Priority One:

Together We Can Beat Global Warming

ALLAN J. YEOMANS

ISBN 978-0-9794799-3-9

Published by Biosphere Media
PO Box 393
Enterprise, OR 97828
USA
http://biospheremedia.org

First published in Australia in 2005 by Keyline Publishing Co Pty. Limited
30 Demand Avenue
Arundel, QLD, Australia, 4214

Library of Congress Control Number: 2007929008

Library of Congress subject headings

Agriculture—Australia.
Agriculture—United States.
Global warming.
Global warming—Government policy—United States.
Greenhouse effect, Atmospheric.
Greenhouse effect, Atmospheric—Government policy—United States.
Environmental policy—United States.
Environmental protection—United States.
Human ecology.
Nuclear energy.
Soil conservation.

DEDICATION

There are many who, for financial or political reasons, require global warming to continue unabated. But much wiser are the others—the people who recognize that destabilizing the world's weather systems can no longer be permitted. The others, who with determination and fortitude will do whatever is within their power to end global warming and halt climatic chaos. If you are one of the others, or if you become one of the others, this book is dedicated to you.

and to my wife Christina May Yeomans OAM*
'the wind beneath my wings'

*OAM Order of Australia Medal

Contents

List of illustrations

Preface to the
international edition

Global warming is a problem and a challenge unlike any we've ever faced. The standard responses to environmental problems, and even much of the thinking behind them, are not working. All too often they are making things worse.

This book is different. It is based on solutions. The rapid development of soil organic matter, nuclear energy, biofuels—all of these have been extensively tested and proven to work in a variety of situations. We can do more than just slow global warming. Together, we can beat it.

The book you hold in your hands had its start in the mid-1980s, when Allan Yeomans began to see that global warming was the most serious economic and environmental threat we face on this planet. He is an inventor and problem solver. He could not contemplate the problem without coming up with a feasible solution.

As a young man, Allan Yeomans studied nuclear physics, chemistry, and engineering. As a competitive sailplane pilot he acquired a practical and extensive knowledge of weather patterns and phenomena—otherwise, as he puts it, "you don't stay in the air." His father, P. A. Yeomans, pioneered the Keyline system of soil development in Australia, and Allan took an active role in both the development of subsoil plows and the practicalities of managing land for rapid creation of fertile topsoil.

This combination of practical and scientific knowledges came together in what he recognized as a viable solution to the problem of global warming. In our modern era of specialization and separation of theory from practice, few people understand or appreciate how rapidly soil organic matter can develop under appropriate management, particularly in temperate zones. It is not common knowledge in academic circles, in government agencies, or in the nonprofit sector. "When I finally sat down and did some back-of-the-envelope calculations, it became apparent that soil could solve the global warming problem," he recalls.

Yeomans presented this concept to a gathering on sustainable agriculture in California in 1989 (see page 373), along with his thoughts on the undue influence of the oil and agrochemical industry. "I thought people would realize that this is good way of solving greenhouse problems. But the concepts weren't accepted, and the word didn't spread as I thought it might." He recognized that few others had his combination of practical and scientific knowledges, and he began to feel a responsibility and a duty to write about the solution he saw in a way that others could understand it.

In 1992 he began gathering more information and writing. Global warming, he says, was constantly portrayed as either not happening, unavoidable, or safe anyway. Almost all the reports, columns, and articles tended to discount both the dangers and the opportunities for solving the problem. After many years of research and writing, he published this book in Australia in 2005 (www.yeomansplow.com.au).

For a generation and more, environmental movements have focused on species and local ecosystems, along with all the sub-problems arising from human decisions such as pollution, energy, family farms, land degradation and desertification, colonialism, food security, and sustainable agriculture. To beat global warming, we need a broader grasp, one that helps us understand the causes of the problems and create effective solutions. We need to grasp process as well as events, incentives as well as policies, the biospheric carbon cycle as well as sources and sinks, wholes as well as parts—for which our language, our habits of thought, and divisions of knowledge are ill suited.

This book embodies that broader grasp. It will refresh some people and discomfit others. You've been warned.

Peter Donovan
Biosphere Media
Enterprise, Oregon, USA
http://biospheremedia.org

Introduction: our future

UNPREDICTABLE weather and climate change caused by global warming poses the greatest single threat our world and all humanity have ever faced. The danger can no longer be ignored. I believe it is possible to stop global warming. I believe it could be accomplished in less than ten years. I also believe the prevention of global warming can be achieved at near zero cost. This book shows how we do it.

The effects of global warming are much worse than we are encouraged to believe. Global warming is destroying the accumulated wealth and prosperity of all nations, rich and poor alike. The environmental costs of climatic change are already horrendous and are escalating. In countries all across the globe, people are dying right now because of global warming. The resulting loss of human life will ultimately dwarf the death toll from all the world's wars combined.

A myriad of minor environmental issues, being forced down our collective throats, is systematically blinding us to the dreadful and deadly serious reality of the destabilization of world climates. Apart from excessive human population growth, the only environmental threat with long-term and meaningful significance is the phenomenon of escalating climatic instability caused by global warming. Its prevention must be our absolute and overriding priority.

Global warming is an anthropogenic problem, a human problem, created by us changing the total quantity of greenhouse gases in the earth's atmosphere. The principal greenhouse gas is carbon dioxide, CO_2. Since the industrial revolution, mankind's activities have massively increased its total quantity.

The carbon from which anthropogenic carbon dioxide derives comes from two distinct sources.

Firstly, it comes from our use of fossil carbon to supply energy for human civilization. Fossil carbon exists in the earth's crust as coal, peat, oil, or as a variety of natural gases. When these materials burn they combine with the oxygen in the air in chemical reactions that produce mainly carbon dioxide and water vapour. The chemical reactions also produce usable heat. We burn these materials to produce steam to spin the turbines that generate electricity in our power stations across the country.

1

Fossil fuels and the heat they produce are also used to run our self-propelled transport systems. Jet fuel powers our air transport. Petrol (gasoline), diesel, and natural gas power our motor vehicles.

Burning these fossil carbon fuels to run power stations and transport systems releases carbon dioxide directly into the atmosphere. There is no possible way of commercially collecting and compressing the carbon dioxide for some later, yet-to-be-invented disposal system.

Fossil carbon materials are also used as the raw material in the production of a wide range of petrochemical and agrochemical products. The main products are agricultural chemical fertilizers, plastics and explosives. Carbon dioxide is discharged into the atmosphere in the production of all these products.

Secondly, carbon dioxide is produced in agricultural soils as their fertility declines. Fertile soil contains large quantities of carbon in the form of soil organic matter. The important thing to realize is that there is about twenty times as much carbon in good topsoil as in all the air above it.

The massive worldwide use of agrochemicals to produce food crops is destroying the fertility of agricultural soil by breaking down the soil's organic matter. The quantity of carbon dioxide released into the atmosphere from the destruction of this organic matter is gigantic. That quantity far exceeds the total released in the manufacturing of all petrochemical and agrochemical products.

The release of carbon dioxide from the destruction of the world's farmed soils is similar in quantity to all that released from the burning of fossil fuels.

The increased level of carbon dioxide in the atmosphere is trapping the sun's heat in ever-increasing quantities. The temperature of both the earth's surface and atmosphere is increasing dangerously. That is what global warming is. And that is our problem.

The object of this book is to show that global warming can be stopped and to show how easily this can be accomplished. In addition it is also to demonstrate that halting world temperature rises and returning world climates to normal will cost virtually nothing.

It must also be understood that if global warming is to be halted then the fossil carbon industries cannot continue to exist at their current huge size.

Three basic ideas form the foundation of this book:

First: The simple and economical enrichment and development of agricultural soil can extract out of the atmosphere all the excess carbon dioxide that has accumulated over the last 75 years. And it can all be removed in less than 10 years. This is mankind's one trump card. But it can only be played once, as the worldwide availability of suitable agricultural land is limited.

Second: There is no economic necessity whatever for us to be completely reliant on fossil fuels for our energy supply. Economically viable alternative energy systems for power generation and motor transport are now available. These are assessed in chapter 11. As excess carbon dioxide is removed from the atmosphere by increasing the fertility of agricultural soils, a rapid switch to these alternative energy systems will maintain normal carbon dioxide levels and maintain climate stability forever.

Third: Fossil carbon companies, their public-relations organizations, and their lobbyists have seconded world environmental movements to a massive extent. They fund many of them and their operations. They are thus able to manipulate such organizations to secure continuing and ever-expanding markets for fossil carbon products. They manipulate environmental information. They have turned too many environmental movement members into their own foot soldiers, their pawns, their frontline troops, to unknowingly assist them in the marketing of fossil-carbon-based products. The myriad of strategies and techniques whereby environmental issues have been twisted, or in many cases actually invented, to sell fossil fuels and fossil carbon-based chemicals is covered in detail in chapter 9.

The fossil carbon industries are powerful and their obvious preference is, like all industries, to survive, to expand and to prosper. Therefore, they constantly condition public opinion and manipulate governments and legislators throughout the world to suit their aims and plans. It's now time for us to stop being so compliant. It is now the time for us to exert equal pressure to gain what is needed and stop global warming.

1

Your world can't afford global warming

THE alteration of world climate patterns is an extremely deadly and frighteningly irresponsible game to play. Scientists know how serious it is. Climatologists know about it. Oceanographers know about it. Insurance companies know, and are now factoring the huge cost increases into premiums for new policies. Politicians are told about it, if they ask. But if you are an average citizen, the whole thing seems just too confusing. Simple clear facts and information that would allow a reasonable person to achieve a workable understanding of the problem, an understanding that allows for practical and sensible assessment of possible solutions, is very difficult to obtain. Why is this so?

Sherlock Holmes, in one of Arthur Conan Doyle's books, said to Dr Watson, "To solve the mystery, first look for he who will benefit". The same concept expressed in an older language is "*Cui bono*" meaning, "To whom the good?"

The crucial element involved in global warming is carbon. Carbon is the most common element in all organic matter, that is plant and animal life. When burnt, carbon combines with oxygen from the air to form carbon dioxide. It happens when we chemically "burn" the sugars in our body to produce energy, consuming oxygen and exhaling some carbon dioxide in our breath. Plants are different, they consume carbon dioxide and release oxygen—but they require energy to do it and this energy comes from sunlight. The carbon cycle we often hear about basically refers to the continual removal of carbon dioxide from the atmosphere by plants, the eating of the plants by animals and the subsequent release of carbon dioxide into the atmosphere. The problem arises because we are currently adding extra carbon into the cycle in large volumes.

Coal, oil and natural gas are mainly carbon formed from the remains of ancient plants and animals. Extracting this fossil carbon and burning it directly produces excess atmospheric carbon dioxide. Agriculture based on chemicals derived from fossil carbon also releases carbon dioxide into the atmosphere by breaking down soil organic matter. So global warming is caused totally and absolutely by the fossil carbon industries in all their forms. The fossil carbon industries are the only ones who benefit from obscuring and confusing this simple basic reality. Solving the greenhouse problem ultimately hurts only the coal, oil and natural gas industries and the petrochemical industries, no one else. This would certainly be Sherlock Holmes' analysis for Dr Watson.

People who work in these industries must invariably become adept at distorting or ignoring the facts and the realities. People who work in the tobacco industry had the same problem, but with tobacco the truth is now out. The truth with fossil carbon materials is much harder to obtain and our ignorance is more deadly to us than it was with tobacco. With fossil carbon fuels the fiction is still almost universally believed.

When you do collect all the information together, this is what you ultimately find: it starts with carbon dioxide—a naturally occurring gas in our atmosphere. When I was at school in the 1940s and 1950s, they taught that the atmosphere contained approximately 280 parts of carbon dioxide per million parts of all the other gases, or 0.028%. That small quantity of carbon dioxide in the atmosphere created a greenhouse effect that kept the surface of the world at an average temperature of 15°C (59°F). Carbon dioxide levels in 2004 reached 375 parts per million (ppm) and are rising continuously at over 2.5 ppm per year.

The "greenhouse effect" gets its name from garden greenhouses, where glass roofs and walls allow sunlight in to warm the interior but stop heat radiating back out. Because the solar heat is "trapped" inside the greenhouse, its internal temperature rises and tropical plants can be grown in cold climates. Carbon dioxide in the earth's atmosphere acts like the glass in a greenhouse, trapping the solar heat near the earth's surface. There are some other gases, which have the same effect as carbon dioxide, and it is common to refer to these and carbon dioxide collectively as "greenhouse gases". But the fact remains that the percentage of carbon dioxide in the atmosphere is the largest single factor responsible for setting the average temperature across the entire world. This global greenhouse effect has been maintaining this planet at life-supporting temperatures for a billion years (1,000,000,000), and life as we know it couldn't live without it. The problem is that we now have too much carbon dioxide in the atmosphere; and humans put it there.

In 1894, the concept of global warming and a world greenhouse effect was merely a philosophical concept. Svante August Arrhenius was a Swedish chemist who decided to do the arithmetic. He divided the world up into a series of unique squares then worked out the effects of increased carbon dioxide levels and solar radiation effects on every single square. He had no computers so he had to do all the calculations by hand. That's how he spent all of 1895. Arrhenius calculated that a doubling of world carbon dioxide levels would increase world temperatures by between 5°C and 6°C. The United Nations–sponsored Intergovernmental Panel on Climate Change (IPCC), using the most modern and sophisticated computers, a few years ago announced the probable upper limit for global warming, following a doubling of atmospheric carbon dioxide levels, at 5.8°C.

Arrhenius was right on the mark, but at the time nobody was interested. Svante Arrhenius was also interested in electrical conductivity, and for his work in this field he won the Nobel Prize for Chemistry in 1903.

The chemistry of terrestrial life is ultimately based on chemical reactions that occur in the presence of liquid water. Life as we know it needs a temperature well below the boiling point of water (100°C or 212°F) and comfortably above its freezing point (0°C or 32°F). Our average world temperature of 15°C (59°F) is ideal. We humans developed in a world where 280 ppm was normal and stable. With a stable level of atmospheric carbon dioxide, worldwide weather patterns themselves were reasonably stable and, more importantly reasonably predictable. We could therefore plan ahead, build towns and societies and great civilizations. Throughout the history of civilized man the greenhouse effect from the carbon dioxide in the air acted like a couple of warm blankets, keeping us at an even and comfortable temperature.

Unfortunately things have changed. The use of fossil fuel as a prime energy source to power our more advanced civilization, and then our coating of agricultural land with oil-based fertilizers and chemicals, have increased the quantity of carbon dioxide in the world's atmosphere by 30%, from below 280 ppm to over 360 ppm. The extra carbon dioxide is the equivalent of an extra blanket. We used to have three blankets. Now we have four.

Since 1860 the earth's average surface temperature has risen somewhere between 0.5°C and 0.7°C (1°F and 1.2°F). The United Nations Intergovernmental Panel on Climate Change (IPCC) had confirmed the temperature rise as 0.6°C above preindustrial levels, even before the Kyoto conference in 1997. The temperature rise is exactly what computer climate modelling said it would be as a result of the measured increase in levels of carbon dioxide and other greenhouse gases. (Chapter 4 discusses climate modelling in more detail.) With the recent industrial expansion of India and China, world greenhouse gas emission rates have accelerated, and in consequence we can expect accelerated rates of temperature rises.

The only good news is that the massive amount of water in the earth's oceans acts like a brake, delaying the rate of atmospheric and shallow ground heating. On the land areas of the planet, below a metre or so (just a few feet), ground temperatures become stable and have little effect on a planet's surface environment. Oceans cover over 70% of the surface of our planet and those oceans are a couple of miles deep. Without the oceans, the warming would already be between 1°C and 2.4°C (1.8°F and 4.3°F). The bad news is that despite the delaying effect of the oceans, the consequences of global warming are going to be much worse than most of us ever imagined.

Admittedly, the temperature changes that have happened, and will happen in the near future, do seem small in comparison to what we experience in our day-to-day living. But don't be fooled; those temperature changes dramatically affect and in turn control the world's weather. As the oceans warm up, the regular pattern and flow of mammoth currents in the deep oceans of the world will destabilize. Ocean currents, circulating from the tropics to the poles, are responsible for distributing most of the heat energy around the world. They utterly dwarf heat distribution by general atmospheric circulation. Disrupting the pattern of these ocean currents will cause a destabilization of world climate systems far more serious than might be expected from simple temperature changes.

At the International Conference on global warming held in Kyoto, Japan in December 1997 the following predictions emerged:

By 2050, the predicted average temperature rise was expected to be a minimum of 1.6°C (2.9°F).

Over the next 100 years, the predicted average temperature rise was expected to be 3.5°C (6.3°F).

Resulting sea-level rises were forecast to be between 150 mm and 950 mm (6 inches and 3 feet).

Then in December 2000, the IPCC changed their forecasts. They subsequently increased their maximum expected temperature rise over the next 100 years to 5.8°C (10.4°F). So now, with almost total certainty, we can expect a minimum mean world temperature rise of around 0.5°C (almost 1°F) every ten years. This would be a greater temperature rise than has ever occurred during the entire span of human existence. At the peak, or the glacial maximum of the last 100,000-year ice age, the oceans were just 1°C to 2°C (1.8°F to 3.6°F) cooler in the equatorial oceans and 6°C (10.8°F) cooler in the latitudes of Europe, North America and New Zealand.

The average temperature rise over the whole world is always difficult to accurately determine, but must be somewhere between the two extremes, maybe around 4°C (7.2°F). A temperature rise of this magnitude, occurring over only 100 years, would almost certainly initiate climatic conditions that have not occurred since the evolution of Cro-Magnon and Neanderthal man. It must be appreciated that it took a temperature rise of just 5.8°C to end the last ice age.

At The Hague conference on global warming held in November 2000, the scientists and delegates agreed that the forecast maximum world temperature rise expected by 2100 should be increased from 3.5°C to a possible catastrophic 6°C. That temperature is more than enough to induce a massive Greenland ice meltdown.

This planet has probably not seen sustained temperature rises at these rates for many millions of years, if ever. So we just don't know, and can't predict what will happen to the world's climate. We do however, have very good information on what happened when the temperature rose by this same amount at the end of the last ice age, and that change took tens of thousands of years to occur, not a mere 100. With those temperature changes, sea levels rose a full 330 feet (100 m) to their current levels. However, sea-level rises are only limited by the amount of ice in the world to melt. A sea-level rise of 12 m to 15 m (40 feet or 50 feet) is probably a conservative estimation if any significant proportion of that ice melted. But a rise like that would flood most of the major seaport cities of the world. Places like Florida and the Pacific island states, just to mention a few, would vanish under water. Even the rise of 950 mm (3 feet) predicted at the 1997 Kyoto meeting will absolutely end the very existence of several Pacific island states.

Sea-level rises are bad enough; but changes in weather patterns are even more frightening and immediate. Tropical cyclones usually form over oceans only when the surface temperature is above about 27°C (80°F). A 1°C (1.8°F) rise in sea-level temperatures will widen the zone of the subtropical cyclones, right around the world, by an average 375 miles (600 km). This widening of the cyclone or hurricane zone is already happening as we have seen. It has already caused considerable loss of life and major damage. The widening will continue. It will be inconsistent and unpredictable. It is the unpredictable changes in local and regional weather patterns that will take the greatest toll; and now everywhere we are seeing these effects.

Paradoxically, one of the effects of global warming is a slight cooling in the stratosphere. This will cause cyclones to penetrate to higher altitudes and therefore become more energetic and much more destructive. The frequency with which these cyclones lash coastlines and penetrate deep inland will rise and house insurance premiums will rise accordingly. Storm surges, coupled with even the minimum predicted sea-level rises, mean many coastal areas will become simply uninsurable. Quixotic efforts by green movements to conserve tiny patches of "fragile" coastal wetland habitats from urban development will look ridiculous, when at the same time thousands of miles of coastline will be inundated by devastating storm surges resulting from global warming. These people are marching to the beat of a very illusory drummer.

Our world's weather is tightly interrelated with the oceans and the pattern of deep ocean currents circulating the globe. This pattern of ocean currents plays a greater role in local weather phenomena than is generally realized. For example, looking at a world map we see that the balmy French Riviera is actually further away from the equator than cold Chicago, or the

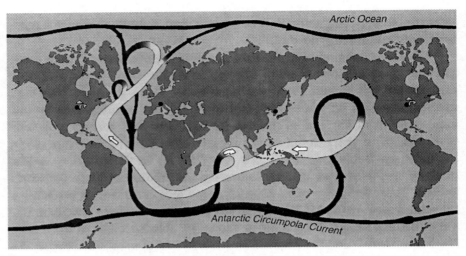

The Oceanic Conveyor showing its links to the North and South polar currents. Warmer currents are shown light, colder currents dark. Dots show Chicago, Korea, and the French Riviera.

whole of South Korea.

Europe is warmed by ocean currents that originate in the Equatorial Pacific. They travel around South Africa and up through the Bahamas, where they pick up more heat, before moving on up to the North Atlantic. The Gulf Stream forms part of this ocean water movement.

Westerly winds pick up this surface-level warmth from the North Atlantic and carry warm moist air east, over Europe. In the process water is evaporated from the ocean, increasing the relative amount of salt in the water. The evaporation also cools the water left behind. This cooler, saltier water is heavier, and so flows down and southward in deep ocean valleys, all the way back around South Africa and on, ultimately to the Northern Equatorial Pacific. The result is a giant, continuous, circulating current, which takes 1,600 years for a round trip.

This giant thermohaline circulation of ocean water and heat energy has been dubbed the Oceanic Conveyor. It conveys massive quantities of heat from the Southern Hemisphere to the Northern Hemisphere. The general stability of the world weather we now live with depends on the consistency of this global heat flow.

Sunshine usually supplies the heat energy to warm the continents but the Oceanic Conveyor provides a massive 25% of the heat that warms the United Kingdom, and Western Europe down to the French Riviera. If the Oceanic Conveyor flow rate slows, Europe will freeze over. Wallace S. Broecker of the Lamont-Doherty Observatory of Columbia University, New York, in a report published in *Science* (Vol. 278, November 1997) calculated that if the conveyor stopped, winter temperatures in Europe would drop by

11°C, that's 20°F, in just ten years! Those numbers are still valid.

Oceanographers from the University of Bremen, Germany have discovered an irregular warming in the southern section of the Oceanic Conveyor. The heat therefore is not moving north as normal and that means trouble. The Oceanic Conveyor is starting to stop!

Huge changes in world climate in the past seem to reflect the ability of the Oceanic Conveyor circulation to assume more than one mode of operation. Broecker reported that ice records showed past changes in the flow of the Oceanic Conveyor had been massive and that associated changes in the world climate had been "large, abrupt and global". The ice records indicate that the Oceanic Conveyor has "jumped from one mode of operation to another" with transitions occurring "in a few decades to as little as a few years". These effects were common several thousand years ago during the last ice age, but so far have been generally absent during our current interglacial period. The final transition from the last ice age to this interglacial period took about 7,000 years and was completed by around 6000 BC. That's about when the Sumerians invented the wheel.

We can't predict exactly what is going to happen over the next few years to world weather and to us from the altered climate. However, we can get some idea of the drastic nature of change by studying how almost imperceptible effects on the planet's surface triggered previous massive environmental modifications. Also subtle evidence is there that indicates the tiny but probable causes of those changes.

How do we know what past climates were like? Our information relies on examining air and dust particles, pollen and other environmental indicators that are entrapped in falling snow. If snow doesn't melt and is covered with more snow, it finally forms into ice sheets; a telltale diary of world weather can build up that can span millennia. This happens in both the high northern and the high southern latitudes. Drilling machines with hollow drill bits are set up on these ice sheets and penetrate thousands of feet into the ancient ice.

Round columns of frozen ice that contain the evidence are extracted through the hollow drill bit as the drill progresses down. In this way we can obtain extremely accurate samples that tell us many things about our Earth's past life. The history of the atmosphere and the world's climate can be laid out as in "a book of time" that goes back for 100,000 years. Even longer periods can be mapped by examining geological indicators and ancient sediments.

Core samples, recently taken by drill rigs set up on the Greenland ice cap, contain unnerving surprises and a wealth of information about the transition to our current interglacial period. These cores show clearly the start of the break up of the northern ice sheets that commenced about 15,000 years ago and how the break-up process lasted through until about 6000 BC. The first smelting of copper happened 1,000 years before that; at a time when sea levels were 100 feet (30 m) below today's levels and many of the world's continental shelves were deserts or forests or savannas.

The cores also show that the transition out of the ice age wasn't smooth; in one short fifty-year period the average environmental temperature rose a full 7°C (12.6°F). It wasn't a simple daily fluctuation; that was the average for the whole world and involving an incredible world climate change. That temperature change is more than you would experience moving from Niagara Falls to Miami or from Scotland to the Greek Islands. And it all happened in a fifty-year time slot.

We don't have to go far from Europe to find evidence of how quickly major ocean currents are starting to change. In the North Atlantic, measurements in the early 1980s showed deep ocean water, part of the Oceanic Conveyor, flowing slowly from the Greenland Sea into the Norwegian Sea. The water was measured moving at 10 cm per second, or about a quarter of a mile per hour. In an incredible directional change, measurements taken ten years later showed the flow had totally reversed. The deep ocean water was flowing at 1 cm per second back into the Greenland Sea. That represents an enormous change in heat energy delivery in the area (*Journal of Climate*, Vol. 12/3297 and *Deep-Sea Research* Vol. 46).

The circular flows in the earth's oceans are not easy to visualize. It also seems impossible that they could ever change significantly in less than centuries. But not so. Direction changes can be abrupt and take only a few days, not centuries.

As the water runs out of a bath, it forms a stable spinning vortex. Give the water a quick stir in the opposite direction, and a new stable vortex will form, revolving in the opposite direction. If there are no significant energy input changes, resulting from shape changes or heat input changes, then this new flow state will always be less stable than the original. After a short time, and very suddenly, the pattern will flip back to the original direction of rotation. It takes less than a second. That's the type of quick-change that can happen in the world's oceans.

We are raising the temperature of the atmosphere. We are altering the direction of prevailing winds. We are significantly altering the energy stability balance in the world's oceans. Some will flip. It could happen any time. If we continue to feed ancient buried carbon into the earth's surface systems then global warming will become effectively irreversible. When particular ocean flow systems change they will be remembered by the year they happened. Unfortunately, it could take a thousand years for them to switch back.

In the North Atlantic, temperatures and ocean flows are changing. Dramatic evidence comes from iceberg numbers. Since 1912, when the *Titanic* hit one and sank, the International Ice Patrol has been tracking and warning shipping of dangerous icebergs south of latitude 48° North. The number of icebergs that drift down the Labrador and Eastern Canadian coast varies

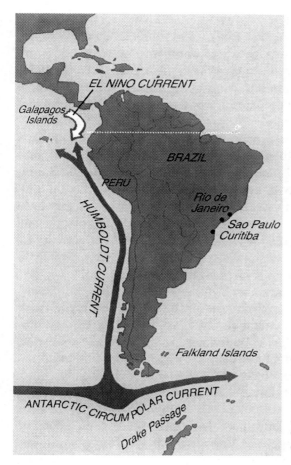

The Drake Passage restricts the flow of the Antarctic Circumpolar Current and helps generate the Humboldt Current. Shown also are the periodic El Niño Current, and the Brazilian city of Curitiba, discussed later.

but averages about 500 per year. In 1999, for the first time since the service started, not one single iceberg-warning bulletin was issued.

There is another major ocean circulation which evidence suggests is also changing. From the southern tip of Chile, a cold current from the Antarctic, rich in nutrients, flows up the west coast of South America. It is known as the Humboldt Current. The nutrients in this current fed an enormous fishing industry in Peru. Peruvian fisherman supplied the world with anchovies. Every few years, around Christmas, a warm tropical Pacific current would sweep in and ruin the catch. Sea temperatures off Peru would rise quite rapidly, but not necessarily disastrously. Because it happened at Christmas time, the current and the effect was called El Niño meaning "the God Child" Jesus.

These El Niño events in Peru are now seen to be part of a major ocean and atmospheric energy interplay that spans the entire Equatorial Pacific. Normally the easterly trade winds blow from South America to New Guinea. These constant winds blowing on the ocean push water towards the Solomon Islands in the Western Pacific and the surface of the ocean builds up a little higher than normal in this region. An El Niño occurs when the easterly trades winds reverse, or slow down. The winds no longer hold the wall of water back. A great wave of warm water washes back across the Pacific and finally hits the South American coast and alters the Humboldt Current. Here it builds up again before initiating a more leisurely bounce back across the Pacific. It is like a wave in a bathtub sloshing from one end to the other, only on a larger scale.

Atmospheric pressures measured in Darwin, on the northwestern Australian coast, and Tahiti seem to oscillate in unison with El Niños. An El Niño (EN), in combination with this Southern atmospheric pressure Oscillation (SO) is now described as an ENSO event—from the initials.

El Niños are now known to materially affect weather in the Northern Hemisphere. Researchers at the Weizmann Institute in Rehovot, Israel reported that the droughts in Australia caused by El Niño events correspond with rapid rainfall rises in the Israeli Hills. El Niños are therefore likely to affect rainfall in most of the eastern Mediterranean.

What actually triggers the start of an ENSO event is still a little confusing. The 1997–98 El Niño was in many ways the strongest ever recorded. There are theories that involve phenomena described as "Roses Waves" and how they bounce off the Western Pacific boundaries and initiate El Niño events by generating another phenomenon called "Kelvin Waves". None of the theories even vaguely predicted the enormity of the 1997–98 El Niño.

Weather in the tropical Pacific and its El Niño events are now being blamed for the giant northern hemisphere drought that affected a wide area of the northern middle latitudes. The areas affected included the United States, Southern Europe, the Mediterranean, and both Southwest and Central Asia through to Pakistan. The timing of the four-year drought corresponds almost exactly with sea-surface temperatures in the eastern tropical Pacific from 1998 to 2002.

The intensity and duration of El Niño or ENSO events certainly seems to be controlled by what happens to the temperatures in a volume of water called the Western Pacific Warm Pool and how the winds blow across this pool and on to the rest of the Pacific Ocean. The Western Pacific Warm Pool is an area of ocean as big as Australia or the lower 48 U.S. states. It has the hottest average ocean temperatures in the world, at around 28°C (82°F).

The Western Pacific Warm Pool is an area of relatively shallow water surrounded on the north, east and west by deeper ocean. It is bounded on the north by the Caroline Islands and extends northwest to the Mindanao Trench off the Philippines. To the south, it is bounded by the northern coast of New Guinea. The Gilbert and Ellice Islands, near the international date line, mark the northeast boundary. Guadalcanal, the British Solomon Islands, and Santa Cruz Island are contained within the pool. The Coral Sea off the Australian coast and south of the Solomon Islands is not included in the Western Pacific Warm Pool and seems to behave differently and

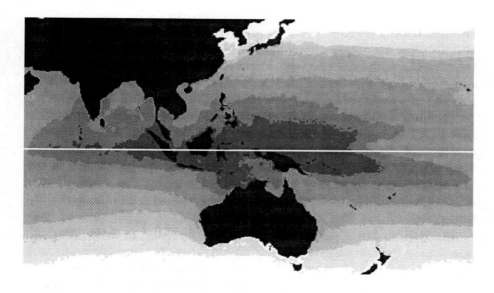

The Western Pacific Warm Pool. Darker shading means warmer water.

independently.

El Niños are becoming worse. The massive 1982–83 El Niño, when it hit South America, sent water temperatures soaring. Measured seawater temperatures rose a full 8°C (14°F). They rose over 4°C (7°F) in just one day. The Peruvian fishing fields were destroyed, and many say have never really recovered. The effect on the Peruvian economy was devastating. El Niños occurred in 1972–73, 1982–83, 1987–88, and then semi-continuously and erratically through the 1990s. The 1997–1998 El Niño was reported in the editorial of *New Scientist* in September 2001 as being the "El Niño of the century" and causing general havoc around the world, costing an estimated US$32 billion. (The term *billion* here, and throughout, means one thousand million, not one million million as sometimes used in Europe.)

I am a member of the American Association for the Advancement of Science and so receive the journal *Science*. Since 1980, the world has had two "El Niños of the century". The February 1999 issue of *Science* Vol. 283, No. 5405 also reported that global warming was boosting the intensity of El Niño events. This report also noted: "El Niño-related weather extremes had caused 23,000 deaths and $33 billion in damages around the world".

At the time, Kevin Trenberth and Timothy Hoar of the National Center for Atmospheric Research in Boulder, Colorado suggested it was probably the longest in the last 2,000 years. El Niños now are so altered they no longer behave like El Niños—they too are now unpredictable.

Daniel P. Schrag of Harvard University's Department of Earth and Planetary Sciences discovered some ancient coral in Indonesia that was dated as 125,000 years old. From this coral sample Schrag was able to show that

El Niños have been with us, off and on, for all that time. Even with those past El Niños the frequency was approximately the six-year cycle length we were familiar with a few years ago, but now that's not the case. *New Scientist*, commenting on both Schrag's and a flood of other evidence says, "it makes a strong case that the climate system is changing beyond all recognition".

The long El Niño in the 1990s affected weather everywhere. Devastating floods hit Los Angeles. In early February 1992, the Mount Wilson observatory in Southern California recorded 1 foot (300 mm) of rain in four days. State officials indicated that statistically, floods of this magnitude in the Los Angeles area could only be expected twice in any one century. This bland reassurance that it is just a statistical phenomenon is not based on the world's new type of climate where statistics no longer apply. Now we have a climate in a state of permanent instability. Just prior to these "50-year" floods, from 1986 through to 1991, California suffered a long continuous and unpredicted period of drought. Water supplies were rationed to agriculture and to cities. Estimates for economic losses exceeded four billion dollars. Incredibly expensive oil-powered desalination plants were, and still are, being seen as a possible alternative water supply. Weather changes regularly turn the state's southwest into a tinderbox. In 2003, 1,000 homes and 20 deaths was another cost Californians paid for global warming.

ENSO events also seem to be substantially and intimately related to the Indian monsoons and the annual melting of the Himalayan snow. These combined effects over relatively small regions then influence, and may even control climates throughout the world. Certainly, they control the climate over the entire Equatorial Pacific from Indonesia to Peru. And the Pacific Ocean does cover almost half the world. The Pacific Ocean is comparable in size to the total of the combined areas of Africa, Europe, North and South America and the North and South Atlantic oceans. It is not hard to see how it can influence the entire world climate.

As is becoming typical, the 1982–83 ENSO was the beginning of the end. That event triggered severe storms in western North America, unprecedented cyclones in French Polynesia, and horrific droughts from weather pattern changes in North Africa. It is glaringly obvious that these climate changes caused the droughts and the resulting starvation suffered by the people of Ethiopia and Somalia at the time. The 1982–83 events are now typical of the new weather instability.

The Western nations in particular, but indeed all the world's massive expansion in the use of fossil fuel as its prime energy source, and all the world's massive expansion of chemical-based agriculture, have changed the nature of the earth's atmosphere. That is where the blame lies. Global warming has turned El Niño, the God Child, into the Angel of Death.

Undoubtedly, over the last few million years the biggest events in global climate have been the ice ages. Through most of that time ice ages have come and gone in cycles of about 100,000 years. But changes associated

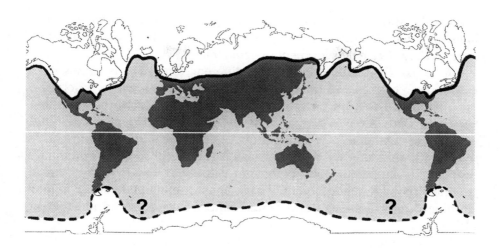

Ice-age earth showing ice cover prior to 20,000 years ago.

with ice ages were so gradual that life would have had plenty of time to adjust, either way. We are now in the warmer period between ice ages, a so-called interglacial period. Interglacial periods generally seem to last between 10,000 and 20,000 years. Unfortunately, this one, this otherwise "standard" warm interglacial is overheating. Rapidly. The world's ecology, us included, does not have the usual time to adjust to such changes.

Modern humans first appeared about half way through the last 100,000-year-long ice age. That ice age started breaking up about 15,000 years ago—say 13,000 BC. The last Neanderthal died about 30,000 years ago.

About 8,000 years ago, we modern humans started to grow our first crops. They were the edible grass seeds. We slowly selectively bred and modified these grasses into wheat and barley.

For most of the time that modern man has existed, the world was actually in ice age mode. What was living like? What is an ice age like? During an ice age the world is certainly different, but perhaps not as different as is often thought. In an ice age the whole world just doesn't freeze up. In the last ice age, mankind did not sit in smoky caves rugged up in smelly animal skins, waiting 50,000 years for the ice to melt. It wasn't like that. Although large ice sheets covered northern latitudes of Asia, Western Europe and all of Canada and the northern United States down to about Chicago, most of the people that lived during those periods would never have seen ice or snow in their entire lives. Some humans migrated up into the cold of Europe after glaciation peaked out and stopped moving south. They of course would have seen plenty of ice and snow. The Neanderthals would not have been pleased losing their cherished winter apartments to the carpetbaggers, this time from the south.

If you lived in Southeast Asia or India, Africa, Australia, South America or

Mexico, the Middle East or Central America, you would hardly have noticed life being any different to what it was just before the industrial revolution. (And the large-scale development of democracies.)

Of course there would have been differences around us as has been mentioned. Jungles and rainforests could have existed where deserts are now. Deserts could have existed where jungles and rainforests are now. Sea levels were lower by hundreds of feet and in consequence coastlines would have been markedly different by the exposure of more of the world's continental shelves. World weather patterns and local climates would have been totally shuffled around compared with what we see today. But in general the main changes would have been entirely geographic. Good conditions and bad conditions would simply have occurred in different places.

Ocean temperatures would be cooler, possibly by as much as 6°C or 7°C (10°F to 12°F) in the middle to polar latitudes. But tropical oceans would still have been as warm as a heated swimming pool, perhaps 1°C or 2°C (1.8°F to 3.6°F) cooler than now.

The northern hemisphere, where most humans now live, the cold of the ice age was most fearsome. In those times, the warm ocean currents that warm present-day Europe could easily have been meandering in other directions. Near the end of the last ice age, the giant sheet of ice covering all of Canada and half the United States began melting at its southern boundary as world temperatures rose. The ice sheet shrank towards the north. Then suddenly, 8,000 years ago it did a U-turn and re-advanced well down into Wisconsin before its final retreat north. That final retreat north marked the end of the last ice age. Civilizations in the Middle East, and in Central and South America, were unperturbed by these northern ice sheet movements. They would not have been noticed.

The regular 100,000-year cyclic nature of ice ages and their possible astronomical triggering effects are discussed in the next chapter. The fact that sequencing ice ages can occur at all, I think, is very possibly linked to the current arrangement of continents. The continents of the world have not always been in their current position. They have been drifting over the surface of our planet since the original break up of the giant continents of Pangaea, Gondwanaland, and Laurasia some 250 million years ago. The phenomenon is called continental drift. The relatively recent movement of the Caribbean Plate to block up the equatorial waterway between the North and South American continents is a good example of continental drift in action. That was three million years ago.

The particular geographical layout of the world today is somewhat peculiar. Centred on the South Pole we have Antarctica, an island continent surrounded by 12,000-foot-deep oceans (over 3,500 m). Centred on the North Pole we have the Arctic Ocean and this ocean is effectively an inland sea.

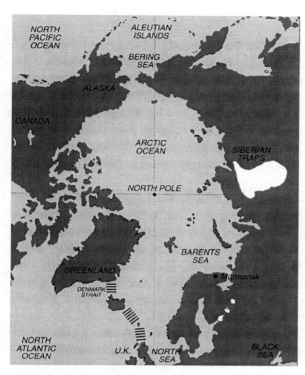

Denmark Strait. Arctic Ocean currents flow counterclockwise. The GIUK gap is shown as hatching. The Siberian Traps, shown white, are basalt flows that are associated with the Permian-Triassic or P-T mass extinction of 250 million years ago. This P-T extinction is discussed a few pages further on.

The Arctic Ocean is surrounded by the landmasses of Asia, North America, Greenland, and Iceland. The Arctic Ocean is also the shallowest ocean on earth. Its average depth is only 3,900 feet (1,200 m) whereas the average for the world's oceans is three times this. Its average temperature should therefore change three times as fast. At this time what this means in terms of global warming can only be speculation.

The biggest openings to this inland sea are between Scotland and Iceland. They are small openings. To illustrate the small size of the Scotland-Iceland opening, the island of Madagascar would block it off completely. There is also a narrower but significant access through the Denmark Strait, between Iceland and Greenland. Greenland and the many islands of northeastern Canada are almost linked. Ocean circulation between them is limited as it has to thread its way through a maze of minor channels. The relatively tiny Bering Strait, between Asia and North America, is the only other opening. The Bering Strait is narrow. It has even been crossed on a wind-surfer. The Bering Strait is also the one and only connection between the Arctic Ocean and the warm waters of the Pacific Ocean.

Before the continents drifted into their present position, some 40 million years ago, and gave us an inland sea at the North Pole and a very large landmass at the South Pole, it is doubtful if a regular pattern of ice ages could have occurred at all. The tropical ocean waters would have easily circulated right to the poles and probably kept them totally free of any permanent ice formation.

However that is certainly not the way it is today. Because of the current layout of world continents, it is difficult for the heat from the tropics to be transported, by ocean currents, to either of the polar regions. And so we have very significant polar ice caps. The current juxtaposition of continents is unique in the geographical, topographical and oceanographic history of our planet. It is also why we are so vulnerable to small fluctuations in world greenhouse effects. Small changes in the composition of our atmosphere, especially changes that alter its optical characteristics, do inevitably alter the structure and pattern of world climates.

Temporary reversion to ice-age conditions for surprisingly short time periods occurred quite regularly during that last long meltdown from the ice age. The final significant hiccup that started 12,900 years ago and ended 10,700 years ago is referred to as the Younger Dryas period. It's named after a flower that thrived through the period. The drier, dusty conditions, characteristic of ice-age conditions in Greenland at the time, changed over a frighteningly short twenty-year period. This change established a totally different and wetter climate for the island.

The Younger Dryas hiccup return to glacial conditions was originally presumed to have occurred worldwide, but researchers at the Research School of Earth Sciences at the Victoria University, Wellington, New Zealand, seemed to have proved the opposite. New Zealand didn't get colder during the Younger Dryas; some evidence suggests it got wetter, but definitely not colder. The fact that Europe can freeze independently and quickly, and for little apparent reason, indicates that unsuspected changes in ocean circulation patterns are the likely trigger.

The idea of rapid changes in climate being brought on by changes in ocean circulation is supported by more recent evidence. An extremely short period of unusually warmer weather occurred around 850 AD. This sudden burst of climate change saw the establishment of Norse and Viking cultures at least as far west as that land mass they named Greenland. And as we have seen, the name stuck.

Iceland too, was actually free of sea ice for more than 300 years after the Vikings originally gave it that inhospitable name. Nordic wanderers even established temporary settlements in far-off North America around this time. Then the North Atlantic cooled about 2°C during the 13th and 14th centuries, and the Greenland colonies perished. The last Greenlander was found frozen solid, still fully clothed, by the crew of a ship blown off course in 1540. Greenland has rarely seen much green since.

The weather was then quite reasonable until around 1600 AD when a little ice age started. It was nothing compared to the earlier more definitive Younger Dryas Period. That chill lasted until 1900 AD. The same bout of cold weather stopped Napoleon on his march into Russia. Strangely, during that time, some Canadian glaciers crept down their valleys further than at any time in the last 50,000 years.

The past very rapid weather pattern changes in the North Atlantic and Arctic Ocean strongly support the concept that various "stable" ocean current configurations can exist, and that these can be switched from one configuration to another by minor changes in atmospheric composition. Even as recently as 1920, we saw a sudden general Greenland temperature rise of 4°C. This was soon followed by a slow cooling back to normal conditions. There is no solid explanation for the fluctuation.

In all these occurrences the pollution of the atmosphere from burning fossil fuel hadn't yet touched the dial on Mother Earth's electric blanket.

Several climate modellers are now forecasting temperature rises in the polar latitudes of 10°C to 12°C (18°F to 21.6°F) within 25 years. That's five or six times the change that wiped out the Viking colonies on Greenland. The Viking wipeout took at least a century. Just to contemplate temperature changes of these magnitudes was inconceivable just a few short years ago. Those forecast temperature rises, and they have indeed started rising, will be more rapid than the fastest temperature changes ever found in any ice core sample from anywhere on earth.

The energy that powers the mighty ocean currents comes from sunlight. We have just increased the sunlight energy retention characteristics of the earth's atmosphere by almost 30%. The three blankets that make up our carbon dioxide blanket and keep the world livable are now four. And the world is starting to sweat.

The whole concept of human-induced rapid weather pattern changes over vast areas of the earth's surface is terrifying meteorologists and oceanographers throughout the world. Most scientists involved in research on climate change now concede that such changes can truly be expected. Changes of the expected magnitude in time periods measured in weeks and months are seen as terrifying. Before global warming, extremely short time periods were at least decades. The great climatic changes that moved the world into and out of ice ages in the past generally took hundreds, or more likely thousands of years, and would have been virtually imperceptible to people living at the time.

This time the fossil carbon companies want us to accept such climate changes within one generation. They want us to accept the notion that global warming is inevitable. It suits them for us to turn a blind eye on the horrendous costs and horrendous consequences.

How can such rapid changes come about? Well snow and ice cover appear to hold the key. Snow, glaciers, and pack ice are very poor absorbers of solar radiation. They reflect most of the light that hits them. That is why they appear white and why you get snow-blindness if you don't wear eye protection in the snow. Incoming solar energy is mostly reflected back into space from snow or ice cover. If we make allowance for the irregularities in the surfaces, it is a fair approximation to say that ice and snow reflect back

75% of incoming solar radiation. Whereas in contrast, open ocean absorbs about 75% of solar radiation. This leads to a positive feedback mechanism; more snow or ice cover means less absorbed heat, so the temperature drops allowing the snow or ice to last longer. The Arctic ice sheet thus acts like a massive self-stimulated heat switch. More ice covering the ocean means less absorbed sunlight, allowing yet more ice cover. Less ice covering the ocean means more absorbed sunlight, and warmer water, and still less ice cover.

When seawater freezes, relatively salt-free ice is produced; the remaining saltier, and therefore denser cold water sinks to the bottom. In the Arctic Ocean, this cold bottom-water is walled in by barriers. The barriers could be thought of as mountain ranges on the sea floor. We have the barrier joining Greenland to Iceland under the waters of the Denmark Strait; it's called the Greenland-Iceland Rise. Another barrier joins Iceland to the Faeroe Islands, and on to the Orkney Islands (just south of the Shetland Islands), and then across to Northern Scotland; it's called the Iceland-Faeroe Ridge. There are two low points in the ridge through which a constant cascade of cold, salty, bottom-water from the Arctic Ocean pours down into the deep North Atlantic Basin. The water there is almost four miles (6 km) deep.

The military call this line across the North Atlantic the GIUK gap from the Greenland-Iceland-United-Kingdom Gap. It was virtually the only way for Russian submarines to get out into the world's oceans. They could always be detected passing through the GIUK gap.

Arctic Ocean bottom-water also overflows the Greenland-Iceland Ridge on the west coast of Iceland. A giant cataract or waterfall exists 2,000 feet (600 m) below the surface waters of this Denmark Strait. The dense Arctic waters pour over this waterfall and on down a long submarine valley into the North Atlantic Deep. The water descends 2 miles (3.5 km) with a flow rate of five million tons per second. That's twenty times the flow of the Amazon River. (An imperial ton is less than 2% bigger than a metric tonne. Conveniently they are almost the same.) This submarine valley is a mere 650 feet (200 m) wide and the top surface of the flow is just 650 feet (200 m) below the surface. It's a cold dark raging torrent (as reported by John A. Whitehead of Woods Hole Oceanographic Institution in *Scientific American*, February 1989).

How global warming will change the patterns of the underwater ocean currents is almost impossible to predict. But if the formation of Arctic sea ice is slowing, then the supply of dense, cold, bottom-water must be diminishing. If we take no action to halt the warming, ocean currents will change. There is no doubt. What we do know about these deep ocean currents guarantees that, for Europe, it is not going to be very pleasant. As we will see later.

Melting sea ice can have a direct effect on ocean currents but there's no effect on sea level. It's simple physics. Ice takes up more room than the same mass of water. Ice is lighter and therefore floats. When sea ice melts the

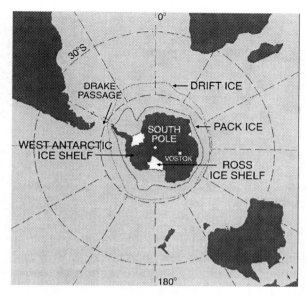

Ice on the Antarctic continent can be several kilometres thick. The continent is surrounded by pack ice; drift ice surrounds the pack ice. The restriction at Drake Passage to the clockwise direction of the circumpolar current becomes obvious in this view.

package shrinks and occupies exactly the same space that the underwater part of the ice took up before it melted. An over-full glass of water containing floating ice protruding out the top won't overflow as the ice melts. Likewise, sea level doesn't change when floating pack ice melts.

Pack ice forms and exists in the Arctic Ocean in enormous quantities. Indications are that a permanent, floating, polar ice cap has been in existence now for over 15 million years. Over this time span, the ice cap would obviously vary considerably in size, shape, and depth. It would be subject to fickle changes in ocean currents around the relatively small entrances into this giant inland sea. The sea ice pack has no direct effect on sea levels.

Not so for ice on landmasses.

Melting of sea ice cannot alter sea levels in any way. But the melting of snow and ice buildups on land most certainly can, and does. Sea levels around the world change dramatically with the waxing and waning of continental ice cover.

Antarctica is a landmass covered in ice. This ice is not floating on water. If it melts or if its minute rate of flow to the sea increases for whatever reason, sea levels will rise. Antarctica is an extremely cold place, and the ice can't all melt, and it won't all melt. However on the Antarctic continent there is a massive accumulation of ice called the West Antarctic Ice Sheet. If this ice sheet melted it would produce a world sea-level rise estimated at around 18 feet (5.5 m). Worse still, the ice doesn't have to melt. It has only to move from over the land to into the sea. The floating icebergs cause an immediate sea-level rise.

The massive Antarctic glaciers that form much of the West Antarctic Ice Sheet move very slowly. They are held back by thick compacted sea ice blocking the glacier exits to the ocean. Small ocean current changes could

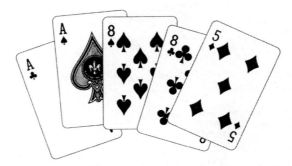

"Dead Man's Hand"—Wild Bill Hickok's poker hand when he was shot in the back of the head in Deadwood, 2 August 1876.

accelerate the fracturing of this sea ice barrier, initiating a very sudden rise in glacial flow rates into the Antarctic Ocean. This type of event could occur in less than a decade and this would raise sea levels rapidly. This would not be good. It is generally conceded that this process, once initiated, would in all likelihood be irreversible. Nothing could stop the ice flow. Instantly reverting the earth's atmospheric carbon dioxide levels back to those that existed before fossil fuels would not stop the flow.

Andrew Shepherd at the Centre for Polar Observation and Modelling, University College, London and his colleagues have been monitoring the movements of the largest of all the glaciers in the West Antarctic Ice Sheet by satellite. They claim it is now losing ice faster than snowfall replacement. Shepherd says; "This is the first time we have seen an Antarctic glacier retreating". Because of this he adds, "The concern for sea-level rises are real". If this observed rate of glacier retreat simply stays at its current rate we will see rises of over three inches (80 mm) every ten years. As we note further on, this rise was actually predicted in 1997. Unfortunately, glacier retreat is actually accelerating. There is also a huge ice sheet over land in the high northern latitudes. The most important is the Greenland ice cap. Greenland is a big island. It's two-thirds the size of India. Recently it's been reported that the Greenland ice cap has started to melt and to move. If we continue the global warming gamble, then Greenland ice really becomes the unpredictable wild card. It is kilometres deep. It is even more frightening than the threat from continued Antarctic melting. The United Nations–sponsored International Panel on Climate Change (IPCC) in 2000 issued a warning that has not been rescinded. The warning is that a 3°C rise in temperatures throughout Greenland would trigger an irreversible melting of Greenland's sheet ice.

In 2003, *Science* Vol. 302 reported that huge glacial surges are triggered by Greenland's fairly common seismic events. It is now considered that these could involve tens of cubic kilometres of ice moving several metres in just minutes. Apparently it slides on the super-compressed and somehow

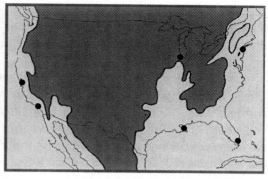

Showing the coastlines of Europe and the United States if global warming is allowed to melt three-quarters of the polar ice. Such a melt is in the cards, and it could happen over the next 100 years.

density-inflated water under the ice.

At the same time GPS (Global Positioning System) data collected for the NASA Goddard Space Flight Center in Maryland show the speeding up of Greenland ice flows occurring in weeks. The totally unexpected rapid ice movement is thought to result from increased meltwater seeping under the 4,000-feet (1,200-metre) thick ice sheets and acting as a lubricant for the ice flow. The lubricating effect has never before been considered.

Such a Greenland melt, as the IPCC warn of, would result in a very definite world sea-level rise of 23 feet (7 m). It would mean that shipping and docking facilities in every seaport, on every coastline, in every country anywhere on earth, would be useless. We might bet the farm, but we can't bet the whole planet.

Today we are currently between ice ages. We are in an interglacial period. Before the last ice age and around 100,000 years ago the planet was at the warmest part of that earlier interglacial period. Sea levels were then 18 feet (5.5 m) higher than they are now. We know that at the time Greenland had lost most of its ice and was almost ice free. The loss of Greenland ice accounts almost exactly for the sea level that then existed. From this it would appear that the West Antarctic Ice Sheet has previously been inherently more stable than the Greenland ice sheet and has maintained its ice volumes throughout at least one previous interglacial period. Greenhouse gas levels, if we permit them to continue climbing, will skyrocket to levels twice what they were when Greenland ice totally melted. This time Antarctic ice cannot be expected to remain stable at such high and unprecedented atmospheric carbon dioxide levels. The Western Antarctic Ice Sheet is rapidly approaching total unpredictability. If it's not there already.

Sea-level rises have started and are going to accelerate. The actual amount of rise even in the near future is very difficult to predict with accuracy. That they will rise is a certainty. Oceanographers gave us what they believe to be expected minimum and maximum rises back in 1997. Predictions were between 6 inches and 3 feet (150 and 950 mm) over the next 100 years.

Just like the change in average world temperatures, these rises in sea levels, on face value, do not appear to be too frightening or excessive to contend with. After all, aren't daily tidal fluctuations of 5 to 10 feet (around 1 to 2 metres) common along many coastlines? But predicted sea-level rises are added to the inevitable extreme high tides. Coastal lands are often very flat so even small sea-level rises can affect towns well inland from current tide lines.

Others predict far greater rises than 3 inches, often as much as twenty times these estimates. Aircraft and satellite surveys of the Amundsen Sea sector of West Antarctica indicate glacial thinning doubled during the 1990s. If all the ice melts, just in Antarctica alone, sea levels will rise 70 metres (235 feet; *Science*, Vol 306 October 2004).

Even without melting ice caps, sea levels will rise because the ocean water expands as it warms. As world-average air temperatures rise from excess greenhouse warming, the warmer air will begin to warm the mass of ocean water. Its temperature rise is delayed but it is only a delay. There is more than 250 times as much weight of water in the world's oceans as air in the entire atmosphere. The Earth's oceans average over 11,000 feet (3,300 m) deep. It is sobering to realize that the first 33 feet (10 m) or so of the world's oceans contain as much heat energy as our entire atmosphere right out to the fringes of space. That is why the rate of warming is delayed.

Average sea-level rises caused by the thermal expansion of water are 16 inches for every 1°F rise in ocean temperatures. That's 730 mm for every 1°C.

Although sea-level rises are delayed by their very mass, it is small comfort to the more than 80 million people in Bangladesh who are already subject to the effects of severe storms and flooding from global warming. Forty million people is often considered as a very conservative minimum estimate for the number who will suffer and die over just a relatively short period from global warming and its immediate consequences.

Other countries and areas where sea-level rises will mean excessive costs in loss of life and property include: Argentina, Brazil and Surinam in South America, large areas on the coast in the Gulf of Mexico, especially places like New Orleans and the Mississippi delta country; in Africa, Mozambique, large areas of Nigeria, Senegal, Gambia and parts of Egypt; in Europe, The Netherlands, Venice and northern areas of the United Kingdom.

Venice saw its first major flood in 1966. Water rose to almost 7 feet (2 m) above the "standard for mean sea levels" established in 1897. Some of the almost priceless art in the old city suffered terrible damage. Because of underlying geological structures, the city is actually sinking at a rate of 1 mm per year, but added to this is the global warming effect, which is raising sea levels by 4 mm per year. So things won't improve for Venice and its treasures. Both will be lost as the water rises. The whole world will lose when Venice has to be abandoned to be sacrificed on the altar of the fossil carbon industries.

In the Indian and Pacific Oceans, the Maldives, Pakistan, Thailand, Bangladesh, China, Vietnam and Indonesia are all at risk. Coastal cities will then be awash from no more than minor storms. Some of the small island states will simply disappear. Many of their citizens will die. They will die as the severity of typhoons and hurricanes exceed all previous maximums. They will die while the "theory of global warming" is being disputed by academics manipulated by oil money.

Those words were written before the 2004 Boxing Day earthquake-generated tsunami. While global warming and its allied climate change cannot produce such severe and almost instantaneous effects as happened that day, increased severity of storms and storm surges on elevated sea levels will produce less severe events but occurring in ever increasing numbers.

Australia is an island continent. It has the longest national coastline in the world, 19,000 miles (30,000 km) long. If you include the 12,000 surrounding islands and the hundreds of estuaries, bays, tidal lakes and lagoons, the coastline is nearer 44,000 miles (70,000 km). Rising sea levels will affect all of those 44,000 miles. Ecological changes will be enormous.

In many countries the conservative cost estimates of sea-level rises exceed 5% of the gross national product, and that generally is merely the cost to hopefully achieve some form of ocean wave or tidal protection. In many countries that will not be affordable.

The accumulated wealth of human society, towns and cities, roads and railways, shipping terminals, factories, office blocks and schools, could all be under water in a few short years, a huge waste. For many it would mean starting all over again. Global warming risks are a gamble no one anywhere on earth can afford. (Except for the fossil carbon industries.)

Apart from eventual sea-level rises, there is a nasty downside to ocean heat content. Normal ocean water in some areas is actually quite warm, and therefore contains enormous quantities of stored heat already. This heat is near the surface. The cold water might be a mile down. If a flip should occur somewhere in the ocean's circulations, then these vast stores of surface heat energy could quite suddenly add to atmospheric warming effect. More and more informed and thinking people are now considering this a probability. The oceans could become, not a dampener to rapid global warming, but a stimulator to a greatly accelerated and runaway global warming phenomenon. These things could happen within five to ten years, but nobody knows. However, hard evidence on general global warming and what it is costing is flooding in. It's everywhere.

On the other side of the Andes, east of Peru with all its anchovy and El

Niño problems, is Brazil. Generally when the media reports on activities in Brazil they will invariably highlight discussion on the so-called destruction of the Amazon rainforests. It is always portrayed as an ecological disaster and receives a constant stream of orchestrated criticism. The media never lets up. The Amazon rainforest, it is inferred, somehow determines the ecological and wellbeing of the entire planet. This ploy conveniently diverts our attention on global warming away from the oil fuel industry and concentrates our attention on some battling Brazilian farmers. This is wrong and unjust.

There is a law in Brazil that says petrol must contain 25% ethanol. The ethanol is produced from sugar cane and so does not add to the world's total atmospheric carbon dioxide level. There are 170 million Brazilians and they drive a lot of cars. That single law makes Brazil the most environmentally responsible country on earth. The oil companies do not like the ethanol laws. Likewise it can be argued that oil companies would not like beautiful Brazilian rainforest timbers that, in so many applications compete too successfully with their oil-based plastics.

The Brazilian city of Curitiba, with some 1.6 million inhabitants, is a wonderful example of how a well-managed sustainable city should function. The city has a fast convenient urban transport system and although the inhabitants own more cars than people in other Brazilian cities, they rarely use them with such a pleasant mass transit system available. This should be newsworthy but media talk is always concentrated on the Amazonian trees and rainforests. For information on Curitiba see *New Scientist* Vol. 134, No. 1825.

The rainforest and the tropical swamps or wetlands of the Amazon have been marketed as the "lungs of the world". That's plain nonsense. Mature rainforests release as much carbon dioxide as they absorb. Or almost, for some is released back, not as carbon dioxide but as marsh gas (methane), from the rotting vegetation on the forest floor. Rainforests do not produce any excess oxygen. A stable rainforest, in terms of influencing the greenhouse effect by reducing atmospheric carbon dioxide levels, is a complete nonentity. In this aspect only, rainforests are greenhouse neutral. But overall, sadly, they are not even neutral.

One of the most glossed over realities of wetlands, and especially the dense tropical wetlands such as exist in the Amazon basin, is that they are a massive producer of greenhouse gases. They don't minimize global warming, they make it worse. NASA, the U.S. National Aeronautics and Space Administration, in conjunction with INPE, the Instituto Nacional de Pesquisas Espaciais, the Brazilian space agency, conducted a series of atmospheric composition determinations over the Amazon basin. An array of tethered weather balloons was established, and aeroplanes crisscrossed Brazil. It was all part of the Amazon Boundary Layer Experiments ABLE-2A and ABLE-2B. The first, ABLE-2A was conducted in July and August of 1985.

ABLE-2B was conducted in April and May of 1987. The tests were part of the comprehensive Global Tropospheric Experiment. From this, and from other closely allied research, some very interesting, greenhouse-relevant information emerged.

Over the Amazon area, it was found that the atmospheric carbon dioxide levels would drop to 340 ppm during the day and then overnight would rise dramatically to a high of 370 ppm, just before sunrise. It happens every day and that was expected. What was found that was alarming was the constant, and in total, massive production of methane from the wetlands below. Methane is not something that gets recycled within the forest. Methane stays in the air and methane is between twenty and twenty-five times more potent a greenhouse gas than carbon dioxide. So in effect, wetlands, through the growth, death and decomposition of plant life are in effect turning atmospheric carbon dioxide into the far more greenhouse potent greenhouse gas, methane.

Tropical wetlands account for approximately 60% of all wetlands and current updated estimates of methane production from tropical wetlands are now put at 55 million tons per year. To put that in perspective, call methane twenty-two and a half times worse than carbon dioxide, so just tropical wetlands produce the equivalent of 1,235 million tons of carbon dioxide per year. That's about the yearly CO_2 production from 100 million automobiles. Sadly at this time wetlands are no great asset to our planet despite the colourful rhetoric to the contrary.

The greatest real threat to any rainforest or wetland with their timeless cycles of decay and regrowth is that global-warming-induced climate and weather changes will, in so many places, stop the rain. Droughts will become common. No rain means no rainforest. In 1992, part of the eastern Amazon basin had become tinder dry after months of "unusual drought". One well-placed lightning strike at the time would have started horrendous and wasteful fires. The whole thing could have literally exploded. That time the Brazilians were lucky. Their luck ran out in the southern hemisphere summer of 1997–98, when huge areas of dry South American rainforests burst into flame. Such fires will become the new norm.

The increasing severity of ENSO events generated by global warming has also brought dreadful famine to much of northeast Brazil, but it has generated negligible media coverage in the Western press, and no coverage whatever suggesting global warming as the prime cause.

Darwin's studies of the amazing variety of species on the arid Galapagos Islands were a big factor in his discovery and appreciation of the processes of evolution. The islands sit right on the equator in the eastern Pacific Ocean off northern Peru. Well-dated sedimentary deposits indicate sea surface temperatures in the Galapagos Archipelago were very stable and varied little. Even during the Last Glacial Maximum they were only 1°C on average cooler than temperatures just a few years ago.

Our use of fossil fuels has so changed weather patterns in these islands that the environment that created their amazing species diversity now no longer exists. During current El Niños water temperatures are running 3°C higher than prediction. The millennia-long period of weather stability has finished. Water temperatures 5°C higher than normal now last for months on end. Yearly rainfalls that once averaged less than 20 inches (500 mm) can now exceed 9 feet (2.7 metres).

Marine species suffer most. Local hammerhead sharks have vanished. There is widespread coral bleaching. Barnacle species, common to the islands, have nearly all died. Marine iguanas, which do not occur elsewhere, are dying from starvation and will soon almost certainly vanish. The edible seaweed, their stable diet, won't grow there any more. The rare and multiple varieties of Galapagos bird life will soon cease to exist.

Today Darwin would find little to study of any meaningful and significant interest in the Galapagos Archipelago.

As reported in *New Scientist* in July 2003, Toby Gardner, of the University of East Anglia in the UK, has been compiling data on coral formations in the Caribbean. The Caribbean reefs were created by a particular form of hard coral. Analysis completed 25 years ago showed the species existed on about half the reefs in the area. That reef-building species now only exist on just 10% of the Caribbean reefs. This means that the coral reefs of the Caribbean are now close to total extinction. Causes are complex and often interrelated but two things seem to stand out. Sea temperatures are consistently at record heights, resulting it is suspected from global warming, and secondly, silt and agricultural chemicals are changing growth patterns of the coral types. The loss of hard coral from higher levels of agricultural chemicals is also occurring on the biggest reef system in the world, the 2,000-km Australian Great Barrier Reef. It is observed that the further away from agricultural runoff, the healthier the reef and the greater the biodiversity, and both by a big margin. What was found in the Caribbean was that soft corals are surviving but the reef-forming corals have almost vanished. (The term *biodiversity* has only recently entered the English language. Biodiversity, in most dictionaries, is now generally defined as the measure of individual species living in a nominated area. In biology, a species is generally considered as a group in which the members do, or are capable of, interbreeding.)

On the western side of the Pacific, Southeast Asia is also suffering. Rainforests are burning for want of rain. On a regular basis we now see dreadful fires in Borneo and the results of their choking smoke on the people. Poor visibility attributed to this smoke caused the crash of an Indonesian Airbus A-300 flight out of Jakarta in September 1997. All 234 people on board were killed.

Peat bogs are fossil fuels not quite completely fossilized. Peat bog researchers in the UK, France and the United States now estimate that

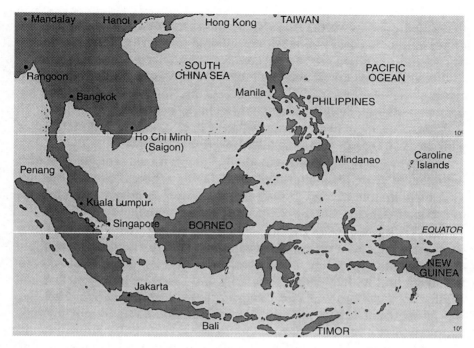

Southeast Asia, from New Guinea to Mandalay, from Hong Kong to Bali.

Indonesia, Borneo and Sumatra contain 20% of the world's store of peat-bog-trapped carbon. The burning rainforests have set these peat bogs on fire and it could be impossible to put them out. They behave like burning coal seams. If they continue to burn they could add as much carbon dioxide to the atmosphere as is generated by the use of fossil fuels in the whole of Europe. This would further accelerate global warming.

Unprecedented forest fires started in far eastern Russia in 1997. In six months, 2 million hectares on the Pacific coast and the nearby island of Sakhalin were destroyed.

Towards the end of the 1990s Papua New Guinea (PNG) in the east equatorial Pacific experienced widespread starvation resulting from the first-time-ever droughts on that normally wet tropical island. Rainfalls plummeted everywhere. Normally August rainfall in Tabubil, in the New Guinea Highlands, averages 34 inches (870 mm). In August 1997 they got just an inch and a quarter (32 mm). In September there was no rain. An Australian National University report at the time indicated that 540,000 rural Papua New Guineans had insufficient food to survive. These people normally grow their own food and are well-fed and well-nourished. The RAAF (Royal Australian Air Force) had to fly in massive quantities of food aid from Australia.

Copper exports are a major factor in PNG's economy. The cargo vessels that ship the ore out via the rivers were stuck in the mud at the bottom of the empty rivers. The national economy suffered drastically. Then the tinder-dry rainforests caught fire and the country was blanketed in smoke haze.

These disasters are claimed by interested parties to result from natural cycles in the severity of El Niño or ENSO events. But that is wrong. They are the typical dire consequences of global warming in action.

Climatic changes in the Northern Pacific have now been definitely linked with the ENSO events spanning the whole central Pacific.

In Japan in 1991, big changes in weather patterns really got going; rainfall increases in some areas exceeded 350% of the expected annual average. Typhoons, unprecedented in their frequency and severity, caused billions of dollars in damage. But the water could not be stored.

Japan once had a dry period about every twenty years. Water-supply dams were built accordingly. However, since 1996 dry periods come about once every four years. Japan now needs twice as many dams. Groundwater has made up the difference temporarily, but these are emptying fast and as they do, buildings sink and collapse. Tokyo's ground surface sink rate was measured at 40 mm per year (1.5 inches). Osaka was 10 mm per year. Nagoya was 20 mm.

In another unrelated study on global warming in 1997, Japan's Institute for Environmental Studies, using August as a test month, forecasted that a 1°C temperature rise would result in an ongoing additional death rate in Japan of 600 people each and every August.

Methane, at a good twenty times more potent a greenhouse gas as carbon dioxide, is not a substance to trifle with. It seems incongruous that the Japanese are actually assessing the fuel energy potential of extracting methane from methane hydrates out of the deep ocean sediments off their east Pacific coast. When burnt as a fuel, it turns into carbon dioxide and water. The Japanese naturally want cheap energy, but if they use this supposedly cheap methane, it will prove to be very expensive in the long run as it will significantly ramp up global warming.

The Iberian Peninsula, on the other side of the world, is also suffering from global warming. Spain in 1992 and 1993 experienced their second worst drought in the whole of the twentieth century. Billions of dollars have had to be earmarked to channel the waters from the Pyrenees Mountains to the now, ever-drying Spanish South.

The previous year, off the coast of Spain in the Mediterranean, hundreds and possibly thousands of striped dolphins died. The most likely cause was that their starvation triggered the release of an accumulation of chemicals that had built up in their own fat. The starvation resulted from a lack of nutrients in the abnormally warm Eastern Mediterranean waters. This was coupled with a drop in organic matter supplies normally delivered via runoff from the nearby coastal areas. There was no rain, therefore no runoff. By 1993, the entire Mediterranean area was experiencing its fifth consecutive year of drought.

Incredible and costly engineering projects have been planned and rushed through to cater for the ever changing and dryer weather patterns of the Mediterranean area. Almost every city from Nicosia, on the island of Cyprus to Lisbon, in western Portugal is now continuously running low on water. Climate modelling, adjusted for our constantly modifying atmosphere, predicts even drier conditions ahead for the countries of the Mediterranean. Many parts of southern Europe will become so drought prone that historically normal dairy production is expected to cease entirely.

Bushfires were not common in Europe once. With changing weather patterns they are now, and they will get worse. Forest and brush fires of unprecedented severity are taking a dreadful toll. Too many people are dying. Too much property is being destroyed. A heat wave hit Europe in 2003. Nothing like it had been seen before. In France over 14,000 people died of heat exhaustion. The U.N. Food and Agriculture Organization reports for 2003 an increase in bushfire damage in France of 30%. In Portugal bushfires and brush fires are not uncommon, but the U.N. reports in 2003, fire and fire damage increased by 300% over the average for the previous twenty years.

Sometimes there is also irony in these climatic changes and climate change effects. Several years ago oil was found in the North Sea. It was a boom to the British and Norwegian economies. Oil rig platforms were designed and built during the 1970s to extract this new "wealth". The final result being that the whole North Atlantic weather has been changed for the worse by the increased global warming, so current North Sea oil platforms are at serious risk. New rigs have to be redesigned. Old rigs have to be strengthened. Since the 1990s oilrigs have been designed with support legs much higher than those designed in the 1970s. It's ironic but even oilrig designers now recognize what is happening to world weather. Since 1960 the average height of waves in the North Atlantic has increased by an astonishing 50% (Sheldon Bacon of the Institute of Oceanographic Sciences at Wormley, UK, as reported in *New Scientist* 29 August 1992).

The oil companies scored another "own goal" when on 5 January 1993 the bulk oil carrier *Braer*, carrying 84,000 tons of crude oil, went aground on the rocks off Garth's Ness in the Shetland Islands. None of the oil could be salvaged. The global-warming-generated weather was too dreadful and the sea was too rough. It was a disaster. Huge waves, abnormal even for the treacherous North Atlantic, prevented any hope of salvage.

What in particular caused this enormous increase in average wave size in the North Atlantic? It appears it was probably the combination of two things. The first being a change in the atmospheric pressure relationship between the semi-permanent Azores High in the northeastern Atlantic off the coast of Portugal, and the semi-permanent Icelandic Low. The Azores Archipelago is an idyllic group of Portuguese islands, 950 miles (1,500 km) east of Lisbon. They are one of the few spots where the volcanic chain forming the Mid-Atlantic ridge, protrudes above the ocean surface. The second thing affecting the wave size was a new and increased differential in the North Atlantic sea temperatures. The combination apparently forces the North Atlantic winds to blow east for longer periods, and as the Oceanic Conveyor itself starts to misbehave, the waves grow bigger.

So much for the North Atlantic. The Southern and Tropical Atlantic may have a totally different and unusual problem to consider. It will undoubtedly be one of many. The yellow-bellied sea snake (*Pelamis platurus*) is a widespread inhabitant of the Pacific. It is descended from the cobra, but is considerably more venomous, being five times more deadly.

The sea snakes of the Pacific are a fairly late evolutionary development. They seem to have evolved after the Americas became joined by continental plate movements about three million years ago. The Caribbean Plate drifted in from the Eastern Pacific and blocked the water passage between North and South America. The Caribbean Plate could hardly be called a "continental plate", more of an "island plate", as it is only about the size of Western Australia or Argentina. As a result, the yellow-bellied sea snakes never made it to the Atlantic. Their habitat follows the warm Pacific and Indian Ocean currents, down to the Cape of Good Hope on the southern tip of South Africa, and stops there. The South Atlantic, on the southern tip of Africa, is a little too cold for their liking, so they never got around the corner into the South Atlantic. That is at this time of writing.

Sea-temperature rises that have already occurred in many parts of the world, if repeated on that short strip of southeast African coastline, would open the doors for the yellow-bellied sea snake, and its brothers, and its cousins, to move into the naïve and innocent waters of the Atlantic. They would thrive in the Caribbean. Atlantic marine life did not evolve a natural tendency to avoid sea snakes. Atlantic salmon have been shown to happily try to eat them with obvious and unpleasant consequences.

Sea snakes can be prolific breeders. In 1932 a dense line of sea snakes (*Astrotia stokesii*, a brother of the yellow-bellied sea snake) was sighted in the Strait of Malacca, between Malaysia and Indonesia and Penang and Singapore. The line was 3 metres (10 feet) wide and 100 kilometres (60 miles) long. Imagine a river of very poisonous sea snakes that long in the balmy waters around the blissful islands of the Caribbean.

Tropical diseases are another threat looming with frightening implications for our very near future. If we permit global warming to continue, the supposedly safe Western world can expect a widespread and deadly influx of tropical diseases. We can expect malaria, leishmaniasis and its variation Yellow Fever, and schistosomiasis to move out of their confines in the tropics and spread north and south. They will move further south than they are now in South Africa and South America. Schistosomiasis, like malaria, is a parasitic disease and falls second only to malaria as a parasitic world killer.

These diseases will move into Australia. Malaria cases are already being reported regularly in north Queensland.

In the Northern Hemisphere we can expect tropical diseases to spread into North America and the countries of southern Europe. West Nile virus, a leishmaniasis-type virus, is now in New York City.

Let us not kid ourselves that tropical disease control in First World countries has been successful because of the development of drugs. Tropical diseases have become extremely resistant to drugs. Control results more from natural periods of cool weather coupled with excellent hygiene than from brilliant medicine. In countries where these diseases are endemic, a general population immunity has been developing over centuries or more probably millennia. In the cooler countries of the world such general population immunity is nonexistent. Evolved population immunity unfortunately requires a lot of people to suffer and die.

These diseases are already spreading. The spread has not yet manifested itself to any great extent so we still have a little time available. We have about the time it takes for babies today to grow into teenagers. But we don't have more time than that as climate change accelerates.

Paradoxically at this time, in some areas, Greenland ice is actually accumulating slightly, which illustrates what could occur in Europe and Canada. We can't tell. At the moment, and also for how long we can't forecast, Europe is rapidly getting hotter. Floods, droughts and fires, once unheard of in the previously benign European climates will for a while it seems, become common and their severity is predicted to become progressively more devastating.

Once upon a time Europe was never generally considered as an area prone to flooding. But that has certainly changed. Extreme floods are now becoming common in all of Central Europe. As the new millennium commenced, the worst flooding in at least half a century occurred along the Rhine River. Both the Maas and the Waal rivers exceeded all previous flood heights. At least 30 people died in the Low Countries. Damage was estimated at US$2 billion. In August 2002 a flood occurred in the Elbe River basin and up into parts of the Danube. Damages exceeded $12 billion. Such flooding has never previously been recorded in any European historical records. There are records in Dresden, Germany that tell of ten extreme floods occurring since the thirteenth century. The two highest peaking at 27 feet and 29 feet (8.2 m and 8.8 m). That August 2002 flood peaked two feet higher at 31 feet (9.4 m).

Today, in Europe such disasters are becoming commonplace with costs spiralling almost out of control. However, the Europeans are still force-fed the concept that using cheap coal to generate their power underpins their standard of living. Surely that must now become an obvious public relations marketing myth. Even if coal, gas and oil were free, the world couldn't afford the costs of the resultant ongoing floods and droughts and fires and tornadoes.

Then, just as suddenly Europe will get very cold as continuously chang-ing weather patterns will again drastically alter European climates. An oceanic heat flow, originating way back in the central Pacific and given a boost on its way through the Bahamas, will be cut off, or massively reduced. More than 25% of the heat energy that has always warmed Europe comes from these warm ocean currents. Cutting or even reducing this energy flow will increase the duration of winter ice and snow coverage over Northern and Central Europe. The albedo is a measure of the amount of sunlight reflected back into space from the planetary surface. The extra ice and snow cover will increase the albedo and so increase the local cooling effect, thereby increasing the duration of ice and snow coverage further.

As soon as just one summer thaw is missed, the ice and snow buildup can become permanently established. Then in a few short years global warming will likely produce a localized European-only ice age. Europe, on the same latitude, could acquire the climate of northern Siberia, while in complete contrast the Arctic Ocean will be warmer.

One might think that increasing snow cover in Northern Europe would help offset sea-level rises caused by melting ice in either the Greenland or the Antarctic ice caps. But these ice caps are enormously thick. Their thickness is often measured in kilometres. The additional snow cover in Europe would be trivial by comparison. It would have negligible affect on world sea levels.

The establishment of an ice sheet cover depends on large quantities of moist air at the higher latitudes to produce the snow. But if it is there, and in quantity, then in a few seasons excess snowfalls, compressed by their own weight, can form an almost instant, although thin, ice sheet. For Europe, this reflective cover adds to the threat posed by ocean circulation changes.

The British Isles are extremely vulnerable to the effects global warming will have on weather in the Arctic Circle and to ocean current flows in the Atlantic. Their weather and their warm air also comes from warm tropical surface waters flowing north. The English fogs are formed when cold Arctic Ocean currents flowing down the English Channel chill the warm moisture-laden air off the Atlantic. It's this mix that creates the English "pea soup" fogs. The English are renowned for talking about the weather. This time it's very serious. The North Atlantic and the British Isles are areas where global warming indicators are very apparent.

The Royal Botanic Gardens at Kew in Surrey, England were established in 1759 by the mother of George III and donated to the country by Queen Victoria in 1840. It has an area of 360 acres (146 ha) and contains samples of more than 25,000 plant species. (One hectare is 2.471 acres or close enough to two and a half acres). Kew Gardens, as it's usually called, is also an important centre for botanical research. The weather there is typically English—pleasant sunshine and often long periods of drizzle. It has always been fairly benign.

On 15 October 1987, disaster struck. Southern and Eastern England were lashed with tremendous storms. The sedate Kew Gardens was devastated. Trees that had stood for 200 years were destroyed. The glass in the glasshouses, where the greenhouse effect kept tropical plants thriving, was shattered. Wind gusts to 100 mph (160 km/h) were recorded in the area. Nineteen people were killed in the storms. Almost twenty million trees were reported destroyed. Damage estimates exceeded $3 billion. It was dubbed "The great storm of 1987", nothing had ever been seen like it. It was the "once in a thousand years" disaster.

In January 1990 it happened again. At Kew Gardens wind gusts were recorded 20 knots (36 km/h) stronger than the worst winds of 1987. Eighty rare tree specimens that had survived the 1987 storm were destroyed within the gardens themselves. The glasshouses again sustained dreadful damage. This time the storm was more widespread; 120-knot (220 km/h) winds were recorded right up into Scotland.

New and ferocious storms are not the only indicators of frightening and extensive weather pattern changes as global warming takes hold. Temperature records in the UK have been kept since about the 1850s. The 1980s were shown to be the warmest decade ever recorded. The 1990s were hotter still. The record for the highest temperatures since records began was broken six times in the decade, with 1998 the hottest year. And temperatures continue to rise.

The United Kingdom has never been considered a nation prone to drought. It sounds impossible but now it happens. Unusually high temperatures in continental Europe brought warmer and drier air that produced drought in England's southeast. While the northwest of England had been experiencing slightly higher than average rainfalls, severe drought plagued the southeast of the country for five consecutive years. Rainfalls in some areas were down by 70%. Many small creeks ran dry that have never ever been known to stop running. Ever. Rivers had levels lower than any previously recorded.

Because of the sudden end to reliable weather patterns, serious consideration is being given to pumping treated sewage effluent back upstream for reuse. There are proposals to construct channels to bring water from the wetter northwest of the country down to London and the southeast. The cost would be staggering. But even that would not be enough, as more money would be needed for newer systems when the new weather pattern are found to be subject to even more unknowns. The times of useful weather predictability in the United Kingdom have ended.

Following the severe droughts, weather patterns changed again. In the year 2000 the UK experienced the worst floods in recorded history. Towns were inundated that had never ever been known to flood before. Now severe flooding is a regular occurrence throughout the land.

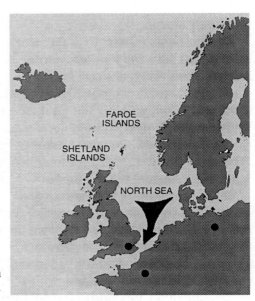

A storm surge coupled with a high tide funnels into the English Channel.

In the United Kingdom, as in many parts of the world, rats breed when the weather warms in spring and summer. In the United Kingdom, when the winter snow falls and the temperatures drop, the rats freeze to death. That's the way it was, but the winter of 1999–2000 was particularly warm, and the rats survived in huge numbers. With the following summer came a rat plague. People in the United Kingdom can probably expect this to be a regular occurrence from now on.

The east coast of England has another problem. The North Sea, at its northern end, is open to the Arctic Ocean, and at its southern end it is almost closed off by the very narrow and shallow English Channel. It's narrow enough that people swim across almost regularly. Strong and prevailing winds over oceans not only make big waves, but they also raise sea levels on the downwind side of the ocean. Storm winds produce a storm surge. A sea level difference of three feet or one metre is not uncommon. Funnel such a surge into a narrowing channel and surge heights magnify. If such a storm surge is coupled with a high tide, severe coastal flooding can occur. The English Channel in width and depth has a distinct funnel shape.

In 1953 a severe storm in the North Sea brought all these factors together. A massive surge raced down south and into the English Channel. Sea walls were breached in Holland, Belgium and the eastern coast of England. In total over 2,000 people died. In Holland 1,800 people died. Farmlands along the coast were so badly inundated by the flood surge and the collapse of sea walls that they were never recovered. Some of these farmlands are not even land any more. They are shallow estuaries. They will probably never resurface, as an odd local geological phenomenon results in a constant lowering of land levels in the area by inches a year. Adding to the problems of general sea-level rises, it is also reported that tide heights are increasing in the area faster than anywhere else in the world. The increase is approximately a quarter of an inch a year (6 mm).

New and massive sea walls were constructed following this 1953 disaster. Coastal erosion from wave pattern and tidal changes have already removed 25% of the salt marshes in Essex alone, exposing these sea walls to the full frontal attack of the now enlarged ocean waves. New and bigger sea walls will now be built further inland. In this part of the English Channel, Britannia no longer rules the waves. Global warming does.

On the other side of the world to the United Kingdom lies China, the most populous country on earth with 1.3 billion people. The Chinese government now has a policy of one child per family, a policy easily circum-vented by simply not registering additional children. This probably adds another 100 million or so to the population estimates. Therefore, almost one quarter of the world's population lives in China. That population relies on just 7% of the world's agricultural land for food.

The ecological problems facing China are frightening. One sixth of the total land area is desert, and this is now increasing at an alarming rate. It is estimated that in the period from 1950 to the year 2000 the desert areas doubled in size. Lakes in China are drying up. Of the 1,066 lakes in Hubei Province alone, more than two-thirds dried up over the forty-year period from 1949 to 1989.

Quite erroneously, much of the blame for the drying of these lakes, the enormous increase in erosion, and the vast increase in desert areas, is attributed to deforestation. Rarely is mention made of the effects that global warming is having on the climate and weather patterns of China.

Official figures for deforestation, in the forty-year period commencing in 1949, show a decrease in total forest area from 12.7% to 12%. These figures were reported in *New Scientist* in 1 July 1989 along with a report on a book, *China In The Valley*, by He Bochuan. He Bochuan, a professor of philosophy of science at Zhongshan University, Guangdong, laments the loss of China's forests. It seems most unlikely that this 0.7% decrease in forest area could, in consequence, increase desert areas by the equivalent of 15% of the country's total area.

Using wood decreases the use of energy-consuming alternatives, so de-forestation characteristically is blamed for everything. Surely it would seem most unlikely that a tiny, almost theoretical 0.7% decrease in Chinese forest cover would have the effect of drying up hundreds, or possibly thousands of lakes across the country and result in massive silt buildup in the Yellow River. In some places it is reported that this silt buildup increased the water level by 33 feet (10 m). It doesn't make sense that such a minuscule decrease in a country's forest cover could cause the "unusual" flooding that affected half of all the provinces of China. The flooding caused the Yangtze River to become another "Yellow River" carrying half a billion tons of silt and yellow mud into the sea each year. The "hug a tree" and use-plastics people are barking up the wrong tree, expecting us to believe such conclusions.

It's more reasonable to suspect that global warming and the massive increase in the use of state-subsidized agrochemicals, especially nitrogenous fertilizers as reported in *Newsweek*, May 1995, is creating most of China's environmental problems.

According to a "Policy Forum" article in *Science*, Vol. 288, June 2000, the reality is that total forest cover in China has actually risen. They state that between 1950 and 1995, total forest cover increased by 8.7%. There has been a decrease in native forests and a marked increase in fast-growing timber plantations.

Various and consistent predictions have been made on the effects of global warming on China. It is believed that much of the steppe (prairies or savannas) would become desert. The weather in China would become much hotter and considerably drier, and the country would experience regular and severe cyclones. In consequence there would be a reduction in wheat production and rice yields and an estimated 50% reduction in the soybean harvest. Also as a result of global warming, the predicted 20-inch (0.5 m) rise in sea levels by the year 2050 would flood and devastate the low-lying East China plains, destroying thousands of acres of fertile and high-yielding rich alluvial soils.

Widespread famine in a country comprising a quarter of the world's population, a country maintaining the largest army on earth, controlled by a single centralized authority and well-armed with nuclear weapons, is a disconcerting concept.

In world history we see it is common for nations to go to war to ensure ample food supply for their machinery of state. Remember Chinese leaders a few years back did say that China had a big enough population to "comfortably survive" a global nuclear war. Their problem now must be how to survive global warming.

There is often a lot of sulphur in coal. The World Bank estimates that localized atmospheric sulphur dioxide pollution is costing the Chinese economy US$45 billion per year just in lost production. Major cities throughout China and Southeast Asia have experienced a 400% increase in atmospheric pollution in twenty-five years. Sulphur dioxide levels run four or five times higher than WHO (World Health Organization) safe limits. If in these cities fossil fuels continue to be the major source of energy, then the annual cost of preventing the resulting sulphur compounds entering the atmosphere has been put at $87 billion per year.

The World Bank states that pollution in China resulting from their current massive use of fossil fuels now kills 218,000 people per year. The bank states this will increase to 850,000 per year over the next twenty years, unless extreme measures are undertaken to reduce atmospheric pollution. China can no longer afford the high price of cheap energy.

Trouble in Guyana.

Along with sulphur compounds, several other chemical compounds are discharged into the air from the burning of fossil fuels. They become aerosols. Aerosols are a name given to both tiny particles of solid materials and tiny droplets of liquid when dispersed in a gas; generally in air. Aerosols alter the optical properties of the air. Some aerosols also produce acid rain. The massive accumulation of aerosols in the air over India and western China from burning fossil fuels, not only in India but, more importantly in central and eastern China, is modifying weather patterns and monsoonal rainfalls.

Indian monsoons are actually an enormous annual sea-breeze effect, whereby hot air rising over the Indian subcontinent sucks in cooler moist sea air off the Indian Ocean, producing rain. The annual monsoon season lasts about four months and accounts for some 70% of Indian rainfall. Indian agriculture is naturally heavily dependent on monsoonal rains.

Aerosol haze is casting a cooling shadow over the subcontinent that decreases the monsoon effects. Also the ground is not warming but the upper air is. The warming has a tendency to form upper-air inversions which prevent rain cloud formation. While some areas in the south are expected to experience increased rainfalls, most areas will not.

Indian food production will suffer. Severe disruption to the Indian monsoon system will affect a country with a billion people. We can expect that food aid to India will be a likely necessity in the very near future.

Guyana is a small country on the northeast coast of South America, nestled between Venezuela and Brazil. It is typical of the world's small developing nations. Guyana has a population of just 700,000 people. It is extremely mountainous and so 90% of the population live on their narrow coastal plain. The Dutch established colonies in the regions of Essequibo, Demerara and Berbice at the navigable river mouths along the coastal plain. The Dutch, as was their way, built simple, effective sea walls and created rich sugar plantations along the low-lying narrow coastal strip. Wide belts of mangrove swamps protected the sea walls from the tropical Atlantic.

The Dutch ceded the colony to Britain in 1814. The capital then became Georgetown, just north of the old Dutch town of New Amsterdam. The country became the Co-operative Republic of Guyana on 23 February 1970. During the 1970s the new government, as is the wont of most bureaucracies, nationalized the major industries and the standard of living declined in consequence. Mangrove trees then became the main source of firewood for cooking. Mangrove swamps were cleared, exposing the old sea walls, which then began to rapidly deteriorate.

Global warming, more intense storms and rising sea levels have now come into calculations on the economy of Guyana. To protect this country from the virtual elimination of its total gross domestic product, sea walls would need to be constructed along most of the 300-mile (500-km) coast-line. A sea wall capable of withstanding sea-level rises currently forecast for the next 100 years would cost something like US$2,000 per yard (metre). Unfortunately, Guyana is not a rich country and the wall won't be built; it seems now that sea-level rises and increased storm surges will be an actuality.

The fertility of the soils in Guyana will decrease markedly from salination caused by the periodic sea flooding that has already commenced. Food and sugar production are expected to decline rapidly.

Although Guyana is small and undeveloped it has a well-developed and resilient democratic structure. Its main industries are bauxite mining (the ore from which aluminium is produced) and sugar. To replace the loss of income from sugar exports there will be a consequential massive expansion in the exports of rainforest timbers. Undoubtedly, the citizens of this poor country will then be blamed for contributing to global warming. Around the world, the few embassies that this poor country can support will likely be stoned and sprayed with graffiti by the green pawns, the foot soldiers of the fossil fuel industries.

Let's have a look at Central Africa and *The Snows of Kilimanjaro*. The book was written by Ernest Hemingway. The adventure movie stared Gregory Peck, Ava Gardener and Susan Hayward and was made in 1952. Kilimanjaro is in Tanzania. Because of its ice and snow cover, it's called Africa's Shining Mountain. It's a volcanic mountain and at 19,344 feet (5,896 m) is the highest mountain in all of Africa. It was first surveyed in 1912. The latest NASA satellite photos show that 82% of the snow cover observed in 1912, and believed to have formed more than 11,000 years ago, is gone. Many meteorologists expect the snows of Kilimanjaro to be all gone by 2015. Africa will have lost its Shining Mountain.

Further north, Africa is a dry place. From the Indian Ocean, near the entrance to the Red Sea, through to the Atlantic Ocean and the Gulf of Guinea, there lies a vast area of land called the Sahel. It is the semi-arid land, south of the giant Sahara Desert and down to about 10° south latitude. Climate predictions based on greenhouse computer modelling say this area should become more prone to drought as greenhouse gases accumulate in the atmosphere. The models tell us that much dryer desert conditions will

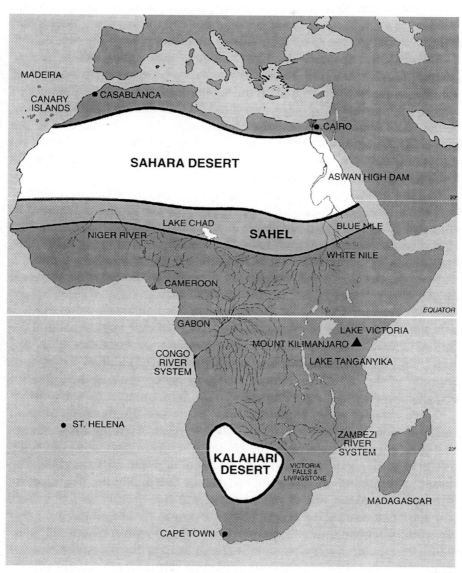

Wet tropical central Africa drains to the sea via only four main river systems. Overflow from Lake Victoria flows into the Nile. Also shown is the Aswan High Dam and Mount Kilimanjaro, as well as the general location of the Sahel.

move south into the Sahel from the Red Sea right across to the extreme west coast of Africa.

Well it's happening. Weather patterns are changing. For a thousand years, life in the Sahel has been based on simple subsistence farming. Farmers sow their crops based on expected future weather. When that future weather proves to be drier than is customary, crops fail and we call it a drought. But droughts don't last that long; next season will be back to normal. That's how it was, but not any more. The larger countries south of the Sahara are Mauritania and Spanish Sahara on the Atlantic Coast, then west to Mali, followed by Niger and Chad both bordering Lake Chad, then Sudan, then Ethiopia and Somalia on the Indian Ocean east coast. In the media the droughts and the starvation in these countries are blamed on everything and anything, but never on the warming of our globe from the fossil-fuel-induced greenhouse effect.

In 1967, rainfall in much of the Sahel was dropping. It has never in any year since reached the pre-1967 averages. Dreadful droughts occurred in 1972 and 1973, and again but worse in 1983, 1984 and 1987 and 1990. The 1990 drought was the worst of them all. Rainfall patterns in the Sahel have been declining in step with rises in temperatures in the southern oceans.

Even so, the media still blames the droughts in the Sahel on the local people, who it seems, after many hundreds of years of survival suddenly decided to overgraze and destroy the vegetation that made their very existence possible. "Destruction of the rainforests on the Atlantic West Coast and the Gulf of Guinea" was thrown in for good measure. None of this made any sense; it didn't have to, just so long as the issues stayed clouded. But now, in scientific circles at least, opinion is swinging rapidly towards the influence of global warming as the prime reason for the devastation in these countries.

Large areas of India, Southeast Asia, Africa and the northern areas of South America can expect declines in grain yields resulting from climate changes. Studies presented to the United Nations in April 1992 indicated a drop in grain production and grain yields of between 10% and 15%. The same study pointed out the quite substantial rise in famine. The number of people at serious risk of malnutrition will rise quickly to 400 million and approach one billion people within 50 years. It's virtually certain that the world will have at least a quarter of a billion "environmental refugees" within this period. A well considered estimation says that the environmental refugee problem, resulting from world climate changes and rising sea levels, will be 40 times bigger than the world refugee problem existing at the end of World War II. Our use of "cheap" energy will prove to be very expensive.

In southern African countries, over the last ten to fifteen years, weather patterns have changed producing generally drier conditions throughout. The southern African drought of 1991–1992 was the most devastating of the century.

The mighty Zambezi River is the biggest river in southern Africa. It forms the border between Zambia and Zimbabwe (formerly Rhodesia) and plunges over Victoria Falls near the town of Livingston. The Zambezi catchments include almost all of Zambia, half of Zimbabwe and about a third of Angola. Also the trickle of water that drains from most of Botswana, and the northern rivers of Namibia (formerly South West Africa), ends up in the Zambezi. Finally, the Zambezi flows through central Mozambique and into the Indian Ocean.

Every country in southern Africa, except South Africa itself, uses the waters of the Zambezi River. With the lower rainfalls experienced in southern Africa, enormous projects are being designed to dam the Zambezi and its tributaries. One such project involves a pipeline almost 250 miles (400 km) long, running from just below Victoria Falls through to the dry southwest of Zimbabwe and on to the town of Bulawayo. In the process, the water would need to be elevated over 3,000 feet (1,000 m), one of the highest pumped-lifts in a city's water supply in the world. The enormous power requirements to pump the water this high would probably come from additional dams for hydroelectric power—also on the Zambezi or its tributaries.

The combined population of the six countries in the Zambezi River catchment area is 47,000,000 people. Who owns the waters of the Zambezi River? Whose claims are going to be valid, and who will determine this? It is a problem in the making.

Should global warming so change weather conditions in southern Africa that we see thousands die as the rivers dry, will our oil-industry-dominated media ever even hint that the greenhouse effect and fossil fuels had something to do with it? It's unlikely.

The South Pacific Convergent Zone is a general area, or zone, of storms and winds in the eastern part of the South Pacific Ocean. According to New Zealand's National Institute of Water and Atmospheric Research (reported in *Australian Science*, Vol. 19, Number 9, October 1998), this zone has moved 90 miles (150 km) east since 1977. The zone's movement has brought drought and depressed rainfalls to Fiji, New Caledonia and Vanuatu. In Fiji, it slashed sugar production with subsequent effects on the vulnerable national economy. The same change caused the drought and resulting food shortages in Papua New Guinea. According to the report, New Zealand's weather has "substantially warmed" over the last twenty years with significant weather pattern changes. The New Zealand institute predicts things will get worse as global warming intensifies.

The temperature in the Western Pacific Warm Pool, mentioned earlier, is rising consistently. Year by year the Transcontinental Demarcation Zone stretching across Australia is creeping down the Australian east coast. These changes mean that the "cyclone belt", the area in which tropical hurricanes can be expected, is also moving down the east Australian coast. Sydney, at latitude 34° south, is no longer a cyclone-free city as its residents have at great cost become aware. More than eighty percent of the east Australian

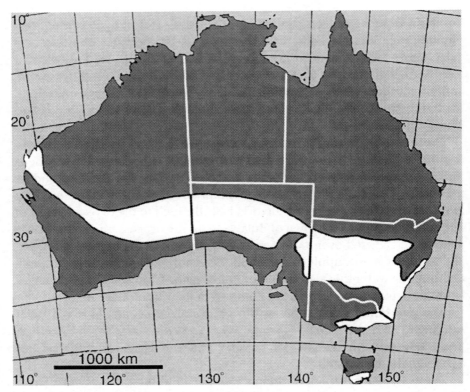

The Australian Rainfall Transcontinental Demarcation Zone separates the predominantly summer-rainfall areas (north) from the predominantly winter-rainfall areas (south). Within the zone itself patterns can vary, often from year to year.

coast can now be included in the cyclone belt. It is no longer confined to northern Queensland. Tropical cyclone "Sose" got as far south as New Zealand in April 2001.

Australia and New Zealand are efficient and affluent Western democracies. Neither of these countries is overpopulated. Loss of life from unexpected weather phenomena resulting from global warming will be minimal. In broad terms it will simply cause minor reductions in the general standard of living. Some farming areas could receive additional rainfall with beneficial results. However, it is extremely unlikely that the areas benefiting would ever compensate for those areas that will suffer from the changes. Climate modelling predictions are becoming realities. The capital cost of change is high.

The Australian Transcontinental Demarcation Zone marks the divide between two distinct climate types. In general north of this zone, weather patterns produce predominately summer rainfall and south of the zone winter rains dominate. The zone itself is fairly narrow, about 60 miles (100 km) wide on the west coast where it starts at Exmouth Gulf and Northwest

Cape about 60 miles (100 km) north of the Tropic of Capricorn. It heads southeast and by the time it reaches the Great Australian Bight, near the West Australian border, it has widened to form a zone up to 300 miles (500 km) across. It arcs across the Great Australian Bight, through the middle of South Australia, where it again turns slightly south as it passes through central New South Wales hitting the Australian east coast centred on Sydney.

Greenhouse computer predictions say the demarcation zone should gradually move south. It appears to be happening as predicted. In central New South Wales, around the city of Dubbo, rainfall records for the first half of the twentieth century, although varied, showed a distinct rainfall peak through May, June, and July, Southern Hemisphere autumn and winter months. In recent years there has been a complete reversal in weather patterns. These same months are now the driest months of the year. December, January, and February, the summer months, are now the wettest months. A new, short, high-rainfall pattern in the spring has also established itself, probably temporarily. But that is, predictably, quite impossible to predict.

Farming in these areas can adapt easily to these changed weather patterns, but not so in Queensland. El Niños have always been a part of Queensland's climatic pattern. They used to bring drought conditions for a single season, on average about once every six or seven years. But El Niños have changed. The longest El Niño event ever recorded became established and continued for the entire first half of the 1990s. Normally El Niños last a season, but that 1990s El Niño lasted half a decade. Drought in inland Queensland seemed never-ending. Hundreds of thousands of cattle and sheep and untold numbers of kangaroos died the slow death of starvation and thirst. Bankrupt farmers left their farms and/or properties (ranches, to use the U.S. term) in droves.

These were not people who were irresponsible. These were not people who had overstocked, overgrazed and willfully and stupidly destroyed the land that had been in their families for generations. These were people who had learnt to live with nature and generally improve on it. What they hadn't learnt was that oil and coal extracted from the earth all around the world was altering the rules of survival. The weather patterns that their farms, their lives and their livelihood had been structured around were both changed and now ever changing.

There are three states on the Australian east coast. The coastline is 2,000 miles long (3,300 km). Drought is common in Australia, but generally occurs in different areas in different states at different times. At the beginning of the millennium we saw the entire eastern half of the country in the grip of drought. Such a drought is almost unprecedented. It covered an area as big as from Houston to Minneapolis and back to the Atlantic seaboard.

As the country dried out, the fires started. Strong hot winds made many unstoppable. In Canberra, the national capital, 400 homes in what are normally quiet suburban streets were razed. The nearby Mount Stromlo National Observatory had for many years been the most significant observatory in the Southern Hemisphere. The entire complex was completely destroyed. It is doubtful if it will ever be rebuilt, but efforts are underway.

Australian and U.S. firefighters now regularly cross the Pacific when help is needed. Both countries are needing each other's firefighters more and more as global warming takes hold.

Australia became an importer of grain for the first time since a colony was established here in 1778. The grain came from the United States.

It's happening all over the world. Weather patterns and local climates are changing. As a result, the most suitable form of agriculture for areas also changes. Croplands may become only good for grazing. Tree lands may suit grain cropping. Grazing lands may become deserts. Almost overnight, support facilities are in the wrong place. Railroads and grain handling facilities, stock yards, abattoirs, power lines, roads and even towns would suddenly be better some place else.

Water supplies to cities suddenly become insufficient. Dams are too small and must be enlarged, if catchment areas allow. Or new dams must be built. For other cities and their water supplies, the opposite is true. Water supplies to the suddenly wetter cities come from dams whose spillways were never designed to handle such massively increased flow rates and become prone to failure.

When things are all in the wrong place, efficiency goes out the window. The efficiency of a society creates its standards of living. Surely we can afford to pay a little extra for our raw energy to prevent such massive and costly waste. The U.N. reports for 2003 that fires in Russia consumed 24 million hectares. That's double the previous year, and it was bad.

In New Zealand, across the Tasman Sea from Australia, it's a similar story. Parts of New Zealand record rainfalls amongst the highest in the world. One inch (25 mm) is a lot of rain for every day of the year, but in some parts there, that's what they get. In steep mountainous country, such rainfalls allows for the building of pristine, high-altitude dams and lakes to generate exceptionally efficient and inexpensive hydroelectric power. In New Zealand many of the lakes were already there.

Electricity consumption accounts for roughly a third of the cost of producing aluminium. New Zealand produces a lot of aluminium using their totally clean hydroelectric energy source.

In 1989, the country experienced its first-ever severe drought. Power rationing was imposed for the very first time in history. The whole New Zealand aluminium industry was threatened. That time, luckily the rains came in the nick of time. However, as a result of this scare a move gained momentum to abandon the New Zealand aluminium smelters. It has been suggested that they be relocated across the Tasman Sea to Australia where electricity generated by burning millions of tons of Australian coal might be more reliable.

What a mad kind of logic! The drought in New Zealand was caused by climate changes induced by burning coal and oil. Are we to stop using New Zealand's hydroelectric power and burn more Australian coal? And that of course produces even more climate instability.

The central area of the United States, comprising the Great Plains and the prairies, and all that vast area bounded to the west by the Rocky Mountains and on the east by the Appalachians, all drains down the Mississippi and the Missouri rivers into the Gulf of Mexico. It's the land Napoleon sold for $15 million to help fund his war with England. This vast catchment area stretches north to just across the Canadian border, west to the Rockies and east to the Great Lakes and the outer suburbs of Chicago on the shores of Lake Michigan. Even the Chicago River in downtown Chicago can flow backwards into this vast watershed, simply by closing some of the navigation locks on its lower reaches.

The Great Plains had a history of stable predictable weather patterns, and rainfalls. That is until now. The once-rare drought years are now becoming more frequent and wildly irregular. The farmers and ranchers, and the industries built around them, are suffering badly. They now get "good years" where once every year was a good year. As a result, the nation itself, like all other nations, will have depleted wealth, and be poorer because of the weather changes.

The 1990s El Niños were in full swing and what a swing it was. In the North American summer of 1993 the rains came! Des Moines, Iowa is about 450 km (280 miles) west of Chicago. It is not even on the Mississippi or the Missouri Rivers. It's on the junction of the Raccoon River and the Des Moines River, which in turn flow into the Mississippi a few miles downstream. Des Moines is a long way inland; as far from the Gulf of Mexico as Chicago is from New Orleans. The water had a long way to go to reach the sea. The Raccoon River rose 25 feet (8 m) higher than any preconceived prediction. It turned much of Des Moines, a city with a population of 393,000, into one vast lake.

Few construction projects are ever designed to withstand the statistically possible monster 500-year flood. No one ever expects to see one. But downstream at Hannibal, Missouri, the flood crest exceeded 32 feet (9.8 m). That is above the hypothetical 500-year flood height prediction of 30 feet (9.14 m). Five-hundred-year flood height predictions were exceeded throughout seven of the hardest hit Midwest States. Cost estimates for the flood damage exceeded $15 billion.

Unpredictable flooding can now be expected at any time, even in the very near future, in these states. They are no longer 500-year events. Farming enterprises are no longer predicable and reliable and in consequence, farmland is no longer as valuable. The $15 billion damages bill is negligible in comparison to the drop in farmland values. The total cost is therefore gigantic, but will never be truly calculated.

Expensive and devastating flooding can only occur in an area when it is a new phenomenon and is not catered for in the original designs and layouts of the roads, towns, airports, power lines and rural properties etc. When planning is undertaken, it is always based on historic climatic conditions. If we change the climate, as we are doing now, then the planning has all been in vain. We all become vulnerable and if not directly, then from inevitable increases in weather-related insurance premiums. It is confirmed that disasters and catastrophes, entirely resulting from or related to weather severity have increased fourfold since the 1960s. Ultimately, one way or another we all pay those extra premiums.

Dr Andrew Dlugolecki is an advisor to the U.N. Environment Programme. He is also a director of CGNU. CGNU is one of the world's biggest insurance groups. Damage growth is now rising at 10% a year. Dr Dlugolecki succinctly pointed out that by 2065 the damages done by global warming and the resultant climate changes would then exceed world GDP. It would mean a serious decline, or at best a stagnation in living standards around the world.

Every year in the United States up to a thousand tornadoes rip across the country causing severe destruction and loss of life. The average over a recent 50-year period was 810 per year. That's how it was. Then in May 2003, 400 tornadoes hit the United States in just one week. Nothing like it had ever been seen before. Australia was hit hard the same year. Australia averages about 20 tornadoes a year. Bad ones were rare. But not any more. With the weather changes in recent years, Australian tornado damage bills have started to skyrocket.

Cygnet Lake is located near the centre of Yellowstone National Park. The area has been dominated by lodgepole pine for the last 13,000 years, and the historical occurrences of severe bushfires can be determined by analyzing ash from the burnt pines in sediments in the bottom of the lake. Hot dry weather caused extensive fires, which destroyed much of Yellowstone during 1988. Prior to this, severe fires occurred at a rate of about two or three per thousand years (*Science*, Vol. 287, March 2000). Now they are becoming a regular occurrence there.

In October 2003, the worst fires to ravage California swept through the "unusually" tinder-dry southern areas of the state. Three-quarters of a million acres were burnt out. Twenty-two lives were lost. Over 2,600 homes were destroyed. This new extreme vulnerability of California to such weather conditions and the resulting horrendous damage is rarely, if ever, discussed in relation to general weather pattern changes resulting from global warming. But of course it is!

At that exact time in Australia, the final race of the Gold Coast INDY was stopped mid-race as "unusually" large golf-ball-sized hail pelted the city. After the hailstorm went through, the race restarted and was completed. (It was won by Sebastian Bourdais driving for the U.S. Lilly, Newman and Haas team.)

South of British Columbia on the eastern side of the Rocky Mountains in Montana is the beautiful Glacier National Park. There were about 150 glaciers in the park in 1850. There are now 37 left. Daniel Fagre of the U.S. Geological Survey predicts that if the melt rate continues, they will all disappear over the next thirty years. Every single glacier in Glacier National Park will be gone.

The Western United States fills its water supply dams from the annual snowmelt in the mountains to the east. Global warming will change the melt and rainfall patterns. The cities, the agriculture and the industries of the Western United States can't be moved overnight. Therefore, new and massive water storage and reticulation systems will have to be built in an endeavour to cater for the constant change. Even if fossil fuels were free, the money saved still couldn't cover the cost of these suddenly needed new projects.

The U.S. National Oceanic and Atmospheric Administration tells us that the 1999 North Atlantic hurricane season was the fiercest ever recorded. Wind speeds exceeded 210 km per hour (130 miles per hour). William Gray of Colorado State University warns, "We are entering a new era of more intense hurricane activity along the U.S. East Coast". The series of storms that came out of the Caribbean in 2004, including the horrendous "100-year event" hurricane Ivan is a grim taste of what's to come. It is interesting to note that mentions of global warming and the cancer of climate change in the reporting of these new weather phenomena are always conspicuous by their absence.

North to Alaska. In much of Alaska and Siberia the ground is permanently frozen. In both places, roads, buildings and airports are built on the solid permafrost. Thomas Osterkamp of the University of Alaska, Fairbanks reports that in some areas the permafrost is thawing "at rates approaching 20 centimetres per year" (8 inches per year). As a result, airport runways are fracturing, buildings are tilting and falling down, roads are caving in. The extremely expensive Trans-Alaska Pipeline is structured on the permafrost remaining permanent. But over the last thirty years things have changed. Along the pipeline it's thawing, and long lengths of pipeline will require rebuilding and restructuring.

To add to these problems permafrost contains large quantities of methane; and methane is twenty times more powerful as a greenhouse gas than carbon dioxide. This methane is released to the atmosphere as the permafrost thaws.

Now Arctic sea ice has started to melt and disappear. It has been reported that the area of the giant Arctic ice cap is decreasing by about 30,000 square kilometres a year, that's over 7 million acres a year.

Not only is the area of sea ice decreasing, but so to is the thickness of the ice sheet itself. Average ice thickness in the Arctic Ocean, north of Greenland, shrank from about 21 feet (6.5 m) thick to about 14.75 feet (4.5 m) during the 1980s alone.

In August, in the first year of the new millennium, the Russian icebreaker *Yamal* arrived at the North Pole. And there was no ice there. The North Pole was open ocean.

The New York Times (19 August 2000) and *BBC World News* (20 August 2000) were the first to report on the voyage of the *Yamal* in the Arctic Ocean. The reports originated from Dr Malcolm C. McKenna, a paleontologist, and Dr James McCarthy, an oceanographer at Harvard University, who were on board the *Yamal* at the time. The report stated that the thick pack ice, usually covering almost the whole Arctic Ocean, was thinning and breaking up. After their arrival at the specific location of the North Pole, they continued on to the next ice flow. The ship had to travel several miles into the shattered pack ice before they encountered material thick enough for the visitors to get off the ship and safely walk around on the ice. In the same report, Dr McCarthy also commented that Arctic sea ice during the 1950s and 1960s was almost twice as thick as it was during the 1990s. This has been confirmed by declassified U.S. Navy submarine reports.

Meanwhile at the South Pole, a monster iceberg broke off the Ross Ice Shelf in Antarctica. The 183-mile-long iceberg is one quarter of a mile thick (295 km long and 400 m thick). An iceberg this size would have to last years. Satellite records, started in 1977, have never before located an iceberg like this one, reported Matthew Lazzara of the Antarctic Meteorological Research Center at the University of Wisconsin-Madison. And they should know.

The current arrangement of the continents give us world climates enormously sensitive to the influence of small changes in heat flow, and we are not appreciating this vulnerability. At this moment the future we are creating is an unpublished experiment. It is unplanned and the reality is that we are being frighteningly irresponsible. Too many lives are at stake. We are risking too much of our total national and international assets.

We are conducting an experiment using the continents in their current unusual configuration and then boosting the heat input from the sun. Nobody knows what damage we are doing and what it will cost humanity. We are doing this by raising atmospheric carbon dioxide and greenhouse gas levels higher than at any time in the last 20 million years. That is a time well before even the current cyclic pattern of ice age existed.

The Yucatan Peninsula, in northeastern Mexico, forms the southern side of the Gulf of Mexico.

Sixty-five million years ago, an asteroid, or meteor, around 6 miles (10 km) in diameter and travelling at around 10 km per second, hit the earth on what is now that peninsula. It came in fast and low from the southeast. The energy from the impact was the equivalent of 10,000 atomic bombs going off

Sixty-five million years ago—sudden climate change and the end of the dinosaurs.

at once. The impact zone is still there and it is 300 km across. The dinosaurs could easily have handled the explosion. But then, as is happening now, the earth's tiny and fragile atmosphere was overwhelmed. An asteroid-created "nuclear winter" spread across the world as dust particles and the smoke from a burning world ecosystem mixed into the atmosphere and filtered out the life-sustaining sunlight. It now appears that other smaller and related impacts occurred around the same time as the Yucatan impact, and these contributed to this sustained period of nuclear winter.

Plant life stopped virtually overnight. The food chain was broken. Few survived. It terminated the age of the dinosaurs. It is estimated that 90% of all living species were wiped out. Probably several billion individual independent species of some form or other were in that horrific total. How long the nuclear winter lasted, or how long the period over which the mass extinctions occurred, is difficult to determine. It could have been less than 50 years and it could be as long as 10,000 years. Less than 1,000 years is more likely, but then less than 1,000 years is almost impossible to pinpoint.

The event is called the Cretaceous-Tertiary extinction, the K-T extinction.

Finally however, when the dust settled and sunlight could get through in full force, new plants grew in profusion. This fed a new evolutionary explosion on that ancient almost empty world. Some tiny mammal-like creatures, the very first mammals, which had only recently evolved, and some of the smaller reptiles were among the survivors. These new animals, in particular the mammals—the world's new breed—won the new evolutionary race.

Two hundred and fifty million years ago there was another massive extinction of life on our planet. It is called the Permian-Triassic extinction, or the P-T extinction. It was the worst one ever. In that event about 95% of all living species on the planet became extinct. A meteor impact did not cause this extinction. Admittedly, there is some debatable evidence that an impact may have had some contributing effect, but apparently it was not the real villain.

If the Cretaceous-Tertiary extinction can be described as like a "freezing cold nuclear winter" then the Permian-Triassic extinction should be described as a "scorching hot fossil fuel summer", for it was caused by carbon dioxide levels rising sufficiently to initiate runaway global warming.

This is what probably happened. A series of large outflows of molten lava spewed out of geological fault lines in an area that is now part of eastern Russia. The series of lava flows were similar to the lava flows that regularly, and in some places almost constantly, occur in Iceland today. Volcanoes are not all the same. Most volcanoes are short-term events. They are usually fast, explosive and dramatic. The lava flows in that ancient Russia were a series of slow ponderous events spread over a long time, possibly half a million years. One outpouring of lava would occur. It would solidify. Then the solid rock would be covered by another outpouring. Such lava flows, when they occur often form a series of step-like ridges. The Swedish word for steps is "trappa", so such lava flows are called "traps". Those lava flows that occurred 250 million years ago formed the Siberian Traps. The basalt flows cover an area the size of Germany and Italy combined.

Each time the lava flowed, large quantities of carbon dioxide were released into the atmosphere. It is hard to know for certain, but it seems that the total quantity was probably comparable with the quantities resulting from our massive extraction of fossilized carbon materials from the earth's upper crust. Some estimates suggest that over the long-term formation of the Siberian Traps the released carbon dioxide would have increased world temperatures by, very roughly, about 5°C.

What we are doing by our massive use of fossil fuels and our destruction of organic matter in soils is adding greenhouse gases to the atmosphere that, according to the IPCC (the United Nations–sponsored Intergovernmental Panel on Climate Change) estimates will cause a similar world temperature rise. The IPCC suggest possibly 5.8°C. Such a temperature rise will most certainly cause a significant percentage of species to become extinct, but nothing remotely like the Permian-Triassic, the P-T extinction of 251 million years ago. For a P-T-like extinction to occur requires a world climatic change to occur that needs the temperature to rise a further 5°C than that currently predicted by rises in anthropogenic carbon dioxide levels. That's a total of 10°C or 18°F rise in world air temperatures.

Our current use of fossil fuels cannot add enough greenhouse gases to the atmosphere to make this occur. But we very possibly could be triggering effects that might just make it an all-too-terrible reality. And the trigger might be a hair trigger. And the consequences would probably be irreversible.

What is the point in humanity taking such an incredible gamble?

At the bottom of any pond or sea or ocean, both in the time just before the Permian-Triassic extinction and in times today, there is and always will be massive quantities of decomposing biological residues. As they decompose they produce methane, and we know methane is twenty times more powerful a greenhouse gas than carbon dioxide. In all shallow water, the methane constantly bubbles to the surface as "marsh gas". The methane in the bottom of deep oceans doesn't bubble to the surface. It stays there. Under the extreme pressures and in the extreme cold at the bottom of the world's oceans, the methane combines with water and freezes into snowflake-type crystals of methane hydrate. There in the deep cold on the floor of the oceans the crystals accumulate. A 4- or 5-degree Celsius rise in the temperature of the seas and the oceans will start the methane hydrate crystals to thaw on a massive scale. That's about 7 to 9 degrees Fahrenheit. As that happens untold millions of tons of methane gas will inexorably bubble up to the surface and escape into the air. That extra methane in the atmosphere will be more than enough to raise world temperatures by the additional few degrees that created the greatest extinction in the history of planet Earth.

It can happen. There is twice as much carbon in the methane hydrates frozen at the bottom of oceans than there is in all the known fossil fuels of all types, anywhere in the world. The quantity is considered to be around 10,000 billion tons. We know it can happen because it has already happened before. Fifty-five million years ago the ocean waters did indeed warm gradually. The reason is as yet unknown. But we do know the critical threshold was reached, for quite suddenly the methane started bubbling up. Sea surface temperatures rapidly rose 8°C and deep ocean temperatures rose 5°C. Those temperatures changes ended the Paleocene epoch. The Paleocene epoch is the relatively short period between the end of the dinosaurs at the K-T boundary 65 million years ago and the extinction of 55 million years ago.

It took at most just a few thousand years for temperatures to peak out. It took about 250,000 years for temperatures and conditions on the planet to finally restabilize. In the unlikely event that that threshold was exceeded tomorrow morning, humanity and our civilization, as we know it, would probably not last a hundred years. So depending on your personal age, you might have grandchildren, but you would be unlikely to have great grandchildren.

Sediments build up on continental shelves to considerable thicknesses. Organic matter in these sediments also creates frozen methane hydrates. Warming can trigger, what people are now calling giant methane "burps". When this happens in the sediments near the steep edge of a continental plate it can trigger massive mudslides down the underwater cliff faces. Such mudslides generate massive tsunamis and, around the world, is one of the most common causes of large tsunamis. As the world slowly warmed, ending the last ice age some 12,000 years ago, it seems such submarine landslides slides were undoubtedly a feature of that global warming.

Off the coast of Norway and just north of Scotland is a sensitive area for such slides. Seven thousand years ago one particular slide generated waves estimated to be 65 feet (20 m) high in the Shetland Islands off northern Scotland. If this new global warming triggers similar slides off the Norwegian coast the funnelling effect in the North Sea would probably wipe out London.

The U.S. Naval Research Laboratories at the Stennis Space Center in Mississippi have recently found evidence that methane hydrate ice crystals are considerably less stably entrapped than previously believed. We are going to see methane bubbling out of the shallower seas much sooner than we thought.

Six hundred million years ago, the continents had drifted up near the equator to form a string of large wet tropical island continents. There was no polar continent at the South Pole as we have today, nor was there a semi-inland sea at the north pole. The high rainfalls on those tropical island continents caused massive and continuous widespread weathering of the exposed rock faces. A cycle would commence. Rock weathering processes would extract carbon dioxide from the surrounding air. This reduction in turn reduced the normal greenhouse effect.

Eventually things would get too cold. Large sheets of ice and snow would form on the higher tropical land surfaces. This reflected incoming sunlight back into space. The Earth would get colder still. Sea levels would drop further, and the cycle would start feeding itself. It is now thought that within a mere thousand years or so, the world and all the oceans would become covered with ice. Ocean ice would form a kilometre thick right up to the equator!

A phenomenon, now dubbed "Snowball Earth" would come into existence and the planet would go into hibernation. During the long cold period, world temperatures apparently averaged -50°C. That is -60°F. The whole world would be like our present Antarctic in winter.

Some life survived; probably near warm ocean vents in deep oceans.

Over the next possibly ten million years, volcanoes continued to pump out carbon dioxide into the atmosphere. The levels rose inexorably. It is believed carbon dioxide levels peaked out at levels several hundred times what we have today; possibly as high as 10,000 ppm.

A highly exaggerated greenhouse effect would finally win, out generating super global warming. It is thought that within as short a period as a century or so, all the ice covering the planet would melt. It melted as global temperatures rocketed from an impossibly low of -50°C to an impossibly high of +50°C. That's from -60°F to +120°F.

For the last three million years the world's landmasses have been located about as they are today. Ice ages and interglacial periods still cycle but currently they are not the exaggerated phenomena of those times. We have to keep it that way.

Today, for us and for all things that live on planet Earth, there is only one very serious problem facing us. The thin surface of the planet is where we all live, and the surface of our world is overheating. We can't let it happen. We have to fix it. And we have to fix it now.

World temperatures and world climates are determined by the quantity of carbon dioxide in the atmosphere. It is the blanket that keeps the world warm and stable. Change the thickness of the blanket, and a totally new and erratic world climate will establish itself. That new climate will not be concerned if our cities are below the new high tide level and our basements get flooded twice a day. It will not care if a billion people starve in new deserts or drown in unpredicted floods. It will not blink if for some totally unpredictable period, totally new areas of land are suddenly, almost overnight suited to grain growing. Areas that are, unfortunately, hundreds of miles from the existing silos, rail terminals, and road networks that serviced yesterday's world grain production. And of course it will be unconcerned with the extinction of hundreds of otherwise viable species whose habitats are suddenly and totally altered beyond recognition.

Ultimately we will all pay. We will pay in higher food prices, power charges, road costs and often in the abandonment and relocation of whole towns and infrastructures. This is the cost to us of continuing to use oil and coal and natural gas as our major source of energy. Fossil fuels no longer have a cost benefit and we are now paying the price. We will pay, and we will pay, and we will pay again. For we are not creating a stable "warmer" world; we are creating an unstable "warming" world. A new stable climate is an utter impossibility while carbon dioxide levels themselves are constantly rising. And even if we peg carbon dioxide at existing levels, stability is impossible until world ocean temperatures achieve stability and the new pattern of world ocean currents is finally established. The oceans of the world are so massive and can absorb so much heat that it will take many decades, and probably centuries, before any unknown and untried stability has any hope of forming. The cost of the cheap energy experiment is proving prohibitively expensive.

Our only guarantee against never-ending disasters and massive loss of life is to restore carbon dioxide levels to those that have existed for the last few million years. That means a cold turkey termination of our habit of burning fossil fuels to power civilization. It means an immediate switch to the wholesale utilization of energy sources that don't produce greenhouse gases and don't destabilize world climates and sea levels.

That is what we must do. It is urgent. It is imperative, and it is totally achievable. (How and why it can be done is explained in chapters 5 and 11. What we do is summarized in chapter 12.)

It is also a financial necessity. On price alone, a barrel of oil regularly exceeds the cost of many non-fossil-fuel energy sources. Coal is a cheaper energy source than oil, but has many hidden costs; coal mining and transport alone kills far too many people to be considered a cheap energy system. Non-fossil-fuel energy sources can be made sufficiently competitive with coal and oil. In many cases they are already. But that really doesn't matter as any cost incurred in abandoning fossil fuels as our prime energy source will be zero or negligible, in comparison to the cost of continuing their use. The cost of not abandoning fossil fuels is horrendous and escalating. In human life alone, 20 million people are expected to die of starvation as a direct result of global warming by the year 2050. That is the price of cheap energy.

The greenhouse effect is increasing the temperature of the earth's surface with frightening results. There is now no doubt. It is not the temperature rise itself creating the danger, it is the way that the temperature rise can so significantly and so destructively change well-established weather patterns and world sea levels. It will get much worse, but it can be fixed. It can be fixed without taking away the family car, without us all riding bicycles every-where, and without decreasing our standard of living. The simple things that we must do will be strenuously resisted by the powerful lobby groups who manipulate and influence governments and government agencies. Those lobby groups are employed by the oil, coal and gas industries and their offshoots, the most significant being the agrochemical industry.

Global warming is caused by our excessive use of fossil fuel and our excessive use of chemical fertilizers in agriculture. The effect is manifesting itself in disastrous ways in almost every country on earth. Not since the threat of atomic war has the world been placed in such a vulnerable position. Changing the surface temperature of a planet is much more important and much more terrifying than is ever commonly admitted.

Slow but meaningful events, such as continental drift and oscillations in astronomical patterns, change climatic conditions on earth over periods of thousands of years. The Earth's atmosphere and climate will slowly vary decade-to-decade, or even century-to-century, but weather conditions are fairly consistent and predictable. Most life forms can survive such slow climatic changes as they have time to relocate, modify or evolve. However, they can't survive meaningful, globally significant events occurring over relatively short time periods, such as caused by asteroid impacts or large-scale geological upheavals. Rapid climatic changes are deadly. Large-scale extinction of species is the rule. Shifting average global temperatures just a few degrees either way over a short time period will always lead to massive disruption of established ecological systems.

The term *nuclear winter* was coined to describe the overall world weather conditions following a large-scale nuclear war. In such a conflict, after the violence and destruction of the exploding bombs, the major threat to living things is not from radiation. It never has been. It is the resultant dust clouds that would permeate the atmosphere and shield incoming sunlight, and in turn generate global cooling. That is the most threatening effect.

Global warming is the opposite and at least equally as deadly. Huge increases in atmospheric carbon dioxide levels resulting from fossil fuel use are now overheating the world's biosphere.

As noted previously; sixty-five million years ago a large asteroid hit the planet in what is now Mexico's Yucatan Peninsula. The dust and debris from the impact created a nuclear winter of unprecedented proportions. The cold conditions persisted long after the impact. That impact, and the resultant climate modifications, ended the reign of the dinosaurs.

Sixty-five million years ago the warmth of sunshine could not get through the atmosphere, but the earth's warmth continued to radiate out into space, so world temperatures dropped. Now, 65 million years later, the sunshine gets through OK, but with the atmosphere's rapid and massive increase in carbon dioxide and other greenhouse gases, the warmth can't get out. Inexorably, world temperatures climb. We are beginning to experience the start of a thousand-year-long fossil carbon heat wave.

What we are concerned about in the greenhouse effect is not that it is there at all, for it is one of the prime factors that created the environment and the atmosphere in which we evolved and live. What we are concerned about is the frightening ease with which man's activities can rapidly change the levels of this greenhouse effect, and in consequence modify the total environmental balance of the planet.

It is awe-inspiring that the tiny and seemingly insignificant quantity of carbon dioxide, and related greenhouse gases in the atmosphere, control our world's surface temperature. They control all the world's climates, and every environment existing anywhere on the planet.

(The interrelationship between carbon dioxide and the minor greenhouse gases is discussed in more detail in chapter 4.)

Those minute quantities of greenhouse gases determine the water content of the atmosphere, the melting and forming rate of glaciers and the water level of the world's oceans. They determine where coastlines will be and whether those coastlines will be out on the edge of the continental shelf, or as sea levels rise, maybe fifty miles inland.

They determine whether rainforests will stay rainforests or whether they wither and die. They determine what land can be used for agriculture and the rainfall that land receives. Those minute quantities of greenhouse gases also determine the consistency of that rainfall. They determine whether it be summer rains or winter rains, or storm rains, or droughts or floods. Outside of geological events, the quantity of greenhouse gases in the atmosphere is the only variable that determines the flow of deep ocean currents, how much heat they carry and importantly, which way they flow.

Extracting once safely buried fossil carbon materials for energy and to produce agricultural chemicals has already increased the quantity of greenhouse gases by well over 30%. In consequence we are now witnessing the never-ending disruption of world weather systems and patterns and the resulting violence.

In the sediments that accumulate at the bottom of the world's oceans are entrapped huge quantities of methane and carbon dioxide. Unlike the methane formed in swamps, paddy fields and wetlands, the gases stay put at the bottom of the oceans. The intense cold, the enormous pressures and the quiet stability of the deep oceans prevent the gases bubbling up to the distant surface. But this stability is like a newly opened beer bottle: no shake, no bubbles. Unfortunately our global warming is beginning to destabilize the flow and temperatures of the world's deep ocean currents. We are introducing a shake to the system.

It is alarming as nobody has any real knowledge of what might happen. But it is logical that destabilizing these deep ocean currents will alter the temperatures on the ocean floors. Some areas will get cooler and the frozen gases will stay where they are. But where temperatures rise, it could suddenly release huge quantities of methane and carbon dioxide up to the surface and dangerously add to greenhouse warming. It is often speculated that giant expanding bubbles of these trapped gases are the explanation for the strange mysteries of ship losses in otherwise calm seas. If rising ocean temperatures cause gas releases, then they alone would almost certainly generate runaway global warming, and for any foreseeable future, the whole thing becomes an irreversible scenario.

That world weather systems are being destabilized, there is no doubt. Confirmation of the alteration of world weather patterns, of glacial move-ments, sea level changes and modifications of deep ocean currents, is flooding in. The confirmations are coming from weather stations, from satellite observations, from oceanographic monitoring stations and from a multiplicity of other information sources all over the planet.

Today the evidence confirming global warming has been finally and almost totally accepted by an overwhelming majority of world climatolo-gists. At The Hague conference on global warming in November 2000, 160 countries were represented by delegates and scientists: they too concluded it was happening.

The world's climate determines the whole pattern of human activity on the planet. The total costs, economic and social, of all our past wars will be less than the costs of the climatic change we are bringing about. Wars always eventually end. One side usually wins.

This book is about how we put an end to unpredictable climate change and how we terminate the looming threat of runaway global warming. We can do it. And we can do it all in a few short years and it can all be accomplished at utterly negligible cost. It's how we all can win. But we must start now.

2

How we fix global warming

OUR global warming and climate change problem is caused by excess quantities of greenhouses gases altering the optical characteristics of the world's atmosphere. Of all the greenhouse gases that concern us, carbon dioxide is the most significant. Where does it come from? We must understand the fundamentals of problems or we will never be able to solve them. With understanding we will appreciate how we have been, and are being, blinkered.

Originally all carbon dioxide comes from volcanoes, and that source will be pumping it out into the air long after mankind has gone. This delivery of carbon dioxide has been consistent for a few billion years. Admittedly there have been a few hiccups along the way when some areas of the earth would experience excessive volcanic activity. Over eons, the surface ecology evolved to stash it away at the same rate as it discharged from the world's volcanoes. Equilibriums became established. Humans, unfortunately, are digging up the stash, dumping it back in the air and putting the whole system out of balance.

Getting down to fundamentals. When you light a fire you burn "something", and what you burn was once some form of plant or animal structure. It was alive, and the chemistry of life is both built on, and is totally dependent on, the chemistry of the element carbon. It is the basic material of all living things. The carbon atom has the unique ability to chemically link itself, to itself infinitely, and also to link to a whole range of other elements. These links form never-ending chains and structures, sometimes of astounding complexities. The original energy used to form these complex carbon compounds is always, and has always been, the energy of sunlight absorbed on plant leaves by photosynthesis.

When the remains of living things are buried beneath the ground, and out of contact with air for many millennia, chemical reactions stabilize and the once-living things become fossils. The fossil materials that concern us in our problem of global warming are coal, oil, natural gas and sometimes peat. When any of these fossil forms re-emerge on the surface to be burnt for their energy or alternatively manufactured into ultimately degradable products, the carbon in them is converted back into atmospheric carbon dioxide. This increases the total carbon content of our planetary biosphere.

By extracting and using fossil carbon materials we are adding carbon to the biosphere that has been in storage and out of circulation for countless millions of years. As a direct consequence carbon dioxide levels in the atmosphere rise and greenhouse warming is exacerbated.

On the other hand, when we burn wood we are simply shifting carbon that is already in the biosphere, from one form to another; from wood to carbon dioxide. Then when timber regrows, the process is reversed; carbon dioxide is converted back to wood. Greenhouse gas levels are unchanged.

Deep ice core drillings at Vostok on the Antarctic continent show conclusively that in the 400,000 years before the massive mining of this buried fossilized carbon material, atmospheric carbon dioxide levels were surprisingly consistent. In that entire period, levels never once exceeded the levels that we had rapidly climbed to by the late 1900s. There is more information on the Vostok research results in the next chapter, along with reports on other research that shows pre-1980 carbon dioxide levels not being exceeded for as far back as 22 million years.

Global warming is the problem we face. As such there are two forms of non-atmospheric carbon placement that concern us. The first of course is in the fossil forms. (Limestone is also a fossilized form of carbon, but is not particularly relevant to our current global warming problem.)

The second storage form that concerns us in determining a solution to greenhouse warming however, is much more dynamic. It is the mass of carbon residing in our world's soils and in our world's living biology. And what then becomes of supreme importance is that we can massively and easily increase that quantity. That will solve half the problem.

Prior to the advent of the industrial revolution our requirement for energy for transport was satisfied by the horse, and what it ate. For power, the water wheel to grind our flour, and wood to supply us with heat. Animal skins, plant fibres and wood were our plastics. The rains came to constantly power our water wheels. Fibres were easy to grow. The regrowth of timber catered for our small population's tiny energy requirements. Life, for most of us, was harsh but simple. Just surviving occupied most of our time.

Then the rapid development of industry, an ever-rising standard of living, an unchecked and even encouraged population growth created an enormous and unprecedented increase in energy requirements.

We uncorked the jar containing the genie of fossil fuel with its vast store of ancient sunlight energy. Unfortunately, it's taken half a century to find out there is no such thing as a free lunch.

Burning these fossil fuels released the long-buried carbon. The carbon burned to become carbon dioxide. The very carbon dioxide that once upon a time prevented the very existence of oxygen-breathing life. The types and varieties of fossil fuels and how they can be easily replaced by fuels that won't contribute to Global Warning is discussed in chapter 11.

Fossil fuels are not the only culprit creating the mess that is global warming and climate change. There is another and it's an almost intimately related culprit. It's also near equal in guilt.

This second source of carbon dioxide into our atmosphere derives from the discharge of the gas from the wholesale destruction of soil organic matter and its conversion back to carbon dioxide. Our living soil is being killed and destroyed. Amazing as it may seem, some simple arithmetic clearly shows that the volume of this source of carbon dioxide pouring into our atmosphere is of comparable volume to the total coming from the burning of fossil fuels. This is true but it's an extremely well-concealed truth. Soil fertility degradation is a topic where facts and truth have been systematically twisted, distorted and hidden for very obvious commercial and marketing reasons.

Nevertheless the facts are available, albeit not readily. One of the many, and I believe the most, informative and valuable consideration and discussion on the destruction of the fertility of agricultural soils is in a collection of essays compiled as *The Albrecht Papers.*

The Albrecht Papers were published by Charles Walters, Jr. of *Acres U.S.A.* magazine, Kansas City, Missouri. My wife and I stayed with Chuck Walters in Kansas City and he visited us when he was in Australia. For many years Dr William A. Albrecht was Professor of Soils and Chairman of the Department of Soils at the University of Missouri, College of Agriculture. See chapter 6, "The Albrecht Papers" (page 152).

There are three things that contribute to the destruction of the fertility of agricultural soils. They are agricultural chemicals, monocropping, and inversion tillage. All three have a massive impact on soil organic matter. All three have the effect of breaking it down and releasing the carbon into the air as carbon dioxide. Therefore all three contribute massively to global warming. The three processes are considered in detail in chapter 6.

In stark contrast to truth and reality, the claim that receives the greatest publicity as a contributor to atmospheric carbon dioxide levels is the clearing of forest lands. This is portrayed as a monumental disaster. Yet this "claim" approaches complete fiction. The forest story is a logical and well-considered marketing ploy. In the ploy the general use of timber as a material of construction is portrayed as a crime against the planet. Children are constantly fed this fiction in insidious TV cartoons, where trees are portrayed as innocent and helpless "good guys", always to be protected, and at any cost. Reality is that in general, tree numbers aren't even in decline.

For decades the majority of Western countries have been growing vastly more timber and creating more forest than they actually consume. The often-voiced complaint that much of this timber is grown in plantations is a clever but factually illogical criticism. Actually growing timber and using the wood acts as a positive hindrance to atmospheric carbon dioxide buildup; it is not in any way a contributor to global warming. Preferably wood should be used to replace plastics and other high embodied-energy products; the reverse is madness.

The greatest biological source of carbon dioxide feeding the greenhouse effect comes from the destruction of the fertility of the world's soils. Any argument that tree felling and rainforest clearing cause global warming fades into insignificance compared to carbon dioxide produced from soil fertility decline. Timber has to rot or be burnt before the carbon in the wood can revert back to gas in the air. More timber houses get built than get burnt down, so the construction of timber houses is a very effective carbon dioxide sink.

The clearing of dense rainforests for agricultural use becomes especially insignificant if the exposed land is farmed in a sensible and soil-enhancing manner. That is, farmed so that the depth and fertility of the soil increases. Burning off timber and thereby not harvesting or utilizing the valuable wood for houses etc., will however be a contributor to global warming until soil fertility is developed. But burning is totally logical if the wood is being used as a fossil fuel replacement. It is unjustified waste not to utilize this alternative energy source.

The flames and the smoke of a burning rainforest make for good television. A "save the rainforest" campaign is also a convenient way to shift the blame for global warming to the Third World. The truth is that, almost totally, global warming and climate destabilization is a derivative of Western agricultural practices and the West's consumption of fossil fuels. But for oil companies, funding irrational rainforest causes makes good marketing sense.

Amazonia, the total Amazon River catchment area, is not "the lungs of the world" as the environmental marketing lobby claim. It never has been and it never will be. Rainforests, indeed any forests, are totally carbon dioxide neutral. Forests do nothing.

A stable forest, during the day, breathes in carbon dioxide and breathes out oxygen. But at night the process is reversed. The forest breathes in oxygen and breathes out carbon dioxide. That's short term. Long term is no different as the carbon trapped in the plants ultimately falls as litter on the forest floor. The litter rots and decomposes and releases the carbon back into the air as carbon dioxide. Think about this—if this was not so, million-year-old rainforests would have to be buried in their own litter, or else the floor of a rainforest would have to be a coal seam, or a peat bog. And we all know it's not like that. The litter on the ground in a rainforest can be scratched through with your fingers. It's very shallow.

Deep rich soil can trap and store as much carbon dioxide as any rainforest. That same deep rich soil can also grow a healthy food crop and grow one every year and for ever. Forests are stagnant entities. Soil fertility is the key to restoring global climatic stability—not trees—and definitely not fertilizers, not ever.

The meaning of the word "fertilizer" has been distorted. Fertile should mean healthy fertility.   The term has been cleverly and substantially expanded to now encompass the whole range of plant stimulants and soil additives—from the once highly favoured and popular cow manure, through to pure bottled ammonia gas. Today manufactured chemicals are called fertilizers.

The term "chemical fertilizer" is clever and astute marketing. Chemical fertilizers have nothing to do with fertility. They function more like "speed". They are like a soil amphetamine. One of their functions is to break down and destroy soil organic matter. This stimulated breakdown releases nutrients within the humus that is normally required to sustain soil biological activity. So for a few years crop growth can be increased. Unfortunately for the soil and the farmer, each year more fertilizers—those so beautifully misnamed soil drugs—need to be purchased and applied to produce an ever-diminishing yield. It's a diminishing yield of food with diminishing nutritional levels. In the process, soil biological activity is terminated. Soil biological activity is no longer there to break down virgin rock particles and so can't deliver new nutrients and elements to the soil. Using fertilizers made farmers finally come up with the term "worn-out soils". And no wonder; these processes and reversing these processes are discussed in detail in chapter 5.

Soil organic matter has slight variations in meaning and our use here should be clarified. It is generally nominated by determining soil carbon content. Sometimes the term is expanded to include surface litter. Sometimes it may also include actively growing plant material. In this book "soil organic matter" is limited to the more commonly accepted usage and so refers to plant material that is already in the process of breakdown and decomposition, all the way through to its eventual conversion into humus and humic acid molecules. The weight of fresh surface litter is not included. Also, as is common, soil organic matter here includes the mass of living soil microbiological activity involved in the process of plant breakdown and humus formation. Soot is pure carbon, as is a diamond. It is not a carbon compound and here it is quite rightfully not considered as soil organic matter.

Generally to determine organic matter content, a soil sample is heated until all the carbon and carbon compounds are burnt off. The carbon dioxide is collected and the organic carbon content is calculated. Some soils do contain high levels of soot, generally from ancient excessive anthropogenic burning. This is notably so in Australian soils. In these cases an oxidizing agent process is used on the dry soil sample. This is done to avoid the soot carbon affecting organic carbon content determinations.

In Australia, in the production of sugar from sugar cane, it is common for state agricultural departments to advise growers to use chemical fertilizers at rates exceeding two tons of chemicals per hectare, per year. (Ton and tonne are close enough to equal.) It takes a lot of crude oil to produce those two tons of fertilizers and all the chemical sprays used along with it. Big money is involved and so the destruction of soil organic matter, unfortunately, becomes an ongoing process.

To make matters worse, agricultural quota systems for many crops, all round the world, are deliberately constructed to limit the number of acres or hectares that can be farmed. These systems seem always to be systematically designed so that no limit is placed on the quantity of produce actually produced. The limit is placed on the area that can be farmed. Area is limited but not quantity. This naturally encourages the use of massive quantities of chemical stimulants to produce maximum crop quantities from the restricted areas allowed. This practice and its destructive consequences are expanded on in chapter 6.

You will often have seen statements from supposedly green protagonists criticizing farmers and their tractors for the discharge of carbon dioxide from these implements. This is a laughable "red herring" and is obviously used to stop us urban dwellers becoming interested in the discharge of carbon dioxide from chemical-induced soil destruction. Even the biggest farm tractor rarely burns more fuel than a family car. In addition, they are all diesel powered and therefore more fuel-efficient than the petrol-powered family car. The argument becomes even more ludicrous when we consider as an example that the farming community in Australia amounts to no more than 3% of the total national population. So in comparison to cars there are very few tractors in the nation. Australian farming is however, very efficient. Australia not only feeds itself but is a major world supplier of food, wool and many other agricultural products.

Farmers around the world might use a litre or so of fuel to drive their tractor over a couple of acres of land. In so doing they might well be spreading the equivalent of two, three or even four tons of oil, previously converted into agricultural chemicals, on that same land area. The oil to drive the tractor amounts to a few litres. The oil to make the agrochemicals amounts to tons. The enormous contribution made by the use of agricultural chemicals to the buildup of greenhouse gases in our atmosphere, to my knowledge, has never before been seriously considered, except here in this book. It's enormous.

When it is realized that world agriculture is such an important factor in increasing carbon dioxide levels in the atmosphere, it must also be realized that changes in agricultural practices might reverse it. And they can. Fortunately, techniques now exist for the very rapid rejuvenation of our agricultural soils. Practices can now be implemented that rapidly and massively increase the weight of organic matter within soil. In this way soils can rapidly be returned to their former excellence and even beyond, up to extreme levels of fertility. Because of careful lobbying and astute funding by those that make their money by catering to farmers working now unhealthy and infertile soils, agricultural departments and agricultural colleges rarely promote such concepts.

It must never be forgotten: humus and organic matter is the stuff of fertile soil. The composition of humus and organic matter in soils is generally accepted as being 58% carbon by dry weight. Soil organic matter is decomposed plant life. All plant life sources its carbon supply from carbon dioxide in the air around it. Excess carbon dioxide in the air is causing global warming, but improving soil fertility means less carbon dioxide in the air.

Provided the numbers work out, it is obvious. If we increase the basic fertility levels of our world's agricultural and grazing lands we can stop global warming in its tracks. And the numbers work out exceptionally well.

Building soil fertility to halt global warming: the simple basic arithmetic

All the carbon dioxide that has been discharged into the atmosphere from the burning of fossil fuels and all the carbon dioxide that has derived from the destruction of the fertility of world soils is not all still in the atmosphere. A huge quantity has been absorbed into the world's oceans. Our soils therefore don't have to absorb all the carbon dioxide they discharged into the air as they were denuded. So fortunately they actually have some excess capacity available to cater for the atmospheric buildup from fossil fuel use. That is why world soil enhancement can restore atmospheric carbon dioxide levels to normal. The absolutely essential proviso is that fossil fuel use is concurrently, progressively reduced to negligible quantities. Otherwise our newfound climatic stability from enhanced soil fertility will be short-lived and then total destabilization will be utterly irreversible. We can only play the soil fertility card once.

This is the sequence. All life ultimately starts by green leaves or green algae extracting carbon dioxide out of the air and manufacturing carbon compounds; compounds that become the building blocks of life. As plants grow, oxygen is released and recharges the air for more complex life forms to breathe. Normally when plants die they become soil organic matter and ultimately can then become permanent humus. (There is a small but interesting exception. It is a life cycle that exists near hot volcanic vents in some of our deep oceans. The energy source is the local volcanic heat. Search "hydrothermal-vents smokers" on the Web.)

Rich soil contains large quantities of organic matter. Very rich soil can contain as much as 20% organic matter. In good soils in cold climates where decomposition of roots and litter is slowed, organic matter content can often stabilize at levels well above 20%. The majority of the soils of the world however, have organic matter contents ranging between 2% and 10%. Even deserts, apart from the windblown sand variety, usually contain around 0.5% organic matter. Otherwise how else could deserts bloom after their rare rainstorms?

It is not only apparent in the field but also well documented in agricultural literature, notably in Albrecht's writings, that using "modern" agricultural practices, soil organic matter content invariably drops by around 50% of its original value over a period of thirty or forty years. Further decreases in organic matter content, after that initial 50% drop, occur at a much slower rate. Decreases in soil fertility from poor farming practices occur irrespective of either soil type or location. Most of our Western world's soils are now at or below this 50% level. The levelling occurs because some humic acid molecules are extremely stable and stoically resist agrochemical attack.

How fertility declines and how it can be reestablished is discussed in the chapters on soil and soil fertility. Happily for the planet, creating fertile soil is a much faster process than destroying it—although this is not generally appreciated, for it is very rarely taught or even discussed in most agricultural schools.

The control of fertility in our agricultural soils has an enormous bearing on global warming. So we need to understand the relative quantities of carbon involved in the world's soils in relation to that in the world's atmosphere.

Global warming has to be fixed and the utter reality is that ordinary people are the ones that are going to make that happen—not experts, not academics and certainly not state bureaucracies. Therefore, as much as it is possible, it is essential that we all personally get an appreciation and general understanding of the problem and the fix.

Quoting huge numbers with lots of noughts is confusing and usually becomes meaningless. That's why it's fed to us. But that's not good enough. We have to have a comprehensible perspective. We have to know what statements and claims are plausible and do actually reflect reality, and what is simply well-oiled marketing fiction.

Let's start with what we know. The earth is covered with a thin layer of air a few miles, a few klicks, thick—a klick being a kilometre. That's our atmosphere. That layer of air weighs about the same as a layer of water 34 feet deep (10.3 m deep). (If air is cooled enough it becomes a liquid.) Liquid air is slightly less dense than water, so as liquid air our atmosphere would be 39.2 feet deep (11.9 m). The fact is there is not much air on this planet. Our layer of air contains a small, but until recently a relatively constant percentage of carbon dioxide. In the 1940s the air contained just under 280 parts of carbon dioxide gas for every one million parts of air. For the few thousand years before the 1940s it was nearer 270 ppm. By 2000 it had risen above 360 ppm and the rate of increase is accelerating.

The gases that occur in small quantities in the atmosphere are usually measured in parts per million or ppm. So for example, 360 ppm of carbon dioxide means there are 360 parts, or bits of that gas in the atmosphere for every million single bits or parts of everything else. As a percentage it would be written as 0.036%. Rarer gases are often nominated in "ppb" which is parts per billion. Sometimes you may see these terms written as ppmv and ppbv. The term ppmv means "parts per million by volume". For us there is little difference.

In simple terms, the problem of global warming is caused by the increase in carbon dioxide in our atmosphere causing an excessive greenhouse effect. This is discussed in detail in chapter 4.

At 280 ppm, how much carbon dioxide are we really talking about? What does it all mean? To answer we need a little more visualization. Freeze carbon dioxide and you get dry ice. If we took all the CO_2 (carbon dioxide) out of the atmosphere and froze it, it would form a vast white blanket of dry ice covering the entire surface of the planet. Just a few years ago the blanket would have been slightly over one sixteenth of an inch thick or just under two millimetres (1.86 mm). The carbon dioxide content of our atmosphere by the year 2000 had reached 360 ppm. The extra 80 ppm can be imagined as a layer of dry ice less than one thirty-second of an inch deep (0.021 inches or 0.53 mm).

Global warming is happening because we have increased the quantity of carbon dioxide in the atmosphere. Imagined as dry ice it went from just under 2 millimetres thick to just under 2.5 millimetres in 60 years—from 0.075" thick to 0.095" thick. Your fingernail is about 0.4 mm thick. So the dry ice got one and a half fingernails thicker. It went from about four and a half to about six fingernails in thickness.

Carbon dioxide is made of one atom of carbon combined with two atoms of oxygen. So let's just consider the excess carbon atoms causing global warming at the 360 ppm levels. Those atoms would form a layer of soot, or carbon dust, a mere 0.007 of an inch (0.18 mm) thick, covering the entire surface of the earth. A sheet of newspaper is about that same thickness. (The density or specific gravity of soot varies between 1.8 and 2.1 times as heavy as water, here it is averaged at 1.95. By comparison a commonly accepted range for the density of fertile soil is from 1.3 to 1.4.)

That tiny 0.007 of an inch (0.18 mm) of carbon is causing the erratic climatic changes the world is now beginning to experience. That tiny quantity of carbon, in the form of carbon dioxide, is the villain causing our crazy, destructive, unpredictable global warming.

We cannot leave the stuff there in our atmosphere. We have to remove it. If we don't, then very dangerous and even more expensive global warming effects will manifest themselves. Temperatures all over the world will rise even faster than is happening already. Temperatures will then go on rising for centuries to come as lagging ocean temperatures try to catch up.

Climates will become totally destabilized and unpredictable.

But we can stop it!

We have looked at the atmosphere, now let's look at the soil. The 58% carbon content of soil organic matter means that a typical average density agricultural soil, 12 inches (300 mm) deep, and containing 5% organic matter, can be imagined as a layer of soot a quarter of an inch thick (0.246 inches or 6.25 mm). A soil containing 5% organic matter is not a rich soil. So even in poor soil we still have the equivalent of .246 of an inch of carbon and our global warming problem is caused by just 0.007 of an inch of carbon.

Soil having an organic matter content of only 5%, therefore, holds over 35 times as much carbon as that causing global warming. That's why soil fertility concepts are so important and why increasing the fertility levels of our soils can fix global warming.

They talk about it, but we simply cannot trap the excess CO_2 in the oceans. We don't know how to, even if we wanted to. Also to play with, and somehow manipulate the surface of the world's oceans, to have them absorb carbon dioxide at some vastly altered rates, seems incredibly risky. It's too big a gamble to even contemplate.

So we really only have the land to trap the excess. And we really only have the land we actively use or farm. But that's OK. Humans know about land and know about farming. Some parts of our world have been farmed successfully for more than forty centuries, as is so interestingly described by Professor F. H. King in his 1911 book *Farmers of Forty Centuries*.

What do the numbers look like? Can it be done? Yes, as we will see. The land area of planet Earth is 29% of the total surface area of the planet. We use, or actively control as farmlands, rangelands, parklands etc. about 30% of that land area. So we control at least 8.5% of the total surface area of the entire planet. Third World countries, depending how they are defined, account for less than a quarter of that total.

The extra carbon dioxide causing global warming equates to 0.007 inches (0.18 mm) of carbon spread over the whole planet, but we have limited ourselves to just 8.5% of the earth's area to fix the problem. But it's enough. If we magically scraped together the carbon causing global warming so that it only covered the land we farm or control, then it would still be only 0.081 inches (2.1 mm) thick. Amazingly that is still less than one third of the quantity of carbon in the first foot or three 'hands' of an agricultural soil with just 5% organic matter.

As we have seen, such soil easily contains a quarter of an inch of carbon atoms.

To fix global warming we need to put that 0.081 inches (2.1 mm) of carbon back into that 8.5% area of the earth we actively control. That quantity of carbon is the same as in a foot of soil with just 1.6% organic

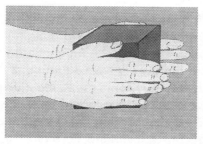

A horse's height is measured in hands. A person's hand is about 4 inches wide, and the hand unit is currently defined as 4 inches, which conveniently is very close to 100 mm, or a tenth of a metre. A block with sides each of 1 hand is therefore approximately 1 litre. A hand print, a palm print or a pad is generally very close in area to a 4-by-4-inch square, or a 100-mm-by-100-mm square. So we could say, 9 prints (palms or pads) to the square foot and 100 to the square metre. (So officially redefining a hand as exactly one tenth of a metre would be wonderfully logical and useful.)

matter content. There is more than that in most desert soils.

All we have to do is ensure that our soils are managed in such a manner that their fertility levels rise that necessary 1.6%. It only has to happen on the lands we farm and manage right now, but when it does, all that excess carbon dioxide in the air causing world climatic change will vanish.

Soils that once held 5% organic matter and now hold half that, can easily be restored to 5% and even higher. Prairie soils, such as those in the United States that once had up to 20% organic matter and have been gradually reduced to levels often below 5%, can also be restored to their original richness. They can rebound rapidly back to those 20% levels.

Recreating the richness of the soils of the American prairies could almost on its own normalize world carbon dioxide levels.

All agricultural land the world over has the potential to be restored to its former fertility level. Even better, with judicious management most soils can have their organic matter profitably elevated to well beyond those original levels.

With the right agricultural changes in place (see chapter 8), that 8.5% of the world's area is easily sufficient to mop up the excess carbon dioxide causing our global warming. The problems of global warming thus become no more than the problem of turning the equivalent of 0.081 inches (2.1 mm) of atmospheric carbon atoms into stable productive soil organic matter. Practically, economically and technically we can do it easily and world climatic stability would be instantly restored.

Relative to world agriculture and the world's soils, the buildup in atmospheric carbon dioxide is nothing. It is easy to reverse and fix. Yet we are allowing that buildup to continue, and we are allowing it to destabilize our world's climate and weather.

The soils most easily rejuvenated are the mineral-rich soils. Mineral-rich soils simply respond faster than mineral-poor soils, but the response of both is always amazingly rapid. The simple techniques are discussed in chapter 8.

Actually very few of the world's soils are mineral deficient to any prohibitive extent. (Technically we should say element deficient.) The problem is that the minerals or elements are locked up in chemically stable rock particles and thus unavailable to plant life. Unfortunately, the excessively slow natural way of freeing up elements for biological use is through rain. Raindrops absorb carbon dioxide and so rainwater is slightly acidic. This acidity increases the weathering effects on rocks. Weathering slowly releases minerals to soil and plant life. Fortunately, active organic matter can break down rock particles and make minerals available to soil life many times more effectively. That's one of its established functions. Without this process land life could never have developed as it has.

The mineral- and humus-rich soils of the Western nations have now unfortunately become organically poor. These are the worn-out soils we hear so much about. They have also in effect become mineral deficient as minerals have stopped being released. Nevertheless in almost every example, the basic rock material is not itself deficient, so the increased soil biological activity possible when strong agrochemicals are avoided can rapidly release the essential elements to plants.

The farmers of the Western nations are already equipped, more than anyone else, to handle and physically implement the simple changes necessary to recreate rich fertile soil. Indeed, many farmers are already doing this. They are our organic farmers and grow our organic food and fibres. They are the farmers who have totally and systematically abandoned the concept of chemical-fed agriculture. Some have changed entirely for moral or ethical reasons. Most have changed because it makes good sense. Almost without exception, these farmers actually make more money from the better prices they generally receive. Practitioners of organic farming and farming based on soil development concepts have found that yields soon generally exceed their chemically addicted neighbours. This is documented later in Strategy 37.

The agrochemical establishment image, that high farm yields and increasing world food production requires ever increasing inputs of chemicals and chemical fertilizers, is wrong. Organic farmers know this but organic farmers don't have a loud voice in the halls of power, so governments give most support to chemically based agriculture.

The restoration of world soil fertility levels, especially in the developed worlds where declines are endemic, can reverse global warming. Such changes in agricultural practices should start now. They must become the new "conventional" agriculture.

This change in agricultural practices will give us the breathing space we need to bring on line alternative energy producing systems that don't endanger our tiny and vulnerable atmosphere.

We have to start immediately to change our agricultural practices for only then we will have enough time to win this global warming War.

Don't believe the propaganda of the oil industries' lobby groups. We will not need to decrease our standard of living. We will not need to abandon the family car. We will not need to live the austere life of a Tibetan monk and we will not need to ride to work on a push-bike. Our food on the other hand will taste better. It will be more nutritious, we will be healthier and, most certainly we will live longer. An additional bonus in some areas will be a halt in the current continuous loss of arable farmland to salination. Salination stops and actually reverses itself as soil fertility returns.

Rising water tables that contribute to salination will cease to be a problem. Rising water tables result in part from the use of ever increasing volumes of irrigation water. Soils lacking organic matter can't retain moisture efficiently. In consequence huge quantities of excess water are necessary to maintain soil moisture levels. Soils with low and declining fertility levels require chemical fertilizers and stimulants for crop production. Soil fertility and soil organic matter levels drop and the salination cycle repeats.

The innate worth of high soil fertility, how it prevents and cures soil salinity, and why trees are not the answer is discussed in chapter 8 and also generally throughout this book.

Birth of the soil fertility concept

This simple and so beneficial solution to global warming seems obvious in retrospect. But it wasn't. Generally things are always clearer in hindsight. In this however, I was fortunate. I grew up in a household where soil conservation and soil fertility enrichment were in constant discussion, where concepts were developed and where erosion control and on-farm water storage ponds were dinner-table conversation. My father, P. A. Yeomans, wrote several books on the concepts he developed and pioneered. I studied engineering at Sydney University and was very involved in the agricultural concepts. I saw the trials, watched the improvements and saw the ultimate development of a practical, viable, economical and profitable sustainable agricultural system. I was particularly involved in the design of equipment to make the system economically viable. The agricultural system that ultimately developed from all these efforts became the Keyline system. It is unique in many aspects, but in reality is still only a wise and astute modification to, and a development from farming and farming practices that have endured for millennia (see chapter 7).

Even with my agricultural background, the interrelation between agriculture and global warming would still not have been at all obvious, for the reality is global warming and climatic change are actually meteorological phenomena. However as a hobby I started flying. I became a glider pilot

The author in a Libelle 301 sailplane over the Murray River during the 1975–76 Australian National Championships. Glider flying time in a typical race day is four to five hours and distance flown might be 500 km. Initially the glider is towed to 2,000 feet by a light aircraft and released. Tow plane engine time is typically about eight minutes per launch. The glider then uses rising air currents to periodically gain height to fly the assigned task. Eight minutes engine time for five hours flying time is probably why oil company support for the sport of gliding is conspicuous by its absence.

and for many years raced sailplanes. Sailplanes are high-performance gliders. To race sailplanes a pilot has to develop an intimate knowledge and understanding of meteorology. Otherwise you can't stay in the air.

This probably uncommon combination of an intimate knowledge of soil fertility levels and how they can be enhanced, coupled with a detailed knowledge of the composition of the atmosphere and associated atmospheric phenomena, was fortuitous. With these two disciplines, a practical and viable solution to reversing global warming and restoring climatic stability suddenly looked feasible; a definite possibility. It soon became quite obvious that just simple changes in agricultural practices could solve the problem of climate change. A great deal of study and research totally confirmed the original concepts. I had already known energy systems were available at reasonable cost that could prevent warming recurring (see chapter 11).

By slightly changing our Western agricultural techniques to a combination of early sustainable agricultural practices and efficient modern mechanized practices we can do it. We can rapidly extract the excess carbon dioxide out of our overburdened atmosphere and from it create or recreate rich, wonderfully fertile and hugely productive agricultural soils.

It is not difficult to do and it is now urgent. If we all decide to fix global warming, we can fix it. And with a little common sense, it won't cost a cent.

Changing from fossil fuels to different energy sources

Concurrently we must switch to other energy sources and we must be aware that, despite the propaganda, no other energy system is as lethal to our total environment, and to us, as burning fossil carbon. The era of our world running on fossil fuels must now end. It is over. Not because we are running out of fossil fuels, as that's effectively impossible in any foreseeable future, but because global warming is too risky, too deadly and already too costly.

For the fossil fuel industries it is just business. For the oil companies, it is just business. These people don't want the prevention of global warming to become a reality and they act accordingly. It is not necessary to invent some world conspiracy to explain their actions; the marketing of fossil fuels creates one automatically. Oil company customers burn oil. Burning a ton of any fossil fuel produces between two and three tons of carbon dioxide. It's a sad but uncompromising reality: fossil fuel companies are utterly dependent on the continuation of global warming and allied climate change.

It's doubly sad with oil, as oil, being an incredible mix of hydrocarbon compounds, will always be an invaluable raw material for the manufacture of petrochemical products, plastics, pharmaceuticals, etc. Oil is also the best general-purpose engineering and industrial lubricant. To burn this valuable resource just for its energy content is inexcusable. And of course, to turn it into agrochemicals to drench the rural lands of the world, destroying their fertility and organic matter, is equally inexcusable.

Alternative energy systems for power generation and transport that actually prevent global warming are here now, and they are competitive. Most of the alternative transport fuels will be grown by farmers and mostly in the tropics and subtropics (see chapter 11). Most fortuitously, this would help Third World societies self-fund themselves out of their perpetual poverty.

Despite what is always implied to delay their implementation, no new technologies have to be discovered. Nothing new has to be invented. Even if the costs of alternate fuel systems were, say, five times the cost of fossil fuel systems, which they are not, they would still be cheap. For they are safe, and they are logical, and they are economically sound, and they will save us all from the horrendous costs of cancerous climate change.

Our main problem in changing is political. In agriculture many Western farmers now spend more money on oil-derived chemical fertilizers and the necessary pesticides and fungicides to keep the resultant unhealthy crop from self-destructing, than they spend on all other farm inputs combined. In consequence agricultural chemical companies have vast sums of advertising and public relations dollars to spend to buy agreeable and placatory editorial to support their agrochemical sales.

The problem for the world is that fossil fuel companies and the agrochemical companies will always strenuously resist any changes in the status quo. They will put up tremendous opposition. They will not only continue, but in the future will significantly increase their massive public relations campaign to stop any change. We have seen their public relations campaigns. They are very effective and very influential. It's an effort not to be influenced.

Remember the never-ending series of articles, stories and "scientific reports" to establish that cigarettes, despite all the evidence, weren't really dangerous to our health? This isn't any different. When cigarette companies started to lose the cigarette battles, they moved to China and to Third World countries, but they didn't give up. Before cigarette advertising was restricted, the hero and heroine in movies and TV shows rarely smoked. After the restrictions we saw characters in lead roles smoking cigars. Cigars were a good start. Now you may have noticed all the TV shows have the hero smoking? Clever aren't they? If you check you will find cigarettes sales climbing. Oil advertising companies know the tricks. Just like the tobacco companies, they lose a few battles, but they never give up the war. With cigarettes, individuals have a choice. With global warming there are no individuals. We are like conscripted passive smokers.

Now we are being conditioned to allow, and accept, atmospheric carbon dioxide content rising to double the already dangerous levels we are currently at (now over 360 ppm). That is a rise to 700 ppm. A few years ago they pushed for a public acceptance of 500 ppm. They may even suggest higher limits be accepted as atmospheric readings continue to climb.

We should never tolerate such criminally insane proposals. We must cease tolerating the fossil fuel industry's blatant irresponsibility and self-interest.

Individually but cohesively we can stop global warming

If the necessary and now urgent changes are to happen in agriculture and energy, then they won't happen because Big Business wants them to happen. Don't forget, for Big Business, there is absolutely no money in healthy soil. And big money is not yet in alternative energy.

Nor will the necessary changes happen because governments in their wisdom decide to do something. The main aim of any government is its own personal survival. If we sit pat and do nothing, it will be a very long time before governments come to see soil fertility as a vote-catching issue.

It is doubtful that changes would happen from union action. Individualistic farmers and collective union muscle rarely see eye to eye. However, to be just, there are some unions that do sometimes show surprising levels of general community responsibility. In such matters these unions must be applauded.

So the changes must start with us, the people. Fixing global warming has to be a real grass roots movement. As citizens and consumers we can indeed make it happen. We can have more impact on the fertility of our world's soils than any union, any government, any government agency, any inane regulation, and more than any big business conglomerate.

For example, if food processors and retailers see a big market shift by consumers to purchase more organically grown food, things will rapidly change and soils will improve. It works like this: organically grown food is grown most successfully and most economically on humus-rich soils. If we as consumers show a massive preference for organically grown food, demand organically grown cotton and organically grown wool, farmers will have to change to cater. They will change their methods of farming and their soils will start to change and improve in consequence. Organic matter content will rise and atmospheric carbon dioxide levels will fall. Demanding organically grown produce will have a definitive influence on global warming. It's also healthier. Actually, nutrient for nutrient, it is generally cheaper.

In addition, as we improve our soils we must also change our total reliance on fossil fuels to power our societies. Alternative energy systems must be fostered and encouraged. We are fortunate that at last alternative energy systems are feasible, practical and economical. Fossil fuel costs may often be a little lower than alternative energy costs, but only if you totally exclude the cost of destroying the stability of world weather.

The process by which the fossil fuel and the agricultural chemical industries manipulate public opinion is given a great deal of detail throughout this book. This manipulation must be understood clearly so that suitable countermeasures to global warming can get established.

Plants and trees and animals grow and die, the carbon dioxide recirculates back into the soil and the cycle repeats. We can shift the balance so that the soil retains much more during the cycle.

But extracting fossil carbon from deep geological formations is absolutely a one-way street to global disaster. So let's not be fooled. We have to be well prepared to combat the unending deluge of misinformation on global warming that continues to be heaped upon us.

Restoring the fertility of our world's soils is essential, and changing to new energy systems must happen concurrently. That way we will stop global warming. How we can ensure that what is needed actually takes place, is I hope, the message throughout this book.

Preventing global warming and the resultant climate change is easy.

But some people don't want it to ever happen.

3

The atmosphere, ice ages, sunspots, internal heat and volcanoes

G LOBAL warming stems from the greenhouse effect, which we talk about in detail in the next chapter. The greenhouse effect controls world surface temperatures by restricting the re-radiation of solar energy back into space. Naturally occurring internal planetary radioactive decay also warms the planet but this effect is comparatively insignificant. There is no other heat source.

We know that the greenhouse phenomenon keeps the surface of our world at a comfortable living temperature. We now know we have upset the stability of that entire phenomenon by changing the composition of the relatively microscopically thin atmospheric skin that coats the earth's surface. More and more this extra warming effect is going to influence every human being on the planet. It is going to influence all societies, all governments and all nations.

The greenhouse effect and global warming must therefore be made comprehensible and understandable, so we can make environmental decisions based on reason and common sense. No longer can our decisions be based on the rantings of some so-called green movements. Nor can they be based on the diverting imagery created by the oil companies' public-relations gurus. Nor can we allow our energy and our environmental responsibility and enthusiasm to be diverted into insignificant and doubtful causes that may well self-destruct in an overheated world.

It is essential for us to acquire a basic, but sound and rational, understanding of our atmosphere so we can monitor the myriad of often irrelevant environmental doctrines we are expected to swallow. The atmosphere and its movement are not easy things to visualize, but it is worth trying.

On movie sets when the director wants to create the image of a person walking on a cloud he might use a fogging machine. (Coincidentally, the machine uses dry ice which is carbon dioxide frozen solid.) It produces an ankle-deep white fog that lies on the floor. When you watch this fog, it seems to rise and fall. Waves move across it. It sometimes might pulsate, and it all seems to happen in an eerie sort of slow motion.

On a much larger scale, that's exactly what our atmosphere looks like. That is what it would look like if you were looking down at it from a high-flying jet. It is however transparent, so you can't actually see it. So we have to use a little imagination. The never-ending waves and pulsations, the constant rises and falls in the top surface of the atmosphere change the local depth and thickness of the air. Down on the surface, under all that air, we feel the difference as variations in our local atmospheric pressure. When we measure these pressure variations and plot them on a chart and then join up all the equal pressure points, we have our familiar weather maps with their high- and low-pressure areas. The areas are usually called high-pressure systems or low-pressure systems.

The constant changes in temperature, moisture content and air move-ment occurring within the thin skin of atmospheric gases clinging to the surface of the planet we know as weather. Climate is the name we give to the average weather that occurs over large specific areas of the earth's surface.

Weather is controlled by many factors. The land, in more northerly or more southerly latitudes, receives less sunlight than does land nearer the tropics. Different land is warmed and cooled at different rates, and in turn, warms and cools local air masses. This differential has a big effect on our weather. The warming and cooling expands and contracts the air volume and this causes the waves and pulsations mentioned earlier.

The earth is revolving and drags its atmosphere around with it. The irreg-ular distribution of continents, their size and shape all affect the otherwise even flow of air masses, which would normally result from a continuously revolving spherical world. The nature of the land surface, whether it be covered in grass, trees or desert, has a big effect. The depths of oceans, their local temperature and salt content have their effects. The giant rivers of deep, cold, salt-rich water that circulate at the bottom of all the oceans of the world have profound effects. Some of these deep ocean currents almost totally determine the weather and weather patterns throughout Europe. The Arctic and Antarctic ice packs that reflect so much sunlight and heat back into space also massively affect world climates.

All these interrelated phenomena create and control the variety of cli-mates that cover the planet.

There is not very much to our atmosphere. It really is a very thin skin. You may drive 10 miles to the supermarket on the surface of the planet. Yet no man has ever been down 10 miles into its interior, and if you go up 10 miles, you are in the unbreathable outer edge of space.

One of the major problems in discussing the planet's atmosphere is that the discussions are always couched in terms meaningless to anybody who doesn't live with such numbers. It's like the national debt. It's like Monopoly money! How can we even think of solving the problem of global warming and how can we even begin to understand it, if the problem is always stated in terms that are unfamiliar and in numbers and proportions that are meaningless? The talk is in megatonnes, parts per million, parts per billion, gigatonnes and so on, and their often incomprehensible abbreviations; to most of us most of these units and symbols have no meaning whatever.

So let's try and get some perspective, and also, let's expand on the concept of considering the composition of the atmosphere as separate individual layers and as liquids as we did in chapter 2.

On a spherical world globe such as you might find in a school room, the atmosphere would be about as deep and as significant as the film formed by dipping the globe into a dish of very light salad oil. The slow movement of this thin oily skin around our globe, if we revolve it, would be the same as the movement of air on our planet.

Let's imagine our world globe model as being about eight inches (200 mm or a couple of hand widths) in diameter. As the world is roughly 8,000 miles in diameter (12,756 km at the equator), one-thousandth of an inch will therefore represent one mile or 5,280 feet. (1 mm will represent 64 km.)

In this model, the deepest mine in the world would be 0.002 of an inch (0.05 mm) deep—that's about the thickness of a cigarette paper. The average depth of all the oceans of the world is about 0.003 of an inch (0.075 mm) or less than the thickness of the paper you are reading. Our highest mountain, Mount Everest, is 29,000 feet or 5.5 miles high (8,800 m) in the real world. In our model it would be less than 0.006 of an inch high (0.14 mm). That's half the thickness of your fingernail.

The atmosphere of our planet, the air we breathe, gets thinner the higher up we go. On our little globe, at 0.008 of an inch (0.2 mm) above the surface, the air would be so thin you couldn't breathe. You would die. That's about the thickness of two pages of this book.

By the time you get to a height represented by the thickness of a paper clip on our 8-inch globe, the reduction in atmospheric pressure would be such that your blood would long since have boiled away, as boiling point temperatures drop with decreasing pressure.

Our model world is also very smooth. It would be like a big ball bearing with a few tiny scratches representing deep ocean troughs. Those scratches would be deeper than the mighty mountain ranges are high and the thin atmosphere would barely reach the top of the higher mountains.

The atmosphere is made of gases, the main ones being nitrogen, comprising about 78%, and oxygen, comprising almost the rest. All the other gases combined: argon, carbon dioxide, water vapour, ozone, methane, nitrous oxide and minute traces of several other gases don't add up to more than 1%.

Now substances take up a lot more room when they are in a gaseous state, than when they are in a liquid or solid state; for many gases a thousand times more room. If a layer of water 12 inches or three hands deep was all turned into steam or water vapour it would have expanded and become a column of steam 1,000 feet (300 m) high. It would still be the same amount of water, the same weight of water, but steam is a gas and takes up a lot more room.

The same applies to our atmosphere, but let's look at it in reverse. If we could magically turn our atmosphere back into a liquid, it would become a mixture of liquid oxygen and liquid nitrogen. That liquid mix would cover our planet with a layer 39 feet (12 m) deep.

You would still have the same quantity, the same mass of oxygen and nitrogen, the same number of atoms, but now it would simply be condensed to a liquid state. Of course, both oxygen and nitrogen cannot exist in a liquid state at the temperatures on the surface of the earth, as their actual boiling points are well below even our coldest natural temperatures, but the concepts help our understanding of just how little mass, how little weight, is actually there.

Looking at it another way: atmospheric pressure is 14.7 pounds per square inch at sea level, or about 1013 millibars, or 1013 hectopascals, or 760 mm of mercury (depending on which version of the metric system is currently decreed). In other words, a column of air covering one square inch of the ground and extending out to space weighs 14.7 pounds. A column of water, one inch square and 34 feet high, weighs exactly the same and produces the same pressure at its base. The air covering one square centimetre on the ground weighs a little over one kilogram and that's the same as 10.3 m of water. In aviation the figure of 1013 millibars has been nominated and is the universally accepted pressure standard for altimeter settings at sea level.

When considering global warming and the greenhouse effect, it is so very important to recognize and appreciate that the total mass of the atmosphere directly above our heads is so tiny, and in consequence, so dreadfully vulnerable.

Just think about it, how much beetroot juice would it take to colour a 30-foot (10-metre) deep water tank or pool from the bottom to the top? Not very much. If you could vaporize exactly the same quantity of beetroot juice as the percentage of carbon dioxide in the air it would be enough to colour a column of air, with the same size base but extending all the way up to the outer reaches of space. Carbon dioxide just happens to be transparent to visible light, but that doesn't mean it is not there. If CO_2 were red we would now be able to see our atmosphere slowly getting redder year by year.

Back to our 8-inch globe, and considering air as a liquid so as to more easily understand its vulnerability, the atmosphere would then represent a coating over our globe, a mere six-millionth of an inch thick, that's 0.00016 mm.

Comparing this to coating our little model world with one coat of household paint—the paint would be one thousand times thicker, and one thousand times heavier, than the liquefied atmosphere coating our model world.

Vulnerable—could there be any doubt?

Visualizing the atmosphere as if all the gases were somehow condensed into their liquid form is a way of giving the problem a perspective that is both meaningful and valid. For example: on our planet the quantity of air that makes up our atmosphere is relatively tiny, whereas the quantity of water that forms our oceans is gigantic. The oceans of the world average about 12,000 feet (3,600 m) deep. Even if the oceans were spread evenly over the entire planet and all landmasses were flattened out, the entire planet would still be covered with an ocean 8,000 feet (2,500 m) deep. We have the equivalent of 8,000 feet of water and a tiny 39 feet of liquefied air. There is a small quantity of water dissolved in the air as humidity but in this exercise the quantity is meaningless. That's 2,500 metres of seawater to 10 metres of air. So air is less than 0.5% of the stuff covering our planetary surface and water is 99.5%. There is 250 times as much water as air.

It becomes obvious why our atmosphere is so vulnerable to pollution. To pollute the oceans as much as we are polluting our air, we would each have to buy an extra 250 cars and then drive them all at once, and drive them just as regularly as we are driving our single car now. We would also require 250 times as many coal- and oil-fired power stations.

Technically, the actual depth of the gaseous atmosphere is not really a finite thing. At any height there is still some air above you, it just gets thinner and thinner. It's thicker and denser near the surface because the weight of the air above compresses it. Theoretically, the atmosphere extends up for hundreds of miles, but there is really nothing there. At those heights it is almost the vacuum of true space.

In an ordinary commercial jet flight, when it levels off to cruise, we could be well over 40,000 feet (12 km) high. At that height, the vast majority of our planet's atmosphere is underneath us. Next time you are going some place in a jet, look out the window and think about it. It tends to make a person realize just how little air we have here, and just how vulnerable it really is. All the world's weather and all the world's life is down there below you.

The only significant things affecting us above that height are minute quantities of ozone gas and oxides of nitrogen. These protect us from the more harmful frequencies of ultraviolet light radiation that forms part of incoming sunlight. When this ozone is destroyed we have the creation of the ozone hole through which ultraviolet rays can penetrate down to the earth's surface and give us, amongst other things, skin cancer. Ozone and its formation are discussed later.

On our Earth the fine balance between absorbing too much heat from the sun and not quite enough is determined in the main by the quantity of carbon dioxide in the atmosphere. That quantity of carbon dioxide in our atmosphere has been remarkably stable over several hundred thousand years. That stability, before the advent of fossil fuels, was self-maintaining within a relatively narrow range.

Vostok is a Russian research base on the high Antarctic Plateau. It is one of the coldest places on earth and holds the low-temperature record, at -89.6°C. The ice at Vostok has accumulated in layers over hundreds of thousands of years. The station sits on ice 2.5 miles (4 km) thick.

The Vostok area has the longest continuous record of ice deposition in the world. The scientists there have a drilling rig that cuts into the ice like an apple corer and collects samples down to a depth of over 2 miles. Analysis of the core samples has established how world atmospheric carbon dioxide levels varied over a 400,000-year period.

In all that time, a time that spanned four ice ages, carbon dioxide levels varied only slightly. They peaked out at 300 ppm (parts per million) just once, and that was 300,000 years ago. In today's world we have forced the levels to 360 ppm and they are rapidly climbing. Temperatures are following a few short years behind.

We can go back even further. A research report in the August 2000 issue of *Nature*, Vol. 406, described an elegant and brilliantly simple testing process for determining past atmospheric carbon dioxide levels. The system works by analyzing the boron-isotope ratios in precipitated calcium carbonate found in ancient marine planktonic foraminifer shells. The researchers were Paul N. Pearson and Martin R. Palmer of the Department of Earth Sciences, University of Bristol, UK. The deposits were laid down on flat-topped seamounts in the tropical North Pacific. The sea bottom there has been geologically stable for at least 60 million years.

Their analysis showed that for the last 22 million years atmospheric carbon dioxide levels had never risen above 300 parts per million. Those levels were never ever exceeded until the 1950s and 1960s.

The results are disturbing because they show that by mining and burning fossilized carbon and by destroying the fertility of agricultural soils, we have increased world carbon dioxide readings to levels that have not existed on this entire planet for at least 22 million years.

What we are moving into is a man-made, total-world, environmental disaster. We have to stop it happening before it eventually becomes uncontrollable and irreversible.

Prior to the 1940s, the quantity of carbon dioxide in the atmosphere was determined by the mass and distribution of life on the planetary surface. This mass and distribution, of course, is subject to subtle influences but is generally consistent. Carbon deposits lying deep beneath the earth's surface did not previously affect atmospheric carbon dioxide levels and therefore climatic variations.

There are of course, other influences on the world's climate. These need to be considered as they are too often used to instill doubt on the extreme dangers of our massive use of fossil-carbon-derived fuels and products.

Over thousands of years there has been a natural pattern of small recurring changes in the earth's orbit. Although these changes appear almost insignificant, however, they have been enough to create and terminate ice ages. The subtle orbit changes have somehow been enough to slightly shift the balanced interrelationship of life and carbon dioxide and thus overall world temperatures.

A theory on the cyclic nature of ice ages was first suggested by a Scotsman, James Croll. His theories were originally published in *The Philosophical Magazine* in 1864. Croll's original ideas were upgraded and refined by a Yugoslav astronomer, Milutin Milankovic, in the 1920s and 1930s. In the years since, these concepts have in general become widely accepted. Admittedly there are other theories, such as the effect of our solar system passing through waves of nebulous interstellar dust, so to a certain extent the jury is still out on what combination exactly trips the ice age trigger.

These are the known and established facts: ice ages have been occurring about every 100,000 years for about a million years. Out of each of those 100,000-year periods, 80–90,000 years is actually ice age. The remaining 10–20,000 years is a period of somewhat warmer climates, called interglacials. We are currently in an interglacial period and have been since just before the Egyptians started building their pyramids.

There are three main astronomical cycles in the Milankovic model and they correlate with the frequency of the ice ages and the fluctuations within them. The first and most significant component in the model is a slight shift and return in the earth's orbit each 100,000 years. The earth's orbit changes from a slightly elliptical shape to a more rounded form, and then reverts back to the elliptical shape. It is a very minor change but is linked very accurately to the now well-known frequencies of ice ages.

Secondly: the earth spins about its axis of rotation daily, and this axis is tilted with respect to the plane of the earth's orbit; it is this tilt that gives us our summer-winter seasonal variations. This total tilt of the earth's axis oscillates backwards and forwards in cycles lasting roughly 41,000 years.

Thirdly, the daily spin of the earth, a tiny twenty-four hour cycle, creates a spinning top effect. When a spinning top slows down slightly, it develops a characteristic wobble. The earth is the same and it too has a wobble. The earth's wobble takes between 19,000 years and 23,000 years to complete its period. In the time of the pyramid builders, the North Star would not have been the accurate indicator of true north that it is today. This apparent shift in the position of the fixed stars is called the "precession of the equinoxes" but it is our Earth, not, as was once thought, the stars that are wobbling.

The last eight ice ages have occurred within the last million years, and *Homo sapiens*, that's us, have been around for about 100,000 years. Humans therefore have experienced and lived through maybe just one single ice age. *Homo sapiens* and before that, *Homo erectus*, or possibly *Homo heidelbergensis*, our probable evolutionary ancestors, survived and evolved through the trauma of five, or six, or maybe even more, ice ages.

Before that, according to the geological record, it appears that cyclic ice ages were not a regular thing at all.

One of the most intriguing things about these climatic fluctuations and the ice ages is that the actual astronomical variations in the earth's orbit—its shift, its tilt, and its wobble—seem so tiny and so inconsequential. Yet they still manage to cause ice ages by somehow triggering enormous weather and climatic fluctuations.

Even more intriguing is that the 100,000-year cycle that sets the time and frequencies of the ice ages is actually the weakest of the three astronomical fluctuations. Yet deep drilling of ice cores, and investigations of sediments laid down in long past mud deposits, nevertheless conclusively establish the 100,000-year cycle of our planet's ice ages over this last million years.

A period of 41,000 years and a period of 19,000 years, the time period of the other two cycles, don't divide evenly into 100,000 years, nor are they multiples of each other. So there are variations in temperatures, ice formation and the associated weather in each particular ice age. Every ice age was a little different. And so was each interglacial period.

The overlying pattern of 100,000 years, however, is extremely consistent and leaves little doubt as to the interrelationship of glaciation and astro-nomical fluctuations. The lesson we learn is that it does not take much to totally change the weather patterns of the entire planet.

The changes in world atmospheric temperatures, between glacial and interglacial periods, are determined by collating many phenomena. One piece of evidence of temperature changes and their magnitude is demon-strated dramatically by the formation of glacial moraines.

A glacier is a giant river of ice, flowing and moving down its home valley until finally it descends to an altitude warm enough for it to fracture and melt. Or, as in Antarctica, the glacier can end up reaching the ocean and either melts there or breaks away and forms icebergs.

Moraines are formed where the glacier ice melts. The rocks and debris gouged from the sides and floor of the valley are carried down within the moving ice and finally dumped. This material forms a wall across the valley. The appearance, when you actually look at one, is like a long river of ice suddenly ending as a wall of rocks.

For example: in rare cases, in some wide valleys, a glacier will form walls on either side of itself and have the appearance of an elevated ice freeway with rock sides, sometimes 60 feet (20 m) high running down the centre of an otherwise flat valley floor. These moraines can be miles long with an ice-free valley floor visible on either side. All these dumps, in their various forms, are called glacial moraines.

The flow speed of a glacier can be as slow as a few inches a century as in Alaska and Antarctica, or as high as 16 feet (3 m) per day for the Fox Glacier near Mount Cook on the South Island of New Zealand. The Fox Glacier must undoubtedly be one of the fastest moving glaciers in the world. You can actually hear it moving.

When significant and long-term climate changes occur and temperature rises become well established, the glacier retreats relatively abruptly back up its valley to a new stable location. At the old location is the moraine containing the debris of sometimes thousands of years of deposition. It forms a wall, and as silt and other debris arrive, they eventually form a seal between the rocks and boulders and other debris and a lake is formed. The existence of such lakes is quite common throughout the world. The formation of these glacial moraine walls created most of the many lakes in the southern island of New Zealand and most of the lakes in other parts of the world at similar latitudes.

The positions of the end of glaciers in valleys are dependent on average temperatures prevailing over the time the moraines were forming. Knowing the altitude of a particular moraine we can determine what those prevailing temperatures might have been.

The very existence of these lakes dramatically evidences the existence of past variations in world atmospheric temperature patterns and the effects they create. They also show that the climate periods were much longer and more stable than the one our global warming is initiating.

Other clues to world temperature changes and their magnitude include the rise and fall in the altitude of snow lines. These lines are indicated by fossilized and semi-fossilized vegetation deposits on the mountainsides.

When all the information is collected from these and other sources, it indicates that the variations in average world temperatures in the biosphere, causing or resulting from the establishment and termination of ice ages, is less than 5°C or about 9°F. Additionally it is generally thought that tropical sea-surface temperature changes are a good two degrees higher still. Temperatures over continents can double that again.

These temperature changes may not seem important, especially as in our daily experience we see changes varying by much more than that in just a few minutes. However we are talking about world averages. And they are very important.

Sunspots are also often mentioned as a possible influence on our planet's weather. Sunspots are round cooler patches on the surface of the sun. They are like volcanoes, only they erupt intense magnetic fields, not ash or carbon dioxide or lava like terrestrial volcanoes do. Sunspots don't cover a substantial area of the sun. In photographs they look like half a dozen small grapes in a large flat fruit bowl.

The well known 11-year sunspot cycle seems to be half of a 22-year solar magnetic cycle in which the magnetic polarity of sunspots reverses each 11 years. Sunspot activity very slightly affects the 1,370 watts per square metre solar constant. Also there is a slight cyclic variation in total solar emissions over periods of less than 100 years. In the longer term therefore, these effects do not seem to be related in any significant way to glacial cycles and ice ages as they tend to average out over their relatively brief cycle.

In the short term however, they can affect human activities and civilizations. An increase in total solar activity between the years 1100 and 1250 did appear to coincide with relatively warmer weather in Northern Europe. It was this added warmth that encouraged the migration of Vikings to Greenland, and even on to North America.

Likewise the thermal energy released from volcanic activity is totally insignificant when considering global warming and world climates. A volcano does however spew out dust, and sometimes the dust is in sufficient quantities to alter the optical characteristics of the atmosphere. That is the only possible way a volcanic eruption can affect total world weather, but even then it can only be for a short period, just while the dust settles. Admittedly every few tens of millions of years catastrophic geological events occur that massively change the world environment. Mankind has never seen such events.

There is now absolutely no doubt that the recent warming of the earth that has occurred in the last forty years cannot be blamed either on orbital changes, nor on sunspot activities, nor on overall solar emissions. Nor can this warming be blamed on any Milankovic glacial cycle, for the reality is that according to their postulated long-term effects, the earth should be very, very slowly cooling—not rapidly warming, as it is.

Neither does the internal heat of the earth soaking up through the mantle have any significant effect on our weather and climate. Just below the earth's crust, temperatures do soar to thousands of degrees, and yet the influence of all this internal planetary heat has less than a tenth of a percentage point effect on the earth's surface temperatures. In other words, the temperature of this entire planet, from one side all the way through to the other is, in the long term, determined by the heat of the sun and the related greenhouse phenomenon—a massive planetary phenomenon that we are rapidly changing.

The climates and the weathers of this planet are ultimately determined by the amount of heat that comes to us as sunshine. The amount of heat energy arriving as sunshine in our part of the solar system is called the solar constant. The solar constant is an incredible 1,370 watts per square metre. Where most people on earth live, it drops to about 1,000 watts per square metre mid-day, mid-summer, depending on the clarity of the atmosphere. That's like a 100-watt light bulb per square foot. Or for the whole world, it's like 130,000,000,000,000 electric radiators, each a thousand watts, and all shining down on the earth's surface. That's 130 trillion of them.

That is the energy that drives our entire weather system. That is the energy that powers the flows of the giant ocean currents. And a little of it is the energy that powers virtually all living things.

The greenhouse effect is an entirely optical phenomenon. Technically it's an electromagnetic phenomenon. That's why these things are so important and why we need to know some of the relevant details.

The energy from the sun comes to us as sunshine, and sunshine is light. So what controls our weather is the optical characteristics of our atmosphere. Some things are transparent to light at only certain wavelengths (or colours). Some things are partially transparent. Some things are totally transparent. A layer of some materials, no more than one or two atoms thick, can block out sunlight completely. A piece of black paper, a thin film of plastic, a sheet of aluminium foil, the chrome plating on a car, a blush of spray paint, a linen shirt, all can totally prevent sunlight getting through.

Light coming to us from the sun is a mixture of a whole range of colours. We see these colours in a spectrum or in a rainbow. The mix of colours in natural sunlight is extremely consistent, and we have evolved so we don't notice the mix at all, nor can we differentiate the component colours. When we hear a mixture of sounds we can hear the mix of different pitches, or frequencies, that make up the sound. When we see a mixture of colours we only see the final mix. What we see as green may not be green light at all, but a particular mix that seems green to us. Green light appears green, but sunlight appears to have no colour at all and is described as white light.

At both ends of the colour range there is just a little bit of sunlight that we can't see. At one end there is infrared, i.e. just beyond red. At the other end there is ultraviolet, or just beyond violet. Some night-hunting animals can actually "see" the infrared coming from warm-blooded prey. Others creatures are sensitive to some of the ultraviolet wavelengths.

All objects radiate some light energy, whether visible or not. As they cool they radiate less. If not too hot, radiation is generally infrared. We may not see infrared radiation ourselves, but we can feel it. We feel it as warmth. Above about 600°C many surfaces start to glow red. Objects are then described as red-hot and we can see the radiation.

The actual surface of the sun is around 6,000°C and at this temperature it's much hotter than red hot, it glows white hot. It is very much hotter in the deep interior where nuclear reactions are continuous. Temperatures there are in the millions of degrees.

Light is a wave of electric and magnetic fields, a so-called electromagnetic wave, but if you think of it like a wave on the surface of water you won't go far wrong. All waves have some common properties: wavelength (the distance between the crests), frequency (the number of crests passing per second) and velocity (how fast the crests move). The wavelength, frequency and velocity are thus interrelated. In a vacuum (and pretty much in air), all light waves travel at the same speed and we need only consider either the wavelength or frequency. The wavelength multiplied by the frequency always equals the velocity of light so either term can be used.

A nanometre is one billionth of a metre. The wavelength of ultraviolet light ranges from 280 to 400 nanometres. Visible light, i.e. violet, indigo, blue, green, yellow, orange and red lights have wavelengths ranging from 400 to 760 nanometres. The infrared wavelengths go from 760 to 50,000 nanometres. Gamma rays and X-rays are also electromagnetic waves and have wavelengths of less than 200 nanometres.

Above a wavelength of 50,000 nanometres we have microwaves. Longer than a wavelength of about 80,000,000 nanometres or 8 cm, we get into the radio wave band. Radio waves are generally described by their frequency, instead of their wavelength. Longer wavelengths correspond to lower frequencies. In the electromagnetic spectrum a wavelength of around 8 mm is called EHF (extra high frequency), then descending comes SHF (super high frequency), UHF (ultra high frequency), VHF (very high frequency), HF (high frequency), MF (medium frequency), LF (low frequency), and VLF (very low frequency). With ULF (ultra low frequencies), frequencies are around 100,000 cycles per second and have wavelengths around 10 kilometres long. Wavelengths can be virtually any size, up to light years long, but these would be almost impossible to detect.

Waves that convey radio signals can generally pass through wood and bricks and plastic. Electromagnetic radiation in the visible spectrum will penetrate water and glass and petrol to a certain extent, but not thick oil. Infrared radiation hardly penetrates solid materials at all.

The electromagnetic frequencies of raw sunlight cover a fairly wide spectrum, but a good 40% arrives as visible light. Gamma rays, X-rays and ultraviolet rays amount to about 10%. The remaining 50% is composed of a broad spectrum of infrared radiation.

The light-absorbing characteristics of our tiny and vulnerable atmosphere control the quantity of energy we receive from the sun and it controls how much of that energy is re-radiated back into space. The optical characteristics of our atmosphere decide the climate and the weather of the world we live in by balancing the amount of energy coming in and going out. Normally, changes in our atmosphere occur only slowly, usually over many thousands or even millions of years.

However, major changes in the earth's optical characteristics can occur rapidly, often after dramatic geological events. The air then becomes loaded with dust. The input-output heat balance rapidly changes. This occurred most noticeably with the eruption of Mount Pinatubo in the Philippines in July 1991. Generally within months and rarely more than within a few years the particles settle and the atmosphere clears. The original heat balance is restored. There is little permanent disruption to life and to ecosystems. With the Pinatubo eruption the average world surface temperatures dropped by over 0.5°F (0.3°C) for two years, but in complete contrast, and because of polar air circulation in the high northern latitudes warming actually occurred.

After an impact with a large extraterrestrial object, say a few kilometres in diameter, things are different. The atmosphere does not revert to "normal" in a matter of months. The world changes totally. Massive global extinctions occur. The world's ecosystems are altered forever. Eventually a totally new world environment forms, and a new heat balance becomes established.

A stable heat balance is the only thing that establishes stable climatic systems, which in turn controls our weather and determines the energy and power of our ocean currents. Ultimately that balance is the factor that decides whether we will be surviving in an ice age or living in an interglacial period as we are now.

Massive changes in climate can be, and are tolerated, but only over geological timescales. For most advanced life forms, changes can only be tolerated when long periods of time are available for adjustment or evolution. Only very primitive life forms can survive on a world in a constant state of erratic and unpredictable change.

Humans can adapt. Animals can adapt. But only so long as there is time to adapt. But the rate of adaptation certainly cannot be sped up a thousandfold, and a thousandfold increase in adaptation rate is what would be needed to adjust to current fossil-carbon-induced global warming.

4

The greenhouse effect, the ozone hole, the light, the heat and the gases

G LOBAL warming is caused by a greenhouse effect. This greenhouse effect is the conversion of light energy into heat energy, followed by the entrapment of that heat energy within the atmosphere of our planet.

How a greenhouse works

A glass-enclosed greenhouse is used to create a warmer climate within the greenhouse than exists naturally outside the greenhouse. Tropical and subtropical plants can be grown in the warmer artificial climate. The entire air and surface temperature of the earth is determined in a similar way. Our planetary temperatures are therefore described as resulting from a total world greenhouse effect. Greenhouse effects result from the optical characteristics of the covering over the greenhouse, as was mentioned in chapter 3.

White-hot surfaces, such as the surface of the sun, radiate white light. Slightly cooler objects, but still red-hot, radiate red light. Cooler objects still, objects cool enough to touch, radiate infrared light. Infrared means beyond red, and is not visible to human eyes, but we feel it as heat.

The glass in the walls and roof of a greenhouse is almost transparent to visible sunlight. The sun shines through the glass, and objects inside the greenhouse absorb the light energy and warm up. As the objects get warmer they radiate this warmth back out, but now they are radiating the energy as infrared light. Glass is transparent to white light but is not transparent to infrared light. The light, converted to heat energy, is trapped.

Some of the infrared light coming from the objects within the greenhouse is simply reflected back off the glass and stays inside the greenhouse. Some of the infrared light is absorbed by the glass as it tries to get through. This now warmer glass in turn radiates energy. Some of the energy is radiated to the outside and escapes, but the rest is radiated back into the greenhouse. The temperature inside the greenhouse slowly rises. Eventually the glass, and the materials inside the greenhouse, get hot enough that as much heat is lost to the outside as the sun is pouring in. A warmer internal greenhouse temperature eventually stabilizes.

It depends on the conditions, but generally around 25% of the heat loss from a greenhouse is due to radiation from the glass. The rest is lost by conduction, for example, the heat might soak into the ground, or by convection, as outside breezes cool the glass walls. Such breezes blowing on the glass can increase heat loss dramatically. This is the reason why greenhouses are often double-glazed. Usually in a greenhouse most of the heat loss results from this convection.

Our atmosphere acts like the glass in a greenhouse. It too lets the sunlight from space through and down to the ground. The ground warms up and radiates infrared light back into space. However, certain gases in the atmosphere, the oxides of nitrogen, methane (the marsh gas that bubbles through your toes in swamps) and carbon dioxide (the bubbles in soda water and soft drinks) are opaque to infrared light. These gases act exactly the same as the glass in a greenhouse. The infrared is re-reflected again to the ground. And so the earth's surface warms up.

There is no air in space, and so there can be no convenient breezes in space to help cool the earth down in the manner that glass is cooled in a greenhouse. Obviously, conduction and convection effects can't apply to a whole planet, as a planet resides in the vacuum of space. It is heat radiation alone that is relevant to overall planetary surface temperatures. Radiation is the sole way by which a planet can shed heat, or for that matter, any celestial body. Of course there are geological and nuclear energy phenomena occurring deep within our planet, but these have surprisingly negligible short-term or direct surface-temperature effects.

The stream of solar energy that constantly bathes our planet has little variation. Weather and climate variations depend entirely on whether that sunlight energy stays in our atmosphere, our soil and our oceans, or is ultimately reflected or re-radiated back into space. The movement of the sun-derived energy through all these systems is called the greenhouse effect. The prime controlling factor in the magnitude of the greenhouse effect is atmospheric carbon dioxide. The levels of carbon dioxide in our atmosphere, and the absorption of that carbon dioxide into the geology of the earth's crust, into the oceans, into the planet's living biomass, and into soil fertility enrichment processes, are all intimately interrelated and determine the surface temperature of the planet.

All life on this planet controls, and is in turn controlled by, the relatively minuscule carbon dioxide content in our planet's atmosphere. We have to realize that by digging up and burning ancient buried carbon deposits, we are massively increasing that content.

Electromagnetic energy and the greenhouse effect

Sunlight warms the earth's surface and the earth's atmosphere in a couple of different ways. The particular process is determined by the wavelengths of the incoming electromagnetic radiation. Light is simply visible electromagnetic radiation.

At an altitude of 275,000 feet or 52 miles (84 kilometres), the majority of the dangerous short-wavelength gamma rays and X-rays in raw sunlight have been screened out by upper atmospheric effects. This happens in what is almost, but not quite, the vacuum of space. These effects are negligible as far as global warming is concerned. Infrared and visible light are the important ones. Starting with longer wavelengths, infrared radiation is in general absorbed by the gases making up the atmosphere before it reaches the ground.

The greenhouse gases in the atmosphere, having absorbed this heat energy, immediately re-radiate it out, but now in any random direction. What happens is that an individual molecule of the gas will absorb a photon, that is a single "particle" of light energy, and a little while later shoots another photon out at pretty much the same wavelength it came in at. Some of these photons will be reabsorbed, some will be re-radiated back into space, some will get all the way through the atmosphere and warm the planetary surface. Sometimes a molecule that has absorbed a photon collides with another molecule before it has a chance to shoot a photon back out. When this happens the energy is not re-emitted but instead ends up increasing the speed of the molecule. This increased speed manifests itself as an increase in temperature of the gas. Convection currents then distribute the heat through the surrounding air and warm the total mass of the atmosphere.

The other greenhouse warming process involves shorter-wavelength radiation. The majority of this radiation is visible light. The light, or more correctly photons of light, come straight down through the atmosphere until they hit a cloud and are reflected directly back into space, or they penetrate straight through to the earth's surface. During any one day it is usually a combination of both. The absorbed radiation warms the ground or the ocean. The heat soaks in. The temperature of the ground can then be warmer than the air in contact with it. So the air gets warmed by conduction. This warmer air moves away from the ground and in turn warms the atmosphere by convection.

All objects emit heat radiation, and the wavelength of that heat radiation is determined by the temperature of the radiating body. The ground is relatively cold and can only radiate infrared radiation. Infrared radiation has a lot more trouble getting past the greenhouse gases to outer space and the heat is trapped.

Thus we have energy arriving from the sun in the form of visual light that easily penetrates our atmosphere. It hits the ground and is absorbed. As it is now trapped, things warm up. So the greenhouse effect basically depends on the optical qualities of our atmosphere. As more infrared-absorbing gases enter the atmosphere, the effect intensifies.

Optical processes can be affected by minuscule quantities of matter. For example, a household mirror reflects almost all light shining on it. That light is reflected back by the metallic coating on the back of the mirror. The coating can be mercury, silver, or aluminium and is usually between one and two millionths of an inch (30 nanometres) thick. A nanometre, or nm, is one billionth of a metre.

A piece of aluminium foil wrapped around a light globe won't let any heat or light radiation in or out. A thin coat of white paint, or a thin coat of black paint, will make an incredible difference to how much an object will heat up in the sun. The white paint is cool. You can fry an egg on the black paint. Smoke a piece of glass with a candle. The coating will be microscopically thin, yet the bright sun appears as a faint orange ball when viewed through the glass. A good 99% of the sun's energy has been blocked.

The colour effects of a film of oil on water occur because the film of oil has thinned out to where it is no thicker than the wavelengths of the light shining on the oil. The differences in the thickness of the oil film trap different wavelengths. What you see is not actually a true spectrum but white light minus the particular colours of the true sunlight spectrum. You see that peculiar spectrum of not-quite-right colour.

If gold and mercury contact, a layer of mercury, as thin as a few atoms across, will immediately coat the gold, and the colour of the gold vanishes. Those few atoms of mercury are extremely difficult to remove to expose the underlying gold, but eventually the mercury will evaporate into the air. Never let your gold wedding ring touch a drop of mercury. What you actually see is a tiny opaque layer of mercury atoms. The coated gold looks a little like silver or platinum.

That's how little is required to alter optical phenomena. And so, it bears repeating. The entire greenhouse effect is an optical phenomenon, subject to control by seemingly insignificant quantities of matter. Because of this our power to change the temperature of our entire planet is awesome. We are now like small children innocently playing with fully loaded guns. And the fossil-fuel industries keep telling us not to worry.

Greenhouse effects are not just confined to the backyard greenhouse and the atmosphere of planet Earth. Our two neighbouring planets, Venus and Mars, are excellent examples of planetary surface temperatures massively modified by greenhouse effects. The planets of our solar system have wildly different atmospheres resulting from the unique variations in their planetary evolution.

The atmosphere of Venus was originally assessed as probably 96% carbon dioxide and about 3% nitrogen; the rest a mixture of various gases. Calculations based on this level of carbon dioxide predicted surface temperatures could be as high as several hundred degrees. Both predictions have since been confirmed by space probes.

In the unlikely event it ever existed, life on Venus was never able to entrap the planet's carbon dioxide and safely lock it away under the surface as limestone deposits, oil deposits, peat or coal beds, and certainly not as fertile soil. All the carbon dioxide that was ever in the atmosphere of Venus is still there. Its greenhouse effect, with all that carbon dioxide in its atmosphere, has established a completely stable but scorchingly hot, lifeless world. Ground temperatures on Venus were found to be around 475°C (850°F). The atmospheric pressure on Venus is about ninety times as high as here on earth.

The planet Mars, on the other hand, was forecast as a place of extreme cold. Our space probe visit to Mars confirmed the forecast exactly. The actual composition of the atmosphere is virtually the same as on Venus. However the Martian atmosphere is so thin that the warming caused by a Mars' greenhouse effect is lost to space. The ground-level atmospheric pressure on Mars is about 6 millibars, whereas on earth it averages 1,013 millibars. In consequence, the surface temperatures of Mars range from a cold -20°C at midday, to an extremely cold -120°C at midnight.

Like Earth, the atmospheric temperatures and the ground surface temperatures on these planets are almost totally controlled by the quantity and composition of their atmospheres. The modelling of surface temperature modifications by greenhouse effects is well understood. The predicted surface temperatures on Mars and Venus were almost exactly the temperatures found when the interplanetary space probes finally got there and checked them.

If planet Earth did not have an atmosphere containing gases with significant greenhouse effects, the average temperature would not be plus 56°F (15°C) as it is now, but zero Fahrenheit (-18°C) and with the same wild daily temperature variations found on other planets. This predicted temperature for our planet uses the same formula that so accurately predicted the temperatures of our neighbouring planets. There are now no unexplained mysteries in the correlation of global temperatures with greenhouse gas levels in any planet's atmosphere.

If we had no atmosphere on earth things would be very different. We can use the moon to illustrate this perfectly. The earth and the moon are both, on average, exactly the same distance from the sun. The nighttime surface temperature of the moon can drop below -150°C and the daytime surface temperature can exceed 100°C. The moon's average surface temperature is about 33°C cooler than the earth's average. The earth's atmosphere and its resulting greenhouse effect gives us the extra 33°C of warmth and mitigates the inhospitable 250°C variation in daily temperature which would otherwise occur and make life on earth, at least as we know it, impossible.

We know the temperatures that occur on earth. We measure them all the time. We can forecast with confident accuracy and reliability how hot our changing atmospheric carbon dioxide level is going to make our atmosphere and our ground temperature. Just what these temperature rises will do to world climate, rainfalls and sea levels are the frightening unknowns. But we can be sure it won't be pleasant.

Extra: How heat energy moves

Heat energy can be transferred, moved, or conveyed in three different ways.

The first is by radiation. All objects constantly absorb and radiate out heat radiation. Heat radiation and light radiation are really the same. Heat radiation is usually considered as light radiation that is just outside our capacity to see. It is invisible, although you can feel it.

The radiant heat emitted from an object is proportional to the fourth power of its absolute temperature. So, if you double the absolute temperature of an object its radiation will increase sixteenfold. If you increase the temperature threefold, it will radiate out 3 x 3 x 3 x 3 times as much radiation as it did at the cooler temperature. That is 81 times as much radiant heat.

If a surface is exposed to a similar adjacent surface with a higher temperature, both surfaces continue to radiate and both surfaces continue to absorb the radiant heat. Because of this quadruple multiplication factor, the cooler surface rapidly absorbs extra heat from the warmer surface. This happens until both reach the same temperature and radiating and absorbing effects become equal.

The heat we feel from a radiator, and the warmth we feel on our hand near a light globe is radiation, but to be more precise it is electromagnetic radiation. Apart from quantity, the difference between radiation emitted from your hand and that from a light globe is simply the respective wavelengths of the electromagnetic radiation.

The second way heat energy moves is by conduction. Heat can be transferred from one object to another by conduction, if the objects are in contact. The molecules or atoms in a substance are always bouncing around a bit. The hotter the object the more they bounce around. When a hot object comes into contact with a cold object, the more violently moving molecules in the hot object crash into the molecules in the cold object and cause them to start bouncing more vigorously. So the cold object heats up. The process is called heat conduction. Heat conduction burns your finger when you touch a hot electric iron.

Thirdly, heat can be transferred from one object to another by convection; that is when the actual object itself, containing the heat, moves. The hot electric element in a hair dryer warms the air in contact with the hot electric coils by conduction. The warmth, or the energy, in this now warm air is conveyed, or carried, to your wet hair as the air moves.

This process is convection. Convection can be natural or unforced as in the case when warm air rises naturally, warming the air above, or it can be forced, as the example of the hair dryer where a fan pushes the warmed air along.

The composition of the atmosphere

To understand what determines the extent of the greenhouse effect on earth it's wise to have some basic knowledge of the properties and composition of our current atmosphere. Otherwise we are too easily fooled, and too many people want us to be.

The composition of our atmosphere is nitrogen 78%, oxygen 21% and argon 0.9%. All the rest of the gases—carbon dioxide, neon, methane, krypton, helium, xenon, hydrogen, nitrous oxides, carbon monoxide, nitrogen dioxide, sulphur dioxide and ozone and various man-made gases make up the remaining 0.1%. There is also both water and water vapour, which we'll count separately as atmospheric water content can vary enormously. It can vary from virtually zero to the huge quantities occurring during a storm.

The pressure in our atmosphere drops off with height, similar to the way water pressure drops off as you rise to the surface from a dive. Proportionally, air pressure does actually drop off faster as you ascend because air is compressible, so its density, or weight per unit volume, also drops off with height. Whereas, even under extreme pressure, the density of water varies little.

Temperatures don't follow that simple pattern. Starting from ground level and rising we are initially in the troposphere, where just about everything that directly concerns human life happens, from growing our food to flying our planes, from drizzling rain to towering tornadoes. In the troposphere, temperatures constantly decrease with height at an average of about 1.1°F (2°C) per 1,000 feet (300 m) to about −69°F, or about 101°F below freezing (−56°C). At this point the temperature stops dropping and we enter the stratosphere. The behaviour in temperature defines the boundary. The boundary between the troposphere and the stratosphere is called, appropriately enough, the tropopause. This boundary can be as low as 25,000 feet (8 km) over the poles and as high as 50,000 feet (15 km) over the equator.

The troposphere contains 80% of all the air on this Earth of ours. When you look out the window on that inter-city jet flight we previously considered, 80% of all the world's air is underneath you and that air controls the temperature of the entire planet. It is a sobering thought.

The area defined as the stratosphere tops out at about 160,000 feet, or 30 miles (50 km). In the stratosphere the temperatures stay at their low readings until slowly rising again to about 50°F (10°C) in a thin band called the mesosphere. At a height of around 60 miles (100 km) temperatures again fall to low readings. They then start to rise again as we merge into interplanetary space where temperatures rise to as high as several thousand degrees. At these heights however, there is so little mass involved that such temperatures are almost purely academic. Our skin can't tolerate boiling water but we sit in saunas with air temperatures well above that of boiling water. The air may be hot but being so light there is little heat energy in it. Variations in temperatures of thousands of degrees would not even be felt in the thinness of space.

At an altitude of 30 miles (50 km) or so, only about 0.1% of the world's air is still above you; yet this thin air is still sufficient to protect us from incoming meteors. We see them as shooting stars as friction burns them up travelling through this high thin air.

What is climate modelling?

Climate modelling is the simulation on computer of most of the variables involved in predicting weather patterns and climatic change.

In climate modelling relating to the greenhouse effect, usually all the greenhouse gases and their effects are given a "carbon dioxide equivalent" rating. The quantity of each gas is converted into the quantity of carbon dioxide that would give the same greenhouse effect. Apart from CFCs (chlorofluorocarbons) most of the greenhouse gases are fossilized-carbon-use related and therefore fairly intimately related to pure carbon dioxide concentrations. The simplification therefore does not distort the essential validity of calculations. Changing greenhouse gas concentrations can then be studied as an exercise in one variable—the equivalent total of CO_2.

Climate and weather modelling works something like this.

First you might get the temperature of the local ocean current, and let's say you already know that it's moving south. There might be a high-pressure system sitting off to the east and you know air revolves around a high-pressure system in a certain way, counterclockwise in the Southern Hemisphere, clockwise in the Northern. You have collected measurements, the humidity of the air and its temperature and pressure at various heights.

At the time of the year the warmth from the sun is a known quantity. The air maybe has a measured quantity of dust from a recent dust storm, and that will affect heat getting through to the ground. This too must be allowed for. Summer is approaching. You know that the ground is much wetter than it normally is because of recent rain showers. You have a whole stack of records that show what happens when similar readings occurred in the past. In addition you have worked out some rules that give you a rough idea how each of the conditions you've measured affects other phenomena. You then put all this information, and as many rules as seem applicable, into a computer and press "go".

Because there are so many variables, the bigger and faster the computer is, the better. What you want the computer to do is to move all these variables around according to your rules, and give you back what all these readings will be, let's say, a week ahead. Short-term, this is called weather forecasting. Long-term, it's called climate modelling. Climate modelling implies covering a much larger area than that taken into account in weather forecasting.

In practical terms, with weather forecasting in most parts of the world, the most accurate weather forecast for tomorrow is firstly that it will be the same as today. To this is added modifications based on information gleaned from weather maps, satellite cloud images, and even the location of recent rainfalls. A final forecast is then made. This method is hardly climate modelling, but is generally reliable in the short-term.

Prior to the advent of powerful computers, long-term forecasting was based on considering what similar weather patterns in the past had produced and basing a forecast on history repeating itself.

This method of forecasting is difficult without a mass of accurate records. Of course for long-term climate forecasting in a global warming scenario, the records themselves unfortunately now come from a somewhat cooler world. With modern powerful computers there is now less reliance on simply looking at patterns in the past weather. Both weather forecasting and climate modelling now depend more on knowing how all the variables interact and using these "rules" to let the computer work out what will happen. The accuracy is improving constantly.

The greenhouse properties of the atmospheric gases

The greenhouse effect of an individual gas is determined not only by how much of that gas is up there, but also how well the gas absorbs and then re-radiates energy or simply scatters it. Those wavelengths of electromagnetic radiation that a gas molecule absorbs best are determined by the size of the gas molecule and how strongly the atoms within the molecule are bound together, or how "flexible" the molecule is. Each gas has its own unique capacity to absorb sunlight at particular wavelengths. Additionally, the significance of the effect will vary if it occurs at a high altitude or a low altitude because of previous screening. The gases that make up the atmosphere are evenly and totally mixed throughout all altitudes. The only exception being at altitudes where particular gases are being chemically or structurally modified by some external influence and mixing is not yet complete.

The molecules of oxygen and nitrogen in the atmosphere are too small and too rigid to interact with either visible or infrared light and do not have any greenhouse effects. The molecules that comprise the gases that concern us most are slightly bigger, more flexible and a little more complex. They can interact with infrared light and so have an important part to play in the greenhouse effect.

These gases are carbon dioxide (CO_2), methane (CH_4), nitrous oxide (N_2O) and various other compounds of nitrogen and oxygen, loosely labeled NO_x. Then there is ozone (O_3), and finally the compounds of carbon combined with chlorine and fluorine and generally labelled chlorofluoro-carbons, or CFCs. Although ozone is a potent greenhouse gas, the quantities involved are too tiny for its greenhouse effect to be of any real significance.

CFCs are the man-made gases used in such things as refrigerators and spray cans. The CFCs are important both because of their interaction with ozone and because of their not totally insignificant greenhouse effects. Ozone and the ozone hole are discussed later in this chapter.

Some of the wavelengths in solar radiation are absorbed by a few green-house gases, some are absorbed by only one and some are not absorbed at all. One of the reasons that the refrigerant gases, the CFCs, are a significant greenhouse gas is that they affect wavelength ranges that are otherwise unaffected by the main greenhouse gases. This effect of the CFCs is in addition to their ability to destroy the high-altitude ozone layer that helps in shielding us from cancer-causing ultraviolet radiation.

All the greenhouse gases combined currently make up less than 0.1% of the atmosphere. Water however is a wild card. When water evaporates into the air, it becomes humidity or water vapour. And atmospheric water vapour acts as a very powerful greenhouse gas.

Apart from water precipitation effects—clouds, fogs and rain, etc.—all the greenhouse gases are thoroughly mixed and dispersed throughout the predominately nitrogen-oxygen atmosphere.

For an exercise to appreciate the relative quantities and importance of the atmosphere's constituents, let's imagine that we take all the greenhouse gases combined and separate them out. We then put them in separate layers away from the main nitrogen-oxygen mix. Imagine them as individual self-contained layers on the surface covering the whole planet and then let's measure them. For this exercise we will omit humidity and cloud formations and also assume the gases are at normal ground temperature and pressure. We are talking about gases, not liquids.

That layer of greenhouse gases would be about nine feet (3 m) high. The layer of gas would not reach the ceiling in a one-storey bungalow. If we then condense the gas layers into our hypothetical liquid form, the total layer of greenhouse gases would be no more than about an eighth of an inch (3 mm) deep. Of that only a very tiny but very dangerous added fraction is causing our world to overheat.

Carbon dioxide (CO_2)

Carbon in the form of carbon dioxide is the most critical component in the greenhouse effect. All the gases in the atmosphere that influence the earth's greenhouse effect interrelate and overlap in their ability to absorb and affect sunlight, but carbon dioxide is the key. In the atmosphere carbon dioxide lasts forever. It doesn't break down into something less able to cause greenhouse heating. It can only be physically removed. Some soaks into oceans, but the rest can only be extracted by the processes within living things.

Over millions of years in our world's long geological history, huge quantities of carbon have been transformed via biological processes into oil, gas, coal and limestone. It must be clearly appreciated that in the short term, in terms of a few hundred years or less, it can only be extracted by the creation of additional biomass and increased soil fertility.

It must also be noted that the man-made sources of carbon dioxide on earth are either closely connected, or often identical to, the sources of the other major man-made greenhouse gases. In general they are derived from producing and burning fossil carbon for fuel, or from destroying soil organic matter and microscopic soil life by excessive use of chemical fertilizers generally exacerbated by other damaging agricultural practices. In a similar manner the production of almost every minor greenhouse gas is associated with a carbon-dioxide-producing process—gases such as methane, nitrous oxide, the CFCs and ozone. Conveniently and for simplicity the minor gases are given a "CO_2 equivalent" rating. The measure of carbon dioxide accumulation in our atmosphere, either itself only or including the minor gases, is thus an excellent measure of, and correlates exactly with, the constantly rising levels of "natural" disasters we are now experiencing.

In the beginning, carbon dioxide, being one atom of carbon combined with two atoms of oxygen (dioxide = two oxygen), belched out of volcanoes in huge quantities, where it became a major component of earth's primal atmosphere. It is still being discharged from the thousands of active volcanoes under the oceans and across the earth's surface.

The whole process of life started by taking some carbon from the air, mixing in some water, adding tiny traces of other elements for variety, and then warming it all with sunlight energy. There were probably a few lightning flashes thrown in to kick-start the life-developing chemical processes. (Alternatively, some believe life may have initially started using carbon dioxide coming from undersea volcanoes and vents which dissolved in the surrounding seawater, and the energy of the geothermal activity to power up the life-generating process.)

Multiple reactions occurred in these processes, and complex organic compounds were formed. These complex compounds then became the building blocks for even more of the complex chemicals of life. In this process the oxygen in the original carbon dioxide was released into the atmosphere to eventually support the development of aerobic metabolic processes, i.e. life based on oxygen use or consumption.

There was once much too much carbon dioxide in the air for humans to breathe the stuff. However over hundreds of millions of years, primitive plants, microbes and bacteria absorbed the carbon dioxide from the air. They also absorbed the sunlight energy that shone on this primitive world. Most of these complex carbon compounds, with their entrapped solar energy, became part of the rocks that form the earth's upper crust.

Two billion years after the formation of the earth, the carbon dioxide levels had been massively reduced and oxygen, because of living processes, became a significant ingredient in the atmosphere. The oxygen-consuming life forms then developed rapidly. After another two and a half billion years, the atmosphere and the earth's environment changed towards generally what we know today. These new types of environments suited the evolution of well-developed life forms. Mammals eventually evolved, then came the evolution of the primates, and finally mankind.

As plant life grows, sunlight energy becomes trapped as chemical bonds within carbon-containing molecules. When we burn a piece of wood, the complex organic material that makes up the wood recombines with the oxygen in the air to re-form the original carbon dioxide. The energy released as heat and radiation from the fire is the energy of the sunlight, originally utilized to grow and form the wood.

In our bodies, we can combine oxygen with the complex carbon molecules at much lower temperatures and at much slower and controlled rates. This produces the energy we need to function. In the process, we also produce carbon dioxide, which we discharge in our exhaled breath. This energy-producing system is extremely compact. It is twenty times more effective at energy production than that used by most lower life forms, especially those primitive, microscopic life forms that need to rely on carbon compounds that are only randomly formed.

Despite its importance to our global warming problems, there is actually very little carbon dioxide in our world's atmosphere, relative to the other gases. Recalling our liquefied carbon dioxide example, all the liquid CO_2 in the atmosphere would be about one-tenth of an inch thick; that's about two and a half millimetres. The crazy and dangerous weather changes we are now experiencing are occurring because we have added just 0.020 of an inch, or half a millimetre, to that imagined liquefied carbon dioxide blanket covering the earth.

Methane (CH$_4$)

Methane is the second most influential greenhouse gas following carbon dioxide. It is at least 20 times more potent, but relatively small quantities are involved.

Both methane and nitrous oxide (considered next) have one special importance when considering global warming. In the longer wavelengths, carbon dioxide and water vapour don't have much effect on planetary re-radiation. Methane and nitrous oxide do. They trap many of the infrared wavelengths that are missed by carbon dioxide. This gives them an importance way in excess of what would be expected by their relatively small quantities.

Methane is composed of one atom of carbon and four atoms of hydrogen. Its chemical formula is CH$_4$. Methane is constantly being produced on the planet both naturally and anthropogenically. It is constantly being broken down by oxidation into carbon dioxide and water. Methane's life in the atmosphere as methane is short, only about 10 years, but the resulting carbon dioxide lasts indefinitely.

Apart from its contribution to global warming, excess methane in the atmosphere has other downsides. Methane migrates up into the stratosphere where it breaks down to water and carbon dioxide. The water from this breakdown then forms thin wispy clouds. The sequence of events in these breakdown processes exacerbates the destruction of our ozone shield.

A constant buildup of water vapour and ice crystals in the otherwise very stable upper stratosphere suggests all kinds of very unpleasant but likely scenarios as the ice crystals can catalyze any number of reactions. We don't know what the consequences might be. Unfortunately, research on these effects is quite noticeably not well supported. Just possibly because it would be to the detriment of the fossil carbon industries' image.

Atmospheric methane had previously been produced almost entirely by anaerobic bacteria digesting dead plant material. Anaerobic bacteria don't require and often can't tolerate the presence of oxygen. Methane is also formed this way in the stomach of all herbivorous animals. This factor gets a lot more publicity than its relative quantity warrants.

Herbivorous animals as a source of methane have definitely risen with the increase in world cattle and sheep populations. However, the increase is not nearly as significant as is constantly insisted, for grazing lands have always been inhabited by grazing animals, whose populations have only ever been limited by grass growth, and of course the carnivores that inevitably move in and hunt the herbivores.

Vegetation decomposition produces methane in any situation when air supply is restricted. Methane is thus formed in large quantities by vegetation decomposing underwater. The so-called marsh gas in swamps and rice fields is methane. Big increases in rice production have meant significant increases in the discharge of methane into the air. At the same time however, large areas of swamps or wetlands have been cleared and turned into grazing land. This reduction in swamps and wetland areas has just about compensated for the extra methane from the world increase in rice production. Wetlands and rice fields contribute about equal quantities of methane to the atmosphere. Most of these wetlands are in the earth's northern hemisphere. Incidentally, dryland rice, which is the majority of rice grown in Australia, produces very much smaller quantities of methane.

The constant call for the preservation of swamps and wetlands in effect becomes a call to increase global warming and sadly therefore a call that harms the total ecology of the whole planet. Filling in swamps or wetlands will do more good than harm. Our priorities have to be seriously and not irrationally reconsidered.

The tundra areas of Siberia and Alaska are frozen swampland and contain incredible quantities of methane that has been trapped in the ice over countless centuries. This methane is starting to be released into the air as the tundra thaws due to global temperature rises. Another positive feedback loop is thus being created, forcing further global temperature rises. In addition the seawater flooding of freshwater-based coastal lowland vegetation will also contribute to methane generation.

We now dump our rubbish in landfills where there is no oxygen supply. It ferments to form methane. In the past our rubbish used to end up in the top few inches of soil where it broke down aerobically and didn't produce methane. It did produce some carbon dioxide but more importantly, it improved and produced soil. We don't do that now.

The methane from airless landfills is now sometimes extracted by driving steel pipes into the landfill mass to tap this gas. It is then collected and burnt as an energy source. The burnt methane is finally discharged into the atmosphere as water and carbon dioxide. This carbon dioxide production is a far less undesirable outcome than having the methane escape directly into the air.

This sequence is actually sustainable. The rotting material in landfills was once plant life. This plant life grew by utilizing atmospheric carbon dioxide. The whole process from atmospheric carbon dioxide to plants, to trash, to landfill, to methane and finally back to carbon dioxide, although tiny, is a reasonably sustainable energy recycling system. This is only pro-vided there are no fossilized carbon inputs, either as fuel or as agricultural chemicals to overload the cycle.

Food waste and sewage waste is better recycled to produce rich soil, but collecting methane from food waste dumps for energy production is an excellent second choice.

Methane also resides in huge quantities in coal seams. This dates back to the original formation of the coal seams from vast ancient swamps. So methane, along with some carbon dioxide, is commonly the main constituent of coal gas. In the general mining of coal, these gases are constantly being released into the atmosphere.

The additional worldwide methane release that is now overloading natural atmospheric methane breakdown comes from the production and treatment of fossil fuels. Radiocarbon analysis of atmospheric methane reported in *Nature* (Vol. 332, pp. 522–525) indicated that even as far back as 1988, at least one third of all the atmospheric methane then existing in our world came from fossil fuel productions and use. Atmospheric methane concentration is now rising at around 1% of its current level per year, as measured at the Cape Grimm Observatory, Tasmania. That's almost exactly in line with the numbers for fossil fuel usage.

In grim confirmation, ice core samples taken at the Russian Vostok station in Antarctica show past variations in world methane levels to have fluctuated between 350 ppbv (parts per billion by volume) to 650 ppbv over the last 160,000 years. That is more than *Homo sapiens'* total time in existence. But just in the last few years we have increased those concentrations to 1,700 ppbv. The rate of increase in atmospheric methane levels is now between 14 and 17 ppbv each year, as reported by Houghton, Jenkins and Ephraums in *Climate Change*, IPCC *Scientific Assessment* (Cambridge University Press). Ten years ago both French and Soviet researchers were warning that atmospheric methane levels were already rising 50 times faster than at any time in the previous 160,000 years.

What do these numbers mean by comparison? The figure of 1,700 parts per billion is another way of writing 1.7 parts per million (ppm). Carbon dioxide levels have risen 80 ppm but methane has at least twenty times the greenhouse effect of CO_2 so it has the warming equivalent of 34 ppm of carbon dioxide.

The public relations ploy of blaming all methane buildup on cows is a giant red herring. The press produces more wind than the cattle.

Nitrous oxides (NO_X)

The oxides of nitrogen are potent greenhouse gases. Fortunately they are there in relatively small quantities. In addition to global warming effects, nitrous oxide in the atmosphere readily combines with moisture to form nitric acid, one of the more deadly components of acid rain. Until man's relatively recent industrialization, the levels of nitrous oxides in the atmosphere had been quite stable.

There are natural sources of atmospheric nitrous oxides. Some soil bacteria and termites produce nitrous oxide. These have not changed much. But we know that nitrous oxide levels in the atmosphere are rising dangerously and dramatically. One quite reasonable estimate suggested that the level of nitrous oxides will rise to ultimately become a 10% contributor to total global warming within 30 years. These additional nitrous oxides entering our atmosphere come from fossil-fuel power stations and automotive exhausts.

The other and equally significant source of the nitrous oxides comes from our massive use of nitrogenous fertilizers and other nitrogen-based agricultural chemicals. These chemicals not only release their own nitrogen compounds into the atmosphere, but by breaking down soil organic matter, they excessively release the nitrogen that is a constituent of all good fertile soil. This soil nitrogen enters the air generally as nitrous oxides.

Atmospheric water, the wild card

The amount of water (H_2O) and water vapour in the atmosphere varies widely. In the dry air over hot parched deserts, water content can be almost zero. Whereas in the tropics, in thunderstorms, the total water content could well weigh more than the total dry air mass itself. Normally, localized atmospheric water content is constantly varying from day to day, while the average world total stays constant.

The amount of water vapour in the air is usually expressed as relative humidity and written as a percentage rather than parts per million as is the case with other gases. At 100% relative humidity no more water can evaporate into the air at the particular air temperature—the water vapour in the air has reached saturation. If the relative humidity is very low we have nearly dry air. The air's total water content can only exceed 100% relative humidity if the air also contains solid or liquid water, such as snowflakes, raindrops, minute droplets like those we see as a warm breath in cold weather, or as cloud formations.

Another term used to describe atmospheric water content is absolute humidity. Absolute humidity is the actual mass of water vapour present, and provided no water is added or no moisture is forced to condense out by cooling, the absolute humidity will not vary with temperature.

The maximum weight/mass of water vapour that a volume of air can hold rises as the air temperature rises, and falls as air temperature falls. If a parcel of air containing some quantity of water vapour is cooled, its relative humidity will rise to 100%. Any further cooling will cause some of the water to condense out and form clouds, or dew. The temperature at which this happens depends on the absolute humidity and is called the dew point.

Often you might notice all the clouds in the sky appear to have flat bottoms and all at the same altitude. This is the altitude at which the temperature has dropped to the dew point and moisture condenses out of any rising warm air and forms clouds. For any large mass of air the cloud base will rise during the day as the air mass warms. At high altitudes tiny ice crystals can form out of wet saturated air and persist in the upper atmosphere for hours, and sometimes even days. Being ice, they won't readily evaporate back into the parent air. This phenomenon produces the common "anvil" formation on the top of thunderstorms. While the droplets in the rest of the towering thunderstorm can evaporate away, or fall as rain to the ground, the frozen misty anvil top will spread and form a thin layer of high cirrus cloud, sometimes covering the whole sky.

Water has a molecular structure with just the right size and flexibility to absorb and re-radiate infrared energy and so must be considered as a greenhouse gas. Because of the huge quantity in the atmosphere, water is far and away the most powerful and influential of all the greenhouse gases. On a normal comfortable day at 25°C or 77°F and 50% relative humidity, there are about 15,000 parts per million of water vapour in the air at sea level, or almost 50 times the mass of carbon dioxide.

The effect of atmospheric water as a blanket stopping heat radiating back into space can be felt when cloud cover moves in during the night. Overnight frosts can't form if an overnight cloud or fog covers the area and entraps the daytime solar heat under the blanket. A cloudy night after a warm sunny day always means the next day will be considerably warmer than otherwise expected.

The majority of water in the atmosphere comes from evaporation off the surface of oceans so there is absolutely no shortage of water on this planet to create humidity and to form clouds. If all the air in the world's atmosphere somehow absorbed its maximum possible quantity of water and thus all the air would have a 100% relative humidity, the process would have used up less than three inches (75 mm) of the oceans' waters. The average depth of the world's oceans is over two miles. Three inches is nothing.

We might ask, why doesn't water vapour itself lead to a runaway green-house effect? The answer is that water vapour content fortunately is self-regulating. If the water content of the atmosphere increases then there will tend to be more clouds. Clouds are very effective at stopping the escape of heat but they also have a very high albedo, meaning they reflect most of the sunlight that hits them back into space.

Long continuous cloudy periods, even in summer, will cause the average temperature to drop. When the temperature drops, so does the dew point and the water simply falls out of the air as rain or snow. The average water content of the atmosphere will therefore regulate itself about some norm, some average. But that norm is determined by the other greenhouse gases.

While water is a powerful greenhouse gas, it is more like a draught horse; it's big but it's controlled by others. The water content of the atmosphere will always rapidly settle down to an average world level. That level is determined by the prevailing level of the more stable greenhouse gases. Carbon dioxide is by far the most significant of these and so carbon dioxide levels ultimately control atmospheric water content. Atmospheric carbon dioxide levels are now 360 parts per million, whereas the water content in humid air can be as high as 15,000 parts per million. But carbon dioxide still holds the reins.

The problem is, when we change the carbon dioxide level we just have no idea what the water vapour content is going to settle down to. Maybe we can steer the draught horse. But that is of little use if we are the ones wearing the blinkers. Browbeaten by the oil companies' PR people, we humans are the ones avoiding an honest observation of where the road is really heading. Alas, we are shirking our responsibility, and the draught horse is almost at full gallop.

The amount of water in the atmosphere as water vapour, or humidity, or clouds, in all their significant and sometimes majestic forms, is ultimately determined by world temperatures and these are determined by the "thickness" of our greenhouse gas blanket. Change the thickness of the blanket, and a totally new world climate and atmospheric stability will have to reestablish itself. But unfortunately no future stability is at all possible while we continue to modify the thickness of our blanket. And even if we stop at some new blanket thickness, any hypothetical stability will be delayed for decades, or even for centuries, while the world waits for the ocean temperatures to slowly catch up.

Again, in simple terms, we used to have three blankets keeping our world stable and liveable and now we have four. Even if we pegged it at four blankets, it would still take a few hundred years for ocean temperatures, sea levels, ocean circulations, world climates and world weather to catch up, and then to finally settle down to some new pattern. We are guaranteed unpredictable weather and unpredictable rainfall for at least hundreds of years. Additionally, there is absolutely no guarantee that a meaningful stability is even possible, ever. Unstable and continuous massive climate fluctuations for thousands of years are likely.

It was OK when natural carbon dioxide, nitrogen oxides and methane levels oscillated slightly over hundreds, or more likely thousands of years. But now, with our massive burning of fossil fuel and our massive destruction of soil fertility with "fertilizers", we are changing these greenhouse gas levels at extreme rates and to extreme levels. In the past these changes have only occurred associated with catastrophic events such as meteorite impacts, or massive widespread volcanic activity, but afterwards things would settle down. It took a few hundred years, or a few thousand years, or sometimes a few million. But the inevitable tendency was to creep back to the prior norms. This cannot happen while we continue to pump CO_2 and other greenhouse gases into the atmosphere. Destructive instability itself becomes the norm.

CFCs and the story of a brilliant chemist

1930 was approaching. It was the time of the great depression. General Motors owned Frigidaire, and the refrigeration industry was starting to boom. Various substances were used as the refrigerant. Frigidaire was using sulphur dioxide. The American Medical Association was highly critical of the poisonous nature of sulphur dioxide. Methyl chloride had also been used but methyl chloride was also a toxic substance. Industrially, ammonia was the preferred refrigerant. However, even then a few people had already died in industrial accidents from ammonia poisoning.

Frigidaire needed a substance that would not burn, was not toxic, would be a good refrigerant and would be cheap to produce. They went to General Motors. General Motors Research Corporation lent them one of their most brilliant industrial chemists. His name was Thomas Midgley, Jr. He had joined General Motors during World War I.

Thomas Midgley was indeed a brilliant chemist. The rapid development of aeroplane engines during World War I demanded fuels with higher and higher octane ratings. One of Midgley's tasks while at General Motors was to somehow increase the octane rating of petrol and therefore increase its efficiency. He succeeded. He invented tetraethyl lead. It wasn't long before every car engine in the world was designed to run on leaded fuels. His brilliance in creating the fuel additive tetraethyl lead was the reason General Motors sent him to Frigidaire to solve the refrigerant gas dilemma.

Midgley solved this problem too. He actually designed a suitable chemical compound on paper, based on the desired characteristics and chemical nature of its components, and then synthesized his molecular design in the laboratory. It worked. He called his chemical dichlorodifluoromethane. He was then able to synthesize a whole group of compounds based on the same chemical constituents. The group of chemicals he called chlorofluorocarbons and abbreviated the name to CFCs.

They were magical chemicals. They were perfect for cleaning circuit boards and radio valves, they were a great foaming agent and were ideal as a propellant in spray cans and they were an incredibly efficient refrigerant. It was 1974 before any significant scientific paper was published suggesting that CFCs could damage the ozone shield that protects land life from harmful ultraviolet radiation.

In those days, we didn't even know that high-altitude ozone protected us from ultraviolet light. It was also quite inconceivable that civilized man could modify the whole planet's atmosphere. Midgley was a chemist. There were no high-altitude meteorologists—no atmospheric physicists there to tell him what CFCs might do. An ozone shield wasn't even a theory in those days. There weren't a lot of motor vehicles around either to burn his leaded petrol. Thomas Midgley, Jr. was indeed a great chemist. He had well over 100 patents credited to him when he died in November 1944.

Ozone, the ozone hole and CFCs

Ozone has almost nothing to do with global warming. Ozone and the ozone hole is a totally different story.

Unfiltered sunlight, the raw sunlight of space, contains ultraviolet light of various wavelengths. Some can break down organic chemical bonds and all life is structured using organic chemical bonds. That's why ozone and the ozone shield is important. It filters out a high proportion of the more damaging wavelengths. The ozone shield was already in place when life moved up onto land. Land life evolved to handle the UV wavelengths not stopped by the ozone shield.

Oxygen in the upper atmosphere stops short-wave ultraviolet light up to a wavelength of about 190 nm (nanometres—a billionth of a metre). It does this by absorbing its electromagnetic energy. Three oxygen (O_2) molecules get converted into two, semi-stable ozone (O_3) molecules. This becomes a shield.

The screening effects of oxygen peter out at wavelengths much above 240 nm but the effect on these lower wavelengths ensures that ozone is continuously being formed.

Above those wavelengths, ultraviolet light is given names. Above a wavelength of 240 nm, up to about 290 nm, the ultraviolet is described as UV-C.

The ozone formed in the stratosphere blocks out the UV-C. At the high quantities involved, UV radiation with wavelengths below 290 nm is very damaging. It easily destroys proteins and DNA. Life on our planetary surface cannot survive when continuously exposed to UV-C. As soon as oxygen was available in quantity, an ozone shield was created. An evolutionary adaptation to live with UV-C was never needed.

From 290 nm to 320 nm we have UV-B. The "B" is for biological. This is the band that land life was mainly exposed to and evolved to live with. These wavelengths are still effective enough to stimulate mutation changes, and as such have contributed to evolution. UV-B gives us a suntan. It can also give us skin cancers if we get too lackadaisical. Ozone does screen out some UV-B even up to wavelengths as high as 350 nm. Ozone absorbs its longer UV in a similar fashion to how oxygen absorbs its shorter UV. The power of the incoming radiation is "soaked up" by being used to break the O_2 molecules into O_3 molecules. The O_3 is then available to absorb longer wavelengths and return to being O_2. This cycle normally continues endlessly.

From 350 nm to 420 nm is the band described as UV-A. It was once considered as almost totally harmless but that's not quite true. UV-A is more penetrating and produces a deeper sunburn but it also produces skin aging effects, wrinkles and skin sagging. In general, sun creams do not screen out UV-A unless they are so marked, e.g. "broad spectrum". Neither ozone nor oxygen shade us from UV-A and land life has evolved to handle this unimpeded radiation.

Above 400 nm it's no longer ultraviolet and no longer dangerous, it's violet or indigo, and it's visible. Light from 400 nm through to red light at 760 nm comprises the total visible spectrum. Above 760 nm it becomes invisible again. It's called infrared, i.e. beyond red.

In summary, oxygen (O_2) stops very short wavelength UV light, and becomes ozone (O_3). The O_3 stops UV-C and some UV-B, and in doing so turns back into O_2.

Unfortunately for us, ozone is very unstable and very vulnerable to contaminants in the air. It can pop back into O_2 before it has its chance at preventing too much harmful UV-B and UV-C getting through to the ground. For example, if, as sometimes happens, a molecule of nitrogen gets extremely close to a molecule of ozone, a rapid series of chemical reactions occur. Initially the ozone is broken down and reforms into oxygen, which UV-B sees as transparent. Finally, the nitrogen is free to go off and destroy another bit of ozone if it gets close enough. This constant inter-reaction becomes a never-ending juggling act maintaining just enough ozone to give us our ozone shield.

Some rise and fall in ozone levels in the upper atmosphere occur naturally. For one thing the levels change with the seasonal variation in incoming sunlight. In addition, recent evidence indicates that the 11-year cycle of sunspot activity does play a small part in ozone formation. If it was really significant then recent solar activity should have prevented or minimized the destruction of our ozone shield.

But it didn't. The shield is slowly deteriorating. It now appears that variations in solar activity have a very much smaller influence on our ozone shield than the CFCs we make and allow to leak into our atmosphere.

CFCs (chlorofluorocarbons) contain the elements chlorine, fluorine and carbon. When a CFC molecule leaks out of a refrigerator and ultimately drifts up into the upper atmosphere, ultraviolet rays break down the CFC, releasing chlorine gas. The chlorine then breaks down the ozone. Chlorine molecules are incredibly destructive to an ozone molecule. A coffee mug full of CFCs taken from a household refrigerator, or a car's air conditioner, contains enough chlorine atoms to destroy 25 acres (10 ha) of the earth's ozone shield and the destructive effect will last for 200 years. The AAAS journal *Science* compiled an excellent and sobering series of reports on CFCs and their effects in their Vol. 261.

Reiterating, the raw sunlight in space hits the first traces of oxygen in our high upper atmosphere and the impossible-to-live-with, very short wavelength UV gets screened out. This process produces ozone from the battered oxygen. Oxygen's role in ultraviolet shielding then ceases. Ozone molecules then screen out UV-B and some of the UV-A radiation. These are the UV frequencies that are difficult to live with. This screening reduces the incidence of skin cancer. In these processes there are no significant greenhouse warming repercussions.

How much ozone in our atmosphere are we talking about? To put it into perspective let's go back to our model where we magically condensed all the atmospheric gases into liquids with the same weight. Now let's do that with ozone. If all the ozone in the atmosphere became a layer of liquid covering the planet it would amount to no more than a thin smear 0.0001 of an inch thick (0.0025 mm). Is that all there is, to protect us from excessive UV solar radiation? Yes. But just as a thin film of sun-screen lotion is enough to prevent sunburn, that thin film of ozone has, to date, been enough to protect surface life on earth.

The tiny quantity is also ozone's vulnerability. Because it is so thin, or really because there is so little of it, it is extremely vulnerable to the effects of strange and new chemicals that have never before existed on the planet.

The physics and chemistry of the upper atmosphere and the formation and breakdown of ozone are difficult to study, and the conditions up there are difficult to simulate in a laboratory. The processes are full of complexities and uncertainties. But one thing we know with absolute certainty is that our ozone shield is deteriorating. It's got holes in it. What is happening? How big are the holes?

The Antarctic ozone hole is an area the size of Australia or China. It is as big as the contiguous 48 states of the United States. It is an area where total destruction of the ozone shield is now a massive annual event. The hole is not fixed over the Antarctic continent. It can drift. It often drifts up over Australia and New Zealand and maybe soon, over South America.

Actually there has always been a small ozone hole over Antarctica that formed regularly every year. It would last a few weeks and then close up again and do no damage, but what we have now is different indeed. It is much bigger and is no longer a short-lived insignificant phenomenon restricted solely to the high southern polar latitudes.

The United Nations Panel on Environmental Effects of Ozone Depletion claimed that a 1% decrease in the world's ozone screen would result in a 3% increase in skin cancer. That means thousands of extra cases and hundreds of extra deaths, particularly in fair-skinned people who regularly frequent the outdoors.

Today, people in the northern hemisphere can also no longer feel complacent. The 1980s and 1990s saw a marked depletion in protective ozone between latitudes thirty degrees north and fifty degrees north. That's from North Africa to London. Just in the 1980s the depletion approached 10%.

It looks as if we can almost count on an Arctic ozone hole—a zero protection hole—to form and meander over Europe and North America in the very near future.

Ozone formation and ozone effects are not confined to high altitudes and high latitudes; there is a downtown variety.

Photochemical smog is the unpleasant cocktail comprising natural fog, exhaust gases from petroleum-fuelled automobiles and the range of chemicals, such as nitric acid, produced by the action of sunlight on this cocktail of gases. Hence "photochemical". When raindrops fall through this mix and absorb the chemicals, the result is acid rain. Ozone is another product produced in photochemical smog.

At these ground levels, ozone still acts as an ultraviolet filter. Although the ozone concentrations near the ground are now dangerously high in our cities, the depth of this ozone-containing layer is relatively small, generally less than a few hundred feet. Because of this, its overall ultraviolet screening effect is small.

Ground-level ozone gas is considered to be a major factor in the death of trees in Europe and North America, as ozone is poisonous. Ozone and acid rain undoubtedly kill more trees than clearfelling forests for timber.

Sadly, when the trees are dead, poisoned by acid rain, they are quite dangerous to harvest as the dead limbs fall unpredictably. So their wood is wasted. Plastics and steel get used instead.

Ground-level ozone concentrations were once around 10 ppb (parts per billion). Currently these levels have doubled to 20 ppb, and in many areas concentrations exceed 200 ppb. Environmental protection levels in the United States were, conveniently for the fossil fuel producers, allowed to be inflated to 120 ppb. Maybe the justification being that data indicated that ozone-induced lung tissue damage does not appear to occur at levels just below 120 ppb. Adopting this upper limit would then not interfere with the sales of petroleum fuels. In England, during a warm summer, readings can well exceed 250 ppb, and stay there for long periods. No action is taken to prevent such occurrences.

Ozone gas at ground levels is an unpleasant story and, conveniently for some, rarely discussed. Ozone is a slightly bluish, highly reactive, and extremely poisonous gas. In the rarefied atmosphere of the stratosphere, its importance lies in its optical properties. At ground level its chemical properties take precedence. Ozone is poisonous even in quite small quantities.

In the lower atmosphere, ozone is produced naturally by lightning activity. Life on earth obviously evolved to handle the levels produced by such weather phenomena. Much more dangerous quantities of near-ground ozone are formed from photochemical smog. This ozone formation and its harmful effects are rarely mentioned in the media.

One of the great ironies is, while we are destroying upper-level ozone with consequent increases in dangerous UV levels, we are concurrently generating large quantities of ozone at ground levels. As we have seen, ozone is extremely reactive with a consequentially short lifetime. So, unfortunately, it is too long and too time-consuming a journey for exhaust-pipe ozone to move up to the stratosphere and shore up our ozone shield.

The same cannot be said for CFC's ozone destruction. The main concern with CFCs results from their exceptional chemical stability and resultant long lifetimes. CFCs do drift up to very high altitudes and enter the stratosphere, and do play havoc with our ozone shield.

Global warming is a different issue. The ozone shield itself is almost totally unrelated to global warming and has no significant role whatever in trapping heat and changing the surface temperature of the planet. Many confuse the two effects, possibly because the distinctions are deliberately never made clear.

Up until just recently, when one read all the press releases and the general literature on the changing atmosphere, it was amazing how much was devoted to CFCs and their affect on upper-level ozone. In collecting references on the greenhouse gases, the volume of references to CFCs and ozone and their interrelationships outstripped everything else. That one phenomenon accounted for more references than all the other greenhouse-gas references combined. Yet ozone, against all other comparisons, is a totally insignificant contributor to global warming. The references infer a relationship to global warming although they always refer to upper atmospheric ozone concentrations and CFC-related effects. Should we wonder why? It is an obvious reality that if the world production of CFCs stopped tomorrow, the producers of oil, coal and natural gas would experience next to nothing in sales reductions. However if calls were made to reduce ozone levels at ground level—only done by reducing automotive fuel use—then things would be different and ozone would vanish as a topic of interest in the media.

CFCs are being replaced by other more benign industrial chemicals so objections to their reduced use is not a marketing issue for the petrochemical industries, for who else will manufacture the substitutes?

The media emphasis away from global warming and onto ozone and ozone holes has only declined because finally larger numbers in the general public started demanding more information on global warming disasters.

Totally independent of their role in the drama of the ozone shield, CFCs are also greenhouse gases. They are actually extremely powerful greenhouse gases, but their low atmospheric concentrations make them a minor force in global warming. Ironically, because of the media emphasis on ozone shield effects, CFCs are already being phased out of widespread use, especially as a refrigerant and in aerosol sprays. As a result, their concentrations in the upper atmosphere began declining in the mid 1990s.

There is one serious problem however with reductions in CFC levels. Figures came out in 1999 that showed that while the rest of the world has been showing considerable responsibility, China was not. Production of CFCs in China expanded and China singularly has now reversed the short-lived welcome decline in world CFC levels. When massive production and use of CFCs finally stops as substitutes are adopted, it will still take a long time before levels become insignificant.

Ground-level ozone results from our use of petrol and diesel to fuel our transport systems. Ozone at ground level can be a killer. Cancer and respiratory disease, cataract formation and blindness caused by high ozone gas concentrations have killed and maimed more people than have ever been, or are ever likely to be killed or maimed from atomic energy nuclear accidents and radioisotopes. In contrast, ozone in the stratosphere keeps us alive by screening out harmful ultraviolet radiations. CFCs and some agricultural chemicals migrate up to the stratosphere and destroy this beneficial ozone.

As always with all things, common sense must apply. It should be applied for nominated specific uses for CFCs. It must be recognized that in some industrial applications, where quantities and leakages are of minor significance, it would be quite irrational to ban these very specific uses on purely emotive grounds. There is a big difference between CFC's relatively tiny use in a few sealed and protected manufacturing laboratories, and their use in millions of car and home air conditioners, household refrigerators, spray cans and fire extinguishers. CFCs must cease being used for such applications.

We must return the composition of our atmosphere to near normal

Fair-skinned humans are very vulnerable to skin damage in tropical localities. With depletion of the ozone shield and the massive enlargement of the areas over the poles, where no protection exists, the ozone hole and the annual drift of this hole out over inhabited areas, both fair-skinned and dark-skinned humans are becoming frighteningly vulnerable to skin damage. But skin damage and resulting skin cancers pose a very small threat to people on this Earth compared to the damage and deaths global warming is already causing. We must also recognize that the frequency and severity of global-warming-related havoc and destruction are rising endlessly.

The average surface temperature of planet Earth was recently 15°C or 56°F. Our then familiar, stable and livable world climatic conditions result from the greenhouse phenomenon and its sensitive balancing act. This balancing act has been relatively stable for a good million years or so. The last quarter of this period saw the evolution of mankind. With the 2- or 3-degree temperature rises now expected, world weather will be in chaos with sea-level rises destroying cities and nations across the planet.

In this last million years the world has experienced tiny fluctuations in atmospheric carbon dioxide levels resulting from volcanic and biological activity. And this, in conjunction with, or resulting from, tiny fluctuations in the earth's orbit, created eight separate ice ages. Remember that the ebb and flow of ice ages is associated with a movement of only few degrees in average world temperatures. Up until now it has generally taken tens of thousands of years for these changes to manifest.

For the last several thousand years greenhouse gases, acting like blankets on a bed, have maintained a relatively stable and pleasant world temperature. But in the period from just before World War II through till now, we have been loading our vulnerable atmosphere with greenhouse gases at an alarming rate. We must never forget that before World War II, we had three blankets on the bed and today we have four. The only reason the world is not sweating excessively today is that our enormous oceans act like a bedroom hot-water bottle, except it's filled with cold water. That's what's holding down world temperature rises. But like any other cold water bottle, the oceans can only slow the warming process until they themselves warm up.

To maintain fossil fuel sales, we are being conditioned by the media and public relations people to accept that a doubling of carbon dioxide levels in the atmosphere is inevitable, and somehow acceptable. That's six blankets. The enormous public relations machinery of the oil and petrochemical industry is trying to convince us that a greenhouse gas level that hasn't been seen on this planet for a hundred million years is really OK!

It is very fortunate, as we shall see, that our civilization finally has the technology to totally and economically replace fossil fuels. But we must also have the desire and take the responsibility to do so.

We had better wake up, before it's too late.

If we endeavour to change our society to create an atmosphere in which the major greenhouse gases are normalized back to near-preindustrial levels, as we must, we are then creating a frontal attack on the fossil fuel petrochemical industries. And they won't like it. They have been happily fooling us for too long. And they like it that way, but . . .

> You can fool all the people some of the time, and some of the people all the time, but you can not fool all the people all of the time.
>
> Abraham Lincoln
> 8 September 1858

We must hope!

5

Soil formation can halt greenhouse warming

THE creation of fertile soil, the enhancement of fertility in existing soils and the re-creation of fertility in worn-out soils, are the only means by which humankind can immediately, right now, today, put the stops on our runaway global warming. Increasing soil fertility necessitates absorbing and sequestering the damaging carbon dioxide gas from the atmosphere into the ground. This is the only way we can obtain some time to allow us to build our new, non-fossil-fuelled energy systems; the systems that will allow us to run our civilization on energy sources that don't change the nature of the very air we breathe.

The act of rebuilding soil fertility to the levels that existed before the advent of current agricultural practices all over the world, and to even beyond those levels, is the only practical action, and soil fertility is the only conceivable carbon sink, that is immediately available and totally controllable by man. Building soil fertility is amazingly easy. To argue that planting trees can achieve the same result is a mathematical nonsense, as will become obvious.

The atmosphere receives a constant supply of new carbon in the form of carbon dioxide from the world's active volcanoes. There are 1,343 active volcanoes on the planet's landmasses alone. There are many more under the sea. There have been 5,000 volcanic eruptions in the last 2,000 years. Over geological times, through biological activity, this carbon dioxide has been split into oxygen and solid carbon compounds. This carbon then accumulates in what are now described as carbon sinks. Effectively they are carbon waste dumps. The carbon accumulates as huge fossil deposits such as coal, oil and natural gas. The carbon also accumulates as huge limestone deposits that are simply fossilized shells and bones from eons of marine life. As well, carbon collects as highly compressed and dissolved carbon dioxide

119

and methane in sediments on the deep ocean floor.

Plant and soil biological activity, and the remains of that activity, is the only other major planetary carbon sink. This sink we can control; all the others, we can't. There is beauty in the concept that a massive increase in soil fertility is the perfect carbon sink to reverse greenhouse warming. Good healthy soil produces good healthy food, and good soil is no more than bad soil loaded with large quantities of various forms of organic matter. Good soil contains plenty of water and plenty of air. Good soil is always teeming with biological activity.

Organic chemistry is the chemistry of carbon-based molecules. Life and all biological activity is composed of complex carbon-based molecules. Soil organic matter is all biological activity in the soil, plus the remains of all previous biological activity in the soil. The chemistry controlling our world's greenhouse effect is the chemistry of carbon compounds. That is why agriculture is so important.

Excess CO_2 in the atmosphere is causing global warming. Man's destruction of soil fertility over the last century by a combination of incorrect cultivation practices and the wide use of agrochemicals accounts for possibly half of that excess. This global destruction of soil fertility has therefore inadvertently created an available carbon sink of enormous proportions. Of course that system can only be used once to absorb the excess.

The difference between poor soil and fertile soil is that fertile soil contains many tons more stable and unstable humic acid molecules per acre from which plants can derive nutrients. Fertile soil also contains tons more dead and decomposing plant roots and soil life. Fertile soil always contains an abundance of living microorganisms and earthworms all busily digesting and decomposing the residues of dead plants. Every single molecule in every bit of soil organic matter anywhere is made of carbon atoms. New organic matter has to get its carbon from the carbon dioxide in the air. Soil biological activity produces in turn its own waste products and that is humus and humic acid molecules. The importance of humus and humic acid is discussed later in this chapter.

It is amazingly easy to generate good soil from bad soil. To do so, use of agricultural chemicals must be avoided, and cultivation must not invert the soil layers. Then, all that is needed is water. At least sporadic rain is needed. Good and regular rain or strategic irrigation water is ideal. The rest of the requirements for rapid soil improvement are sensible and practical management techniques.

The agricultural changes required to improve soils worldwide are relatively minor but hugely significant. There are a lot of spin-off advantages, e.g. more nutritious food, better human health, the elimination of excessive soil erosion, reduction in irrigation water requirements and the elimination of salination. And of course, most importantly we stop global warming along with all its current destruction and impending dangers.

After billions of years of geological movement and mixing, there are now few areas in the world where the elements required to produce and maintain rich soil are not already present in more than ample quantities. The minerals are there. They may not be freely available to the plants that need them, but that can be changed by good farming practices and techniques that have been used for a thousand years.

Some soils contain minerals in absolute abundance. These soils naturally respond much faster to management practices that increase soil organic matter. In these soils, changes in the soil colour resulting from the increase in soil fertility can often be seen in a matter of weeks. Minerally poor soils simply take a little longer to develop, but improvements and soil colour changes will be noticeable in months.

If we are going to stop global warming by improving soil, we need to understand what goes on in the top few inches—a hand-width of our planet's land surface, our topsoil and how this is formed from the slightly deeper, biologically inert subsoil.

Soil types vary widely, even from one side of a fence to another, so let's generalize a little. Let's consider a good rich soil, and a typical local environment, and one acre of land. (Thinking in hectares, all quantities can roughly be doubled.)

On top of our acre of soil we could have one or two cows or a few sheep weighing perhaps 2 tons. Or we may have 2 or 3 tons of grain ready for harvest. However, under the surface, the soil life, the earthworms, the soil's biological activity and the byproducts of this activity will add up to a much greater mass.

For a start, there could easily be 25 tons of earthworms. Bacteria, and the whole range of active soil microorganisms, can amount to quantities in excess of 50 tons. (A ton and a tonne are near enough the same.) Decomposed organic matter, mainly in the form of humus, can easily amount to 150 tons per acre. So in this one acre of our typical soil all these components add up to 225 tons (560 tonnes/ha). That equates to around 130 tons of carbon atoms. And 130 tons of carbon atoms had to originally come from almost 500 tons of atmospheric carbon dioxide. (One hectare has 320 tons/tonnes of carbon representing 1,200 tons of atmospheric carbon dioxide.)

These numbers for soil composition and creation are not high. For example, worm counts per acre in the Lower Nile Valley prior to the widespread use of fertilizers often exceeded 200 tons of worms per acre (500 t/ha). The mass of worm casts produced by these worms is enormous. The composition of an earthworm cast is best described as a small piece of utterly perfect soil, and this itself is best described in *Harnessing the Earthworm* by T. J. Barrett in elegant detail. *Harnessing the Earthworm* has a profoundly wise and lovely introduction by Lady Eve Balfour and is published by Faber and Faber.

The United States Department of Agriculture reported on studies of earthworm casts where an estimated 120 tons of casts were being produced per acre (300 t/ha) during one six-month period. It is often noted that active earthworms can produce their own weight in worm casts per day.

Charles Darwin said of earthworms: "It may be doubted whether there are many other animals which have played so important a part in the history of the world as have these lowly organized creatures".

Life in fertile soil is present in amazing variety and abundance. In the Australian CSIRO (Commonwealth Scientific and Industrial Research Organisation) publication *Organic Matter and Soils* (current reprint 1993) they give a typical estimate of the individual number of separate bacteria, fungi and actinomycetes, and their spores, as three billion per gram of soil. In two grams of soil, say half a teaspoon, there are more individual microscopic life forms than there are people in the whole world. Rich fertile land with 20% organic matter content contains over 300 tons of organic matter just in the first 12 inches of soil over an acre. That is 750 tons of organic matter in the top 30 centimetres of soil over a hectare, and rich land can have topsoil several feet deep.

Just one hundred years ago in all of the air above our sample acre of land, from the ground to the edges of space, we had about 17.5 tons of carbon dioxide (43 tons per hectare).

With the widespread use of chemical fertilizers and our massive use of fossil fuel, we have added approximately 5 extra tons of carbon dioxide into the air over every acre of the total planetary surface (12 tons per hectare). That's what we did to our atmosphere in the twentieth century. That extra tonnage is what's causing global warming and the spreading cancer of climate change.

Let us have no doubt about what is happening. Doubt is a deadly weapon fostered and exploited by the fossil fuel lobby to sell their products. We have to know and understand the broader picture and the true reality so we can counter the deliberate spread of confusion and misconceptions.

Reversing global warming by soil enrichment—the numbers

The diameter of planet Earth is 7,917 miles (12,750 km). The total surface area is 196,936,000 square miles (510,000,000 sq km). About 60,000,000 square miles of this is land area (150,000,000 sq km).

We do not have control over the entire surface area of the planet. Seventy-one percent of the area of our world is ocean and the oceans are outside any even remotely safe, quick and feasible man-inspired manipulation. The landmasses themselves usually contain huge areas of wilderness, and untouched wilderness areas are of little value in our fight to reduce and stabilize carbon dioxide levels. But if they can be used, then they should be. There is little sense in endeavouring to maintain some cherished environmental stability in wildernesses facing runaway global warming.

The area of land on this planet that is cultivated and cropped is 5,700,000 square miles (14,500,000 square kilometres). In addition, there is about twice this area comprising grazing land, meadows, prairies and rangelands. There are also golf courses, household lawns, gardens, etc. The combined area of "agricultural type" soils under mankind's easy and direct control is 17,000,000 square miles (44,000,000 square kilometres). This total does not include forest lands.

One way or another, just over 70% of the land area of the world can be described as wilderness. The rest is under some form of human control. These statistics come from the publication *World Resources* and is a comprehensive report by the World Resources Institute, in collaboration with the United Nations Environment Programme and the United Nations Development Programme.

The ratio of total planetary surface area under relatively easy control to total area is 1 to 11.5, or to rephrase it, we control 8.5% of the surface area of the planet. So, to eliminate the excess carbon dioxide causing global warming, each acre of farmland must absorb enough carbon dioxide from the air to eliminate the greenhouse problem on 11.5 acres of the planet's surface.

As was mentioned in chapter 2, on that acre or hectare of land we have to increase the organic matter content by an extra 1.6% to return predictable stability to world climates and stop runaway global warming. (To clarify: if it's now 5% it must go to 6.6%.)

Very poor soils contain maybe 10 to 30 tons of organic matter per acre (25 to 60 t/ha). Very rich soils can easily contain 250 tons of organic matter per acre (600 t/ha).

An acre of soil one foot deep weighs 1,600 tons (one hectare, 300 mm or three hands deep, weighs 4,000 tonnes/tons.) We need a 25-ton-per-acre (60 t/ha) increase in soil organic matter to fix global warming. That represents the 1.6% increase in organic matter content already mentioned.

By just increasing the percentage of soil organic matter by an extra 1.6% in the one-and-three-quarter-acre or three-quarter-hectare block representing each one of us, we save our planet.

It must also be appreciated that the contribution to atmospheric carbon dioxide levels from past soil fertility depletion is gigantic. Simply by employing current Western-inspired agricultural practices, most of the croplands of our world have had their organic matter content depleted by anything from around 1% to more than 10%. Thus a soil which once had 12% total organic matter has become a soil with 2% total organic matter.

With prolonged Western-style agricultural practices, irrespective of soil type, an almost automatic depletion reduces organic matter content by half every forty to fifty years. And the carbon content of that organic matter all finally ends up in the air as carbon dioxide. See "Extra: The Albrecht Papers"

An early photograph showing "Deeper prairie soils of only moderate degrees of development under lower rainfalls in the mid continent" of the United States. Imagine what well-developed prairie soils must have once looked like. The wonderful thing is farmers can now recreate those depth of soils fast and efficiently. All we need is to stop subsidizing agrochemical use and switch our assistance to soil fertility creation.

The dark colour in the photo is a mix of soil organic matter, decomposing soil organic matter and humus. In limestone country the colour changes from the underlying geological material to black rich topsoil are even more dramatic. In such country, as the humus and organic matter is destroyed by agrochemicals, monocropping and soil-inversion practices the ground surface takes on a dirty brown-and-white mottled appearance. From *The Albrecht Papers*, Volume 2 courtesy of Chuck Walters of *Acres U.S.A.*

(page 152) on these soil fertility loss numbers.

The reduction in soil fertility of the vast prairie lands of the United States has discharged into the atmosphere almost exactly the same quantity of carbon dioxide as has come from the exhaust pipes of American cars since 1903 when Henry Martyn Leland built his first "Model A" Cadillac and Henry Ford formed the Ford Motor Company in Detroit. Hard to believe? Yes it is, but there is no escaping the numbers.

Let us examine that. An automobile driven for 100 years, doing 20,000 miles per year, and averaging 20 miles per U.S. gallon of gasoline, would have released into the air about 850 tons of carbon dioxide. One acre of prairie soil losing 5% organic matter content would release 170 tons of carbon dioxide into the atmosphere (30,000 km per year burning 12 litres per 100 km produces 850 tons of carbon dioxide and one hectare losing 5% organic matter releases 420 tons of carbon dioxide into the air).

As a rough but reasonable estimate, let's say there has been an average of 50 million automobiles in general use in the United States, at any time since Henry Ford built his T Model. There are 470 million acres of croplands in the United States. That is nearly five acres of cropland per automobile. Therefore we see that the one automobile produced 850 tons of carbon dioxide and the 4.7 acres of cropland produced 800 tons of carbon dioxide.

The humus and organic matter content of the once-rich soils of Germany—maybe because of their proximity to chemical, and agricultural chemical companies—have deteriorated to a far greater extent than have U.S. soils.

Loss of organic matter from Canadian soils, per head of population, is incredible even by Western agricultural standards. The population of Canada is 31 million. Their croplands alone average over four acres (1.73 ha) per head of population. A 1992 Canadian government report noted that 50% of the organic matter content of Canadian soils had been lost by "poor" farming practices. ("Poor" was not defined in the report.) In round figures, that means that Canadians could have added four times as much carbon dioxide to the atmosphere from the destruction of their soils as has come from every car, truck or tractor Canadians have ever driven. See "Extra: on the destruction of Canadian soils", page 171.

Improving the fertility in the soil in the areas controlled by man is our most powerful means of preventing the impending stampede of climatic change. It can soak up both the CO_2 from soil destruction and the CO_2 from burning fossil fuels. This is the only way we can buy time to develop and expand alternate energy sources that are so essential for the future of all mankind. Of course chemical fertilizer, coal and oil companies won't like it, but they don't pay the bills for all the weather-related damage that is killing thousands of people and almost putting insurance companies out of business everywhere.

Next we need to look at how soil is made to understand how agricultural chemicals and soil inversion plowing can be so destructive.

The derivation of topsoil

The moon and the earth revolve around each other; they are locked together by mutual gravitation. This united pair in turn revolves around the sun. As a result, a never-ending push and pull stirs the earth's interior. Coupled with this, the decay of radioactive elements within the earth produces heat that generates deep convection currents in the thick oozing magma under the earth's thin crust. The two energy systems combine to keep our planet's geology and topography in a constant state of slow flux. It's been like this for four and a half billion years. It will be like that for some time to come.

Hot magma regularly (speaking in geological timescales) oozes up from the earth's molten interior and forms mountains. Wind and rain, and the constant freezing and thawing of water in rock cracks, weather away the cooled magma. Erosion cuts and forms valleys. In turn the valleys are refilled with more weathered material. This loose weathered material is buried and compressed, and so forms new hard rock structures. These rock structures get twisted and bent and are often forced upwards to form new mountain ranges. The process is being forever repeated with slow endless variations.

The geological material on the earth's surface, after weathering and breaking down due to its exposure to the atmosphere, becomes subsoil. This is the material from which life-supporting topsoil is formed. Good, rich, fertile soil is simply weathered, decomposed, geological material in which biological organisms are in a constant state of growth, death, decay and regrowth.

Topsoil is thus a mixture of sand, silt, weathered rocks and clay, inter-mixed with humus and organic matter. Topsoil is biologically active. Soil is richer if it contains more humus and more organic matter. In any good soil, newly deceased organic matter will be decomposed by the action of living bacteria and fungi, ably assisted by colonies of busy earthworms, and finally form humic acid molecules. A constant supply of shed fibrous root structures and leaf litter will perpetuate the cycle and the soil's enrichment.

To increase the mass of humus and biological activity in soil requires more carbon compounds. The carbon can only come from the air. The carbon in the air exists almost entirely as carbon dioxide. And we know that excess carbon dioxide in the air is overheating our planet. It's as simple as that. The soil biological activity extracts the carbon dioxide for us, painlessly and efficiently.

The natural maximum fertility of a soil establishes itself over time. It is dependent on the abundance of available minerals, good access to air, the quantity of sunlight and the nature and quantity of the rainfall, and to a certain extent the presence of grazing animals. In agriculture, the term *mineral* describes both atoms and molecules required for plant growth. The molecules referred to usually do not contain any carbon atoms. I will use the term *minerals* in its agricultural sense.

We can massively increase the maximum fertility of all soil. We begin by mechanically changing the structure of the soil to allow in more air and allow more rain to be absorbed. This is then followed with a cyclic grazing pattern or periodic mowing. What inevitably follows is an explosion in soil life. In this way we begin the approach to maximum possible fertility in the soil. Do this and we start to stop runaway global warming. (The rapid development of soil is discussed at length in chapter 8.) So wherever it is possible, humanity's task in the twenty-first century has to become assisting and accelerating the natural formation of soil organic matter in all the world's soils.

These are the factors involved in soil formation.

The chlorophyll process

The energy to power the processes of life comes to us almost exclusively in the form of sunlight, except for a couple of rare biological environments that use the earth's interior heat as an energy source. Those environments are generally confined to small hot spots that exist at the bottom of some of our deep oceans. In proportion to the mass of solar-powered life they are minuscule.

The most common avenue by which energy fuels life on land starts with sunlight shining on green leaves. A leaf always contains water, which is secreted onto its outer surface. Carbon dioxide in the air dissolves in the minute water film on the leaf to form carbonic acid. That is what soda water is. Carbonic acid can release its carbon dioxide back into the air. Carbonic acid releasing its carbon dioxide is the fizz in aerated water and soft drinks. On the leaf however, the carbonic acid migrates into the leaf.

One of the many giant molecules forming part of a leaf structure is chlorophyll. It's the chlorophyll that makes leaves appear green. Chlorophyll can perform a very useful trick, which is why it is so common and successful. The chlorophyll in the leaf, working in conjunction with a couple of other molecules and using the energy of sunlight, takes water and carbonic acid and reassembles their hydrogen, oxygen and carbon atoms in a chain of chemical reactions. The final assembled molecules ultimately emerge as starches and fats and proteins. Simultaneously, excess oxygen is released into the atmosphere. Plant roots supply the tiny quantities of minerals such as chromium and iron needed to create an endless variety of even more exotic compounds. A molecule of chlorophyll itself apparently needs four manganese atoms and a calcium atom that have to come up through the roots from the soil.

All the ingredients needed to build and produce the richness of terrestrial life are constantly being synthesized in abundance on every continent and on every island on the planet. The process is called photosynthesis because the energy to drive the synthesis comes in the form of photons of light from the sun.

Animals and insects, grubs, worms and fish eat the leaves, the seeds and the roots of the plants. Just through breathing, animals "burn" the sugars, carbohydrates and oils from the plants with the oxygen so conveniently placed in the atmosphere by the plants in the first place. Some of the carbon in this breathing process is exhaled as carbon dioxide. Alternatively, it is excreted or eliminated in sweat, urine, faeces, shed skin, or as cocoons or eggshells. The whole thing is just one more never-ending cycle of life.

The nitrogen process

The other main player in the chemistry of life is the gas nitrogen. Air is nearly 80% nitrogen. Proteins always contain nitrogen. If it doesn't contain nitrogen, it isn't a protein.

To take nitrogen gas from the air and use it to produce large complex carbon-nitrogen based molecules is more complicated than the straight carbon cycle. But nitrogen is needed by both plants and animals. The process for converting atmospheric nitrogen into biologically acceptable, nitrogen-containing molecules is called "fixing" the nitrogen. It works in parallel to the carbon-chlorophyll reaction.

On land, one of the most common processes of nitrogen-fixation is via soil bacteria. Little clusters of these very beneficial bacteria form around the fine root structures of leguminous plants. The bacteria produce tiny quantities of ammonia, which is absorbed by the fine roots. Ammonia (NH_3) consists of one atom of nitrogen combined with three atoms of hydrogen. That is the form in which the nitrogen gets into the plant; and that is where the nitrogen comes from to make plant proteins.

The more common legumes include the clovers, lucerne (alfalfa) and a whole variety of peas and beans. Legumes are any plant belonging to the pulse family that produces dry dehiscent fruit, that is fruit that forms in pods. Lentils, peanuts and soybeans are also legumes.

The little colonies of bacteria on the plant roots are usually called nodules and look like little white clumps of mould growing on the roots. The roots look as if they are diseased but that is wrong. It's the complete opposite. The existence of copious quantities of these nodules on a plant's roots is a good indication of a very healthy plant.

The bacteria normally live in a beneficial symbiotic relationship with the plants. The plant roots supply nutrients to the bacteria and the bacteria supply the plant with nitrogen in the form of ammonia. In larger quantities, ammonia is a very pungent gas, but the tiny and constant supply released by soil biological activity is a safe and normal part of all plant growth.

Ammonia fertilizers force huge quantities of ammonia directly into the root structures and trigger accelerated growth. The powerful ammonia-based fertilizers also poison the bacteria in the nodules, as ammonia is bacteria's own waste product. The plant then becomes completely dependent on a continuous supply of nitrogen fertilizer. It's like heroin addiction. This forced NH_3 feeding can produce larger plants but their nutritional value is reduced. Cattle aren't silly, they won't voluntarily eat grasses made green from heavy dosing with urea.

Some plants can avail themselves of nitrogen directly from the air. This is called direct fixation. It is a relatively slow process. The legumes and their friendly bacteria, however, can fix nitrogen and make it available to other plant life in enormous quantities. In soil where the nitrogen-fixing bacteria have not been killed by heavy applications of fertilizers, yearly additions to soil nitrogen levels by these friendly bacteria can exceed hundreds of pounds per acre or hundreds of kilograms per hectare. (A pound per acre is actually almost the same as a kilogram per hectare.) This is more than any planted crop would ever require. Soil nitrogen levels therefore can be maintained in abundance with a crop rotation program that includes legumes in the system.

Trace elements in plants and soil

Small quantities—often extremely small quantities—of elements other than nitrogen permit the construction of a vast range of other useful carbon-based molecules. Complete understanding of the complex biological chemistry of all these elements is still a long way off, but here are some of the interesting things that we know.

At the centre of the chlorophyll molecule is a flat latticework structure of carbon and nitrogen atoms. The structure is called a porphyrin ring. At the centre of the ring is one single atom of magnesium. There are 137 atoms in the chlorophyll-A molecule, the most common, and 136 atoms in the almost identical chlorophyll-B. And in both there is just one atom of magnesium. Without its magnesium, it could not be chlorophyll, and leaves couldn't function and turn carbon dioxide into useful things, and discharge oxygen into the air in the process.

The heme molecule forms the working heart of hemoglobin, the oxygen carrier in blood. At the centre of the heme molecule is the same porphyrin ring, an exact copy of the inner design of the chlorophyll molecule. At the centre of this porphyin ring however, sits just one single atom of iron. Without it, it could not be heme, and blood couldn't function and do its useful things. And in doing so, ultimately discharge its waste carbon dioxide back into the air. The hemoglobin molecular structures give blood its red colour.

There is another molecular structure not unlike chlorophyll and heme, but very much bigger. It too uses these ring structures, but at the centre of this mass of entwined complexity is a single atom of cobalt. The substance is Vitamin B12.

Vitamin B12 is very interesting. It is about four times as big as the other B-group vitamins. Vitamin B12 appears to be the largest one-piece molecule in human biology. There are longer molecules, but these are polymers, and polymers are really a whole series of identical molecules joined up to form a chain. Starches and proteins are polymers. In the laboratory, to give another example, chemists can link up simple ethylene molecules endlessly and form yet another polymer. That one is called polyethylene, more commonly known as polythene.

B12 is different. A molecule of Vitamin B12 is a very exact structure made up of 181 very specifically located atoms. The precise arrangement was worked out by an English biochemist, Dorothy Crawfoot Hodgkin. She was awarded the Nobel Prize for Chemistry in 1964 for her work in this field.

Without the atom of cobalt, Vitamin B12 cannot be formed. Without Vitamin B12 you would die from pernicious anaemia. We only require an extremely small quantity of B12 to live. The daily requirement for an adult is about 5 micrograms, that is 5 millionths of a gram. The amount of cobalt required is thus extremely small. A teaspoon full of pure cobalt metal is sufficient to form enough Vitamin B12 to last a person for 24,400 years. The term "trace element" can mean a very small trace indeed.

Selenium is another essential element. Selenium is an antioxidant and a typical daily recommended dose is 50 micrograms. Yet in slightly bigger quantities selenium is extremely poisonous. A teaspoon of selenium atoms might last a person 3,000 years. But without any selenium in a person's diet their life would be short.

Calcium is also essential, yet it differs from most other elements in that it is required by our bodies in large quantities. It's not unreasonable to say that most of our body is made of biologically formed plastics such as muscles, tendons, gristle and the walls of veins and air passages. And they are all based on carbon compounds, just like industrial plastics. But this "plastic" body is mounted on biologically formed stone columns, with very high compressive strength. That's our bones and they are made of calcium. That's why calcium is required in such large quantities.

Calcium and magnesium, along with aluminium and silicon are the elements that constitute most rocks found on our planetary surface. Silicon at over 27% being by far the most abundant and is second only to oxygen in total quantity in the earth's crust. Life uses a lot of calcium, a little magnesium and virtually no aluminium or silicon. It uses a very large pinch of salt and a dash of phosphorus and a little sulphur, a little fluorine and a little iron. All the other elements combined, add up to less than 25 parts per million of body weight. They would amount to less than a quarter of a teaspoon. Nevertheless, miss one for too long and one can expect health problems that are a little on the permanent side.

The evolving chemistry of life

Life first evolved in the sea and every element used in the chemistry of life was then, and is now, available in incredible abundance in seawater. In seawater there is every element that exists, there is iodine, gold and even naturally occurring plutonium. All the elements in seawater exist in forms totally available to marine life.

When life first evolved, it could really pick and choose. It would naturally use the easiest chemical or element to do a particular job. Life availed itself of this smorgasbord of chemicals in the sea with relish. As we have seen some of them were used in the tiniest of quantities to do some very particular and unusual job. The surrounding seawater was the fluid in which life's necessary chemical reactions could take place with the water as the universal solvent.

In the sea, living things progressively enclosed themselves in an outer skin for chemical stability. The internal circulating fluids over time were modified from the original seawater to more specialized fluids. Water still is the universal solvent wherein biological chemicals react; and it is the medium that conveys those chemicals to where they need to go. The water-soup mix has however changed in many ways and now varies among the different life forms. Blood plasma and seawater are still very similar. Sterile seawater has even been used as a blood plasma substitute in desperate situations.

The human body itself can be rightly considered as a conglomeration of vats of chemical soups, all interconnected with tiny fibrous pipes. It is so with almost any plant, insect or animal. In these vats and pipes the complex chemicals of life are formed and modified. In them they are delivered and removed, to or from, wherever and whenever required in the body, or in the plant, or in the insect.

Life was well established in the sea before a few adventurous species decided there might be less competition out there on dry land.   The multiplicity of elements found in the sea was integral in the structure of all living organisms. When life forms moved onto the land there was a problem. Land life was stuck with this ocean-based chemistry and so land life needed access to the same complete range of chemicals and elements so available in the sea.

Geological stirring and mixing over a few billion years of Earth's history had produced rocks and geological structures that also contained all the elements needed for life, albeit not always in much abundance. So on land the necessary elements were still all there and they were all around, but invariably they were tightly locked up as very stable chemicals in those rocks.

Land-based life therefore had a problem with the availability of these elements. All the chemical reactions involved in biological processes occur when the elements are dissolved in water, or water-based fluids. In the cycle of land-based life a process had to exist whereby these locked-up elements could be released to become available. A continuous supply of all these elements was an absolute necessity.

Land life came up with a very clever and workable set of processes to solve the problem of ensuring their supply. This is the way it operates.

Most of the rocks on the earth's surface will dissolve in acids to some extent. As raindrops fall, they absorb some of the carbon dioxide in the surrounding air.   Carbonic acid is thus formed.   The carbonic acid is extremely weak, but it's an acid, and it's always there. The rocks will dissolve in this acid but only in minuscule quantities. That's OK, for nature has a lot of time. Thus minerals are released in a form usable by plant and soil life.

The rainwater, unfortunately, also rinses the now soluble, available elements out of the soil. They are rinsed down deep into the earth or away into streams and rivers and finally down to the sea. This process is never-ending and is termed leaching.

If it had not been possible for the leaching process to be prevented, circumvented or slowed significantly, then it is most unlikely that advanced land life could ever have developed. But land life did develop and to such an extent that it easily surpassed development and evolution in the sea.

With the help of the chelating properties of clay, land life started. But clay was not good enough nor plentiful enough for real development, so life on the land found out how to make its own, very much superior chelating material. Land life pulled itself into existence by its own bootstraps. It is important that we appreciate how important these processes are, for by using them we can stop global warming.

This is the chelation process. There is a whole range of strengths that apply in chemical bonds. One bonding process is called chelation. (The word *chelation* comes from "khele", the Greek word for claw. It's pronounced "kill-ation".) This type of bonding applies when single atoms get attached to a type of very large molecule or particle. In this process the chemical bonding action is relatively weak. A particular atom is attached to the main molecule partly by chemical bonding and partly because the atom sneaks into little crevices on the surface of the parent molecule or particle. The crevice is formed like a type of claw and so the attachment is described as chelation.

A chelated element is held with just sufficient strength to no longer be soluble and so not subject to leaching. The leaching process suddenly gets dramatically lessened.

The chelated atom is, nevertheless still weak enough for it to be removed by such things as bacteria, and the fine root structures of plants. And that's the trick. The elements are available to soil biological activity but they won't readily leach away.

There is one further requirement in this process for it to affect the abundance of land-based life. Particles and molecules with the surface characteristics needed to allow useful chelation are not that common and that is a problem. Of all the geological materials in the earth's surface, the only one that occurs in reasonable quantities and has a surface structure suitable for this chelation process is clay. Few rich soils develop without some clay particles in the subsoil material. Very fortunately, common clay is reasonably widespread.

Clays are made up of fine crystalline rock particles, mainly aluminium silicates, sized below 0.01 mm (0.0004 in). Semi-decomposed feldspars are generally the predominant constituents. China clay or kaolin is thought to be formed by the action of hot acid vapours on the feldspars in granites. Clays, being very stable, are not in their pure form a source of useful nutrients. Their value is in their form and shape and their ability to collect passing elements into their structure.

In a nutshell: rainwater falls, absorbing carbon dioxide and forming weak carbonic acid. The carbonic acid breaks down the rocks and releases tiny quantities of life's necessary elements. The elements are chelated onto the surface of the clay particles and plant life and soil life then utilize the chelated elements to grow.

To a plant's fine root structures, the clay particles are like the shelves in a supermarket, and the elements are simply selected as they are required.

After years of intensive cropping these supermarket shelves are emptied and the subsequent crops are poor. The shelves have to be restocked. New atoms have to be released from the rock particles by the carbonic acid weathering process and chelated onto the clay particles. It can take a year or more for the clay particles to be restocked.

Although few farmers realize it, this is the whole point of the ancient and long established practice of fallowing the soil. To fallow the soil is to leave the soil for an extended period in a cultivated but unsown state. This principle also explains why the concept of resting the soil has a certain validity. It has the same effect as fallowing, and ensuring new minerals become available. Effectively the terms are synonymous.

This plant-mineral stocking system using clay works OK, but it has a low capacity. Built into the clay system is an automatic, inherent limit. There is only ever some absolute quantity of clay particles available in any soil. The geological history of the soil determines that quantity, and it can't be increased. The particles are tiny and can be lost to topsoil by being washed or blown away. Trucking in thousands of tons of clay and physically mixing it with the soil is utterly impractical. Despite their noble qualities, the incredibly rich soils dotted around the world could not exist and could never have developed if they only had clay particles to rely on.

But they don't. Life invented its own version of the clay particle, and a much more efficient one to boot.

Enter the humic acid molecule

As plants, bacteria, worms, fungi and all the myriad life forms that inhabit the soil live and die and devour each other, the resulting material becomes humus. The humus breaks down, reforms, and recycles. The end products of these processes are extremely complex molecules of widely varying sizes and stabilities. They are minute in comparison to clay particles, but as molecules they are absolutely enormous. They always have incredibly jumbled shapes and as a result have gigantic relative surface areas for their size, which ultimately is what makes them so significant.

It is absolutely correct to say that the ultimate and perfect end product in the breakdown of decaying organic matter is the humic acid molecule. And what a useful, versatile and essential item the humic acid molecule is!

In laboratories, these giant molecules can be separated out from soil material. In one procedure, the material is washed in alternate acid and alkaline baths and the final giant humic acid molecules are carefully separated into groups. One group of molecules is referred to as humic acid and the other group is referred to as fulvic acid. Fulvic acid is very similar to humic acid and the difference is really academic. Humic acid is often used as a generic term for both forms and I will do the same.

Although called acids both can exhibit alkaline properties at other places on the same giant molecule. They can have a tiny localized structure on one side of the molecule that behaves like a mild acid, and a bit further around the same molecule another area that behaves like a mild alkaline. Exaggerating somewhat to illustrate, we could say that one side of the molecule reacts like caustic soda and the other side like nitric acid. To describe humic acid as an acid is more of a custom than a reality.

The atomic weight of an element is how many times an atom of that substance is heavier than an atom of hydrogen. The molecular weight of a molecule is how many times that molecule is heavier that an atom of hydrogen. An atom of carbon is twelve times as heavy as an atom of hydrogen and so has an atomic weight of twelve, and so contributes twelve units to the weight of a molecule. Oxygen's atomic weight is sixteen, nitrogen is fourteen and hydrogen of course is one. So carbon dioxide (CO_2) has a molecular weight of 44 and ethanol (CH_3CH_2OH) is 46. The molecular weights of humic acid molecules generally range between around 100,000 to 200,000. A molecule of humic acid can therefore contain maybe 15,000 individual atoms. That is an absolutely huge molecule.

However, compared to clay particles, humic acid molecules are minute. But of course, in good soil they are present in the billions of billions. In an acre of rich fertile soil, there can easily be 100 tons of humic acid molecules. That's 250 tons to the hectare.

There are thousands of possible ways in which these molecules can form, and thousands of ways in which the less stable ones can crack or fracture and then the pieces reassemble with other molecules or other pieces. The possible combinations are mind-boggling. It is perfectly reasonable to postulate that there are more variations in individual humic acid molecules than there are stars in all the total universe.

Humic acid molecules therefore come in an infinite number of shapes and sizes. No two are ever the same. But their properties are effectively identical except for their individual short or long-term stability. The chemical stability, and therefore the life span of an individual humic acid molecule, varies widely. Using techniques of carbon dating, some individual humic acid molecules found in today's soils have been shown to be older than the pyramids. On the other hand, some split apart the instant after they are formed, lasting just a fraction of a second.

There is no realistic upper limit on the amount of humus that topsoil may generate. Near the surface in exceptionally well-developed natural grassland soils, the material is a mix of humus and decomposing organic matter containing very little geological material. As one digs down into these soils the proportions change gradually until the composition becomes entirely a locality-specific mix of broken-down weathered rocks, clays and gravels.

One of the chief characteristics of the humic acid molecule involves not the minerals bound within it, but the nature of its outer surface. There are so many nooks and crannies, so many little chemical hooks and snares around these enormous molecules, that they can trap almost anything.

When a nutritious element is released by decomposition of rock particles by carbonic acids and other soil acids, it becomes soluble and consequently vulnerable to the rinsing and washing action of rainwater. However, this can be prevented. The minerals can be chelated, or trapped, and saved on the humic acid's outer surface. It acts like the clay particle's outer surface, only it's much better.

With chelation, the stored elements on the humic acid molecule are no longer soluble, but neither are they so tightly held to be unavailable as a nutrient supply to a growing plant. To the plant, the humic acid molecule is therefore the perfect supermarket shelf, stacked high with all the elements required for a healthy life. Those shelves can hold atoms that will be selected and atoms that won't ever be selected. Clay, as mentioned, also stores elements and compounds onto its outer surface by chelation, but by comparison clay should be better likened to a convenience store. Clay can never be a plant nutrient supermarket.

In all this complex biological, organic, chemical recycling and break-down process, some carbon dioxide is released back into the atmosphere. Some oxygen and some water are also released. The oxygen released ends up in the air as free oxygen. The water released ends up in our streams and rivers or percolates down into artesian basins and aquifers or evaporates back into the atmosphere. The humic acid molecules stay and new ones are formed.

Life slowly adapts to supply and demand and in so doing guarantees its continuing existence. With these humic acid molecules around in such abundance in soil, they have become intimately entwined with, and form part of, all the biological processes in natural soil. Humankind would never have evolved, indeed land life could never have developed, without these fascinating molecules. The story of humic acid is beautifully discussed and illustrated in the CSIRO Australia Division of Soils publication *Organic Matter and Soils*.

Elements or minerals contained, not on the surface of, but within the molecule are not readily available to plant life. They couldn't be if some of these molecules last ten thousand years. But in short-lived humic acid molecules, bound-up minerals are released when the molecule breaks down.

The less stable ones constantly break down and release vast amounts of the more common elements for plant growth and plant bulk. These short-lived molecules are continually being replaced by new ones formed from the constant, natural decomposition of dead plant material. In other words, even some of the supermarket shelves themselves are digestible. But the shelves have to be replaced constantly for a healthy soil to survive and improve.

Many chemical fertilizers function not by actually supplying nutrient elements to the plant as is claimed, but by fracturing and destroying stable humus molecules and extracting their constituent minerals. Charles Walters, Jr. and C. J. Fenzau commented on one of these so-called fertilizers in *An Acres U.S.A. Primer* (Library of Congress Catalog card number 79-50540), saying, "Anhydrous ammonia, it has been noted, burns out the humus supply in a soil system, just as surely as a match touched to a stubble field." Anhydrous means there is no water present so the now widely used anhydrous ammonia is pure ammonia gas.

Not only are the humic acid molecules rapidly destroyed in the process, but also most of the minerals within them are wasted. Adjacent plants cannot absorb the flood of minerals quickly enough, and the humus to trap free minerals has been systematically destroyed. The unused minerals are simply lost from the nutrient cycle. They leach away into the underlying geological matter or into groundwater. Alternatively, they recombine with inorganic chemicals and revert to their unusable inorganic form, effectively turning back into minute pieces of chemically stable rock.

Humic acid molecules have another extremely useful property. They vastly improve soil structure. In dry country, soils with good structure can hold and store more water than even the biggest irrigation dams.

Good soil structure is a term that denotes an increased amount of aggregated particles within a soil. Individual particles are held together by loose chemical bonds, by humus, by humic acid molecules and by a variety of other organic materials within the total spectrum of soil organic matter. Earthworm casts are an ideal example of what we might consider as perfect soil structure.

The particles called crumbs or aggregates keep the soil loose and allow for the penetration and retention of air and water within the soil. The inevitable small cavities, the pores, that form between the soil aggregates in good topsoil are the receptacles to contain essential air and water. The water retention in soil is a wetting and surface tension process and is quite different from the process of chelating atoms onto humus.

The availability of water is naturally subject to local rainfall and irrigation effects and, when this is insufficient, soil activity goes on hold. By storing more water within the soil itself, soil activity can continue through longer dry spells.

Soil and humus, water, soil life and food production are all so closely interrelated. The soil is not a simple single commodity; it's more like a city, or even a nation. A humming, buzzing, working, mining, growing, processing, living, breathing, constantly reproducing system, free to develop, or to be manipulated into stagnation.

Initially, minerals essential for life in soil are released by the carbonic acid in rainwater, but once the process is initiated, the cycle of life, death and decay in the soil produces its own chemicals and acids to break down rock. Some of these microscopic droplets of acid can be a thousand times as strong as battery acid, and a million times as effective as rainwater. It is a wonderful system. But, of course, it has been developing for around 600 million years.

Over time, wind and water erosion exposes new subsoil to the topsoil biological environment. The process is, and must be, never-ending. Contrary to what is invariably preached, this never-ending gentle erosion is essential to maintaining a healthy soil environment. Slow surface erosion or sheet erosion is not the same as the erosion gutters formed by concentrated water flow over incorrectly cultivated, humus-depleted soil.

Geological uplifting raises new land. New mountains are formed and the process is endlessly maintained. The Himalayas, where Mount Everest sits supreme, are actually rising. Every year the Himalayas gain another centimetre. Many mountains in New Zealand are composed from the compressed silt of deep ancient oceans. Those mountains in New Zealand are also getting higher, a little every day. This happens despite the natural constant weathering. It will continue, as long as the earth exists. We will never see our Earth worn down flat by erosion.

Tropical rainforests are a good example of what happens when normal slow erosion processes are virtually halted. The soil building and enrichment process itself then grinds to a halt. In rainforests, the soil is covered and protected by endless trees, vegetation, and fallen litter to such an extent that erosion rates are almost nonexistent. In his book *Earth in the Balance*, Al Gore reports on soil loss in uncleared tropical rainforests on the Ivory Coast. He quotes a figure of 0.12 tons per acre (0.3 tonnes/tons per hectare) per year. The erosion rate must therefore be equivalent to losing a depth of about half of one-thousandth of an inch of soil per year (0.01 mm per year).

These rainforests have been around for many thousands and possibly millions of years, and at any time through those long periods of history, soil depth will have always stabilized and existed in equilibrium. The subsoil minerals are therefore being delivered to the topsoil at absolutely insignificant rates. The very high rainfall means that minerals are leached from the soil rapidly, while the slow breakdown of the subsoil means that the rate of release of minerals into the soil is very negligible. The result is that the equilibrium nutrient levels in rainforest soils are extremely low, and in old growth rainforest soils, practically zero.

The only plants capable of growing in these mineral-deficient soils are the simple cellulose plants like trees and ferns. The only fruits that rainforests produce have little nutritional value and are sweet and sugary as simple sugars can be made from air, water, and warmth and virtually nothing else, and there is nothing else available from these impoverished soils.

The rainforests themselves perpetuate the existence of these worthless demineralized soils. At the incredibly low erosion rates in these tropical jungles, it would take ten thousand years to strip away any meaningful quantity of that leached, mineral-deficient "topsoil" and bring mineral-rich subsoil nearer to the plant zone. Topsoil mineral leaching rates are faster than that. The soil therefore is in a permanent state of almost total mineral deficiency suitable only for woody plants and sugary fruit.

In order to improve the soils in these forests, the subsoil would need to be made available at a faster rate and the leaching process slowed. Given that the rainfall is determined by latitude, geological formations and geographical features, it can be argued that dramatically improving the fertility of these soils can only be done by stripping away the forest cover and allowing the leached surface soil to erode away. Only then the building of fertile soil could occur with the nutrients released from the exposed subsoil. Yet Al Gore applauds the almost total lack of erosion in these Ivory Coast forests, and laments that once the land was cleared the erosion rate rose to "an extraordinary 90 tons per hectare" per year (36 tons per acre). However, even at that rate, it would still take years before the richly mineralized subsoils become uniformly available to nurture the development of rich fertile soil. Well-tended agricultural land loses a little soil every year and is actually the better for it.

Preserving large areas of various rainforest for study, as a habitat for strange life forms, or simply as places to visit, makes good sense. But arguably that is the extent of the worth of a stable rainforest, whose stability itself is absolutely dependent on stable rainfall patterns that every day becomes less reliable.

The much-advocated, so-called protection of impoverished wet tropical soils is not logical. These soils are emotively described by rainforest devotees as "fragile", when in reality they are simply wasted and worthless. Rainforests are not fragile for in them only wood will grow. Tropical rainforests and their soils aren't even bothered by ice ages, unless rain patterns are changed.

Coal is the end product of millions of years of endless rainforest and wet swamp plant growth. Seat earth is the remains of the nutrient-depleted soil found under coal seams. Many seat earths are so demineralized that they make excellent fire clays.

Logically, protecting rainforest soils really equates to not using rainforest timber. The industries that don't wish to compete with rainforest timber are quite naturally the behind-the-scenes supporters of "rainforest protection". They prefer the timber to rot on the forest floor. They prefer we consumers use plastic and thus replace timber. Rainforests are efficient producers of timber. Using that timber will help prevent global warming which is what we must do.

However the enrichment of soil in the temperate and farming zones of the world will always be the prime means by which we stop global warming.

The important thing to appreciate from all the above is that carbon dioxide is 27% carbon and organic matter is 58% carbon. It therefore takes just over 2 tons of atmospheric carbon dioxide to produce 1 ton of organic matter in the soil. Our greenhouse problem is 33 tons of atmospheric carbon dioxide per acre and that problem can be solved by the formation of only 15.3 tons of additional organic matter in each of our agricultural acres (38 t/ha). And rich soil can contain 250 tons of organic matter per acre or 600 tons per hectare.

The process of creating fertile soil and enhancing existing soil fertility levels can only occur by extracting carbon dioxide out of the atmosphere. By creating the right biological environment in our soils we can rapidly generate the production of humus in globally significant quantities.

The creation of rich fertile soil can stabilize our planet's atmosphere, and there is no downside.

The creation of fertile soil can stop the increasingly unpredictable weather changes that are destroying human lives and destroying the accumulated wealth of human society.

And it can all be done in well under ten years!

When we analyse what happened to our once-rich Western world soils, the above considerations can be seen all in total reverse—as a process of soil fertility decline. And that is what we talk about in the next chapter.

Extra: very basic chemistry

It's reasonably accurate to say chemistry is the study of how atoms locate themselves alongside each other, sharing their electrons and so forming chemical bonds; whereas nuclear physics relates to what goes on inside the very central nucleus of those atoms. The nucleus is made up of a mixture of protons, each with a positive charge and neutrons with no charge. An individual proton, or a neutron in the central nucleus, is about 2,000 times as heavy as an electron.

Atoms are tiny. One strand of human hair is about one million atoms in diameter. Atoms are not only small, they are nearly all empty space. The nucleus, made of its protons and neutrons all stuck together, can be considered as like the sun in a model of the solar system. The electrons are like the planets. On the same scale individual electrons would actually be further away from the nucleus than planets are distant from the sun.

The electron itself doesn't even really have much substance to it. It exists more as a wispy cloud, never really being mathematically definable as being at any exact place at any exact time. But the juggle of electrons buzzing around atoms and how atoms share them is the fundamental nature of chemistry. And that is everything we are and everything we touch, and smell and eat and build things from. The number of protons in the central nucleus determines what an atom is, be it iron or oxygen or gold.

The positive charges of the protons is balanced by an equal number of negatively charged electrons surrounding the nucleus. The electrons park themselves in shell-like parking stations, with different parking levels out from the nucleus. The levels are actually called shells, or orbitals, and in each shell there is a particular number of parking spots. An atom is only really "happy" when any shell in use has all its parking spots full. The furthest shell out must either be completely full or completely empty.

The capacity of each shell, moving out from the central nucleus, is two electron parking spots in the first shell, eight parking spots in the second shell, eight in the third shell, eighteen in the fourth shell, eighteen in the fifth, and thirty two in the sixth etc. The inner shells always fill first like the front rows in a theatre. Atoms for all the elements have this same shell structure. In other words the parking stations all have the same basic design. Some are just bigger than others and have more levels.

An individual atom will always try to have the right number of electrons in its parking stations to balance the charge in the nucleus. Depending on the particular atom, the outer shell may therefore be full, empty or anywhere in between. An arrangement isn't really "happy" unless it contains the exact number of electrons required to fill it. So if two atoms with similar problems get close enough together, they can share electrons. In this way they can overcome their imbalances. For example, electrons from a nearly empty shell can hop across to a nearly full shell to bring it up to maximum capacity. Now neither parking shell is only partially in use, and both atoms will be "comfortable". The two atoms can't drift apart. They must remain close together so that the electrons can be shared. The electrons have to stay near their own nucleus to balance the charge on the protons, but they can also run around with the other atom to keep the shell numbers right.

Electrons can also dash across from an outer shell of one atom to an outer shell of another atom, and back again, and thus use up two parking spots at once. This solves another parking position problem. In both cases, the atoms are then bonded, and the attachment is called a "chemical bond". These bonding processes are very much stronger than the very weak chelation phenomenon mentioned earlier.

In a piece of metal the electrons wander all over the place, but still manage to keep balances happy. The electrons form almost a sea and can flow when pushed by a voltage. That is how metals conduct electric current. An electric current is actually the flow of electrons.

When two atoms or more are stuck together in a parking station sharing arrangement, the pair or the little group is called a molecule. Molecules are often very stable.   Water for example is a molecule consisting of two atoms of hydrogen and one atom of oxygen, hence H_2O. In the early days of chemistry, many molecules were thought to be unique substances in themselves.

Oxygen in the air exists as a molecule of two oxygen atoms happily sharing parking stations.   Oxygen has eight electrons, two in the first parking shell and six in the second.   It would like to have two more to fill the second shell up to the stable eight-electron plan.   The two oxygen atoms share two of their outer electrons. This arrangement is not entirely satisfactory for either atom, so an oxygen molecule is always on the lookout for a better deal. When an oxygen molecule comes in contact with something suitable, like a metal, the oxygen readily forms into a more tidy arrangement with the new elements. This process is called oxidization.

Hydrogen gas is extremely light and so was used to fill airships before helium became available. Hydrogen exists as a molecule of two hydro-gen atoms. Each atom is content with its inner shell now apparently containing two electrons; each atom contributes one electron and both are then reasonably happy sharing.

Hydrogen gas is also explosively inflammable which made these same airships poor insurance risks. Two atoms of hydrogen and one atom of oxygen combine violently in the chemical reaction of burning and the reaction releases a great deal of heat. The end product, H_2O, is the very stable, very benign water molecule. The two hydrogen atoms each contribute an electron to fill the oxygen's outer shell and they are quite happy to have their first and only shell left empty. This makes the parking stations in a water molecule much more stable than they are in either the hydrogen molecule, or the oxygen molecule, which is why the reaction occurs so readily. It also means that the oxygen end of the water molecule acquires a slight negative charge while the hydrogen ends are left with a slight positive charge. It is then called a polar molecule. It is the polar nature of the water molecule that allows it to dissolve so many compounds.

The dangerously reactive metal sodium, when chemically combined with the deadly poisonous gas chlorine, produces molecules of sodium chloride—our common table salt, the stuff in the ocean, the stuff you sprinkle on your French fries. Sodium donates the lonely electron in its outer shell to fill the last vacant parking space in chlorine's outer shell.

When atoms combine like this, it is a chemical reaction.   Often some energy is released as heat when the atoms combine. This is an exothermic reaction. Sometimes heat is absorbed during the chemical reaction. This is called an endothermic reaction. In this later case, the reaction only occurs when we heat the substances together and thus supply the extra energy required for the reaction to occur—although sometimes just room temperature supplies enough heat.

Some atoms have the right number of protons to give the right number of electrons to fill the electron parking orbits exactly to capacity. They don't need to share electrons, nor do they want to lend electrons, and so mostly they are chemically nonparticipants. Before 1962 they were described as "inert" substances, then a chemist called Nevi Bartlett showed that it was possible to chemically combine some of the substances, particularly xenon, so now they are called "noble" instead. Helium is like this, and so is neon (as in neon fluorescent tubes), and so also is argon. The other noble substances are xenon, radon and krypton. (This is not the element that bothers Superman, which incidentally, hasn't as yet been discovered on our planet and probably never will.) Radon and radium, by the way, are totally different substances. Radon does not react chemically, but some isotopes of radon are very radioactive.

All other elements are found as small clusters of two or more chemically bonded atoms. The oxygen in air exists as two oxygen atoms bonded together. Nitrogen in the air exists as two nitrogen atoms bonded together. Carbon dioxide consists of one atom of carbon bonded with two atoms of oxygen.

Some substances can combine in huge, repetitive lattice-like arrangements—these are called crystals. Carbon in one of its crystalline forms is called diamond, another form is graphite. Although the atoms in these structures are chemically bonded together, the structures are really not considered as molecules since they can grow to enormous sizes. Most metals have crystalline structures when viewed at microscopic level. Some of these can be extremely stable. Metallic gold, for example, can persist for millions of years without reacting with anything.

Ozone is a moderately unstable molecule consisting of three atoms of oxygen bonded together. The three-oxygen chemical bond in ozone requires an uncomfortable sharing of electrons and as soon as something suitable comes along the third oxygen atom leaves the *ménage a trois* and combines with the new atom or atomic group to form a more stable relationship. Ozone is therefore a very powerful oxidizing agent, tearing apart molecules that are normally quite happy in the presence of normal two-atom oxygen molecules. This is also why ozone is so poisonous.

Most atoms form molecules with rarely more than half a dozen atoms. Molecules (not crystals) with more atoms are simply chemically unstable and atoms like to break off and form themselves into new molecules.

There are two atoms however, on which much larger, yet stable molecules can be constructed. One is silicon and the other is carbon. Both these atoms can hook onto other atoms and to themselves and form extremely large molecules with no problems at all. Silicon seems to do this quite well, although nature never really mastered the trick, or at least never used it to build life forms. Most rocks are based on silicon and oxygen, but that is because they are the most common elements in the earth's crust.

Carbon has virtually no limit on this ability. The chemistry of these large carbon-based molecules is so vast that it earned a special name. Because it was once considered as being exclusively associated with life, it was called organic chemistry. The term now has been broadened to mean the chemistry of carbon in general. The reactions involving all the hundred or so other elements get lumped together under inorganic chemistry.

Most of life's chemical reactions occur in liquid water and one of the disadvantages of complex carbon-based molecules is that many are unstable at temperatures much over the boiling point of water. It is therefore generally assumed that life as we know it can only evolve on planets with surface temperatures firstly below about 200°C to permit the complex carbon molecules to exist; and secondly, probably below 100°C to allow for the existence of liquid water. Liquid water is needed to act as a solvent for the chemical reactions and as a medium to transport the chemicals produced. Under higher pressure water does boil at slightly higher temperatures, so 200°C becomes the possibly upper limit.

Silicon, somewhat like carbon, can form a few large molecules, but not enough and not complex enough to threaten the supremacy of carbon atoms as the building blocks of life. Silicon usually occurs as very stable compounds of silicon oxides and compounds of calcium and aluminium silicates. There are also silicon carbonates. They are all essentially inert, chemically inactive compounds. These stable silicon compounds comprise most of the ordinary rock formations in the earth's crust material.

An English chemist, Frederick Stanley Kipping, born in 1863, tried to create a type of organic compound by interlinking organic carbon compounds to silicon atoms. He experimented with these compounds for forty years and succeeded in creating a whole series of long-chain carbon-silicon structures. Many could exist at temperatures somewhat higher than their pure carbon-based counterparts.

He eventually began to believe the strange compounds he created would be useless. As late as 1937 he commented, "the prospect of any immediate and important advance in this section of organic chemistry does not seem to be very hopeful". The new chemicals were similar to existing carbon compounds but found to be generally more stable and more heat resistant.

In 1941 the first patent was awarded on one of these unique types of chemicals. Because they contained atoms of silicon, Kipping added an "e" to the name, and from 1941 there was an almost explosive development in the new "silicone" materials—silicone rubber, silicone lubricants, silicone sealing material, etc.

Frederick Stanley Kipping died in 1949 at age 85, having finally seen his years of painstaking research come to a great fruition.

Complex molecules based on silicon instead of carbon can exist at very much higher temperatures than carbon-based molecules. There is a vague possibility that higher-temperature life forms based on the silicon atom may have evolved on other planets in the universe. Over a hundred planets have now been confirmed to exist, rotating around other stars in the galaxy, so maybe there is a chance. We will probably never know. Although they can be very stable, large intricate structures based on silicon atoms do not form easily, and so it may well be impossible for silicon compounds to ever naturally form with sufficient complexity to evolve into some form of life.

Of course, silicon life and silicon intelligence may well be created, developed, and evolved in the unique environment of chemical plants and computer factories here on earth. Man himself could be manu-facturing a new life form. It certainly is developing rapidly and most certainly evolving rapidly.

Carbon is involved in the sharing of four electrons and electron park-ing stations. Carbon can combine with four atoms of hydrogen in its most basic configuration to form the gas methane, written chemically as CH_4.

If two atoms of carbon are bonded together, each using one of its parking stations, then each carbon atom has three spots left. If hydrogen atoms utilize these remaining six locations we have the gas ethane C_2H_6. If an oxygen atom, with its two parking stations, is attached in one spot to this molecule instead of hydrogen, the other oxygen spot can be utilized to attach to itself an atom of hydrogen. The formula for this substance is C_2H_6O or more properly CH_3CH_2OH since this form helps indicate the structural arrangement of the atoms. This substance is ethanol, but is known more commonly as alcohol and is the alcohol in alcoholic drinks. In chemistry the term alcohol has a broader definition. Methanol for example is an alcohol. All these molecules have their own unique properties.

The alcohol we drink (CH_3CH_2OH) is really a very simple organic molecule as organic molecules go. Many carbon-based molecules, even discounting the long chain-like polymers, are enormous. Using the analogy of molecules being several atoms bound by their electrons sharing parking stations, you could consider ethanol as a group of interacting car parking levels. Your average humic acid molecule by comparison would be like New York City.

The fascinating and incredibly complex molecular structures that are the building blocks of all living things can only be made because of the carbon atom's ability to form stable molecules with immense variations. By incorporating tiny quantities of other elements, carbon can form an infinite variety of substances with an infinite variety of abilities and characteristics.

Some carbon-based molecules are so strangely structured they can pull other molecules into themselves and form a double molecule, which in turn splits to form two of the original molecules. In other words, we have carbon molecules that can reproduce themselves. That's what life is made of. The now familiar deoxyribonucleic acid or DNA is one of these strange molecules.

6

How Western agriculture is feeding global warming

To reiterate, global temperatures are determined by the optical characteristics of the atmosphere. We are massively modifying those optical characteristics by discharging huge quantities of carbon compounds into the air. The most significant of those compounds is carbon dioxide.

There are other less significant pollutants we add that contribute to global warming—however the majority of these compounds are chemicals produced in association with the production of CO_2. Almost without exception when the generation of CO_2 is stopped, in whatever circumstances, we automatically stop the generation of these associated chemicals.

In the past, volcanoes were the only major source of CO_2. The discharge rates and the sequestration rates of this CO_2 reached a general equilibrium many millions of years ago. That balance recently ceased. Mankind is generating excess carbon dioxide and destabilizing the environment of the planet.

The carbon to produce this excess carbon dioxide comes from two sources. One is from deeply buried ancient carbon deposits existing as coal, oil and natural gas. We burn this carbon for energy and so produce carbon dioxide. The other is derived from carbon held in topsoil in a variety of forms collectively described as organic matter. The inclusion of organic matter is the defining difference between fertile soil and weathered decomposed rock. Incorrect agricultural practices break down and destroy organic matter. This breakdown releases carbon into the atmosphere in the form of carbon dioxide.

It is probable that CO_2 production from soil fertility loss is slightly less than that generated from fossil fuel sources, but even this is debatable. It could be more.

147

Soil fertility loss increases global heating. There is no argument about this, yet soil fertility is being destroyed in every country where Western agricultural systems and practices have been adopted. In most Western agricultural countries, soil fertility has been in gradual decline for well over two centuries. This rate of decline has now been drastically accelerated with the widespread promotion, and in many cases enforced adoption, of quite dangerous crop and livestock production concepts.

Fortunately, soil fertility decline can be reversed. More fortunately, good soil can be created where before none existed. And most fortunately for us in our battle to halt global warming, it can be done rapidly and dramatically. And for a double win, it's invariably profitable.

Fertile soil, cultivated correctly, is totally immune to damaging erosion. It does not wash away in huge quantities down into the nearest valley. Good soil resists erosion beautifully. Fertile soil ecological systems could not have evolved in any other way.

Within the soil environment some slight erosion is actually necessary to expose a replacement supply of minerals from the underlying geological formation and subsoil. Healthy soil always requires a gentle continuous supply of mineral-rich subsoil. Very different are the much-photographed erosion gutters seen in some farmland. These gutters are a symptom of degenerated soil fertility. Filling them with a bulldozer does not solve any soil erosion problem and is a waste of time and money. Soil fertility loss is the problem. Recreating soil fertility is the answer.

The five prime requirements in the creation of true soil and ultimately rich fertile soil where none existed before are: water, air, subsoil, sunlight and grazing animals. The processes and techniques for the creation of fertile soil are considered in the next chapter.

However, before we embark on a program of creating soil fertility we first have to know and appreciate how soil fertility is destroyed. Only then can we stop destroying it, and only then we can start creating it.

Soil fertility is being destroyed in three major ways.

The first process results from the ever-increasing use of agricultural chemicals and so-called fertilizers. This process started in earnest just before World War II, and has been expanding and accelerating ever since.

The second method of soil deterioration results from the increasing practice of monocropping. This is the practice of continuously growing one type of crop, and one type only, on a particular land area, year after year. This practice started in earnest just after World War II.

The third way fertility has been lost results from the specific method by which soil is cultivated. The process of cultivating soil by turning it upside-down creates an extremely unsatisfactory biological environment for natural soil bacteria and fungi. The inversion of soil layers by incorrect cultivation is the agricultural process that has been going on for the longest time. It started during the Middle Ages in Europe.

Let's look at the first of these soil-destroying processes in more detail.

First: chemical agriculture—a horrific mistake

Let's consider the first process. The microbes, bacteria and fungi that all live deep within the soil, their cycle of life, their activity and death, is the only process by which crushed rock particles can be made to yield up in quantity the myriad of elements required by the higher life forms.

The millions upon millions of tons of agricultural chemicals spread on, mixed with, or injected into the agricultural lands of this very Earth of ours, kill soil life. From the use of these chemicals, fertility and the nutrient levels in our soils have experienced a long inevitable decline. Along with the decline of fertility and nutrient levels we are experiencing a decline in the health and the production levels of our crops, our pastures and our animals.

As fertility levels drop, the carbon atoms in the soil organic matter inevitably end up as carbon dioxide in the air. If chemical agriculture had never occurred and world soil fertility had been maintained, not releasing its entrapped carbon into the atmosphere, the current disastrous consequences of global warming would still be at least another quarter century down the track. The rise in CO_2 levels would be half what they now are.

The increase in yields that were characteristic of the so-called Green Revolution in the 1950s and 1960s sprang from a whole range of new high-yielding plant varieties. It's a piece of marketing gobbledygook to say that the Green Revolution had anything to do with agricultural chemicals. Nevertheless agricultural chemicals were marketed and sold to farmers in ever-increasing quantities to supposedly boost production levels. They do, but only for a short period, like taking Benzedrine. Nowadays they are being sold simply to try to maintain production levels in our constantly sickening soils.

Where did this all-pervading emphasis on chemical-based agriculture originate?

The first serious use of nitrogen fertilizers, other than from farm waste, was the use of Peruvian guano. The mining of this guano commenced in the 1830s. This was soon followed by the mining in Chile of naturally formed sodium nitrate.

The use of factory-manufactured nitrogen fertilizers received its first real boost following the cessation of hostilities at the end of World War I, when huge quantities of explosive stockpiles were released onto the agricultural market. In those days, these products were relatively simple compounds.

At the end of World War II, the chemical and explosive factories soon started running out of orders for their wartime newly developed highly sophisticated products. Some major replanning was essential. Modified products with nonmilitary uses had to be developed, and new markets had to be created. The government and the military were then the customers.

They had to be replaced by the government and the farmers. As a result, explosives and biological weapons became fertilizers and farm chemicals. Oil-based nitrogen explosives were switched to oil-based nitrogenous fertilizers. Nerve gases were modified to become pesticides, with fungicides and herbicides following. Organophosphates is the generic class of chemicals used in most pesticides. Organophosphates were chemicals originally developed for the production of nerve gases. Sarin, the gas that terrorists sprayed in the Tokyo subway to murder people, is an organophosphate. The marketing of these modified chemicals must have been well planned. It most certainly has been ruthlessly effective.

The agricultural chemical industry and agricultural colleges advise state soil conservation services and state agricultural departments. The agricultural colleges receive constant financial support from the agrochemical companies. The services and the departments then advise farmers exactly how to use these agricultural chemicals. This constant dissemination of false and misleading information by these bodies institutionalizes a faith in chemical agriculture. Manipulated propaganda and public relations blurbs become accepted "wisdom". The inevitability of an agricultural future based on ever-increasing chemical use then becomes an "acknowledged truth".

The drop in soil nutrient levels from widespread dependency on chemical fertilizers in turn enforces a massive drop in food nutrient levels, to the detriment of our own personal health. The lack of taste in these foods is your tongue telling you the stuff is hardly worth eating.

Unhealthy plants are attacked by all manner of pests and fungi. To them, unlike us, unhealthy plants taste better. They are not readily attracted to healthy plants. All manner of chemical pesticides and fungicides are developed, promoted and recommended to kill the pests and fungi feeding on these unhealthy plants. As this spiral tightens, chemical agriculture booms.

I must point out that there is a variety of fertilizers described as "mineral fertilizers". In simple terms mineral fertilizers are ground up crushed rock. As they are not readily soluble, they are safe. Mineral fertilizers are generally beneficial, and at worst harmless. They are discussed in the next chapter.

It is important to appreciate that of all the chemicals applied to soils, by far the worst destroyers of soil life are nitrogenous fertilizers. Plants need nitrogen to grow, and ultimately it becomes the nitrogen in all our proteins. Nitrogen is supplied to plants in the form of ammonia (NH_3) or nitrate (NO_3). These are available to plant roots from the natural decomposition of organic material and from the nitrogen-fixing bacteria on leguminous plant roots. In this normal structured manner it is delivered in millions of minute and safe doses in all healthy humus-laden soils. More than ample quantities are produced in developed soil.

Nitrogen makes up about 5% of soil organic matter. So in an acre of soil with a few percent organic matter content in the top 12 inches (three hands, 300 mm), there could easily be 7,500 pounds of nitrogen per acre. (Conveniently, rates expressed in pounds per acre are almost identical to the same number in kilograms per hectare, so 7,500 kg/ha.) This provides an abundant source of nitrogen, which becomes available to plants by microbes breaking down and restructuring the organic matter.

Nitrogenous fertilizers in solid form are generally water-soluble nitrogen compounds such as ammonia sulphate and sodium nitrate. Almost all fertilizers are deliberately made water-soluble. The plant is then unable to individually select its own nutritional requirements and is effectively "force fed". Excess fertilizer has to be used to ensure good root contact. This enormous excess is washed away into the river systems or leaches down into the groundwater. Next year's sales of agricultural chemicals are thus assured.

Soil life, bacteria, earthworms, etc. are perfectly adapted to their natural environment, but they haven't had millions of years to adapt to the new concentrations of nitrogenous fertilizers that rain down on them. These compounds are concentrated, water-soluble chemicals, and in the "fertilizing" process they kill the nitrogen-fixing bacteria and can kill all other micro-soil life.

Pure ammonia gas is used to force-feed ammonia direct onto plant roots. Driving through the American Midwest you see a never-ending series of what appears to be small silver-painted fuel depots. But they're not. They are pressurized steel containers full of pure ammonia gas. It is called anhydrous ammonia (i.e. ammonia gas that is not diluted and is not dissolved in water).

Ammonia is a pungent and poisonous gas, and millions of cubic feet of this gas is injected into the cropland soils of the world, every year. The injecting nozzle cuts through the soil to a considerable depth to ensure that the gas is not "wasted" by leaking into the air. The nozzles are spaced rarely more than a few feet, maybe a metre apart, and generally much closer. Within twenty inches (half a metre) of the gas nozzles, every living creature, every worm, every bacterium, every ant, everything, will die immediately.

Carbon dioxide and methane are the most common breakdown products of all this death and destruction. These gases inevitably rise and enter the atmosphere, contributing massively to global warming.

The fact that all is not well with the use of nitrogenous fertilizers is demonstrated by the results of soil tests which can show bizarre results in cropping areas. For example, from chemical analysis it can be shown that an acre of crop might use a total of 100 pounds of nitrogen in the growing process. Now if fertilizer containing 100 pounds of nitrogen is applied to the crop and the crop uses 100 pounds to grow, then things should end up square.

But they don't. After the harvest, you find that total soil nitrogen levels are actually reduced, often by as much as 50 pounds per acre, and sometimes considerably more. It is still somewhat uncertain if the crop gets its nitrogen from the fertilizer-induced breakdown of the biologically produced nitrogen stored within the soil environment, or whether it is force-fed from the applied nitrogenous fertilizer. The point is academic anyway since the soil nitrogen levels are reduced in either case.

Soil tests have been conducted by the University of Missouri at the Missouri Agricultural Experimental Station and on their Sanction Fields since the late 1800s. Soil nitrogen levels have been studied in great detail for over 100 years. In one illustrative set of tests, nitrogen levels dropped 45% over a 25-year period. During the period, nitrogenous fertilizers were added at a constant rate each year to supply 25 pounds of nitrogen per acre. At the beginning of the tests, the soil contained over 6,000 pounds per acre of soil nitrogen. During this 25-year period the soil nitrogen content dropped by 110 pounds per acre per year, despite the addition of the 25 pounds per acre of nitrogen in the nitrogenous fertilizers. If the added fertilizers are included, the nitrogen loss was actually 135 pounds per acre, which is way above plant requirement, as was reported in *The Half Life of Soils* by Dr William A. Albrecht and published in *National Food and Farming* in 1966. It is reproduced in full in the publication *The Albrecht Papers*.

Extra: *The Albrecht Papers*

The Albrecht Papers are a treasury of information on the evolution of soils and the change in soils caused by long-term farming. They are a very large collection of documents published in two volumes by Charles Walters, Jr. of Kansas City Missouri, owner and publisher of the agricultural journal *Acres U.S.A.* (ISBN Number 0-911311-07-06; Library of Congress catalog card number 83-81673; Volume 1 *Foundation Concepts*, and Volume 2 *Soil Fertility and Animal Health*).

The papers include some notes and writings by students but mainly they are the collected talks and lectures of Dr William A. Albrecht. Dr Albrecht was Chairman of the Department of Soils at the University of Missouri College of Agriculture. He became a member of the staff at the college in 1916. *The Albrecht Papers* contain many important observations relating to soils, but in particular, they contain the most detailed collection of thoughts and results on ideal levels of rainfall to produce optimum soil fertility levels I have ever seen.

Albrecht clearly and logically defines the rainfall requirements that developed the rich fertile soils of the plains, the savannas and the prairies of the world. His papers also point out very clearly that rich soil produces healthy animals.

Regular rainfall encourages forest development. High and regular rainfall produces rainforests and tropical jungles. The resultant high levels of surface litter almost totally eliminate surface erosion. However, leaching of essential minerals is continuous and so the development of deep rich healthy soil becomes impossible. Grazing animals barely survive on the poor and limited food supply available in forests.

With very low and irregular rainfall the buildup of soil organic matter and soil fertility is limited. Poor grasses and scrubby trees dominate these landscapes.

Slightly higher but intermittent rainfall is where the grasses grow. Grasses produce copious quantities of seed and although a grass plant will often die in a drought period, the seeds are there to germinate with the next rains. Grasses germinate and grow and quickly produce another seed crop, whereas the same long drought will kill a tree before it can produce seeds.

The ideal situation for soil development exists when rainfall is reasonably regular throughout the year and total rainfall is between say 20 and 30 inches (500 mm to 750 mm) per year. Under these conditions and provided tree growth does not take over, soil fertility and organic matter content will stabilize at extremely high levels and the soils will be remarkably enriched. Naturally, highly mineralized underlying geological structures ensure a higher fertility potential. In colder climates, rainfalls should at least be regular throughout the warmer growing season. These parameters effectively determine the areas where man grows his best crops.

If rainfall levels significantly exceed 30 inches (750 mm) per year then the rainwater doesn't all end up back in the air. Some sinks away into the earth. Plant minerals become exposed to the drift process for a short period each time plants reach the end of their life cycle and go through the decomposition phase. With consistent high rainfalls a constant downward drift of soil moisture becomes established which takes with it some of the minerals released. The loss of soil nutrients is termed soil leaching. The minerals are lost to the soil life cycle; effectively forever.

Transpiration is the evaporation of water from leaf surfaces that occurs during the photosynthesis process. The perfect rainfall is therefore when evaporation from the soil added to transpiration from plants equals total rainfall. There is then abundant water for growth but not enough to generate excessive leaching. High levels of organic matter in the soil can slow the leaching process.

But we are losing organic matter from our soils. The rapid initial decrease in organic matter content of soils to approximately half of pre-cultivation and pre-farming levels, caused by poor cultivation and the high use of inorganic fertilizers, is considered in detail in *The Albrecht Papers*. This is also seen in "Extra: on the destruction of Canadian soils", page 171.

The Albrecht Papers document widespread fertility losses in a variety of soils of 40% in the first 40 years following the commencement of cropping. They also describe a subsequent 40% fertility loss in the following 40 years and indications are that this 40% loss in 40 years is an ongoing phenomenon. Albrecht noted that 120 years is about the maximum time that Missouri farmlands in general have been cropped and the fertility tests confirm the loss rates. What has always offset the fertility declines and kept farming possible was the, until recently, constant addition of farm manure, compost, and farm waste to the cycle. As far back as 1933 Professor Hans Jenny of the Missouri Agricultural Station reported (*Bulletin* 324 of 1933) a similar but lower repetitive fertility loss pattern in Missouri silt loam prairie soils. His tests related specifically to soil nitrogen levels and showed a 33% loss per 60 years. We are also reminded that whether it be 40 years, 50 years or 60 years, no nation can survive such ongoing losses.

The Albrecht Papers also dramatically contrast the benefits of spreading and incorporating good organic matter, such as animal manures, into soils and they document the extremely long-term beneficial effects of such treatments. The papers discuss these factors in considerable detail.

Albrecht discusses the liming of soils to reduce soil acidity. He totally rejects this concept and argues that the benefits of liming are not in some modification to soil acidity, but simply results from the addition of large quantities of calcium to the soil.

These and many others are the wise and thoughtful messages contained within *The Albrecht Papers.*

The loss of soil nitrogen goes hand in hand with the destruction of soil organic matter. The simple inorganic nitrogen compounds left when organic matter is broken down are generally water-soluble and are easily washed away, or in the case of ammonia, escape as gas into the atmosphere.

As soil nitrogen levels diminish and soil life becomes decimated, the rate at which nitrogen can be absorbed into plants diminishes even more quickly. At the same time the natural biological production of soil nitrogen is reduced to negligible amounts. The bacteria that normally fix nitrogen for plant use have all been poisoned. At that point, crop yields become totally dependent on the constant and excessive injection of ammonia gas and nitrogenous fertilizers.

If you play golf, then worm casts dotted over the putting green are considered a "removable hazard". The permanent removal of these hazards is of course a golfing preference. It is generally best achieved by "fertilizing" the green with a liquid fertilizer. The ammonia in the fertilizer makes the putting greens greener, and the worms all die. There are no more worm casts and the procedure is called a success!

And this is what almost all government advisors recommend we do to all the croplands of the world. The end result of the constant use of nitrogenous fertilizers is always the same. And that is, even more nitrogenous fertilizer will be needed and recommended by government advisors.

Nitrogenous fertilizers not only destroy soil organic matter and cause it to discharge into the atmosphere as carbon dioxide, they are also implicated in destroying one of the few natural processes that remove methane from the atmosphere. Methane is an extremely significant greenhouse gas, about twenty times as potent as carbon dioxide. Research at both the University of New Hampshire and at the Woods Hole Marine Biological Laboratory in Massachusetts confirm that the activity of aerobic bacteria in soil is the most significant process by which methane is removed from the atmosphere. They also suggest that inputs of nitrogen-based fertilizers can materially suppress this atmospheric cleansing action.

Another common chemical fertilizer, superphosphate, contains the element phosphorus, also essential for plant growth. Naturally occurring phosphorus is derived from primary geological material broken down by organic activity. Much of the phosphorus in rich topsoil is chelated onto the surface of humic acid molecules and therefore usable by plants. Alternatively, it may be bound within the humic acid molecule and can be released for plant use by the action of microbes breaking down and restructuring these large molecules. Because phosphorus is so essential, the microbes usually keep most of it for themselves. They nevertheless constantly release small but generally significant quantities to plant use.

Some countries, particularly Australia and India, have soils with extremely low levels of natural phosphorus. The phosphorus actually available to plant life can be almost nonexistent in some areas. High levels of soil fertility and microbe activity are needed to release enough phosphorus to grow a crop. To speed up soil development in these soils, one light application of superphosphate is often enough to correct the natural shortage and get the cycle started. Superphosphate provides phosphorus in a form directly usable by plants and capable of being chelated onto humic acid. With fertility-enhancing agriculture, this application will usually suffice until the enhanced biological activity releases previously unavailable phosphorus to the nutrient cycle.

Normally recommended by advisors however, are massive continuous superphosphate applications. Admittedly, initial results can be spectacular. But subsequent crops require more and more to get the same result. Then finally and inevitably the stuff just doesn't seem to work anymore. The soil has become dead, poisoned by excess superphosphate.

In New Zealand for example, it has been regular practice to apply superphosphate at annual rates of up to one ton per acre (approximately 2,000 kg/ha). Applications of 500 to 1,000 pounds per acre are very common and is, unfortunately more than sufficient to massively damage soil biological activity.

High dose rates of superphosphate have an unusual effect on plant cells and this is one of the main reasons it is used. High quantities of superphosphate affect the cell chemistry and force the cell to absorb large quantities of water. The bloated cells in turn bloat the grain or fruit. The fruit or the grain is thus bigger and heavier and so the saleable yield weight is higher. The actual nutrient levels have not risen and may more likely have even decreased. That's why it lacks taste. It's all water. The plants, and their edible products, are sick and unhealthy. But the sick bloated crop still goes to market.

In total contrast to high and destructive application rates, quite small and regular applications of superphosphate can be very beneficial. Phosphorus in particular is not easy to extract from its original geological form, and phosphorus is an absolutely essential element in plant and animal life. In the phosphorus-deficient soils common in Australia, small and safe quantities—50 pounds per acre (50 kg/ha) down to 25 pounds per acre—will actually increase organic matter and humus content, often considerably. To appreciate the amounts involved, 25 pounds of superphosphate could be contained in a common household bucket. It would be about half full. Whereas 1,000 pounds would fill two 40-gallon drums. (For a hectare, we are talking just over 25 kg, say a full bucket, compared to one tonne, or two 200-litre drums.)

It is not all bad. In contrast to their head-office bureaucracy, some state agricultural field officers in Australia, and I suspect elsewhere, are thinking and using common sense. They are recommending and advising farmers to switch to more organic forms of agriculture. They are recommending considerably reduced use of agricultural chemicals. These recommendations are resulting in healthier crops and more profitable and sustainable farming.

We must stop the extensive use of ammonia and urea and all the other varieties of nitrogenous fertilizers in agriculture. Superphosphate, in its various forms and strengths, must no longer be dosed onto the land in poisonous quantities. The use of all forms of water-soluble chemical fertilizers must cease.

Chemical "fertilizers" ultimately necessitate the use of pesticides and fungicides

Chemical fertilizers kill soil life. The dead soil life ultimately converts into atmospheric carbon dioxide, and that's what we have to stop. As a contributor to increasing atmospheric carbon dioxide levels and global warming, the use of agricultural chemicals ranks with coal-fired power stations. This has never before been highlighted. Using agricultural chemicals not only contributes to the release of carbon dioxide, it poisons and kills the very soil biological activity that offers the only real and practical hope of rapidly reversing global warming. And just in their manufacture, there is an oft-quoted rule of thumb that says it takes 3 tons of oil to make 1 ton of agrochemicals.

The use of chemical fertilizers promotes sick and unhealthy crops. While these unhealthy crops are growing, pesticides are needed to ward off insect attacks. The insects are only doing their natural thing. Insects have the job of eliminating sick and unhealthy plants from the environment. This is actually their preferred diet, as mentioned.

The metabolism of insects is different from animals. Each operates in its own niche in the food chains of life. What tastes good to an insect does not taste good to us. A blowfly will turn his nose up at a fresh slab of fillet steak, especially if a nice piece of warm rotting intestine is available nearby. In World War I, maggots were used by doctors to eat away the dead tissue in soldiers' wounds, where gangrene would otherwise fester. The maggots would not touch the healthy tissue. Today the technique is being revitalized and maggots are being bred in sterile conditions with new trials underway.

Nor do insects like the fresh tasty fruit that we humans find so appealing. They like what to us is an unhealthy crop. They like fruit that has been on the table a little too long and is starting to go off. Insects have different digestive systems and have a natural and different role to play.

Indeed insects must wonder at the strangeness of men. Apparently, these humans like to produce sick crops in enormous quantities, seemingly especially for insects. And then they spend fortunes on chemicals to kill all the guests they have so well catered for.

Pesticides are chemicals that are designed to poison insects. But they also poison just about everything else that wriggles, crawls, or burrows on or in our farm soils. The non-selectivity of pesticides is obvious by simply observing what household pesticides kill. Even spiders with their eight legs, that are not insects but are a naturally occurring insect control, have a hard time with household insecticides. These are the same chemicals used on farm crops. There is no selectivity in their action, and chemicals for farm use are usually stronger and more potent than household sprays.

Healthy plants, growing in rich living fertile soil, do not require the dubious assistance of pesticides for their survival. Insects and all their cousins quite happily coexist with healthy plants and animals in rich and fertile soil environments. The health of the plant is the factor that ensures its own survival. Undesirable insect pests will always be present, but kept in check by other insects and birds in any healthy agricultural environment.

Unhealthy soils produce unhealthy crops. The insects that thrive and proliferate on these sick crops are then killed by the billions with pesticides. But because the insects are in ideal conditions, they also breed by the billions. This rapid breeding often allows them to evolve resistance and develop tolerance to the pesticides at a rate far greater than their own natural predators. The numbers of predator insects are always far less than the numbers of prey insects, and chances of favorable mutations decrease with smaller population size. The insect predators therefore always lag behind in developing chemical tolerance and resistance.

Bird life fares even worse. The birds that dine on these swarms of insect pests become poisoned and sicken and die. The birds rarely, if ever, have time to evolve a resistance to the chemicals. Their numbers are relatively few, and their life cycle is much longer. Also, predators invariably accumulate and concentrate in their bodies the pesticide poisons carried in the bodies of their prey. Nonfatal doses soon become fatal doses as they are passed up the food chain.

Rachel Carson's book *Silent Spring* highlighted a new countryside as dead and devoid of all bird sounds. The birds she foresaw as all poisoned by agricultural chemicals. Many have described *Silent Spring* itself as an excess of overkill. But if it was, it was not by any great margin, for despite her book, the worldwide use of pesticides increased dramatically in subsequent years. *Silent Spring* was published in 1962, although much of the material was first published prior as a series of articles in *The New Yorker*. Rachel Carson was originally a biologist with the U.S. Fish and Wildlife Service before becoming a writer. H.R.H. The Duke of Edinburgh once said in an address "I strongly recommend Rachel Carson's *Silent Spring* if you want to see what is going on". Good advice.

It is time that pesticides be put aside and used only as a weapon against plagues, as only that can be considered as a practical and legitimate function. For general agriculture, they cannot be, and must not be, the normal way of life.

A similar story applies to fungi. Fungicides are designed and produced by chemical companies to kill some particular target fungus. At least that is what they claim, but it is not so. There are thousands of varieties of soil fungi that form part of healthy soil and are actually essential in the very creation of that healthy soil. There are also some that do attack crops, especially unhealthy crops. Fungal life is massive and a prerequisite for any healthy soil, but unfortunately, agricultural chemical fungicides are known not to be particularly selective. The injection of fungicides into the soil can kill them all. Consequently, the use of fungicides inevitably and massively decreases soil life and soil fertility. Again, yields soon drop. Fertilizers, produced by the same companies, are now needed and recommended and always in staggering quantities, just to maintain production. It's the same old story.

There are some possible exceptions with chemical fungicides that are applied to above-ground foliage. They often can be made to break down harmlessly before leaching into the soil and so are not able to kill soil fungal life. They can be relatively safe to use and not contribute to the breakdown of soil fertility. Remember that our aim is to circumvent global warming by the massive increase in the organic matter and humic acid content of our soils. A chemical that helps us achieve this aim should be used where necessary. It is not a requirement that food produce must conform to the almost excessively strict definitions mandated for Organic Food labelling.

Insect pests will always be around, and some bothersome fungal activity will always be present. Just as there will always be a few unhealthy plants for them to relish. A fungus or an insect that attacks a particular plant species is rarely significantly harmful to the healthy plant. Only to the unhealthy plant are they a disaster.

Fungal plant diseases can be eliminated or controlled by producing a much healthier plant, and good soil does that. Where monocropping is practiced for any length of time, large areas of any particular crop can always be an invitation to insect breeding and fungal development. Crop rotation solves these problems. One terrible example occurred in Ireland in the mid to late 1840s. By that time the newly structured poor in Ireland lived on potatoes. They were grown repeatedly on the same land. It was monocropping on a national basis. Then a fungus, *Phytophthora infestans*, that probably originated in a variety of Peruvian potatoes, got to Ireland around 1845. The blight decimated the closely spaced crops. Deaths due to starvation and malnutrition resulting from the infestation of potato blight in Ireland exceeded one million people.

The concept that crop rotation and fertile soils produce healthy plants, and the concept that healthy plants readily resist pests and diseases, are not only obvious in the field, but are evolutionary inevitabilities. A healthy plant or animal or even a healthy insect survives, an unhealthy one doesn't. So, wise and thoughtful farming practices become a natural form of biological control. Encouraging the development of beneficial insect predators, either birds or other insects, along with other similar forms of biological control of pests, have always been there on the sidelines. These forms of control must now be used more widely to solve the problems of crop pest infestation. Chemical companies have managed to keep them always on the sideline. And obviously they will try to keep them there for as long as they possibly can.

The use of herbicides in agriculture must receive close and constant scrutiny

The chemical agricultural industry also developed a range of products generally described as herbicides.

In agriculture, when a plant is growing even vaguely in competition with a desired crop, that plant becomes a weed. Roses in a wheat crop are weeds and wheat plants in a rose garden are weeds. Herbicides are agricultural chemicals specifically designed (using the above example) to selectively kill the rose bushes or the wheat.

There are many environmentalists that advocate the total elimination of all foreign chemicals in the production of food. Many thinking people see such extremes as illogical and excessively impractical. Extreme views, if professed too vehemently, can harm a community's sense of environmental responsibility. People don't want to be associated with what they see as illogical options. Issues are avoided. The environment suffers in consequence, and chemical companies win another battle. But big increases in soil fertility mean big increases in human health, and big decreases in global warming. Most herbicides do not destroy productive soil biological activity. Ones that do and ones that don't should be labelled accordingly. Insecticides, fungicides and the majority of chemical fertilizers are broad-band destroyers of soil biological activity. In designing herbicides to kill specific plants the chemists have been much more successful. In general, herbicides are chemically quite different than the chemical poisons and fertilizers that kill fungi, insects, bacteria, actinomycetes (branched bacteria) and our friendly earthworms.

It is often not particularly difficult to design unique chemicals that kill very specific plant species, and I believe their use should not arbitrarily be prohibited. Simple, sensible and safe rules however should apply. The herbicide must break down fairly rapidly after use. The breakdown process must occur automatically and well before it can in any way decrease soil biological activity.

Herbicide use can decrease the amount of tillage required in crop production and thus maintain soil structure. The enhancement of crop yields due to lessened competition can also possibly enhance soil development and increase soil biological activity.

Because of the natural association of herbicides with other chemical agricultural products, they are often given undue criticism when they are simply made by the same companies. The more accurate design of herbicides, and their sensible use, can actually increase food production and could simultaneously increase soil organic matter.

Good soils, soils rich in organic matter and containing thousands of pounds of humus per acre, are fortunately much easier to create than they are to destroy, provided the use of powerful agricultural chemicals are avoided. The propaganda machine of the petrochemical industries has had to hinder and distort public awareness of this simple fact wherever and whenever possible. They try and keep us all in the dark. The general public, the consumers, the people concerned about global warming, are now beginning to see these facts in the true light of day. For the petrochemical industries, it must be like sunlight to a vampire.

Second: the same crop, year in and year out

It's called monocropping, and it too destroys soil organic matter and soil fertility.

Immediately following World War II, war-ravaged Europe had to be rebuilt. It was also desperately short of food. The United States devised the European Recovery Plan. It became known as the Marshall Plan after the then U.S. Secretary of State, George Marshall. There were many factors involved in aid given under the Marshall Plan, but food supply is what concerns us here.

Under the plan U.S. farmers were encouraged to produce huge quantities of food to feed a starving Europe. This was simple. Recipients of vast amounts of tax dollars rarely complain. The U.S. government bought food from U.S. farmers at hugely subsidized prices. Production naturally skyrocketed. The food was then in turn given to Europe. U.S. food production grew astronomically. Food aid was then given to other countries. The U.S. government and American farmers now found themselves "on the tiger's back" with subsidized agriculture. It became too difficult to get off.

By the late 1940s the single-crop concept had become quite widespread in Australia even with negligible subsidies. It was probably for convenience. Also it seemed to be successful in the United States and therefore "the way to go". Farming like everything else has its fads and fashions. In Australia, land was available in vast quantities, and as crop yields diminished new areas could be cleared for farming—as once occurred in the United States. World food shortages keep prices at premium levels and in consequence the concept of monocropping became established in most of the grain areas all over Australia.

In the years following World War II it soon became common practice by governments all over the world to subsidize food but especially grain production. It was not just used by the United States to feed a war-ravaged Europe; the concept spread widely. Subsidized agricultural systems grew like cancers to become onerous burdens on governments and the taxpayers who fund them. Farm subsidies became, and still are, a political issue in every country where they were created.

One of the results of artificially high commodity prices is that farms became smaller. In farming terminology "a living area" is considered as a farm size that can produce a reasonable standard of living for the farmer and his family. Naturally, the specific size varies depending on the nature of the soil, the type of rainfall, the proximity to transport and many other factors. But most important is how much money can be made from the crops produced.

Now if a living area in an agricultural grain belt is say, 1,000 acres (400 ha) without any subsidies, then when grain prices become subsidized the farm almost automatically becomes extremely profitable. The real estate value of the land soars in response. The size of a living area automatically shrinks. Living areas can often be reduced by half, or even a third of the original farm sizes. It depends totally on how much money is paid to the farm in crop subsidies. A living area of 1,000 acres might reduce to three or four hundred acres.

The original farmer becomes a relatively wealthy man. His children grow up. He retires and subdivides his land into smaller farms for each of his children. Each builds their own house and buys their own tractor and builds their own barn. More roads, bigger water supplies are constructed by local authorities. More phone lines are installed. New schools are built and more teachers employed. And it all happens because of an artificially inflated agricultural marketing system. The rest of the community pays for it all, in inflated food prices and wasted tax dollars.

The extra farmers and the extra people in the area resulting from this artificial market structure all have a vote, and naturally do not want to vote themselves out of their homes and out of their businesses.

Eventually a new equilibrium is established. The money made and the lifestyles achieved on the new farms becomes comparable with any other business or lifestyle where similar investment in money and effort is required. A new outside owner buying one of these farms is not only buying into an agricultural business, but is also buying into a complex and artificially distorted socioeconomic structure.

You will find that no matter what the subsidized agricultural product is, the financial support will be distributed in manipulative ways. It will always be dependent on following strict rules about specific total land areas, and often specific plots on the farm. The inevitable result is that vast acreage will continue to be cropped with the same crop, year in and year out. And so this second factor in the destruction of soil fertility was born and consolidated— the concept of monocropping.

Monocropping can often be almost all-pervasive. Australians familiar with the land and agriculture are invariably surprised when driving through the grain areas of the U.S. Great Plains. I know I was. You see no fences. Farming is often a matter of growing grain, and virtually nothing else. There are no sheep or cattle. There are no goats. There are no horses. Many of these farms haven't used fences for sometimes three generations or more. They just grow the same crop year after year. It must be a sad, uninspiring and boring way to farm the land. But the system gives them no choice.

A typical scenario: the farmer wants to borrow money from the bank to put in his crop—OK says the bank, provided it's insured—the farmer goes to the insurance company—OK says the insurance company, provided it's grown to standard agricultural department recommendations. The farmer goes to the local agricultural department and, for some reason we can only guess, they always seem to recommend huge quantities of fertilizers and chemical sprays and of course herbicides. Grow an organic crop? Sorry not "recommended"—sorry, no insurance—sorry, no loan. And the bank might even foreclose on the farm mortgage.

In every case with subsidized agriculture, it eventually becomes necessary to put a limit on the inevitable massive overproduction of the tax-funded food. As a result an even more insidious and unhealthy system comes into being. The remedy dreamed up by government bureaucrats and politicians to correct this overproduction has been to limit the land area an individual farmer could use to produce the subsidized crop. Logically and naturally the farmer uses every trick in the book to produce the most massive crop from the smaller area. He is advised by government agricultural advisors and trained consultants that a higher tonnage of farm produce can only be achieved by using chemically stimulated production. In doing so the absolute mass of the crop rises, its weight rises but its nutritive value plummets. Unfortunately soil fertility and soil organic matter levels also plummet.

Atmospheric carbon dioxide levels climb relentlessly as do tax-funded government stockpiles of farm produce. Nominated land areas are further reduced by government agencies in a continuing endeavour to cap crop volumes. The cycle repeats.

The current system of crop subsidies is used almost universally through the world, and national governments are constantly reducing land area qualifying for subsidy, but never limiting the weight of crop harvested. Chemical fertilizers can stimulate plant growth and increase total crop weight. This means that fertilizers can be poured onto the ground in massive quantities and be a cost benefit to the farmer up to the point where the added fertilizer cost starts to exceed the value of the added yield. Very cute and very convenient marketing!

Why is it that actual production quantities are never limited? Why is it always land area that gets limited? Why is it that often the allowed areas for subsidized crops are confined to very specific and nominated fields within the farm? And of course all these rules and areas are meticulously specified and policed by burgeoning government bureaucracies.

Of course it would have been more practical to pay a subsidy on a specific and limited quantity of produce. But then that might just not have suited certain influential industries. The land area subsidy concept happened to the obvious delight of agricultural chemical companies. Some might even say with their connivance.

The system continues today. It's everywhere. It's in almost every developed society. The farmer is restricted in the size of land he can crop, but subsidized to extract the maximum tonnage out of that limited land area. Under this regime chemical crop stimulants are of course ultimately paid for by the taxpayer. Inevitably using such destructive agricultural practices, pesticides, insecticides and fungicides become imperative, and they are bought with the same funding, that is with our money.

With the subsidized agricultural system the average farmer is not too subtly induced to monocrop just one small specific plot on his much larger farm. Even more devious: if a farmer wishes to rebuild his soil fertility levels by switching from grain, to growing a crop of legumes for example, or possibly using the area as a grazing paddock for a couple of seasons, he can often be effectively stopped. Bureaucrats can do this by simply threatening to withdraw the allocated grain subsidy.

Like puppets on a string the governmental authorities argue that, as the farmer didn't appear to want to grow any more grain, he should therefore lose his grain-subsidized area allocation. This puts him out on a limb. He could own a valueless farm. A system of preventing soil fertility improvements and thus ensuring the continuing use of massive quantities of agricultural chemicals prevails, subsidized in effect by tax dollars.

Agricultural subsidies support agrochemical use and accelerate global warming. Agricultural subsidies must go. Alternatively, and to reduce global warming, subsidies should be paid based exclusively on a measure of soil fertility improvement.

When subsidies are finally removed, as they ultimately have to be and especially on chemically dependent agriculture, the people who become vulnerable, the people who may well lose their shirts, are sadly not those who created the mess. Manipulated bureaucracy, politics, and time, that's what created this mess we know as subsidized agriculture.

In Australia, sugar production from sugar cane has been freed only just recently from this bureaucratic minefield. The United States is all too slowly extracting its agriculture from the subsidization mess. To insure its termination, a five-year-maximum sunset clause should be attached to all such subsidization schemes. The European Economic Community seems simply lost in political infighting and seems not to be getting anywhere, which certainly suits the agrochemical companies. In total contrast, New Zealand in effect and to its credit, went "cold turkey" on subsidies in the 1980s, although it was painful to many.

The constant emphasis on monocropping inherent in all extensive agricultural subsidizing structures constantly depletes the soil of its wealth of accumulated organic matter. The available minerals stored in the soil humus are used up, or rapidly leach away as the humus is broken down by chemical applications. Soil structures deteriorate and the ability of the soil to retain necessary moisture is markedly reduced. No new minerals are released from the subsoil or topsoil by soil biological activity. It can't happen as soil biological activity has been almost eliminated.

Monocropping also became more pronounced as large, high-powered tractors and wide cultivating and harvesting equipment were developed to reduce costs and farm big areas faster and more economically. This system came to be called broadacre farming.

One of the major problems with monocropping is that the pathogens that harm a particular crop are able to breed and develop in excessively huge quantities. With monocropping they have a continuous, idealized, almost exaggerated food supply to support their naturally evolved crop-synchronized breeding cycle. Constantly recurring plagues become the norm. Such plagues just can't occur, or are at least considerably restricted and reduced when land use is continually varied. For example, when grains are grown one year, legumes the next and in the third year the land area is given over to pasture and grazing, plagues don't often happen. The pathogens that damage the crops and constitute the plague have trouble surviving in significant quantities in the varied and changing environment.

With the destruction of the humus, another problem manifests itself. Unpleasant and possibly poisonous minerals and chemicals, once harmlessly chelated onto the large humic acid molecules, are released back into the wider environment. They could be anything from common salt to plutonium. Environmentalists, engineers, and a variety of other experts are called in to solve the "new" soil pollution and soil salination problems. See "The end of soil salinity" in the next chapter.

Yet the answer is obvious. Humic acid is the receptacle or the "shelves" where the elements can be held in store; and in chemically polluted ground there are simply no shelves at the supermarket. The humus, along with its humic acid molecules, has been destroyed. There is no place to harmlessly, safely and conveniently stack the poisons. There are no shelves to hold the nutrient elements, and there are no shelves to safely hold the unwanted poisons.

Monocropping requires ever increasing doses of chemicals to support a mad illogical upstream swim in a fruitless effort just to maintain crop production levels. Eventually after not too many years, crop yields deteriorate even in the once-good soils. This decline happens when the normally shorter-lived humic acid molecules have been fractured and broken down, thereby releasing any internally held nutrients. Almost nothing is left. Of course at this stage, long gone are those nutrients once chelated on the surfaces of the molecules.

But limited quantities of nutrients still exist within the long-lived humic acid molecules. At this point, new and stronger agricultural chemical fertilizers are applied, supposedly, as is advertised quite erroneously, to replace the minerals actually used by the crop. The stronger chemicals are able to break down the very last, very stable humic acid molecules and release the final remaining nutrients. By doing so, crop yields can be partially restored for another few years, before the next inevitable and final decline.

As the humic acid molecules are broken down, the carbon atoms, the building blocks of those molecules, become carbon dioxide. And now, millions upon millions of tons of carbon dioxide from this source have accumulated in the atmosphere, a source as we have noted to rival that from the exhaust pipes of every car on planet Earth.

Without even considering the effects of agricultural chemicals, the combination of "turning the soil" (discussed in the next section) and monocropping results in a total curtailment in the normal, natural production of humus. Natural soil fertility slowly and inevitably deteriorates and the soil humus reverts back to the atmospheric carbon dioxide from whence it came.

With the widespread adoption of the concept of monocropping, world agriculture took a giant step in the wrong direction.

Third: turning the sod destroys the soil

Now let's consider the third most important factor in the destruction of soil fertility, and that is the practice of tilling the soil by turning the soil upside down as part of the cultivation process. It is not as vicious as the excessive use of agricultural chemicals, but it is more insidious and ultimately almost as destructive. The effects of turning the soil develop over a much longer timescale than those of chemical use or monocropping. But remember, farmers have now been turning the soil for centuries, long before monocropping and agricultural chemicals were invented.

Before the practice of turning the soil became established, man cultivated his soil with a forked stick pulled by a horse or an ox. This ancient technique benefits soil microbiological life in three important ways.

Firstly, rain is able to penetrate the cultivated soil and soak in to be retained for long periods. Without moisture, there can be no soil life.

Secondly, the majority of the bacteria that decompose vegetation and root structures and so produce rich soil, are aerobic or air-breathing bacteria. Cultivating in such a way as to allow air into the soil lets these bacteria prosper and get on with the job of creating humic acid. The bad smell of a swamp and the inflammable marsh gas (methane) that bubbles to the surface in the swamp, are produced by anaerobic bacteria. Anaerobic bacteria don't produce soil.

Lastly, root structures can grow and move through the soil more easily if it is loose and friable than if it is hard and compacted. Natural "cultivation" mechanisms exist but they are extremely slow. The growth of tree roots, and the exposure of subsoil when the tree eventually dies and falls, is about as fast as such natural mechanisms operate.

Turning the soil has almost become the standard form of agricultural cultivation, but it was not always so, and unfortunately turning the soil is about the worst form of cultivation we could have devised. It has unfortunate consequences for soil life. The bacteria that break down dead grass root material and produce soil are naturally most happy in the root zone environment. Here there is still sufficient air for them to breathe and they are not exposed to the harsh conditions on the surface. They have been evolving in this environment for millions of years and have modified it and adapted well to it.

The aerobic bacteria that decompose litter lying on the ground surface have similarly adapted well to the environment they created for themselves. They don't actually like to be in direct sunlight as it can get too hot. Conditions can dry out severely and biological activity ceases in the complete absence of water, but in the moist surface litter they thrive, and multiply, and produce rich soil.

However, if the soil is turned over during cultivation, the bacteria that decompose the surface litter find nothing to eat. Their food is buried so deep it is unavailable. The bacteria that happily digested the quite different structures in root material also have nothing to eat. The root material that was their diet is up there on the surface, in the sun—dry, hot and unavailable.

The ancient practice of using a forked stick to cultivate the soil kept it loose and friable but did not separate the bacteria from their food sources. With crop rotation fertility levels were retained or increased. The soil grew rich. The crops grew well. So did everything else, weeds included. Hand weeding, the only drawback to this method of farming, was probably the most time-consuming and tedious task in primitive agriculture. Quite naturally most seeds evolved to sprout on or near the surface, or within the surface litter. Most seeds won't sprout and grow if they are buried too far under the ground. It would have been a wasteful and pointless ability.

Somewhere during the middle ages or a little earlier, a piece of flat board was attached to the forked stick used for cultivation and this turned the shallow cultivated soils upside down. The board was called a "molde board" and the plow became the mouldboard plow. Molde is the Old English word generally denominating the humus-rich top layer of soil. (The spelling became mould in English and mold in American English.) Grain was hand sown on the surface of the mouldboard-plowed ground but the weeds were buried too deep to sprout. The grain grew well and had few weeds to compete against. The never-ending task of hand weeding was thus solved with the invention of the mouldboard plow. Suddenly one man could farm an area as big as he was capable of cultivating and sowing. The area was no longer limited by the constant need to weed out competing and unwanted plants. The manpower required to grow the food supply dropped dramatically. Mankind now had time on his hands to really develop his civilizations.

Turning the soil became synonymous with agriculture.

The use of the mouldboard plow and the later development of the disk plow became the new form of "conventional" agriculture. Plows were soon made out of iron and could go deeper. Then they were made out of steel. Many plows were mounted on a single frame and pulled by teams of horses. Then tractors replaced horses and plows got bigger still.

Naturally it was soon found that the vegetation left after harvest would not readily break down. It stayed there right through until next season and ultimately clogged up machinery. It would not break down because the surface-living aerobic bacteria that normally digested it were too deeply buried by the soil-inverting plows and so they died. In many places it even became common practice to burn off the residue after harvest, to simplify plowing and preparation for the following year's crop. As a result even the possibility of producing any significant quantities of humus literally went up in smoke. The time-proven, preindustrial-age concept of rebuilding and reinvigorating the land by the utilization of a planned pasture and grazing animal phase was forgotten. In North America the practice and its consequences were described:

> The general custom has been, first to raise a crop of Indian corn … which, according to the mode of cultivation, is a good preparation for wheat; after which the ground is respited … and so on, alternately, without any dressing, till the land is exhausted; when it is turned out, without being sown with grass seed, or any other method taken to restore it; and another piece is ruined in the same manner. No more cattle is raised than can be supported by lowland meadows, swamps etc. … Our lands were originally very good; but use, and abuse, have made them quite otherwise. (George Washington in 1768)

In addition, land subjected to continuous cropping, especially where agricultural chemical fertilizers are used, will develop what has become known as a hardpan. A hardpan is a thin layer of very hard dense compacted soil that forms just under the cultivation zone. It only forms where the soil is constantly cultivated with soil-inverting implements. (Forked-stick plowing never produced hardpans.)

Roots find it almost impossible to penetrate these hard compacted layers. If you scratch down into these soils you often find a taproot that goes down a few inches, hits the hardpan, then does a sharp turn and spears off sideways, never getting any deeper.

Neither can rain, unless it is gentle and prolonged, get through these hardpans in sufficient quantities to recharge the subsoil with moisture. Storm rains simply run off in torrents. With any heavy rain, runoff will rapidly accumulate into small rivulets that bite into the cultivated material and wash and erode it away. When this happens the impervious hardpan is stripped bare and left exposed. It's like washing soil off a concrete path. It is a very common and highly visible result of the practice of turning the soil during cultivation.

Agricultural colleges generally teach that a hardpan is formed because of the constant traversing of tractors and farm implements over the cultivation area. As cultivation is often undertaken as a weed control procedure, it is advocated that cultivation should be considerably reduced. It is then recommended that weed management be controlled with herbicides, and crop growth be maintained with fertilizers. The concept is called minimum tillage and it gets a lot of publicity.

"Zero-till", where cultivation is proposed to be eliminated entirely, and "chemicals only" is the promoted method of growing the crop, was advocated and attempted. The system was given a lot of publicity, but it always proved to be a dismal failure.

These processes certainly would suit the agricultural chemical companies, who are great promoters of such systems. For example, the chemical company Monsanto ran advertisements promoting their herbicide Roundup; the caption said "See You Later Cultivator". Roundup is one of the most common herbicides in use in Western agriculture. Roundup is even used in cities and towns as a spray along the edges of lawns and gardens to "trim the edge".

I don't believe hardpans are formed by tractors traversing the land a few times a year as is claimed. It makes no sense.

Many years ago, a long time friend of mine, Dave Adams, who farmed several thousand acres near Forbes in central New South Wales, was driving one of his tractors and his twelve-year-old son Nick was on the seat alongside him. The tractor was an Australian-built Chamberlain Model 354 powered by a 100-horsepower diesel engine, weighing 5.75 tons. The ground at the time had not been recently cultivated. It was wet from a recent rain shower, but not boggy. The boy fell off the moving tractor. A rear wheel of the tractor ran up and over both his legs, over his chest and his left shoulder.

My friend was devastated, but within seconds the boy sat up. He had some trouble breathing, but not too serious. They took him into the local Forbes Hospital. Amazingly, no bones were broken. There was not even severe bruising. Bruising was no worse than a boy gets playing a hard game of football. Nick was kept in hospital overnight for observation. He was sent home next day. Years have passed. Nick is now a man and has a couple of children of his own. He is now farming the family property.

How was it that such an apparently horrific accident did such little damage? There were two major factors. One is that the rear tractor tyres on two-wheel drive tractors are huge and are inflated to very low pressures. The other is that the tractor was not under load. It was not pulling an implement and so there was a negligible torque load on the wheels.

When a farm paddock is cultivated, sown and harvested, implements travel over the ground three or four times in the year. There are spaces between the tyres and so some of the ground surface may never feel a tyre tread all year long. Where the tyres do contact the ground, there is very little ground pressure as the pressure applied can never exceed the original tyre inflation pressure as highlighted by my friend's experience. If you regularly drive over your front lawn with the family car, the very much higher pressures in the car tyres will result in some soil compaction. But the classic subsurface agricultural hardpan never forms in the front lawn. Your lawn might compact near the surface but not deeper down.

I believe, and have always taught, that the formation of hardpans result from a combination of constant cultivation to a fixed depth and general farming practices that deplete most of the organic matter from the soil. Yet agricultural tractor tyres are repeatedly and traditionally blamed for the cause of hardpan formation. Agricultural colleges still teach their students this nonsense.

When plants are potted, the material used always contains extremely high quantities of humus. When you overwater these plants the water comes out the bottom of the pot, and it's perfectly clean. Fill the same container with agricultural topsoil from any extensively cropped and chemically fertilized farmland, and now pour water into the pot. The water again comes out the bottom, but now it's brown, dirty and full of silt. There is a lesson in this little experiment and it is very relevant to understanding how hardpans are formed.

What we can conclude from our observation on potted plants is that when rainwater or irrigation water passes through infertile soil, the very fine dust and clay particles within the soil migrate down through the loose soil material with the water. When they reach the bottom of the cultivation zone they hit the more compact uncultivated soil, or subsoil, and are stopped and effectively trapped. It's like clogging up a filter, and the resulting densely formed hard compact layer is the hardpan.

Excessive cultivation prior to planting does tend to break down the granulated structure of good soil and produce free particles that are prone to migrate downward. It is therefore a valid argument to reduce the total number of times the soil is cultivated or "worked" to what becomes an essential minimum. The argument that says all cultivation should cease (the "zero-till" concept) is based on the totally false presumption that soil fertility can never be rebuilt, and so the presumed inevitable destruction of soil material should be kept to an absolute minimum. This presumption becomes true only when excessive chemical additives are poured into the soil, killing the soil life that produces the fertility, and monocropping is continued.

Water can slowly soak through hardpans but plant roots find them almost impenetrable. The water that does soak through will thus become totally lost and unavailable to any thirsty plant roots. Any subsequent warm weather will quickly dry out the shallow loose topsoil. Plants then wilt and more water is needed. In hot dry conditions water can be needed in as short a time as two or three days. The constant watering carries silt down to form the hardpan. Hardpan formation and the resulting excess use of irrigation water is a major cause of soil salination. The causes and the curing of salination is discussed in the next chapter.

European soils may have been in slight decline for several centuries. The invention of the mouldboard plow probably started the decline but it was insignificant while farm and household manure along with other organic matter was being constantly incorporated back into the soil. Also, crop rotation and the incorporation of a natural grass phase was established procedure. Those practices ceased and today European soils are now as poor as any found anywhere in the world.

Sadly, rich North American soils were in turn destroyed more quickly and more noticeably.

Extra: on the destruction of Canadian soils

In April 1992, Jean Charest, who at the time was Environment Minister for the Canadian government, released a massive and comprehensive environmental report containing twenty-seven separate chapters. This huge report discussed in detail what it considered an alarming deterioration in Canada's water, soil, air and forests.

Fourteen thousand lakes were described as "killed" by acid rain. The report reminded Canadians that 50% of the original organic matter in the soils of the Canadian Western prairies had gone. The report stated that the soil, because of this massive loss of organic matter, had become vulnerable to widespread erosion.

As is usual farmers received most of the blame. Included in the list of mistakes that they were accused of making was the claim that Canadian farmers had "ravaged some of the richest ecosystems in the world". The truth is those farmers were unsuspectingly and in good faith taking the advice of their own agrochemical-lobby-manipulated government agricultural advisors.

The report went on to warn of the deterioration in Canada's freshwater supplies and suggested that this could become a major health hazard. Any such major health hazard would most certainly have resulted from the massive use of agricultural chemicals. These factors were ignored in the report. The report had other predictions. It predicted that within 16 years all the "old growth" forests of British Colombia would have gone. The emphasis is always on "old growth" for a reason unrelated to the reason advertised. Old growth trees are by definition mature trees, ready to harvest, and so compete with plastics and metals, or alternatively, ready to die and rot and ultimately turn into carbon dioxide.

The Canadian Government decreed a $6 billion "green plan" to "address" these environmental problems. One would think that Canadians surely had a right to ask where their agencies would get their advice and information. And surely Canadians had a right to be informed how these vast sums of money were to be spent, or squandered. But it never happens that way.

Jim MacNeill, who was Secretary General of the Canadian Brundtland Commission on the Environment, was cynical about this supposed green plan, as was reported in *New Scientist* at the time. He pointed out that the 14,000 lakes stated to be already lost were destroyed by acid rain produced by burning fossil fuels for energy. He said "The government is spending around $4 billion in subsidies to promote the use of fossil fuels—that is to say we are spending billions to promote global warming and acid rain". He further lamented, "We are spending only about $40 million (that is one hundred times less) to promote energy efficiency ...It's a loser's game", he concluded.

The Canadian experience is one example illustrating the major environmental ills of Western society created by manipulated government agencies. I believe the Canadian government's stated plan was just plain wrong. There are several fallacies in the arguments propounded.

I suggest that the worth of "old growth" forests as compared to continuous growth forests, regularly harvested for their timber, is nothing more than manipulated public relations to prevent timber competing with oil-derived construction materials. There is negligible to zero environmental logic to these, suddenly discovered, "old growth" theories; yet it is what many in the Canadian environmental movement actually believe.

It also seems obvious that the destruction of the Canadian soils was caused by a combination of monocropping coupled with the massive use of chemical fertilizers, plus the continuous dosing of crops with pesticides, fungicides and herbicides, and all this combined with cultivation techniques that endlessly inverted the soil.

Remember that carbon constitutes 58% of soil organic matter. This carbon, when released by destroying the organic matter by these agricultural practices, becomes carbon dioxide in the atmosphere. That is of course, where the carbon atoms go. The generation of atmospheric carbon dioxide from Canadian soils exceeds that from all the fossil fuel burning cars, trucks and power stations in the nation, and by a very considerable extent. It is reasonably argued that it could exceed it by 400% (see chapter 5).

The deterioration in Canada's freshwater supplies must be at least in part caused by acid rain, but to a much greater extent it is due to runoff from farmlands saturated with agricultural chemicals. Any significant acid rain in the Canadian wilderness would be coming from across their border with the United States. This source of acid rain would be by far the most significant. And this cross-border pollution will always be blamed in an attempt to distract attention and responsibility from

Canada's massive use of agrochemicals.

Many of these misguided Canadian environmentalists are the same people constantly endeavouring to stop the state-owned Hydro Quebec authority from building the biggest totally pollution-free hydroelectric generating complex in the world. If the world is lucky these so-called environmentalists and their "land rights" activist friends will fail, and the world will be a much better, healthier and safer place.

Whether these green plans work, or whether they are even designed or expected to work is a moot point. The billions of dollars wasted on such government-funded green plans usually does little more than placate the lobbyists that infest the halls of power. And it pacifies those taxpayers who still believe that government agencies can be trusted to manage a farm better than the farmer who owns the land.

Turning it all around

Just south of Lake Superior and Lake Michigan in the United States is Wisconsin. The soil types in this state are very similar to those in the Canadian province of Ontario on the northern side of the lakes. The original richness and fertility of these soils and their incredible productivity was also typical of the soil types that constituted the Great Plains of the central areas of the United States.

There is a small fenced off area of land just south of Milwaukee in Wisconsin. It's been preserved as a piece of original prairie land. It is a wonderful example of the original grasses and the original prairie soils. It is fascinating and almost unbelievable to behold. There is an immense variety of grasses. They stand shoulder high.

I dug down into this prairie soil with my hands. The top surface is a mass of decomposing litter, which turns into true soil as you go deeper. There is no definite demarcation between the top litter and the true soil. And the soil is deep.

Over the rest of the prairies, all throughout the 20th century, monocropping and turning the soil upside down, and the eventual dosing of the land with agrochemicals year in and year out, changed this incredible material into what became the American Dust Bowl.

And in that process all the organic matter in those rich prairie soils became atmospheric carbon dioxide.

To reverse that process, to absorb millions upon millions of tons of carbon dioxide back into the soil and so commence our control over global warming, we simply have to idealize the soil environment so that earthworms, and all microbiological activity can function at their optimum efficiency and recreate rich fertile soil again.

The rich soils of the American prairies, and the rich soils of the savannas of the world, were developed by grasses and soil biological activity alone. But this is a thousand-year process and we don't have the time. We cannot rely on such a slow process to loosen and aerate and develop our soil to correct global warming.

The life cycles of trees as they grow and die and fall and so aerate the soil is efficient, but it is much too slow for our now desperate need to create masses of planet-saving organic matter. And even the benefit of an uprooted tree is pointless if grasses are not then permitted to develop for lack of sunlight in the loosened, but shade covered soil. Permanent forests are no answer. Permanent forest soils are always poor soils, and stay poor soils.

Grasses and soil cultivation procedures and the implements involved become the important factors in rapid soil development. With the right cultivating implements, if we are wise, we can do the same job a tree does by growing and dying and falling over, and do it three or four times a year. Not just once in a tree's lifetime. New implements can now produce almost perfect soil fracturing, with the exact degree of looseness and friability that promotes maximum grass growth and maximum biological activity. Soil has to be loosened, but not inverted. Soil must be made ready to allow for the easy entry of air and water, and the easy penetration of meandering roots. Today, with chisel plows and subsoiling plows, that total process can be unbelievably fast and extremely efficient.

With good soil preparation and following rain, the grass seeds germinate. They then thrive and proliferate in an explosion of soil creation. The presence of grazing animals in the cycle actually accelerates the rapid soil creation.

In the chapter following we discuss in detail how soil is created naturally and how sensible farming practices can accelerate the process. We also discuss how we, the consuming public, can positively ensure that farmers create fertile soil.

7

History of twentieth-century soil conservation and Keyline

SOIL conservation practices in vogue by the end of World War II, and still advocated by most government departments today, were those designed by the Corps of Engineers of the War Department of the United States in conjunction with the newly formed Soil Erosion Service and various other U.S. government departments. The Soil Erosion Service was set up and operated on soil conservation practices devised from experiments conducted on ten federally funded experimental stations established between 1929 and 1931. Dr Hugh Hammond Bennett proposed both the establishment of these stations and the nature of the experimentation that should be conducted at them to the U.S. Congress. The U.S. Soil Conservation Service was formed in 1933, two years after the stations were established. Dr Bennett subsequently became the first head of the Service.

The U.S. Corps of Engineers and the U.S. Soil Erosion Service together created what has now become conventional soil conservation practices.

By the early 1930s, the American West and central West had degenerated into one giant and very visible dust bowl. This had been caused by generations of farmers monocropping their land and using soil-inverting mouldboard plows to till their soil.

This situation had been greatly exacerbated in the 1920s as the United States initiated the first major developments in mechanized agriculture. The combine harvester was invented. The tractor and the farm truck replaced horse-drawn farm equipment, and cultivation suddenly became cheaper and easier. Excessive cultivation became the norm. These factors led, as Al Gore describes it in his book *Earth in the Balance,* to the "great plow-up" of the late 1920s. This excessive soil-inverting cultivation was soon coupled with an ever-expanding use of chemical fertilizers during the 1930s. It was never appreciated that these were fundamental errors in farming practices and soil fertility maintenance.

Then the knockout punch came. The whole U.S. grain belt was hit with a harsh and prolonged drought. This last blow exhausted the resilience of the soil life and halted plant growth altogether. It left nothing to hold the soil together. The soil structure collapsed, leaving a pile of dust. The skies turned brown from windblown soil, and stayed brown for months.

Franklin D. Roosevelt, president of the United States from 1933 until his death in 1945, had as his prime objective at his inauguration to drag the American economy by a massive spending campaign out of the long and terrible depression of the late 1920s and early 1930s. This was part of his promised "New Deal" for the nation.

Fixing the nation's Dust Bowl was the second objective of the New Deal and was obviously a sound political move. Roosevelt's plan was to pour vast sums of money into various rural projects, and the money would also stimulate the stagnant economy. It seemed the perfect answer.

So "war" was declared on erosion, and the military was heavily involved in the "battles". Similar to the Army Corps of Engineers, the Civilian Conservation Corps (CCC) was established in 1934 as an avenue through which federal money could be fed into the stagnant economy. The CCC then funneled money and manpower into a war against soil erosion. One of the main tenets of the Soil Erosion Service was to prevent erosion by building contour channels. At the time it was described as "terracing" the land. In 1935 the U.S. congress passed the Soil Conservation Act (Public Law 46, 74th Congress), making soil erosion control a federal priority, and the Soil Erosion Service became the Soil Conservation Service. Money was thus fed successfully into the American economy in vast quantities, but as an agricultural initiative, it was an extravagant mistake.

Nobody considered that an assembly that included military generals might not be the best team to fix an agricultural and soil biological problem. But in they went. It was fought like the Great War of only fourteen years prior. The same trench warfare tactics were used, which proved to be incredible disasters in both cases.

The U.S. Corps of Engineers undoubtedly didn't comprehend the true nature of the problem at all. The real crux of the problem was the gigantic decline in the fertility of the nation's soil. Using trenches was no way to fight that battle. Also unfortunately, the Corps of Engineers probably believed the petrochemical companies were their allies. That may possibly be true in war, but not so in peace.

With military precision the trenches were built, thousands of expensive miles of them. They covered the landscape and were called contour banks or check banks. In Australia, we followed the same practice starting in the 1940s, but called them contour drains. They were designed to check, or halt, or slow the flow of water and thus topsoil down the hills, and thus prevent the soil's supposedly inexorable movement into the creeks and rivers of the countryside.

But common sense was not prevailing. As any farmer knows, erosion gutters are invariably formed when heavy rainfall is forced to concentrate, artificially or naturally, on agricultural land. Erosion gutters are ruts cut by fast-flowing water. Concentrating water into trenches is dangerous and invariably increases its velocity. The contour trenches concentrate runoff and in consequence create their own erosion gutters. In many cases such erosion is created where before none existed. Contour check banks, or contour drains, do not prevent erosion. They never have and they never will.

Some strategically placed contour drains can be very useful as a cheap and efficient way to move large volumes of water around a farm to where it is most needed. Designed properly, they can be used to fill farm ponds or dams, and to move this stored water for later irrigation. But as an erosion preventive they are worse than useless. Yet soil conservation services still continue to this day to advise farmers to dig more trenches. Other government agencies hand out low-interest loans and give other tax-funded incentives to guarantee the madness continues. Often too late the farmer finally realizes how stupid the whole exercise has been. Low interest or not, he still has to pay back the loan, and in addition he has the added cost of repairing the often newly created erosion damage.

Trench warfare techniques were no help fighting the U.S. Dust Bowl problem, yet fly over Australia and you see the same folly. The same mistakes are being repeated. In places the countryside is littered with the ugly scars from this insane, expensive and wasteful practice of destroying good land by digging miles of functionless drains.

There was yet more soil-damaging madness promoted by these government agencies: farmers were sold the concept that chemical agriculture could produce bigger yields, and that the maintenance of soil fertility was unnecessary. Practicing such folly guarantees soil erosion as inevitable. And just as inevitably, soil conservation services recommended, and still recommend, building yet more trenches, to hopefully fix the additional erosion caused by the poisoning and destruction of the normally biological fibrous nature of the soil by using the concentrated chemicals. Agricultural chemicals, as we now know, kill earthworms, soil bacteria and fungi—the very things that prevent erosion by their ability to manufacture healthy soil.

It was a case of chemical weapons fighting a biological army and the biological army in this case were the good guys. But there were too many bad guys. Earthworms and soil biological activity lost the battle in the American West. Their casualties ran into millions upon millions of tons of destroyed soil life. The Corp of Engineer's learning curve in soil conservation realities and in understanding and appreciating the biological nature of soil, halted at a plateau of incompetence that has unfortunately been adopted as a standard and gospel by many state soil conservation services throughout

An erosion prevention system near Grenfell in central New South Wales. The system was designed by New South Wales state soil conservation services. The photos show the disastrous results that followed. It is the worst and most damaging erosion found anywhere on this farm.

Right: Chris Yeomans stands in a contour drain as yet not eroded.

A nearby contour drain showing erosion caused by the unnecessary concentration of runoff water into contour drains designed with excessive falls.

the world. Sadly, here in Australia, soil conservation services were among this group of the unwise.

What was needed in the U.S. Dust Bowl of the 1930s was massively increased soil biological activity to reverse the decline in soil structure. This would have stopped the erosion, and stopped the dust flying. But that didn't happen, at least in the beginning. That approach was not promoted. Chemical weapons (fertilizers etc.) were used instead.

The New South Wales Soil Conservation Service was formed just after World War II. It provided for procedures much the same as those of the prevailing U.S. Standard State Soil Conservation District Law. This is actually noted in Bennett's 1939 book *Soil Conservation* published by McGraw-Hill Book Company. Most Australian soil conservation departments continue to this day to dictatorially defend this mish-mash of distorted and impractical concepts in an expensive and pointless waste of taxation revenue.

J. MacDonald Holmes was for many years Professor of Geography at the University of Sydney. His book *Soil Erosion in Australia and New Zealand* is a textbook on the subject. Professor MacDonald Holmes (along with many of his graduate students) was an observer and partly a participant in the original development of my father's Keyline concepts. His 1960s booklet,

Chris Yeomans and an un-
happy farmer. The contour
drains concentrate the water flow into this previously
grass covered primary valley
with horrendous results.

The eroded contour drain
on the right feeds the deeply
eroded valley (centre of picture). Lower left, a delta has
formed of washed soil and
subsoil.

Another view of the eroded
primary valley from under
the wing of the author's
Cessna 180.

The final effect is that the owner wasted a lot of money to create what seems to be his very own Grand Canyon.

The farm owner paid the state authority consulting fees for the erosion prevention designs and in addition paid an earthmoving contractor to build the folly. The erosion shown here was created by a farmer taking the advice of his own state soil conservation service.

Soil conservation services have many examples all across this country of such failed attempts at fixing what is in reality non-existing erosion. Flying over Australian farmland, it is obvious that most of the areas of bare unproductive earth visible are where bulldozers and road graders have been used to form up these endless contoured mistakes. The erosion scars are not caused naturally, nor are they the result of careless neglect. They are caused by farmers following the advice of their own soil conservation services. Alas, only in between these government-designed, man-made scars do any nutritious grasses and crops grow, never on them, or in them.

The Geographical Basis of Keyline is an appraisal of the work. In the booklet he considers "the principles of American soil conservation methods ... have since been largely adopted in this country (Australia) to no great advantage as I see it now".

Back to the U.S. story: the advent of World War II, with its own enormous expenditure requirements, made the agricultural-financial stimulation experiment of the New Deal irrelevant. The severity and the tragedy of the American Dust Bowl also finally came to an end. Two things happened to bring that about. Neither was related in any way to the Corps of Engineers nor any other government group.

In 1933 Fred Hoeme built and sold an implement that became known as a chisel plow. Bill Graham of Amarillo, Texas further developed the implement and it became the Graham Hoeme Chisel Plow. The plow was designed to fracture hardpans and to let air and rainwater into the soil. It was marketed as "The Plow to Save the Plains". Farmers in the Dust Bowl areas started using the Graham Hoeme in the thousands. The chisel plow did not turn the soil upside down, and as a result, soil life began to regenerate.

Secondly, the long drought broke, and *The Rains Came.*

The American author Louis Bromfield (who wrote *The Rains Came*) in his agricultural books *Out of the Earth, Malabar Farm* and *Pleasant Valley,* credits the Graham Hoeme chisel plow with almost singlehandedly ending the dust storms in the U.S. Great Plains. It did indeed become the "The Plow to Save the Plains". And it didn't cost the American taxpayers a dime.

My late father, P. A. Yeomans and I visited Bromfield's Malabar Farm in the early 1950s, and among my more prized possessions is a copy of Bromfield's *Out of the Earth* that Bill Graham signed and gave to me later in Amarillo.

My father was a mining engineer and in 1943 purchased two adjoining blocks of very poor agricultural land at North Richmond, New South Wales, just west of Sydney. The land is 40 miles (65 km) inland from the Pacific Coast. The surface geology is mainly a mix of shale and sandstone. This sandstone, when decomposed, forms the famous beaches of Sydney.

The properties were subsequently named Yobarnie and Nevallan, both derived from family names. I'm the Allan in Nevallan. The area was 1,000 acres (400 ha).

On Yobarnie my father built miles of contour drains, or check banks, constructed as recommended by both Australian state and federal soil conservation and erosion control services. They didn't work. They were totally useless. At best, they simply filled with silt. At worst they created a totally artificial concentration of water that could create erosion on a scale far more destructive than was occurring on adjacent "unprotected" land. They were an incredible waste of time and money. These contour drains had not been government funded, and so there was no bureaucratic interference or objections when they were ultimately bulldozed flat and graded back out of existence.

My father decided a totally new philosophy on land management was needed. After several years of discussions and study, research and experimentation, a practical and economical system evolved. It grew into an overall agricultural concept for the complete design and management of agricultural lands and their soils. My father made several very expensive ripping-type implements to produce the soil texture and soil environment he believed necessary in his experiments in fast soil enrichment, before he obtained his first Graham Hoeme Chisel Plow. This implement greatly simplified the cultivation techniques his ideas and concepts demanded. So we started manufacturing the plow under licence.

Many thousands of farmers visited Yobarnie and Nevallan and, as a result the whole range of what became known as "Keyline farming concepts" spread throughout the country. Farmers, after adopting Keyline concepts, became successful farmers. It was almost an inevitable consequence.

I remember a whole range of titles being considered to encompass these new agricultural concepts before the name Keyline was finally selected. My father's first book, *The Keyline Plan,* was published in 1954 with an initial print run of 10,000 copies. For an agricultural book, it was a best seller.

Keyline planning is based on the natural topography of the land and its rainfall. It uses the form and shape of the land to determine a farm's total layout. The topography of the land, when viewed in the light of Keyline concepts, clearly delineates the logical position of on-farm dams, irrigation areas, roads, fences and farm buildings. It also determines the location of tree belts to provide shade and give wind protection. Keyline concepts also include processes for rapid soil enrichment.

The shape of a landscape is produced by the weathering of geological formations over millennia. The processes are always the same. And so the topography of agricultural land has a basic fundamental consistency. It is the inevitable nature of land shape that river valleys collect water from smaller creek valleys. They in turn are fed their water from still smaller valleys, until finally the water derives from the very first, or primary valleys of the catchment area. In any country, anywhere, when rain shapes the land over long periods of time, it inevitably creates and determines the topography of that land. Ultimately, at the extreme upstream of any river system there always exists thousands of primary valleys. The only variation to consistent topographical shapes occurs where geological features, such as hard rock outcrops, modify normal surface weathering.

A contour is a line meandering over the ground, always at the same height above sea level. The name Keyline was given to a single, very unique contour that occurs in all primary valleys. As you walk up the watercourse in a primary valley, the slope of the valley floor will suddenly increase. That point of sudden steepening is the Keypoint of the valley. A contour line surveyed to run through this Keypoint becomes the Keyline contour for that valley. Because of the consistency in water-formed topographical land shapes there is always a Keyline. The Keyline is always the primary contour and guideline that tells us which way to cultivate when attempting contour cultivation.

It is also a logical starting point for any farm layout planning, and supplies a fundamental principle on which modifications to existing layouts can be based. In planning the layout of a farm or ranch it is often the case that no other contour lines on the property need be surveyed and pegged, just the Keylines for each primary valley. Keyline contour surveying expenses therefore are always minimal.

Normally when any conventional contour plowing is undertaken, a contour line is first pegged or otherwise marked on the ground, then plowing commenced. Cultivation runs are made somewhere between the valley centre line and the adjacent ridge. The first furrow is plowed adjacent to, and parallel to the marked contour line. The second run is of course adjacent to the first and so on.

Let's say for illustration that each run is plowed below the previous run, as in Figure 7.9. Because of the natural topography of rain-formed land

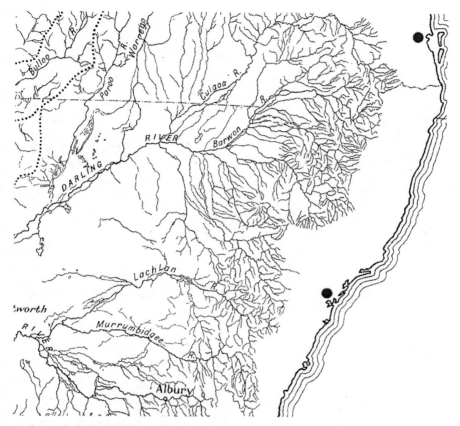

At the end of all these branches, sub-branches, and sub-sub-branches are thousands of even smaller valleys that are the primary valleys so important in Keyline planning. The map is of northeast New South Wales and southeast Queensland and shows part of the catchment areas of the east Australian inland rivers system.

shapes, cultivation runs soon and inevitably depart from the original and accurately marked contour. This always happens and usually after only a few parallel runs.

In conventional contour cultivation this effect is never appreciated and, more often than not, is seen as an apparently unexplainable irritation. Or it's ignored and invariably to the detriment of the land. Because of this off-contour drift, water flow can be directed the wrong way and contour cultivation then creates the very erosion problems it is supposed to solve. Keyline cultivation centres on the planned and logical use of this off-contour cultivation and water drift phenomenon.

In the illustration the length of the guide contour shown might be a few hundred yards long and the picture represents an area on the side of a primary valley. The slope of the land surface is always a little steeper at one end of this line than at the other end. This difference is important

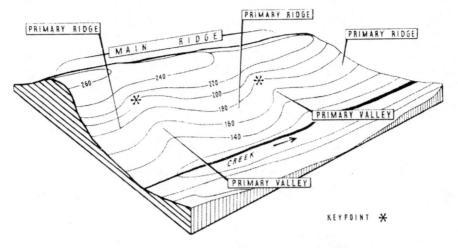

This diagram indicates the terms used in describing Keyline concepts. Contour intervals are drawn in from the 130-foot line to the 260-foot line.

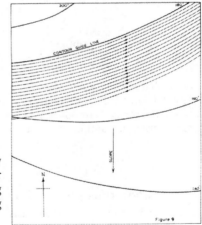

Figure 7.9.   Illustrating how cultivating parallel to a contour line inevitably forces succeeding plowed furrows away from being true contours.

in understanding Keyline cultivation. In the illustration, when plowing by paralleling the guide contour and then progressively progressing down the slope, each successive cultivation run will be slightly lower at the steeper end of the paddock. This follows as each pass with the cultivator will always have the same width, but across each width the vertical height will be slightly different. Inevitably, after just a few passes, the plowed furrows will no longer be on a true contour. They will now have a definite fall one way or the other, in this case to the left. Rain runoff will therefore tend to have a positive flow, or drift along the now slightly descending furrows.

Now, if on the other hand the plowing starts parallel to the true contour

but this time plowing progresses up the slope, then each successive cultivation run will be slightly higher at the steeper end of the cultivation area.
Again the individual cultivation runs will no longer be true contours. The
drift of rain or irrigation water runoff will be reversed. The water will move
to the right.

It's logical to delay the concentration and velocity of rainwater wherever
possible so it makes sense to give water a bias to move out from the
valley centre and not into it. Such drifts dramatically minimize the all-too-
common rapid concentration of rainwater in valleys.

The hundreds of furrows in Keyline pattern cultivation spread the water
and inhibit concentrations. In total contrast the contour banks or drains
advocated by standard soil conservation practices are designed to rapidly
concentrate water into a valley, which naturally increases its eroding action.

Understanding this fundamental concept gives us control of rainwater
drift and flow over the land surface. Of course, if an area for some extraneous
reason is always too wet, reversing the sequence of cultivation will dry it out.

The Keyline contour is extremely important in contour cultivation.
Above this unique contour the valley is steeper than the adjoining ridge.
Below the Keyline the valley is flatter than the adjacent ridge. Thus cultivating parallel to the Keyline contour and moving up the slope drifts water
out of the valley and cultivating parallel to the Keyline contour and moving
down the slope also drifts water out of the valley. If this phenomenon is
not recognized, what is supposedly contour cultivation can manufacture the
erosion that contour cultivation is traditionally believed to prevent. This
subtle but critical feature occurring in all natural landforms determines
surface water movement and this must be appreciated before attempting
contour plowing.

The Keyline contour is thus the transition contour. Above the Keyline,
contour cultivation runs must progress up the slope. Below the Keyline,
contour cultivation runs must progress down the slope. The result of such
Keyline pattern cultivation is that surface runoff water tends to always
drift away from the wet valley floor and out onto the dryer ridge. Erosion
caused by rainwater flow is effectively eliminated. Normally most water
erosion occurs down the centre line of a valley and results from the excess
concentration in water volume and water speed that normally occur there.

Keyline pattern cultivation spreads the flow out over a wide area, rendering it harmless. It also markedly increases the time of contact between the
rainwater and the soil. Water has more time to be absorbed. Keyline pattern
cultivation has the effect of allowing heavy storm rains to be absorbed more
easily into the earth. Generally such absorption only ever happens with
steady soaking rain.

Keylines in adjacent primary valleys are always slightly lower as you
proceed down the main valley or watercourse linking the primary valleys.
The location of farm dams or ponds are decided by using that valley's

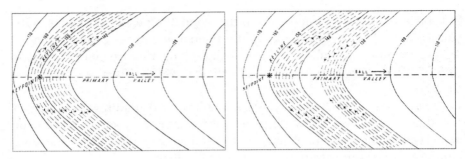

The solid lines are true contours. The dashed lines depict parallel cultivation furrows.

The diagram above left shows a primary valley and its Keypoint along with its associated Keyline. Cultivation has proceeded from the Keyline up the slope and also from the Keyline down the slope. Both drift the runoff rainwater away from the valley floor. Above the Keyline cultivation must always start at a true contour and parallel up the slope. Below the Keyline cultivation must always start at a true contour and parallel down the slope. In other words all cultivation runs must always parallel away from the valley's Keyline.

In the diagram above right the upper cultivation is correct and is proceeding away from the Keyline.

But note how in the lower cultivation area the runs are starting at the 130-foot contour and proceeding towards the Keyline thus forcing runoff to concentrate into the valley centre.

Keyline to determine the highest water level for the proposed dam. A Keyline contour drain can then collect any runoff and help fill the dam. Because of the drop in height of successive Keylines, an outlet pipe through a dam wall will generally approximate the level of the Keyline in the next valley downstream. Generally, with very minor adjustments in levels, dam sites can be logically linked so each Keyline dam can feed, via a contour channel, to the next lower dam. These contour drains can be the same as conventional soil conservation drains but must be almost flat to prevent the erosion soil conservation drains can cause. A fall of 1 in 500 or even 1 in 1,000 is usually plenty. Installing a big outlet pipe is wise when constructing a farm dam as this gives absolute control of the system and pumping becomes unnecessary. Everything is done by gravity.

The design of farm dams, constructed with large irrigation pipes a foot or more in diameter, buried under the dam wall and fitted with valves, and farm dams that can be filled or emptied by contour drains, is a Keyline concept. It is a concept my father borrowed from his experience in gold mining and gold washing in Australia and New Guinea. In gold mining, water often has to be transported for miles, usually through difficult country and it must be done cheaply. In gold mining, even more so than in farming, water itself is gold. Water's collection, storage and cost are of critical importance. The placement of dams with their feeder and delivery channels

An irrigation drain with two flags in position in readiness to hold back and overflow the water stream.

Canvas wall being used to flood irrigate hillside land after previous Keyline pattern cultivation.

The water, released by the valve in the back of the dam wall, moving along the drain under gravity has reached the first flag, filled it, and just commenced to flow over the lip of the drain to irrigate the land below. The fence in the picture is constructed to form the upper limit of the irrigation paddock.

P. A. Yeomans demonstrates his system.

determined by the relevant Keyline contour is the logical adaptation of old mining water-handling techniques to agriculture.

I once found an old contour earth drain, miles long, in the hills near the town of San Andreas in California. It must have been hand built by some of the forty-niners to wash gold from their claim. To me it looked exactly like a Keyline drain on my father's farms.

As sometimes can happen, storm rains occur when farm dams are already full. But that's OK as the Keyline cultivation patterns in the valleys effectively spread the width of the moving floodwater and so decrease its velocity. The valleys become covered with a wide sheet of slowly moving water. Even in steep country the land won't erode.

Keyline's cheap efficient dam construction and water transport systems mean that increasing grass and crop production by irrigating from the on-farm water storage ponds can vastly accelerate soil fertility development.

To irrigate using the Keyline systems the pipe through the dam wall is turned on, flooding the Keyline channel to the next dam. This channel can then be blocked with a pegged down sheet of canvas (called a flag) forcing the water to overflow the channel and flood down the slope. The patterned cultivation spreads the water with ample consistency. The canvas wall is then moved further along the feeder channel to a new location and the process is repeated. Each move takes just a few minutes. In very flat land a slightly different system is used. Either way a person can comfortably irrigate and control water flow rates easily exceeding one acre-foot per hour (one megalitre per hour). The per-acre cost of irrigation equates to simply interest cost on the capital to create the dams and the contour channels, plus the few minutes required for each move. There is no cheaper form of irrigation.

Keyline principles are totally against the concept of concentrating runoff water into manufactured disposal drains that are specifically designed to remove rainwater off the farm as rapidly as possible. Yet the supposedly safe rapid removal of water off a farm is the basis of all current soil conservation principles. In Australia, the driest of the world's continents, such advocacy is almost criminal.

Using Keyline design principles, either land is cleared, or on cleared land trees are planted, to form both windbreaks and shaded areas for livestock. Trees are ultimately harvested and the tree belts replanted.

The other major facet of the Keyline system involves the soil itself. Keyline uses concepts of rapid and economical soil fertility enhancement. As Keyline developed it became obvious that rapid increases in soil fertility from the substantial increase in soil biological activity could and should be an underlying fundamental of all farming endeavours.

The soil in Keyline philosophy is never cultivated by turning the earth upside down. Cultivation is only undertaken using modern versions of the forked stick of ancient agricultural practices. The Graham Chisel Plow was

Aerial photo of the trees on Nevallan. Using Keyline design principles either land is cleared, or on cleared land trees are planted, to form both windbreaks and shaded areas for livestock. Trees are ultimately harvested and the tree belts replanted.

used for years for Keyline soil development until we developed, in the 1970s, an efficient and practical implement, capable of effective subsoiling as well as fulfilling the role of a chisel plow. This implement reached deeper into the soil than a chisel plow but with considerable less soil profile disturbance. The resulting improvement in soil fertility with either implement not only increases crop yields and food production, but also simultaneously reduces costs. Additionally, less water is required for irrigation. For more on subsoiling see "Extra: the forked stick and the subsoil plow" (page 206).

Soil is never homogeneous even if it appears so. In any soil, individual bits randomly clump together and form crumbs or aggregates. The better the soil, the greater the quantity and mass of aggregates within the soil. The bits in the aggregates tend to hold together much more tightly than the assembled aggregates hold to each other. The degree of aggregation defines soil structure.

Soil aggregates however, can easily be broken up and destroyed by tumbling in a cement mixer. Either wet or dry, the aggregates break up. Excessive soil cultivation has the same effect. Land is sometimes cultivated several times to produce a fine seed bed in which to sow. This is a mistake. It is a harmful practice and is being abandoned. Edible crop seeds germinate within soils when humidity levels are high and air is available, not in water saturated soil. However, in any crop preparation prior to planting, at least one cultivation is required, both to loosen compacted soil and act as a weed-killing operation.

The much-publicized arguments promoting the concept of minimum tillage is primarily an argument that the weed-killing cultivation should be abandoned and herbicides be used to control weeds. In the so-called zero tillage concept, crops are supposedly to be grown using only seed and chemicals. Many farmers have tried zero tillage but found (as one might expect) it doesn't work. Wise variations have had some success. In Australia, experience has shown that no-till or minimum-till becomes extremely effective when coupled with annual or biannual, minimum-disturbance subsoiling.

The shape and the size of the aggregates in soil vary considerably. They are typically the size of very small pebbles. The spaces between the aggregates (called pores) can fill up with air and water. If the aggregates hold together well and resist crushing, and have a good general shape so that the pores form nice little connecting channels, then the soil is said to have a good structure. The tiny fibrous roots of plants and grasses love to meander down through the maze of passages in a well-structured soil, hunting for nutrients.

All those little pores and channels have the ability to hold water. The volume held is termed the field capacity. Field capacity is defined as the measure of a soil's capacity to retain water for plant use. Retention is a critical factor so field capacity is usually considered as the volume of water retained in the soil a couple of days after heavy soaking rain. It is what is retained after excess water has had time to drain away.

Field capacity determines how long soil life can function and operate efficiently before another rain shower becomes essential. Rich, humus-laden soil has excellent field capacity. Poor soil has very little. Sand has almost none. Organic farming and Keyline farming practices massively increase field capacity, thereby decreasing rainfall and irrigation requirements.

To initiate the soil building process in Keyline (and in any natural fertility-enhancing process), it is first necessary to grow a crop of almost any form of vegetation. That crop dies, drops litter, or sheds root matter, which in turn decomposes to become soil organic matter and ultimately stable humic acid.

The crop need not necessarily have accepted commercial value. It only needs to be voluminous and readily decomposable. The use of limited quantities of chemical fertilizers, such as lime or superphosphate, to stimulate the volume or mass of that initial crop is, unlike with strict organic farming mandates, perfectly acceptable in Keyline development, but only in the first year. After that, chemical fertilizers must be avoided to ensure a rapid increase in active soil life. It is acknowledged that efficient biological soil-development processes are impossible with continuing high chemical use.

If not constituting the first crop, then grasses and legumes should be utilized in the second growth phase. This second crop has definite commercial value. It can be eaten off periodically, or it can be regularly forage harvested.

Keyline concepts beginning in the early 1950s have consistently advocated the overstocking of confined grazing areas for short periods such as a few days, then moving the stock animals onto a new area to produce a constantly decomposing mass of root matter. This procedure is discussed in chapter 8.

The French biochemist, agronomist, lecturer and farmer, Andre Voisin was probably the first to systematically develop, test and document extreme grass productivity using techniques of accelerated rotational grazing. His book, published in 1959, describes and tabulates his previous fourteen years of research. The system was described but not well documented by Anderson, a Scottish agriculturalist, in 1777.

The development and enrichment of fertile soil are processes that have been known for centuries. Keyline soil enrichment systems merely stream-line the process. Organic farmers are usually familiar with the general techniques. In Keyline the soil building process is accelerated by subsoiling with an implement that guarantees minimum soil layer disturbance. This is then coupled with rotational grazing and, ideally, with low-cost irrigation. The objective in Keyline is to always make the creation of healthy fertile soil a profitable endeavour for the farmer.

There are several facets of Keyline. Over the years since its inception many have been adopted singularly and have proved profitable even in isolation.

Farmers have adopted Keyline layouts for rainwater collection, storage, and irrigation, especially following the successful trials on Keyline tech-niques by Sydney University at their McGarvie Smith Animal Husbandry experimental farm at Badgery's Creek NSW in the 1960s. The University very successfully promoted the Keyline concepts as a form of water harvesting. Although Badgery's Creek is in the same county as Yobarnie and Nevallan, the soil types are not absolutely identical, but the University found the benefits indeed were.

My father and I started the manufacture of the Graham Hoeme chisel plows in Australia in 1952. At the time they were the only type of soil-working implement that would cultivate the soil in the manner needed to enrich soil and prevent erosion. We made the Graham Hoeme under a licence from Bill Graham. The plows were considerably strengthened to suit the harsher Australian conditions.

The acceptance and almost universal adoption of chisel plowing in Aus-tralia has been one of the most noticeable changes in Australian agriculture in the twentieth century. There was not one single chisel plow in the whole of Australia prior to us commencing production. As was the case in most of the world, Australian soils had been cultivated by inverting the sod with disk and mouldboard plows.

Here in Australia I am often asked, "Have Keyline concepts been taken up by many farmers?" Yes they have. Over the last fifty years I have seen Australian agriculture change dramatically. Many of the facets of Keyline have now become "conventional" agriculture in this country. We see Keyline concepts and philosophies adopted everywhere. We see it in the establishment of tree belts, the design and location of farm dams, the general use of contour drains, not to supposedly prevent erosion, but to convey water to and from farm dams and to flood irrigate from these drains.

A Graham plow especially built for a Queensland farmer. It was 69 feet wide, and believed to be the largest plow in the world at the time (1955). (from *The Challenge of Landscape* by P. A. Yeomans, 1958.)

We see it in the widespread adoption of non-inversion tillage practices with the widespread use of chisel plows and the heaver subsoiling plows developed from them.

We also see farmers minimizing or often eliminating their use and reliance on agricultural chemicals. This change has come despite considerable resistance by the Australian soil conservation establishment to most of the concepts of Keyline thinking. It is a marketing reality that big money talks. In consequence, and by a variety of means, government agencies everywhere are coerced by the agrochemical companies into listening to and accepting almost as gospel the promotional material the companies produce. Most governments now accept the fabricated concept that beneficial agriculture totally relies on and is dependent on high chemical inputs. Such indoctrination unfortunately prevents both the enrichment of the world's soils and the entrapment of carbon dioxide into them.

In addition to their use in agriculture, Keyline topographical concepts have been included in several university architectural and town planning courses in Australia, the concept being that the layout of large-scale subdivisions and even whole towns could be planned based on the concepts.

Keyline concepts and designs are becoming increasingly widespread as time goes by. Professor Stuart B. Hill, Ph.D, who holds the Foundation Chair of Social Ecology at the University of Western Sydney, and Martin Mulligan, a lecturer in that faculty, and who is also editor of the journal *Ecopolitics: Thoughts and Action*, recently co-wrote an excellent Australian historical book *Ecological Pioneers*. In discussing my father and the concepts involved in Keyline designs, they say

> Despite its marginalisation by conventional agriculturists, Yeomans' approach to ecological design was, as mentioned above, one of the main sources of inspiration for the development of "Permaculture". The birth of this movement dates

back to 1972 when Bill Mollison—a psychology lecturer and well-known "identity" at the University of Tasmania, and David Holmgren—a student in the Environmental Design Course at the College of Advanced Education in Hobart, began an unlikely but highly productive collaboration. The extroverted Mollison has gone on to establish an international reputation as the "father" of Permaculture; giving inadequate credit to Holmgren and virtually none at all to Yeomans. Holmgren's story is certainly less well known, but of great importance in tracing the lineage of ideas that have manifested themselves in Permaculture design practices.

Keyline practices, once implemented, effectively eliminate all soil erosion. The "battle against soil erosion", the concept of "soil conservation", and the costly bureaucratic industry these buzzwords have created, become irrelevant and unnecessary. Keyline, like classic organic farming, is a soil creation system. It is not a soil conservation system at all. Soil conservation is a negative term and implies merely delaying some inevitable future situation where apparently all the world's soil will be gone.

The Keyline system as originally conceived was not designed to produce organic food, nor was it designed to assist the mitigation of global warming. It was designed to develop poor land into good land, and it was designed to make farming profitable in the quickest most efficient way. To me, Keyline became important in relation to global warming and organic farming because it was a tenet of Keyline philosophy that the best path to achieve its objectives was via the creation of highly fertile soil. And fertile soil is humus-rich soil, and forming humus consumes huge quantities of carbon dioxide.

Although Keyline concepts were never designed with the prevention of global warming in mind, I believe that the widespread adoption of Keyline principles is probably the most practical and profitable change that agriculture should embrace to achieve that worldwide imperative.

My father wrote three books on Keyline farming: *The Keyline Plan, The Challenge of Landscape* and *Water for Every Farm*. I will have them reprinted if indications show it warranted; and maybe also Professor MacDonald Holmes's booklet *The Geographical Basis of Keyline*.

The Keyline Research Foundation was created in 1955 to foster the adoption of "some or all of the techniques" [of the Keyline system and likewise those from] "further development from these basic techniques". [One of the main tenets of the foundation being] "That the permanent development of the soil is the fundamental of the wealth and stability of the nation and the wellbeing of its people".

The Ten Trustees of the Keyline Research Foundation taken at the second meeting of Trustees, August 1955.

From left to right: **Mrs. Rita Yeomans** (my mother), who entertained, advised and catered for often up to one hundred unexpected visitors at the Nevallan farm, almost every week. In addition she was involved with the Flying Doctor Service, the English Speaking Union and the Country Women's Association. She also managed the Brahman stud operation on the farm. **Mrs. Anthony Hordern, Jnr.**, managed her own Southdown stud at Culcain (N.S.W.). **Anthony Hordern Jnr.**, President of the N.S.W. Sheepbreeder's Association. A grazier running Merino and Romney Marsh stud sheep, and also a beef cattle breeder. Professor **J. R. A. McMillian**, Dean of the Faculty of Agriculture at the University of Sydney. **C. R. McKerehan**, President of the Rural Bank of New South Wales. **P. A. Yeomans** (my father), President of the Keyline Foundation, grazier, mining engineer, originator of Keyline Plan, author of several books on agriculture. Professor Sir **C. Stanton Hicks**, Professor of Human Physiology and Pharmacology at the University of Adelaide, Scientific Food Consultant to the Australian Army and founded the Australian Army Catering Corps during World War II. **Sir David R. McCaughey**, a grazier and also chairman of the early Australian wool-exporting company, Elder Smith Goldsborough Mort Limited. His property at the time was Borambola Park Beef Shorthorn Stud, Wagga Wagga (N.S.W.). **John Darling**, Chairman and Managing Director of Darling and Co.Ltd (flour milling and stock-food firm). He was also director of various companies including British Petroleum Co. of Australia, Alcoa of Australia, Perpetual Trustees Australia, Consolidated Metals, and Commonwealth Mining Investments. **Harold N. Sarina**, Organizing Secretary Keyline Research Foundation (former long-term secretary of the Sydney Royal Agricultural Society (R.A.S.), where he was Executive Officer and Registrar from 1933 to 1955. He was also an agriculture and livestock consultant. And **G. B. S. Falkiner** (not shown), of Haddon Rig Merino Stud, Warren (N.S.W.), Vice President of N.S.W. Sheepbreeder's Association, chairman of the Industrial Committee of the Nuclear Foundation and a member of the Council of the N.S.W. Bush Nursing Association.

At the time, probably only the Swedish chemist Svante August Arrhenius (mentioned in chapter 1) had seriously considered the mathematics and also the repercussions on world climates of us constantly adding greenhouse gases to the atmosphere. Most certainly my father and the other members of the Keyline Foundation did not recognize how important was to become the development of the soil, not only to the "nation and the wellbeing of its people" but to the very survival of world civilization as we know it.

8

How we create fertile soil to halt global warming

To put a halt to world climatic change, to stop the greenhouse effect in its tracks, the carbon dioxide in the air has to be converted into soil humus. This chapter is about how it can be done and how we can make this conversion happen.

At the same time as we modify our agricultural systems, we must shift our energy sources away from supposedly cheap fossil carbon systems. We will thus ensure an ongoing world climatic stability, far more economical and far safer than the frightening future we now see ahead of us. The necessary energy system modifications that becomes the other half of the story are explained in chapter 11.

A particular soil may have been consistent and unchanging in its fertility for millennia. If the climate or the functioning environment is changed, the soil fertility level will modify itself. A modification may increase the total organic matter content or decrease it. This happens more rapidly than is generally believed, accepted and taught.

Most soil conservation services and government agencies operate on the premise that it takes "a thousand years to produce an inch of topsoil" (25 mm). This is the basis of the belief that once topsoil is lost, it is lost forever. Soil is constantly portrayed, for all practical purposes, as being totally irreplaceable. These concepts are completely false, and to teach them is irresponsible, or at least naïve.

However, government agencies promulgate these distortions of fact. They do this at least in part to ensure that soil conservation services and their allied agencies are seen by the urban population as noble institutions, preserving threatened national assets from supposedly careless, irresponsible, even illiterate, greed-motivated farmers. These are misleading and false images. For government agencies they justify the imposition of endless, clumsy, inane bureaucratic rules and regulations on a farmer's right to man-age his own farm. It also helps guarantee the survival of the bureaucratic structure.

It frustratingly limits the ability of a farmer or grazier to develop and improve his own land and soil. Almost without exception land owners want to hand on to their children something more than what the land once was. It is the farmer and the owner of agricultural land, nobody else, that really wants the soil to become richer and more productive.

It is easy to improve soil and it is easy to create new soil, providing only that the use of agricultural chemicals and fertilizers are massively minimized, and also during cultivating to any significant depth the soil layers are not inverted. The other necessary requirement, if the land is cropped, is the adoption of simple and sensible crop rotation.

Given a reasonable and regular rainfall, and starting with bare exposed subsoil containing no unique and peculiar element deficiencies or excesses, life will move in. It always does and it always will and new soil will be created in the process. Nature's methods are very practiced and they certainly don't take a thousand years.

With common sense, often soil can be improved significantly in a matter of mere weeks.

A child's sand pit

In a suburban backyard, clean washed sand is used to fill a child's sand pit. Geologically speaking, the sand is usually derived from the quartz material in granite. This pure, quartz-derived sand is almost totally devoid of any of the essential minerals and nutrients required for plant growth. But if that barren material is left unattended for any length of time, plants will sprout and grow. Life will begin to take over. If you have one, then annoyingly, within weeks, the once clean sand pit will need weeding. If not weeded the sand will soon become "dirty". That dark discoloration is decomposed and decomposing plant matter. The creation of humus has started and it is happening in pure clean inert sand!

Bare ground

To illustrate the processes involved in the formation of soil, consider this scenario. Let's start with absolutely no soil at all, located in some remote test area. Let's also start our test with not even a smidgeon of organic matter. All we require is a reasonable rainfall and weathered broken-down rock material. Technically, that material is subsoil. Our test area is as if all true soil has been bulldozed away, leaving the earth bare.

Count down ... zero and go

Within the first few minutes, airborne spores, microbes and bacteria will have arrived and continued their endless individual struggle for survival. Within hours a few bird droppings and other organic debris will have "contaminated" the otherwise totally lifeless earth. Within days plant seeds will also have arrived, carried by the wind, or in bird droppings, maybe between their toes, or even on the boots, paws or wheels of travellers crossing the land.

The first rain to fall will bring additional spores and bacteria, plus a whole variety of different microorganisms picked up by the falling raindrops. The raindrops will also contain dissolved carbon dioxide as carbonic acid. The carbonic acid entering the soil will dissolve tiny quantities of the small inert rock particles and so release tiny quantities of the essential trace elements mixed in the rock particles by past geological activity.

The trace elements, now dissolved in the soil moisture, may start to leach down in the drift and movement of the water into the earth. But many trace elements, after release and after only a very short travel through the subsoil material, will encounter a clay particle and become attached to it by chelation.

Those trace elements, previously tightly bound in inert rock particles, have been freed. They are now available to plant life, waiting on a once vacant "supermarket shelf".

Here and there, seeds will germinate and plants will start to grow. Fine hair-like roots will struggle down into the hard earth looking for nutrients, looking for the essential elements for the plants' survival. The young plants soon form leaves so that photosynthesis can commence. The plant always needs a constant supply of moisture. But sometime after rain has fallen, the near surface material will inevitably dry out. The roots then need to penetrate deeper to find water. Those roots eventually die, or are shed by the plant, and thus become food for such things as aerobic bacteria. The quest for water thus initiates deeper soil development.

These new plants are like the sprouts you might grow on a kitchen shelf. Most of the elements required in this very first initial growth would actually have come from the seed itself. That is the way the seed sprouting process works. Nutrients are only required when the actual roots needed to collect the nutrients have themselves formed.

The windblown seeds of grasses and grains, of legumes and clovers, the plants that are the food sources of the higher animals, will all sprout where they fall. However, they will almost certainly die. As yet not much can survive in this hard, compacted, lifeless subsoil material.

This new dead plant material will be broken down by any hungry microbes carried in by wind and water. The microbes become permanent residents in the forming soil. Small quantities of surprisingly strong acids are produced in the microbic breakdown processes. These acids will decompose more tiny rock particles whose constituent elements will also attach themselves, by chelation, onto any nearby clay particles.

The ultimate end product of the breakdown of the dead plant material, the bird droppings and any organic debris washed or blown onto our test area will be humic acid molecules. These molecules will hugely multiply the available mineral storage capacity of the base material. The supermarket has more shelf space. The presence of clay will no longer be so critical. The subsequent breakdown of some of these humic acid molecules also helps to supply the bulk elements to nourish further plant growth. Some of the "shelves" themselves get consumed.

The good eating plants, the ones that nourish mammals, will not have survived, but quite a few "useless" weeds, having virtually no competition, will definitely survive. Thistles, cacti, and all those plants that have, for us, no nutrient value whatever, can grow and reproduce on only air and water with just the barest traces of the more exotic elements. Some will even prosper.

Many of these so-called weeds have thick woody root structures. These roots are almost devoid of any of the vital elements required for more advanced life. But these hard roots expand with inexorable force as they grow, and in doing so they fracture and crack the hard lifeless soil.

This fracturing and shattering effect is a necessary and essential part of the creation of fertile soil. Rain can now soak in instead of simply running off. Air, necessary for the biological activity of decomposing dead plant material, can gain access into the subsoil.

Within weeks the first plants will become visible to the naked eye. Within months more of the grasses capable of supporting animals will have arrived and germinated. Now, because the soil fertility has begun development, some of these grass plants will survive sufficiently well to grow and ultimately seed.

Within one year our material could no longer be described as decomposed rock or lifeless subsoil. It now has advanced to the point where it must be classified as true soil. It's certainly not rich soil, but it is soil. It's a beginning. The process for the creation of truly fertile soil has started. Within ten years, grazing animals could happily move in and occupy this once lifeless land. A symbiotic relationship would soon establish itself whereby the animal droppings fertilize and stimulate even more grass growth. I say "fertilize" here using it in its true meaning.

Their droppings would further encourage the growth of the better grasses. This is a universal inevitability as virtually every nutritious grass in the world evolved in a self-generating, symbiotic relationship with grazing animals. It must be so. It would be ridiculous to presume that over millions of years the grasses and associated soil biological activity did not evolve so as to utilize the readily and constantly available manure and urine from the grazing animals in their own life cycles. In reality many of the grasses have become almost dependent on such relationships. Healthy grazing animals, nutritional grasses and fertile soil have evolved and combined over time to form highly productive symbiotic relationships.

The cycle begins when the grazing animal bites the top off the plant. The plant no longer has leaves, and with no chlorophyll, can't utilize the sun's energy for growth. The plant immediately switches energy sources and utilizes the carbohydrates stored in its root structures to rapidly regrow its leaves. The plant roots, after being utilized in this regeneration process, are shed like autumn leaves. Microbiological soil life thus gets a crop of dead root material to feast on. Each partly-eaten plant that goes through this cycle generates a net increase in soil organic matter.

The death and decomposition of soil microbes produce rich humus and fertile soil. The grasses in turn thrive in this fertile soil. This whole soil-generation process commences within hours of the leaves being chomped off by the grazing animal. And of course, manure from the animals assists the rapid plant regrowth. Ultimately a general equilibrium is reached between soil fertility, grass growth, and the number of animals the land can support.

Within one human life span, our "test area" of totally bare and barren land would be indistinguishable from the surrounding countryside. Logically, how could it be otherwise? Local conditions will ultimately determine whether the land eventually stabilizes as open savanna, forest land or some combination of both.

I have illustrated how an area of lifeless bare earth would be transformed, with no human assistance, into land capable of producing crops and supporting livestock. Given a landscape of any decomposed rock formations and given any reasonable rainfall, it is quite impossible to stop the generation of soil. With adequate minerals and a regular and adequate rainfall, soil creation is fast.

Lucky for us in our imperative to correct climate change, the rate of soil development can be dramatically accelerated by simple and sensible soil husbandry. This is achieved by subsoil cultivation, non-inversion tillage, the judicious use of good grass varieties and selective and intense grazing practices. By such means fertility development can be underway in 1,000 hours, and the soil can be developed to extremely high productivity in 1,000 days.

The cliché that "It takes a thousand years to make one inch of top soil" is absolute drivel. Yet most of our Western educational organizations teach our children, and force-feed our farmers, this very nonsense! Even officers from the USDA (United States Department of Agriculture) were quoting (*Science*, November 1999) and I presume actually believing, that soil formation occurs at a rate of approximately 0.003 of an inch per year. That's slightly faster but just as silly. It would seem that some of those USDA officers should have spent more time playing in their sand pits, and not burying their heads in it.

Brigadier Sir Cedric Stanton-Hicks C.St.J., M.Sc., M.D. Ph.D., F.R.I.C. and Nutritionist Extraordinary, established the Australian Army Catering Corps, and was its first Director. He was responsible for the health and nutrition of our military forces in the Pacific Region during World War II. Before his death in 1976 he was Emeritus Professor of Human Physiology and Pharmacology at the University of Adelaide.

Describing my father's work on soil development, of which he was quite familiar, Sir Stanton-Hicks writes in his book *The Nutritional Requirements of Living Things*: "After three years he [Yeomans] was able to demonstrate that black soil had formed to a depth of 12 inches where scarcely any soil had previously existed on this rock strewn countryside. Shale and sandstone debris had disintegrated into soil. Thousands of farmers and many distinguished visitors from overseas have witnessed the results of this transformation of a barren tract of land [Nevallan] into a parklike region, carrying fine livestock all year round".

A false image of farmers and farming practices has been foisted upon us

Ranchers, farmers, graziers, subsistence farmers, farmers that farm rice paddy fields or small vegetable plots, farmers the world over are far more wise and responsible than most of us are expected to believe. This reality is totally different from the misleading images that city voters receive from the media, from their academics, and from their politicians. Additionally, they are certainly not the messages distributed by the hordes of conservation and wilderness society committees that have found an effortless way to see themselves on national television.

Unfortunately many of these societies have basic policies founded on illogical and dangerously false premises. Also unfortunately, the usually caring and concerned members of these generally suburban and non-agricultural societies are never encouraged to question the basic wisdom of their organization's policies. Healthy, collective, constructive responsibility is wasted by flaws and falsehoods in the basic premises. The cynically manipulated arguments guarantee a dreadful squandering of human en-thusiasm and concern. The fossil fuel, agrochemical and petrochemical industries always benefit by the diversion of responsible thought and action, especially in agriculture where their market is absolutely huge.

Added to this are politicians who need to establish their own worth and nobility within the minds of their city constituents. Our politicians, driven and guided by entrenched bureaucrats, create incredibly expensive advisory services and then, to the detriment of the total world environment, they impose childish and illogical regulations on farmers to enforce the worthless advice. It is the logic of the agrochemical lobbyists overruling the logic of the

Left: Sir Ian Clunies Ross, first Chairman of CSIRO (Commonwealth Scientific and Industrial Research Organisation) and former Professor of Veterinary Science at Sydney University, on Nevallan. His portrait was included on the reissue of the Australian $50 in 1973. Right: Mr Gill, at the time Chief of the Animal Industry Division of the CSIRO.

The CSIRO is a research organization and not bound by unproven and preconceived opinions. Sir Ian, just before his untimely death in 1959, was organizing a large research project covering several thousand acres to test and document the concepts of Keyline farming concepts for Australia. The research was stopped.

farmer. This way, city dwellers quite erroneously imagine their politicians as caring, concerned and responsible people.

Are we that naïve? Are we to believe that food production and the health and fertility of our soils would be better managed if taken out of the hands of the farmer who owns the land, and given to some nine-to-five bureaucrat in some state or federal capital city? Because that's exactly what we who live in urban and suburban society have done, and still do. Why are we so tolerant of the growth and power of inept bureaucracy? In so doing, we are getting into bad habits.

It is time we stopped swallowing the orchestrated rubbish put out by soil conservation services and the hordes of environmental academics that criticize our farm communities. The majority of the soil destruction that occurs across this world of ours results from government interference, insidious state influences and legislated manipulation of food price structures. Don't blame the farmers.

The only manipulation we, as thinking and responsible citizens, should permit are manipulations that encourage or ensure farm practices become established to directly increase soil fertility. We want and we must demand an agricultural system that will curtail global warming and we need it now. Not tomorrow.

To stop global warming and bring our planetary weather back to stability, the aim must be the rapid production and accumulation of stable organic matter and humus in our soils. We have to have, we must have, farming systems that automatically do that.

Fortunately such systems exist around the world. They are already used by a small band of Western farmers. Classic organic farming is one such system. In general, in countries where bare subsistence farming is the norm, the cost of agrochemicals is prohibitive. Enhancing soil fertility is the necessary optimum. If aid is required then such countries need tractors, not chemicals.

Soil production and fertility creation is a biological process and it happens fastest in the grasslands of the world. This is why the richest soils in the world have always been the grasslands of the world. To rapidly produce rich soil and thereby entrap atmospheric carbon dioxide into the soil, we should use the best system that nature has evolved, then give it a little assistance. That's the fastest and easiest method ever of creating the soil fertility the world and world weather needs.

To produce such soil, employing natural biological techniques with reasonable rainfall, is not anywhere near as difficult as we are constantly encouraged to believe.

Some realities we have to teach:

Firstly: We now have the ability to economically loosen and aerate soil by minimum disturbance subsoil cultivation. This allows the soil to store enormous quantities of rainwater for future use. This also is, in general, the simplest, most logical and most economical means for storing rain.

Secondly: Short dry periods force root structures to search deeper for moisture in the loosened soil. In consequence the soil-building process itself moves deeper. A short drought thus deepens and improves the soil and so can be of actual benefit. If irrigating, space out the times. The topsoil region of biological activity develops into the subsoil and the metamorphosis of the subsoil into true soil begins. Historically animal manure was automatically part of the natural process, so when grazing animals are not used to "cut" the grass then, ideally animal manure should be spread during the grass growing process. It is almost certain that eventually we will discover the grasses' equivalent of "essential vitamins" in animal manures. If such things don't exist then evolution has been missing opportunities.

Thirdly: With the increased sophistication of on-farm dam construction, such as is strongly advocated in the various Keyline books, farmers now have the ability to economically store water from heavy rains. With a simple irrigation system, this water can allow farmers to keep the soil building process and the food production process operating even during excessively long dry periods; see chapter 7.

Overgrazing is grazing more animals and for longer periods than the land will support. When prolonged, it results not only in depletion of total vegetation, but more significantly in depletion of actual plant varieties. Animals eat the best plants first.

Paradoxically, when controlled correctly, overgrazing considerably enhances both grass and soil development. The important proviso being that the overgrazing is terminated before the consumed grass proceeds too far into the regrowth of leaf structure. In this way the more tasty and nutritional grasses are not penalized by being constantly nibbled. The better grasses then survive and will ultimately dominate the pasture.

It may seem surprising, but this overgrazing process is actually the way soil production works in the wild. In the wild, grazing animals move in tightknit herds for protection from predators, and so they always overgraze. They then move on. It will usually be a month or more before the herd returns to that area to repeat the cycle. The one thing the animals can't do in the development of soil, and a wise farmer with a chisel plow or subsoiler can, is to rapidly loosen up the ground to let in air and rain. See "Extra: the forked stick and the subsoil plow" (page 206).

Subsoiling and cultivating with tined implements is one of the main factors in the enrichment of soil and the development of active soil biology. But we must never forget that soil enhancement is the very antithesis of everything being promulgated by the powerful agrochemical industry. This factor may well have restricted the more widespread acceptance of subsoilers and chisel plows, especially in government agricultural advisory services.

We need more good soil and good soil has to be alive. It has to simply teem with microbiological activity. Active healthy soil and soil life guarantees nourishing healthy crops. Without soil life, topsoil is no different than subsoil and that is the crucial difference between the two. In some areas you may hear people describe their soil as being 30 feet (10 m) deep or more. Well it may be black, and it may look rich, but at those depths, active soil life is not possible. There is no air supply at 30 feet and air is an absolute necessity for beneficial microbiological activity. Without it the soil is dead.

Try growing a potted plant in the very best humus-laden rich black soil that's been sterilized in a microwave for a few minutes. The soil life is dead and a nutritious plant is unlikely to grow. Cactus might. If a plant grows at all, it will be unhealthy, stunted and prone to insect attack.

Even after many, many years of poor farm practices, a subsoiler can reverse and nullify accumulated harm to soil structure simply by creating an idealized soil environment. The extra available air and water will encourage a sudden explosion in soil life. Fertility levels will rebound. A subsoiler fractures hardpans and lets air and rainwater penetrate deeply. Rainfall is absorbed almost instantly and erosion-causing runoff becomes negligible. And just as importantly, subsoiling creates billions of spacious comfortable apartments ready for immediate occupancy by the earthworms and the microbes and the bacteria that create humus and form rich fertile soil.

The Australian CSIRO (Commonwealth Scientific and Industrial Research Organisation), in its very excellent and informative publication *Organic Matter and Soils*, ISBN 0643024182, says categorically that the most effective method of increasing soil organic matter is by the utilization of grasses in a pasture phase, which is their technical term for the whole process I have described here.

But the CSIRO is a government research organization and not a government advisory service. Almost all Australian agricultural advisory services, in complete contrast, wrongfully and irresponsibly tell farmers to use more and more chemicals to produce the food and crops. Why can't they communicate? Where do these advisory services get their information from? Indeed governmental agricultural advisory services the world over give their farmers this same twisted, manipulated, chemically inspired advice.

One of the most informative and well-respected books on the subject of prolific grass growth is *Grass Productivity* by Andre Voisin. In this book Voisin describes the high grass production in the Elorn River Valley in Brittany. There, grass production commonly exceeds 50 tons per acre, per year (120 tonnes per hectare, per year). The feed available to soil life, as the grasses shed their roots after harvesting, is also just as massive. Voisin's book demonstrates that by utilizing the technique of selective mowing and grazing, we can produce grass and grass roots and thus enrich soil many times faster than ever occurs in the natural environment.

The systems used around the world to increase soil fertility and food production vary, but every one of them can ultimately be considered as some form of underground "town planning"; town planning designed to encourage and foster microbiological soil life, activity and production— not to kill it as chemical fertilizers do. Whether stated or not, in all such farming systems the world over, the common principle and objective is the maximization of topsoil health and depth.

Large-scale soil fertility enhancement

The ground is chisel plowed or cultivated with a subsoiler. In this way the soil is loosened to readily allow the entry of air and water. Turning the soil or inverting it is thus avoided. A variety of grass seeds most suitable for the specific location is then broadcast or sown into the loosened soil. With moisture present, or when it rains, the grasses will germinate and grow. Generally, high soil humidity, more so than direct water contact, is the key.

From practical experience, and quite contrary to strict organic farming procedures, the very first time grasses are sown, small quantities of chemical fertilizers, such as superphosphate, lime or gypsum can be used and be of benefit to kick-start growth. The use of chemical fertilizers must then cease, or at least kept to an absolute minimum. Their continuing use will prevent the development of colonies of soil-building bacteria and stop the breeding and growth of earthworms. Nitrogen-based fertilizers are always the chemicals to particularly avoid.

There is one class of fertilizers described as a mineral fertilizer. Mineral fertilizers are simply finely ground up natural rocks and are totally harmless to soil life.   Being no more than crushed rock, they are not soluble in water. Notably, the use of mineral fertilizers is approved for organic farming procedures.   The minerals they contain become available to plants only through the natural breakdown of the rock dust particles. The release of the minerals occurs through chemical reactions on the surface of the particles. Mineral fertilizers are therefore always finely ground to increase the surface-area-to-weight ratio.

Only in biologically active soils can this breakdown and delivery of minerals occur copiously. That is why small quantities of chemical fertilizers can be of use to kick-start the soil-building process. Mineral fertilizers could be likened to dust particles that have blown or been washed in from areas with very different geology and mineral content. They thereby increase the mineral diversity within the soil.

When some organic activity is present or becomes established in a soil then the addition of a mineral fertilizer can significantly enhance soil development and fertility improvements.   The very rich soil found below glaciers results, in part, from the slowly moving ice grinding the rock faces into fine powder higher up the valley, in effect producing mineral fertilizers.

Soil biological activity produces strong acids and these are the acids that attack the tiny rock fragments in the soil. As the minerals are released they attach themselves by chelation to the newly formed humic acid molecules within the soil.   Humus and humic acid molecules are created every time the grass growing process is repeated so the newly released minerals always have a home.

Because they are not water-soluble, mineral fertilizers can never produce the concentrated poisonous soup that chemical companies and orches-trated manipulated agricultural departments recommend as the medium in which we are supposed to grow the food we eat.

You don't hear a lot in the media about mineral fertilizers, but then they are not normally produced by chemical companies and there are no big profit margins to be made by just grinding up rocks. Sales of ground-up rock can't fund expensive public relations exercises. But rock dust does enrich our soils.

As soon as a grass crop is fully grown, it must be mown or harvested. If it is mown, surface aerobic bacteria will break down the material and form some surface humus. Or, much more preferably, a herd of grazing animals should be moved in to rapidly and totally eat it out, consuming both the grass and weeds. As stated this short period of intense overgrazing or overstocking is always preferred, after which the animals should be moved off. The grasses have lost their leaves. The plants can't breathe in their essential carbon dioxide. So they rapidly consume the energy in their fine fibrous root structures and grow chlorophyll-containing leaves. The fine roots they then shed. Any legumes in the grass mix can also shed the nitrogen-rich nodules growing on the roots.

There are then in effect two distinct crops. One is the grass leaves that feed the farm animals. The other is the huge crop of dead roots that can now feed soil-producing bacteria and fungi and in turn earthworms who now, with heaps of nourishment, multiply prodigiously.

If there is ample sunshine and the soil is moist, the grass will then go into a frenzy of regrowth. New leaves will be produced rapidly. More roots will be regrown and new nitrogen-producing nodules formed. Earthworms and microbiological soil life will manufacture humus from the cast-off root structures, and soil fertility levels will climb.

Immediately on completion of the grass regrowth, and to keep it all happening, the process should be repeated. Mow it, harvest it, or graze it to produce more fat cattle and stimulate the development of even richer soil. And then do it all over again. And again. It's controlled. It's fast, but it's not artificial. Sometimes the process can be accelerated by adding a few of the most suitable variety of earthworms to the area. Only a tiny number are needed to "seed" new pastures. In the right conditions earthworms are fast breeders. Above the ground the fattened livestock can be sold. The land rapidly becomes more fertile and more productive and consequently more valuable. The land is producing valuable crops in the soil-building process.

Of course, in the same process carbon dioxide is extracted from the air in tremendous quantities, combating global warming.

The mass of root matter beneath the surface is usually very similar in weight to the mass of foliage above the surface. When reasonable growing conditions exist plants tend to retain this balance. In consequence, when the surface foliage is eaten, or collected for forage, an equivalent mass of root matter is automatically shed. If the weather is kind and a little care is taken in the timing process, it is not at all difficult to harvest ten crops of grass per year, and produce ten crops of root mass per year.

Extra: the forked stick and the subsoil plow

The best implements to handle the soil aeration and loosening task are subsoiling plows or subsoilers. These implements are what we could describe as the modern form of the forked stick of ancient agricultural times. The subsoiler can loosen and aerate soil to a greater depth than the chisel plow or the forked stick. It has a narrow knife-like shank which allows it to operate at greater depths without fear of inverting the soil layers. The topsoil and subsoil can then stay where they normally exist. They are not forced to swap places. This is important as the bacteria that are happy at or near the surface, must after cultivation, end up again at or near the surface.

Soil-turning or soil-inverting implements should only be used where very shallow soil preparation is being undertaken; as in seed placement

The Ranson CIC single-tined subsoiler from late 1930s or early 1940s as described in Friend Sykes' marvelous book *Humus and the Farmer*.

during sowing and then only to depths of 2 to 3 inches (50 mm to 75 mm).

The first subsoiler I ever heard of was made in the United Kingdom, in about 1939 by an agricultural machinery manufacturer, Ransome, Sims & Jefferies. The implement was designed to penetrate to quite a considerable depth with little intermixing of individual soil levels. In an old picture of this machine the vertical tine (or shank, the terms are interchangeable in Australian farming) appeared sharp and would have knifed cleanly through the soil. The almost horizontal flat digging point at the base of this implement would have gently lifted the entire mass of soil and subsoil sitting above it. In the process the soil would gently fracture then settle back, with little noticeable disturbance. The very latest subsoiler machine designs in general look almost identical and have that same effect in the ground. The newest and latest machines can be set up with several tines, sometimes as many as thirty.

After subsoiling with this type of implement the most striking feature is the way the soil feels when walked on after cultivation. The earth has a strange spongy feel to it. Pour a bucket of water on the ground and it is immediately absorbed. Storm rains soaks straight in. In following dryer times, this moisture is then available to the probing root structures searching deep in the friable earth.

A subsoiler is not the same as the earth-moving ripper used in mining and road building. Rippers can drag up great compacted clods and leave the ground surface almost impassable to anything but a military tank. The heavy earth-moving ripper also leaves giant open gashes through the soil that are so wide they can prematurely dry out soil moisture. Earth-moving rippers will mix soil layers almost as severely as mouldboard plows. I've seen this happen. Several acres on our old family property Yobarnie, just west of Sydney in New South Wales, were ripped up with large crawler tractors pulling earth-moving rippers during the late 1940s, in an endeavour to aerate the subsoil. What little soil fertility existed in the shallow surface was immediately lost and buried in this ripping process. Almost nothing grew in the subsequent moonscape and it took almost two years before decent grass growth became re-established.

When those first subsoilers were developed farm implements were hauled by one or two horses, or at most by the small low-horsepower agricultural tractors available at the time. It takes a lot of power to pull a subsoiler tine through the earth at depth, so the original subsoilers only ever had one tine. We found on Yobarnie that the implements we were developing worked much better with several tines. Later it became apparent for grass and soil development that the tines are best run about twenty inches (half a metre) apart, although spacing is rarely particularly critical.

Almost by definition, subsoilers operate at depths below all previous cultivation depths and so can strike unyielding stumps and rocks never previously encountered. The good quality cast alloy steels used in modern Australian-made subsoilers were not available when the very early machines were made, and breakages would have been common. Spring-release mechanisms were tried on subsoilers but these prevented deep cultivation, which is the essence of subsoiling. The spring release, "stump jump" action could not hold the tine down in the ground at the desired depths.

Subsoilers were thus time consuming (because of the single tine limitation) and forever in need of repair. Probably for these reasons, subsoilers never became popular in general farming practices despite some outstanding and long-term successes in soil fertility development and erosion control. This has all changed. Modern tractors can pull subsoilers with many tines and the subsoilers themselves are now incredibly robust and exceptionally reliable.

Australia has been farmed for less than 200 years, and in many areas it has still never been farmed. Stumps and sometimes huge rocks are

A modern subsoiling plough, developing soil in rough basalt country, pulls out a basalt boulder.

often found just under the topsoil layer, so subsoiling implements have to be particularly rugged. From many years of my own experience in designing and manufacturing, as near as practical, an indestructible subsoiler, I know how strong they have to be.

The seeds of grasses and plants that never would have survived in old, dry, compacted soil, can be introduced into soil that has been loosened with a subsoiler; then they too will survive and thrive.

A mineral-rich local geology to provide mineral-rich subsoil, combined with regular, but not excessive local rainfall and a sunny climate, have always resulted in the production of the richest natural soils in the world. The grazing animals that inevitably occupy such lands assure the soil-building processes work. The grasslands of the world are the obvious examples of these ideal conditions and subsoilers accelerate natural soil formation.

The combination of grasses and grazing stock is the quickest, cheapest, and most efficient system to put an immediate brake on global warming. However, we also have to produce vegetables, grains and fruit. Well that too is easy. It becomes the natural follow up. With reasonable and regular rainfall, or sensible irrigation, soil improvement is often so rapid that within a year such crops can be commercially produced on previously inhospitable soils. Within just a few years of rapid soil enrichment using grasses, soil humus and soil organic matter can increase to the point where a number of years of single cropping can easily occur with minimal decrease in total soil organic matter. With the addition of animal and possibly human waste, or the addition of compost, fertility can stay high. Any subsequent rebuilding of soil fertility using a grass and grazing sequence can be postponed almost indefinitely, and with care, fertility levels will still climb.

In established orchards, combination cropping works extremely well for both vines and fruit trees. Grasses and legumes planted between rows do not "rob the trees" as fertilizer companies would have us believe. The life cycles of the grasses and legumes increase the fertility of the surrounding soil to the great benefit and increased productivity of the vines and trees.

Most of our food, our grains, fruit and vegetables are of course grown in our most productive soils. However, the natural productivity of these soils has, in general declined drastically over time, and is still declining. These formerly highly fertile and productive soils however are still rich in minerals due to their geological history, even if those minerals are currently unavailable for crop production. The re-establishment of the fertility levels in these highly mineralized soils with soil fertility enrichment practices is particularly rapid and dramatic.

Carbon dioxide can be sequestered back into soil organic matter again in massive quantities by rapid fertility restoration at rates far exceeding those resulting from the production of new soil from scratch. Either way it is all so easily achieved just by slight changes in cultivation techniques combined with crop rotation, and most essentially by the reduction or elimination of the use of harmful chemicals and soluble fertilizers.

Ancient civilizations were not destroyed by soil fertility loss

From the time early humans sowed the first seeds, organized the first harvest and ceased to be foragers and gatherers, they recognized and nurtured the fertility of their soils. They knew fertile soils produced healthy crops. Every successful agricultural society and civilization in recorded history has known and practiced techniques that maintained and increased the fertility and the organic matter content of their soils.

The first and only exception has been our current Western style agricultural system. The result has not only been disastrous from an agricultural aspect but has been a massive contributor to global warming. Healthy crops do not require pesticides, chemical additives, or poisonous fertilizers to survive and grow. Such chemicals are the enemies of healthy and nutritious crops and rich and fertile soils.

Contrary to what is taught, there is no evidence that any ancient civilization ended because of loss in the fertility of its soil. Ancient civilizations ended invariably because of politics, or wars, or more often because of changes in weather patterns. Ancient civilizations often lasted a thousand years or more. And as often noted in *The Albrecht Papers*, our current poor farming practices destroy about 40% of existing soil organic matter about every forty years. It is therefore obvious that those ancient civilizations must have nurtured their soils, for how else would they have survived for such extended periods?

Soil fertility is improved by the addition and incorporation into it of organic waste material. All successful civilizations in the past have used human and animal manure to increase the fertility of their soils, yet the use of human manure is now against the law in most Western societies.

If the objective is to sell chemical fertilizers then such laws are either serendipitous, or extremely clever and astute marketing.

To achieve their aim, all the marketing gurus had to do was dream up a "health threat", and combine it with a not too subtle scare campaign and, lo and behold, laws are enacted that mandate only manufactured agricultural chemicals be used in the production of food and agricultural products in Western societies.

The incorporation of animal manure is still generally acceptable as it is often uncontrollable except in lot-fed situations, whereas the use of collected human waste is easy to monitor and prevent by legislation. Despite the sophistication of our technology the spurious claim that its use will inevitably "spread disease" is always touted. Often the catchall of "heavy metal contamination" is used to justify not using human waste, yet metal ions and even salts are so easily chelated harmlessly onto humic acid molecules. The same humic acid molecules that result from the soil improvement nurtured by the use of the sewage. Currently, inland towns and cities put this material into the nearest river, or bury it. Either way it's a criminal waste that perpetuates and supports the sale of agrochemicals.

There are exceptions to the use of organic fertilizers that are just too difficult for the chemical companies to prevent or conspire against. For example, many coastal societies use fish and kelp to enrich their soil; also plant residue after harvest is often used to enhance soil fertility.

Farming with fire and the Australian agricultural scene

Australia is a big area with a relatively small population. It has an extremely efficient mechanized agricultural industry. Only about 3% of the population is involved in agricultural production. The agricultural community is therefore a small voting block. Before the mechanization of agriculture, as much as 90% of the population of countries would be engaged in agricultural pursuits. In the past, small subsistence farming was more the norm and when these farming people finally got the vote, it became an enormous voting block. As a result, in most developed countries, small uneconomical farms often persist along with their voting powers and their demands for subsidies. This type of large agricultural political power block does not exist in Australia.

Australia is one of the only developed nations whose agriculture has not been structured to almost totally rely on government subsidies and government handouts. Even in times of extreme drought, or following horrendous floods, financial assistance to the Australian farmer has been relatively minuscule. Because of this generally unsubsidized agriculture, Australia is one of the few Western countries where the power of the chemical agricultural companies has had only limited success in establishing effective and manipulative control over governments and their agricultural departments. The freedom to experiment with innovative agriculture and not be penalized by the agricultural regulatory authorities still exists. However, as one now has to be aware, much of that freedom to think and to do what seems best is being whittled away. New regulations restricting land clearing and regulations preventing water collection and use are typical. See "The great Australian river scam" in Strategy 2 (page 274).

As is the case everywhere, both the media and academia incessantly rant and rave about the farming community's destruction of the nation's land and soils. We see it all the time, endless video clips of erosion gullies and salt pans. However the messages are often utterly untrue and the footage dubbed in to suit. It is then touted that land management should come under the stewardship of distant and often ignorant bureaucracies. The reality is that the destruction of soils in the Western world almost invariably results from the insidious establishment of long-term unhealthy alliances between agrochemical companies and government agencies, and trusting farmers taking their manipulative advice.

Like farmers in Europe, in America, in Africa or anywhere else in the world, farmers in Australia care for the land they own. They like to improve their soils. But with constant ever-increasing government interference, with pseudo-environmental regulations that blatantly favour agricultural chemical companies, it's getting progressively more difficult to accomplish these so very worthwhile objectives.

In complete contrast to the sensationalized scare campaigns of ignorant bureaucrats and journalists, soils managed by Australian farmers are probably more fertile, more productive and more charged with organic matter than they have been for millennia. What is endlessly portrayed as some lost but once glorious Original Australian Wilderness is in reality the sorry result of 50,000 years of man's endless and destructive management by fire. Over that time the soil fertility in outback Australia has been slowly reduced to near zero. The drying and desertification of central and north-western Australia was the result of weather pattern changes in those vast region resulting, it is now being suggested, by widespread burning practices that continued for millennia.

Clearing and cleaning the land and redeveloping the soils should now be an Australian national priority. Allowing and encouraging the rebuilding of these ancient soils would be to the betterment of all mankind.

The destruction of soil fertility by the never-ending lighting of forest fires and brush fires didn't happen in North America, although management by fire was widespread. In North America prehistoric man, with his fire, hadn't been there long enough to change weather patterns throughout the country. Very long-term North American rainfall patterns, up until just recently, have been much more consistent than those in Australia. Regular rain encouraged the natural creation of fertile soil. Also, until 20,000 years ago, the Laurentian Ice Sheet covered all of Canada and North America down to south of the Great Lakes. Until the final end of the ice age some 10,000 years ago, remnants of the ice sheets persisted. Such weather conditions were not conducive to incessant and widespread burning. Quite the contrary, in those cold times it was probably hard enough to find enough fuel to keep a cooking fire going. In Australia however there was no such natural brake on the practice of constant burning, and the burning was consistent for possibly an extra 40,000 years.

Soil development and the grasslands of the world

Most of the world's grasslands are distributed in a belt within the temperate and subtropical regions of the planet. Sunlight is plentiful and rainfall is commonly between 15 and 30 inches (400 mm to 750 mm) per year, the perfect range for soil development. These proportions and ratios are explained in considerable detail in *The Albrecht Papers*. The mineral content of the subsoil (being the local decomposed geological material), varies across these vast grasslands, but invariably it is adequate. Although as mentioned earlier, even sand given time can become a worthwhile soil if all the other factors are idealized.

Air, of course, is available in unlimited quantities and its utilization is only restricted by the limitation on its access to deeper soil layers. Subsoil is in no way loose and friable. Generally, it is hard and compact, but not as hard as the rock structures from which it derives. The intercellular spaces, the space between the tiny individual grains of decomposed rock material in subsoil, are minute and contain little air. The bad smell of earth two feet (half a metre) underground is caused by this lack of air. Soil-building bacteria cannot live in this airless environment. But when air is allowed in, bacteria and soil life thrive. They change the nature of the subsoil and slowly turn it into topsoil, no matter the depth. Rich, healthy and living soil is what creates the sweet smell of the freshly tilled earth.

The ideal environment to encourage soil and subsoil life contains millions of tiny air cavities. Virtually all microbiological life that increases soil fertility breathe air, which is why they are called aerobic. Anaerobic, or non-air-breathing bacteria, can still break down waste material but the end product is not humus, and so it's not good soil. Anaerobic decomposition of waste material produces methane. Anaerobic decomposition of saccharides (simple sugars) and other various sugar-like compounds will produce alcohol or vinegar, but it won't produce good soil. Wine producers know that it is essential to keep air out of their process.

There are really only three significant means by which air can be made to circulate in classic subsoil material and so help it change it into classic topsoil material. Firstly, tunnels can be dug by whatever is living in the vicinity—worms, ants, spiders, rabbits. They all contribute to loosening this subsoil and allowing air to enter. All their activities contribute to increasing the total soil intercellular spaces. Worms, if they can be encouraged to breed and have enough decomposing litter and roots to feed on, are far and away the most effective and the most beneficial. For their own comfort, worms often like to bury down into the cooler moist subsoil during the heat of the day, even if there is little food at those depths. Their tunnels still get made.

Secondly, air can be encouraged to circulate in subsoil by mechanically loosening the naturally compact soil structure. Subsoiler plows do this the best. However, it can be done with earth-moving rippers, but these implements are generally too vicious on the overlaying topsoil. Chisel plows are OK but require several passes, usually spread over two or three years. Like an earth-moving ripper, a single deep cultivation with a chisel plow is often too damaging to shallow topsoil.

The other natural process by which subsoil can be loosened and made more friable results from the life cycle of trees. Tree roots have two functions. One is to collect and convey water and nutrients to the foliage above ground. The other, and equally important function is to hold the tree in place, and stop it falling over. Naturally any tree species with a root system that does not hold the tree firmly in place would surely have long since vanished from its position on the bigger evolutionary tree.

As tree roots grow they expand. Enormous pressures, created by osmosis within the tree root, burst the soil. Over time, cracks and cavities are formed in which air and water can accumulate. Millions of little homes are created and soil bacteria and fungi and worms all move in.

Old compacted soils are also loosened and aerated when a tree dies and falls. The upturning tree roots loosen the soil, letting in air and moisture. Around the roots of dead trees, the accelerated soil activity ensures prolific grass growth wherever sunlight can penetrate the canopy. But a tree can take fifty years to grow and to die and to fall over and so "cultivate" and aerate the soil and subsoil in its vicinity.

How often do you see tall lush grass growth in and around the disturbed ground left by a dead fallen tree? How often do you see in a paddock, a line of lush grass following an old excavation trench dug for a water main or power line? Probably often, and probably just seen as a curiosity. The lush grass grows on the edge of the trench where the subsoil has been loosened. It doesn't grow in the centre of the excavated area for that's where the topsoil material has been excessively disturbed, mixed and buried. In the centre the topsoil has been turned and nothing grows.

Of course, trees in general do not go to all this trouble so that the fine root structures of some other plant can take over. So most trees secrete toxins into the soil or onto the soil to keep away intruders. Grasses may be prolific producers of soil, but as far as a tree is concerned they are a serious competitor for soil nutrients. It is no accident that grasses don't grow too well under most trees. It's not just the shade; the living tree often poisons them.

The lack of grass growth in the centre of an old trench line reinforces the lesson that we must stop the current traditional practice of turning the soil when we cultivate, no matter how incongruous that may sound to many of us. The grass growth is always best just at the side of the old trench where the soil has been loosened but not drastically disturbed.

The chisel plows and especially the deeper-reaching subsoiler plows do the job best. Their wise and judicious use, combined with elimination or at least drastic minimizing of chemical use, can generate the extremely rapid soil improvement we need to instantly put a halt on, and eventually correct, our planetary overheating.

The changes necessary to turn agricultural systems that insidiously lower soil organic matter, into agriculture systems that increase soil organic matter are relatively minor, but the results are quite astounding. We therefore need to turn what is now conventional agriculture and utterly unsustainable, into what was once, a few hundred years ago, a different conventional agriculture, and totally sustainable.

In the change to this "new-old" agriculture, we throw away the mould-board plow and the disk cultivator, for they turn the soil. We stop using chemical fertilizers for they kill and destroy soil biological activity. And we stop constantly planting the same crop on the same land year in and year out.

We do however keep the tractors and the pickers. We keep the surface cultivators and the harvesters, and all the equipment that was developed to make farming so much less labour intensive. For what we are now doing is not all wrong, for we do produce our crops and we do produce our food and the system is very efficient. The problem, unfortunately is that current conventional agriculture is both destroying our soil and thus increasing global warming.

As we do this with our agriculture we must re-evaluate the other issues pivotal to the correction of global warming. Those issues are mainly where we get our energy from to run our societies. We have to fix that too. Then the resulting beneficial effects on the earth's ecology, on the earth's atmosphere and on the stabilization of all the world's climates, will be dramatic.

Some pleasant spin-offs

By us demanding and creating this new era for agriculture we will receive some surprising and substantial benefits.

The end of soil erosion

Rich healthy soil, wisely cultivated, just does not erode. Soil erosion will cease to be a problem as we structure the end of global warming. With our new more absorbent soils with enhanced soil structure, retaining and filtering the erstwhile runoff rains, springs will reappear. Our streams, our creeks, and our rivers will once again flow clear, clean and steady. Another advantage we will all receive is the renewed delicious taste of fruits and vegetables grown from the new, rich, well-composted soil. The lovely taste that we instinctively know is our tongues telling us, "this food is good for you".

There will be a huge reduction in the volume of irrigation water required to grow our crops in our irrigation areas.   This is inevitable as highly fertile soil retains moisture many times more effectively than soils with little humus.

And here is another wonderful spin-off:

The end of soil salinity

The buildup of salt in both irrigated and non-irrigated lands around the world is another problem that increasing soil fertility levels solve. The salt causing these problems is common salt, sodium chloride, the stuff we put on our food. The stuff that makes seawater and blood taste salty.

The salt that destroys agricultural land comes from three possible sources. Firstly it comes from the irrigation water being used. Secondly it comes from rising salt-rich water tables and thirdly it can come from the very soil itself.

Most soils throughout the world would have initially contained some quantity of sodium chloride or common salt. The majority of the salt was flushed out by rainwater and ended up in the ocean as a natural part of seawater. Over eons and as the world's soils became established, the soil salt levels declined to a very livable minimum. As the soil fertility increased, the remaining salt not flushed or leached out by rain was chelated into the nooks and crannies of the humic acid molecules forming in the newly created soil. The soil in effect became totally "salt free" and of course rich and fertile.

In good fertile soil, the sodium and the chlorine ions that make up salt are attached by chelation onto the surface of humic acid molecules and clay particles, and become harmless. Many of the very good soils of the world actually contain large quantities of salt safely chelated in this way. Luxuriant plant growth happily thrives in these theoretically saline soils.

Unfortunately modern agricultural practices are reversing the processes that create what to plants are salt-free soils, and the salt soon becomes very visible. It shows up as a dirty white crust covering the bare dead ground. Soil salination soon becomes a "national disaster".

The inevitable stereotypical answer from all environmental academics is to take the land out of production, to abandon it, and to grow useless trees to recreate a vision of some invented "wilderness". A wilderness, incidentally, that is unlikely to ever have existed. The whole concept is extravagant and wasteful. It's wrong.

There is publicity galore for the concept of planting "native" trees as a dewatering and supposedly desalting system. It is impractical and particularly inefficient. The reality is that trees are not going to send their roots to absorb salt-saturated moisture any more than will any other plant.

Transpiration is the process of plants sucking up water from the ground and evaporating it out through the leaves. At this, scrubland trees and bushland trees are not particularly efficient. That trees are the best is a land-wasting fiction. If you check the numbers with your local agricultural department you find that a crop of legumes or even most good grasses is far more effective at transpiration.

The planting of native trees as a means of reversing soil salination amounts to effectively abandoning, for at least decades, what could be and should be valuable and productive agricultural land. It becomes a means only of ensuring intensive agriculture becomes a civilization necessity. Is it just a surprising coincidence that this also so conveniently suits the marketing concepts of the agrochemical industries?

We are destroying the fertility of our soils by the practices of monocropping, inversion tillage and the application of frighteningly excessive quantities of agricultural chemicals. We are needing and using excessive quantities of water to grow our crops. The result in so many places is a ghastly white blush of salt spreading over the land.

Yet in total contrast to all the "doomsday" scenarios, I have seen farmland coated with this dirty white salt blush returned to valuable, fertile and useful soil in just six months. For all intents and purposes, in six months the land has become salt free.

This apparent agricultural miracle is achieved by simply deep subsoil plowing, the spreading of a few mixed varieties of pasture grasses, plus in rare cases a once-only minimal use of a few carefully selected agricultural fertilizers to kick-start plant growth. The formation of humus soon commences. The new humus absorbs the salt by chelation, rendering it totally harmless. The soil is renewed and reborn.

The first cause of salinity results from actually adding more salt into the working topsoil by excessive irrigation. Irrigation water can often contain dissolved salts resulting from the nature of its storage and the canals through which the water is transported. When sodium chloride is in high concentrations, salinity is increased.

The second cause of salination results from unwise cultivation practices that encourage the formation of hardpans under the shallow topsoil. If hardpans form on agricultural land and the land is then irrigated, a proportion of the water will slowly soak through the dense hardpan. Plant roots cannot penetrate these hardpans. As a result there are no deep root structures to collect the water and siphon it up to thirsty leaves. And so the water continues seeping down. The second salination process has commenced.

In the generally flatter irrigation lands of the world there is often an underlying water table. This groundwater can be close to the surface, sometimes as near as 2 or 3 feet (1 metre). It can contain quite high concentrations of salt. In some areas when you dig down to the water and taste it, it can taste as salty as seawater.

A massive quantity of irrigation water, which we can consider as an enormous and sudden increase in rainfall for the region, leaches through the hardpan and adds volume to the salty groundwater. The water table rises, insidiously bringing the salt up to the plant root zones. All vegetation dies. The crops die first. The land becomes useless, and will stay useless for as long as the water table stays elevated and the soil stays depleted. When the farming systems are wrong the water tables rise. In continuous very high rainfall areas the salt is effectively rinsed away in rivers or flushed into deep aquifers.

A soil with high organic matter content can store within itself large quantities of water. The soil is described as having a high field capacity. This stored water can sustain healthy plants for surprisingly long periods. When the weight of organic matter content in a soil increases by some specific quantity, the field capacity increases five to ten times that quantity. However in the depleted soils produced by poor agricultural practices, field capacity is massively reduced. Life-giving water becomes a very transient commodity needed close to the surface in the thin soil layer above the hardpan.

A yearly rainfall of 20 to 30 inches (500 mm to 750 mm), if strategically timed, is more than ample to produce all human food requirements in abundance. This level of rainfall is typical of the major grain belt areas of the world. Less rainfall is sufficient for most grain crops provided the rainfall patterns remain reliable. Unfortunately with global warming, that too is becoming a fragile reliability.

As hardpans become established in our irrigation lands, and organic matter levels drop significantly, the irrigation water requirements increase enormously. After only a few days of hot dry weather following rain or irrigation, the shallow topsoil moisture is lost. A large quantity will simply evaporate. Some will be used by the plant in its growing process. The rest soaks through the hardpan into the subsoil. In hot dry weather a crop can show water stress within just a few days of irrigation, and so require more irrigation.

The loss of soil organic matter coupled with the creation of hardpans have increased the irrigation water requirements for food production enormously. A fivefold increase in water requirements over a few decades is not unusual. A fivefold increase in reality means that on some irrigated farm-lands around the world the equivalent of 12 feet (3.6 metres) of "rainfall" is regularly needed to grow a single crop.

Thirdly salt comes from the very soil itself. In this form of land salination we are not actually adding any salt to the soil at all. There is no overall increase in the total soil salt content. The salt has always been there. What our current destructive agricultural practices are doing is breaking down humic acid molecules and releasing the chelated salt. We are uncorking the genie.

The giant contribution to soil salination problems from the destruction of soil fertility levels receives absolutely no publicity. There is rarely any word of criticism related to soil fertility decline. And if there is, there is never any suggestion that fertility should be rebuilt.

To the hundreds of thousands of acres of salt-poisoned agricultural and irrigation land throughout the world the same basic soil salination causes apply. It is obvious that if agricultural practices don't change, continued salt degradation of even more land is inevitable.

It seems that the understanding of the salination process, and the sensible and logical ways it can be stopped and reversed, has been made unnecessarily confusing, one might suspect deliberately. The realities have most definitely been muddied. Or if not muddied, they have been totally or willfully misunderstood by those who should know better.

Creating increased levels of soil fertility stops and reverses all three processes of soil salination. That means most of the world's manufactured salinity problems will vanish.

Salt problems the world over are the same, and the solution too is always the same. Produce rich soil.

Organic food is ultimately cheaper to grow

Fortunately, where the constant increase in soil organic matter is part of the farm management program, the cost of food produced invariably ends up lower than chemical-based farming. Also, and quite contrary to the statements of the chemical agricultural public relations machine, quantities produced are often higher. The smaller total volume produced is the main factor currently keeping sale prices a little higher. Even now, if food nutrition is considered in the cost equation, organic food costs are lower. But no matter what any apparent additional costs might be for organic food and organically grown products, it is way cheaper than global warming.

The vast majority of farmers I talk to who have commercial-scale operations using organic farming techniques are invariably profitable. They tell me they are often surrounded by other farmers using recommended chemical-based agricultural techniques, who constantly experience management problems, plant health problems and livestock diseases that don't seem to occur with high-soil-fertility-based agriculture. With chemical-based agriculture, the nightmare of constantly buying some new chemical to correct an unfortunate unforeseen result from some previous chemical, keeps many farms hovering on the verge of bankruptcy.

Organic farming currently appears to be slightly more labour intensive, but conversely, has massively reduced input costs. In addition growers usually receive a premium on sales of their organically grown produce, and that helps. Their main problem however, is the small demand. That is obviously where we consumers come in. We can fix that problem and we can make soil-fertility-enhancement agriculture work, both financially as well as environmentally. If food is imported, read the label and buy only organic. By doing this we make farmers in other countries suck carbon dioxide out of the air to make their own humus-rich soil. We make reversing global warming happen internationally.

The requirement for a much broader standardized and designated term to cover any global warming abatement product, process or procedures is discussed later in this chapter. However, at this time of writing, "organic" is the only legally defined term to indicate a soil-enhancing system of agriculture, and it must therefore define what we demand and select at the supermarket. If it doesn't have organic or some similar legal marking on the label to tell you that the growing of that food is fighting the greenhouse effect, then ask for one that does. Demand it. If it is imported and not so labelled, don't buy it at all. It's good to know we consumers can force other countries to change their agricultural practices to help terminate the scourge of global warming. So let's start doing that today! Let's demand organic food, especially if it's imported. We are simply demanding more nutritious food for ourselves and for our families, and voting with the power of the hip pocket for an end to global warming.

Organic farming wins hands down—some documented facts

Organic farming is not ridiculously expensive and hopelessly impracticable as we are constantly being told. We are being treated like mushrooms, "kept in the dark and fed ...". The reality is that changing world agriculture to be more in line with organic farming procedures makes extremely good sense.

A report highlighting the myths and realities of organic sustainable agriculture appeared in *Acres Australia*, a periodical devoted to sustainable agriculture. The report was originally written by Mike Brusko of the U.S.-based Rodale Institute, and its purpose was to demonstrate to "conventional" farmers that many of their beliefs and convictions about the viability of sustainable agriculture are incorrect and to confirm that sustainable agriculture can indeed be profitable. At the same time, the report dramatically demonstrated the insidious success of the agrochemical industries' public relations and marketing strategies.

Brusko reported that Kevin Carroll, of the College of Agriculture at the University of Wisconsin and Margaret Krome, of the Wisconsin Rural Development Center, in 1989 commenced a study to separate fact from fiction. The study's objective was to increase farmers' general understanding of sustainable agriculture. Carroll stated, "My purpose was to look at what kinds of problems farmers face when they actually cut back on chemicals". As part of this study, a sample of 389 conventional farmers were interviewed to determine their perceived obstacles to reducing chemical inputs into their farming program.

Another sample of 177 farmers were also interviewed; farmers who had already reduced, were reducing, or had totally eliminated chemical inputs from their farming program.

The following block summary was included in the article. Significantly but sadly it should be noted here that just about every preconceived conviction held by the conventional farmers in the study was in line with the agrochemical companies' structured images of the supposed uselessness and failure of organic farming concepts.

I have added one additional comment, or interpretation, with relevance to global warming considerations, on what a farmer might expect when switching completely to classic organic farming. Also I would like to note that to my own knowledge, few if any of the low-chemical-input farmers interviewed were availing themselves of the techniques for cheap and rapid soil enrichment previously discussed and used already on many farms here in Australia.

An interesting question was also put to the low-input farming group. They were asked what, if anything, would make them actually increase their use of agricultural chemicals and move away from organic farming. The majority, an outstanding 75%, said, "Nothing. I intend to continue farming the way I do now". If we insist on the unshackling of organic farming and all other forms of soil-fertility-enhancement farming and stop the subsidization of chemically based agriculture, then in our war against global warming, we will win our first battle.

Note the well-accepted myths that conventional farmers believe versus the documented realities obtained from low-chemical-input farmers. In brackets I have added the conclusions/interpretations.

Yields

70.9% think yields will fall if they cut chemicals.

35.3% say yields fell.

17.6% say yields rose.

47.1% say yields stayed the same.

(Yielded gross weight per acre will fall but only slightly and not significantly)

Equipment needs

35.4% say potential for increased equipment needs would keep them from trying low-input methods.

37.6% say equipment increased.

(Changing the type of equipment will usually add costs as using conventional cultivating equipment won't generally allow for very fast soil fertility increases.)

Labour needs

28.3% expect low-input farming to increase their labor needs.

63.6% say labor needs increased.

(Agrochemical are sold on the basis that a quick application of some new chemicals will solve any problem. Their non-use is more time consuming but their high purchase costs vanish.

Pests

38% say potential rise in pest problems is one of the top three reasons they don't cut chemicals.

43.4% say pests were a problem at first.

33.3% say they remained a problem after a few years of farming with fewer chemicals.

(Pest control can be a problem but only in some cases. Organic farming standards dictate zero pest control use any time, but soil fertility increases are not necessarily reduced by minor use of pesticides.)

Information on alternatives

18.2% say lack of good information would keep them from trying low-input methods.

70.8% say finding good advice was a problem at the start of the transition.

(This simply confirms that agricultural advisory services will not readily advise nor assist farmers wishing to convert to organic farming, nor will they advise on methods to increase the fertility of soils. Whereas advice on chemical use always seems to be forthcoming.)

Profits—the bottom line

63.8% say fear of loss of profits is one of the top three barriers to low-input farming.

33% say lower yields cut profits.

76% say lower costs increased profits.

(The objective must be to increase the costs of chemical farming and simultaneously and significantly assist farmers to switch to soil fertility enrichment farming practices such as organic farming.)

Land clearing essential to combating global warming

The reason land is cleared of scrubs and trees is to create agricultural land. The more agricultural land available to grow our food, the less intensive the agricultural system has to be to produce that food. The agrochemical companies always support and encourage moves that restrict the area of land available for food production. For they believe encouraging intensive agriculture is the way to sell their chemicals.

Turn desolate wasteland into a well laid out farm and then decide which is the more beautiful. Yet creating a farm out of nothing is being sold as irresponsible and environmentally incorrect. The environmental organizations that mouth these agrochemical-inspired platitudes need to rethink their reasoning while it is still possible to restore global temperatures.

Greenhouse warming is a constantly expanding disaster against which all other threats to our planetary environment pale, and preserving millions of acres of useless scrublands is a wasteful extravagance that the total world environment and world weather systems cannot afford. Creating huge quantities of useful fertile soil, not fencing off useless scrubland, will prevent global warming.

Whenever it is reported that farmers are clearing woodlands, scrublands, the bush or donga country, or whatever its local description, there is invariably loud and vociferous protests from any number of well-funded, supposedly green, or proclaimed green organizations. These people are funded and orchestrated to lie down in front of bulldozers, chain themselves to trees and get themselves and their manufactured causes well featured on prime time television.

Try talking to these people. It is amazing but so many of them never seem motivated by any logical, intelligent or scientific principles. They simply mouth platitudes. "Protecting biodiversity" is a pet one. Of course "protecting biodiversity" is so vague and indeterminate a concept that it can be used in almost any situation, any time, anywhere.

The politics and money in the "biodiversity industry" and its pointless nature is discussed in "Strategy 24: The delaying tactics of biodiversity studies" and "Strategy 50: Invent a biodiversity crisis".

The only result that will satisfy these environmentally irresponsible environmentalists is a never-ending decrease in the area of world farmlands. That's what they demand. And with that goes the resultant intensification of agriculture. It's gobbledygook.

The total elimination of all soil in the production of food would be a wonderful end game for the agrochemical industries, while they carelessly and cynically accept the inevitability of an overheated, unstable world.

Some self-styled green movements claim that it is their imperative and their exclusive responsibility to "protect trees", all trees, any trees. It is as if trees have some godlike virtue not shared by grasses or grains, vegetables or roses. I'm sure the often used quote "only God can make a tree" was not originally written to imply that God is unable to make any other plants, or alternatively not particularly interested in them. These tree worshippers preach that trees prevent erosion. All plants do. But trees to a much more limited extent. The grasses are much more effective. Tree lovers claim that only trees can stop salt-laden water tables from rising and ruining valuable agricultural land. The trees, they claim, do this by sucking up large quantities of water and releasing it into the air by transpiration from their leaves. But again all plants do. Many are far more efficient and more effective than any of the existing trees, or "native" trees. See previous section, "The end of soil salinity".

Lastly, these protectors of some indeterminate "Natural Wilderness" say wooded scrublands are a natural carbon sink and must be preserved at all cost. This argument in particular is utter nonsense. Woodlands, like jungles, are carbon-dioxide neutral. As a carbon sink, left as they are they must be considered as already full, or maybe as a blocked sink. That's how they have been for millennia. There is absolutely no way they can absorb any more atmospheric carbon than the meager amount they already hold.

Woodlands obviously contain wood, and logically this wood should be harvested in any land clearing process and then used in any way possible. If used structurally it will almost certainly be replacing some oil-derived or oil-consuming product. If not used structurally it should be burnt as a fuel, where it will be replacing the burning of fossil fuels.

Burning wood, or burning any biomass, cannot increase the total quantity of carbon in the biosphere. That can only come from mining buried carbon-based materials, such as coal, gas, oil or peat and then burning it. With the land cleared, the soil can be developed and enriched. The new soil will become a carbon sink many times larger than the previously existing scrub, brush or bushlands, and it will be productive.

The following information, again from the study reported in the Australian CSIRO publication *Organic Matter and Soils*, is a useful illustration of the concept: Over eighty years ago in the southeast of the Australian state of South Australia, very poor quality scrubland was cleared to establish a state agricultural research centre. A test plot was set up on which sheep were grazed and a control plot was retained. As is typical of many Australian soils the land was phosphate deficient. The test plot was fertilized annually with superphosphate at quite low rates (approximately 100 pounds per acre— about a bucketful; common high rates of superphosphate application can be 1 ton per acre or 2.5 tonnes per hectare every year). As we now can appreciate, the low application rate ensured the growth, not the poisoning, of soil biological activity. Over the period the land was used to graze sheep. In no way were any specific techniques to boost organic matter included in the trial. The land was never subsoiled nor cultivated. No soil-developing grasses were introduced. The grasses there were never mown. No selective grazing was undertaken.

Over a period of almost forty years, from 1919 through to 1958, soil analysis on the test plot showed that the organic matter content progressively increased from the originally very low 1.2% to a very respectable 5%, a rise of 3.8%. That is a 300% increase in stable soil organic matter by doing very little.

The biomass in the new thriving grass and grass-related biological activity would easily exceed the living biomass in the original sparse scrublands prior to clearing.

Throughout that long period the organic matter content of control areas remained almost completely unchanged.

In effect, by applying the small amount of 2 tons of superphosphate per acre distributed over that forty-year period, almost 40 tons of organic matter per acre was created. In so doing, 82 tons of carbon dioxide was extracted from the atmosphere. Or 5 tonnes of superphosphate per hectare over forty years removed 205 tonnes of carbon dioxide from the atmosphere. The soil not only became a huge carbon sink but also grew a lot of fine, healthy, wool-producing sheep for the whole forty-year test period.

That South Australian scrubland was originally useless and completely unproductive. It was an ineffectual carbon dioxide repository in that it held only a small amount and was not absorbing any more. Intelligent intervention turned it into reasonably productive land and also a great absorber of CO_2.

There are many supposedly "green" advocates that argue and lobby to turn such enriched farmlands back into their original poor condition and so reverse the process of soil fertility creation. The claim is to restore the land to some supposedly hypothetical better "natural state". They don't consider that the end result they seek in this pursuit necessitates far more intensive farming some place else, and the release of large quantities of carbon dioxide into the atmosphere from the two sites.

This type of narrow single-issue focus has to be recognized as an outmoded and possibly an irresponsible approach to caring for our planet. If global warming is not halted soon, all the myriads of minor environmental issues will become utterly irrelevant. They will simply cease to exist by default. There will be scant left to save.

But we can correct global warming. Those results in South Australia are well over twice the necessary rise in soil organic matter needed in our soils to totally halt further greenhouse warming and commence the road back to climatic stability. Those researchers in South Australia were entrapping enough carbon dioxide into the soil at a rate sufficient to save the world, and they weren't even trying.

If the cleared vegetation had been utilized for home heating or fence building, or any other method of fossil carbon replacement, the figure could easily have become an incredible three times that needed to prevent global warming.

This was actually an accidental serendipitous example of how easily soil fertility can be created.

Financial assistance to "outback" Australian farmers, and where it's applicable, to farmers in other countries around the world, should be given to undertake similar clearing and subsequent soil-development concepts. It would probably be one of the best values for money of any so-called Greenhouse Initiative that politicians like to talk about. With strategic cultivation to enhance subsoil aeration and rainwater retention, the reported development time on that South Australian plot could easily have been cut tenfold.

There are vast areas all across the world where in the same way poor scrubland could be cleared, the soil improved and the land made considerably more useful and productive.

To forestall such logical and responsible action, it is good business, in fact essential business, for the fossil fuel and agrochemical companies to create endless fictions of "biodiversity in crisis".

Soils form from an amazing variety of subsoils and associated geological formations. Some soils may benefit by an initial application of some calcium. Some soils will benefit from the addition of minor trace elements, such as molybdenum. There are very few grassland soils however, that won't respond very favourably and often remarkably to a combination of subsoil cultivation, the addition of a few new grass varieties and controlled cyclic grazing. All highly cultivated soils respond dramatically to a combination of subsoiling, the cessation of monocropping practices and the elimination of life-destroying chemical fertilizers. They all improve as they concurrently absorb carbon dioxide from the air and increase humic acid content.

Tax changes and the use of existing agricultural subsidies to halt global warming

Many countries lavishly subsidize their agriculture. The amount of tax dollars spent on subsidizing agriculture in the United States and in the European Union is awesome. In many countries subsidy systems have operated for decades. As a result the entire agricultural structure of nations has been massively modified. The whole concept of subsidized agriculture has in many cases become totally ingrained in rural thinking and rural life. In consequence, entire national economies are modified. For these reasons the sudden and immediate elimination of agricultural subsidies is almost certainly political suicide. In addition because the structures have been in place for so long their sudden removal could be both morally and ethically unjust.

As taxpayers and as consumers the world over, we are the ones funding "the Beast" of agricultural subsidization. And undoubtedly we will be for a long time to come.

So why don't we make our governments use the subsidy systems, where ever and how ever it exists, to halt global warming? There will be opposition, but that is what we must do. Wherever subsidies exist then a payment system exists. The money structures are already in place, so let's use them.

We can change the whole agricultural subsidy structure with minor and painless changes and create the most effective and most efficient agricultural system possible to generate enormous quantities of rich fertile soil. And fertile soil is the perfect carbon sink to put an immediate brake on runaway global warming.

On the concept of wasteland clearing, we have seen in the Australian CSIRO report on the clearing of scrubland in South Australia that clearing land and developing soil will both increase national wealth and decrease atmospheric carbon dioxide levels. Taxation benefits or other incentives should apply to such clearing and soil enrichment programs. To qualify, total organic matter levels could easily be determined before clearing, and again determined after the soil has started its improvement process. State or federal taxation could be structured to ensure the overall process increases the total mass of organic matter. For example, provided soil fertility and total carbon sequestration showed significant increases, then the cost of clearing and soil development could become a double tax deduction.

As illogical as it is, in many countries today, tax revenue is squandered in actually preventing land clearing and subsequent soil development. Invariably in these cases the result seems always to limit farming areas and in consequence encourage chemically stimulated food production.

In this day and age, it is madness to subsidize any agricultural system that doesn't assist the stabilization of world weather. In the final analysis, most agricultural subsidy systems today effectively destroy soil and in doing so release millions of tons of carbon dioxide and nitrous oxides into the air. Why should we tolerate such nonsense? Now is the time to stop this madness. It is our money they are spending and it is our votes they are chasing. What we humans, and what all other mammals and what all the birds and most of the reptiles on this planet need, is fertile soil. Fertile soil created quickly and in large quantities, that's what we want.

Today when a farmer buys agricultural chemicals and uses them in producing his crop, the purchase of the chemicals are claimed as a tax deduction. The reality is that taxpayers are not supporting farmers by reducing their costs in allowing them to buy cheaper chemicals. The farmer is competing with the farmer next door and he also gets his chemicals cheap. The reality is we are supporting the sale of chemicals. We are subsidizing expanded use of fertility-destroying agricultural chemicals.

This means, in the final analysis, our governments are using the taxation system to support increases in greenhouse gases. And that is just plain ridiculous.

What we must do is demand a few simple changes in our tax laws. The first must be that farmers cannot claim a tax deduction for the purchase of pesticides, herbicides, insecticides, and chemical fertilizers. The reality is that such a tax change can only penalize those farmers and rural producers who wish to continue using excessive quantities of agricultural chemicals. And that's exactly what we want, for it would then only be those few farmers who continue to use such chemicals to almost willfully destroy the fertility of our soils. Fortunately there won't be many like that. In general farmers are very practical people and, if unhindered by incompetent regulators, are totally capable of adjusting rapidly to different requirements.

Buying pesticides, herbicides, insecticides, and chemical fertilizers must cease to be tax-deductible expenses.

Changing the fundamental basics of subsidy calculations

The necessary changes we need to make to existing agricultural subsidy systems are actually small. Many may even seem insignificant, but they will have far-reaching effects in assisting us in the curtailment of global warming and it won't cost us or farmers anything.

One change urgently needed relates only to the arithmetical calculations used to determine food subsidy payments. This change will have enormous effects on reducing global warming. This is it.

As we have seen in every country, current agricultural subsidies and production levels are regulated by the size of the area farmed. When prices received for a crop are inflated by subsidies, it is inevitable for farmers to produce as much produce as possible. The area farmed is used to control excessive production. This effectively mandates chemical-stimulated agriculture to produce maximum crop weight off the restricted area. The soil on that limited area deteriorates until it inevitably becomes simply a substance to hold the plant upright. A plant that is then force-fed chemicals and only kept alive with the equivalent of drugs and stimulants in the form of pesticides, herbicides and fungicides. This whole concept is fundamentally wrong and must be abandoned.

So how, with minimum social disruption, is it possible to change the limited area system? We must change it, but we must change it fairly. Otherwise, subsidy recipients and administrators will end up arguing endlessly over who should receive what, and when, and how often. This would hopelessly delay meaningful implementation. Of course such delays would be to the delight of the agrochemical companies, and possibly even with their connivance.

In essence, all we have to do is change the land-area-limiting basis, to a volume- and weight-limiting basis.

This is neither difficult and nor time consuming. It's actually quite simple. All we need do is take the particular crop area currently allocated to a farm and determine the average yield. This could be done by taking the district or state average yield per acre or hectare and multiplying it by the farm-allocated subsidy area. That determines each farm's maximum subsidizable tonnage. The farmer is subsidized for every ton he sells up to that limit. Above that goes on the open market and gets market price. Produce then becomes the quantity to which a state agricultural subsidy would apply for the farm.

That's all that is needed. The size of the subsidy payment isn't changed. The structural changes in the subsidy system are minimal. Payment calculations are simple. Global warming however, will be massively reduced.

Suddenly the farmer becomes free to farm in the most economical way he sees fit. If he doesn't already know it, he will soon realize that a change to a policy of improving profitability by improving the soil is the way to go. The cheap and simple process of improving soil fertility will make more sense than the endless buying and spreading of agricultural chemicals on some bureaucratically defined piece of farmland. The farmer plants an area each year he considers is a large enough area to produce his allocated tonnage. Produce too much? Then sell it on the free market, or keep it in the silo for next year. Produce too little? Buy some on the open market or sell the subsidy rights. It's his farm, and it's his subsidy, and it's therefore his right to sell it for whatever he can get.

What effect would this have on the capital value of a farm? Could the farmer possibly lose out and therefore protest against such changes? No, such a change would not decrease the value of the farm. The farm should actually be more prosperous, as input costs would be lower.

As the control of global warming is our prime objective, we should ensure that such a change couldn't in any way decrease the value of farmland, nor decrease the subsidy payment a farmer has been structured to depend on. It is in all our interests to make farmers more prosperous. After all with farmers producing more nutritious food, we will all be more healthy.

Valuing a farm receiving subsidies is not difficult. When agricultural subsidies are involved, the capital value of a farm becomes the total of the local real estate value, plus the perceived capital value of the subsidizing system. Currently, and quite logically, subsidies are considered as part of the net return of a farm. Any prudent buyer will therefore include the amount of the subsidy in any calculations determining the "return on capital" for the enterprise. The likely permanence of the particular subsidy will of course be taken into account as he or she assesses what is a reasonable market value when purchasing or selling a farm property. The possession of a subsidy is simply an assessable and negotiable asset.

When subsidies are changed to being based on weight (or volume) of produce, as opposed to being based on specified land areas, the farm still retains its real estate value and the subsidy will again have its own effectively independent and separate value. Provided the new system returns to the farmer at least the same cash as before (and we must ensure that it definitely does) there will be no real argument. Farm values will not decline. So it will all work.

In this way there is no "vicious" or "unjust" or "undue penalty" that can threaten existing farmers. These terms are typically used by farming groups to describe legislative proposals designed to eliminate or significantly re-duce subsidies. Overall reduction in agricultural subsidies is not being suggested. The suggestion, or the proposal, is to keep them, but change them slightly so we can use agricultural subsidies to help control global warming and prevent climate change.

After the modification to the subsidy system the farmer could farm as previously, or he can sell his farm, or if he wishes he can separately sell his subsidy allocation. For it is logical and indeed practical to consider the subsidy as a tradeable commodity. Why not? It would in no way threaten farm viability; it could probably assist. It is also a simpler concept and thus avoids excessive administrative costs. It must never be forgotten that it is in the interest of agricultural chemical companies to prevent such worthwhile changes. They will therefore try and link, or at least imply a link between such changes and some threatened subsidy reduction.

We must be fair to our farmers and ensure their ongoing prosperity. Farmers must be made to feel that it is our sincere wish that they in-crease world soil fertility levels and that we need them to prosper while accomplishing that objective. Also it is our responsibility to ensure that our farmers are not confused or fooled by spurious arguments and misleading suggestions initiated by agrochemical companies and promoted by bent politicians. We must be cognizant that chemical companies will endeav-our to manipulate farmers into protesting against broad-based changes to volume-weight-based subsidy systems.

We must make these changes happen. Contact your local senator or parliamentary representative; ring your local talkback radio station. Write letters to the papers; get the message across. Farm subsidies must be tied to increases in soil fertility and thus the prevention of further global warming.

Remind them: our taxes are our money, and that's the way we want it spent.

By insisting that soil fertility increases are an absolute prerequisite for every form of agricultural subsidy, immediately we are well on the way towards the total prevention of global overheating and endless climatic instability. To change the basis of the system is not a difficult administrative problem. We want it to happen now. It is not difficult to make such changes in a couple of years, maybe within four but that's it. Because if we don't, then within one or two decades, global weather destabilization and continuous sea-level rises will become utterly and totally irreversible. Self-generating global warming will rule out any second chance.

While we pursue these aims to halt global warming we must concurrently consider, recognize and be aware of the type of companies that are, or will be instigating slow-downs to these changes. We should take note of which parties and politicians they support. If these so necessary changes take any longer than two or three years to implement, take note who to blame.

Does this product reduce global warming?

Global warming is the only environmental issue seriously threatening both humanity and our total planetary environment. Our objective must be the complete elimination of global overheating. Other issues must not cloud that objective. It is much too serious.

Does this reduce global warming? We need to know that about every product, every commodity and every service we spend our money on.

I believe we need a term that tells us if a product or service somehow helps in reducing planetary overheating; a term that says nothing more and nothing less, and a term that means no other issues are implied. That must be the label's sole criterion. It must become a symbol we can trust to tell us—"this product reduces global warming".

That being the requirement, the now legally adopted term "organic" used in agriculture is a little too limiting. It has evolved to become a term with a far too restrictive and rigid definition to suit our requirements. It has happened because most organic food organizations worldwide have, with probable justification, always insisted on tight and restrictive definitions. Chemical agriculture, for example, is definitely out, and cannot ever be labelled as organic. But much more narrow definitions have carried through into legislation. In most Western and developed countries false labeling is illegal and can carry heavy fines. In most countries now such foods and food products complying with the tight definitions only can be labeled organic. Products so labelled must comply with both strict growing and handling requirements.

To combat and prevent global warming we require worldwide increase in soil organic matter. That is the prime objective. In consequence the term organic tends to become an almost self-defeating definition. The restrictive requirements also apply to food packaged in an unapproved manner. It applies even if in the production of the food, soil fertility is increased. So just the packaging can disqualify an organic classification. In addition no chemicals can have been used on the area being cropped, usually for a minimum of three years prior. Food preserved by irradiation is automatically disqualified yet food preserved by salting, smoking or pickling can be approved. These processes are far more damaging to food nutrients than food preserved by irradiation.

From a global warming point of view too many philosophical arguments can get entangled with an organic definition. The term is not broad enough. "Semi-organic" is a term sometimes used to describe food produced from a farm in a phase of conversion to true organic status, but even this is too restrictive when the curtailment of global warming is the objective.

Likewise genetically modified crops cannot be labelled as organic. This applies even if they are grown in deep rich and organically approved soil and subsequently harvested and packaged in an organically approved manner. An argument can be put that for thousands of years, ever since the first crops were planted, ever since the first animals were domesticated, human beings have lived on genetically modified food. The DNA of the plant or animal species has been engineered by selective breeding to suit human requirements. Today, except for wild game, everything we eat has been genetically modified or engineered over time. Its DNA has been changed slowly over many generations. Genetically modified has been redefined to mean done in one generation in a laboratory, as apposed to over many generations in the field.

Already by modifying the DNA of our grains we have easily kept food production up with rising world populations. Production is not the problem. I personally believe that despite the many examples of starvation we see in this world today, there is no shortage of food, or at least the ability to produce food. The only shortages are of freedom, and free enterprise, and democracy. Eliminating those shortages and restrictions on incentive would allow ample food to be produced and distributed where and by whom it is needed.

We now have the ability to alter DNA instantly. We can remove bits. We can change bits and in so doing we can massively increase crop yields. And we have. That's what genetic engineering is. We can create in the laboratory totally new species. We will soon be able to recreate long dead species. Such research will always be ongoing. Genetic engineering will continue to happen. One day we will probably see the dodo reborn.

Genetically modified (GM) food and food produce will continue to be grown, and most of us will continue to buy it. GM foods, grown on fertile soil, can be as nutritious as we desire. There is a valid argument that genetically modified foods are a sensible, logical and inevitable reality in the coming future. Of course it must be understood that genetic modification of plant and animal DNA is an extremely powerful tool and should have some form of inspection, or regulatory control.

One major issue of concern with genetic engineering is the development, by agrochemical companies, of crop varieties that are specifically engineered to withstand heavy applications of pesticides. Pesticides produced, incidentally, by those same agrochemical companies. Another is the manufacture of highly productive crop varieties, the seeds of which are sterile, and being so forces farmers to endlessly buy their seed grain through a monopoly of producers. Controlled, obviously by the agrochemical companies.

Controversy has arisen in regard to genetic engineering and patent law. The people created patent law for their own mutual benefit. The inventor discloses his clever, unique and useful ideas to the people for their free and unrestricted use. In exchange the people grant the inventor a monopoly on the invention for a maximum period of twenty years. Invention is thus encouraged to the benefit of all. If in some particular field minor imperfections in our patent laws are too easily exploited by inventors to the actual and significant detriment of the people, then in that field the people should cancel inventors' rights to monopoly for their inventions. To do otherwise is silly.

The pros and cons of genetically modified food is a totally different issue from global warming. In general, few agrochemical companies are involved in genetically engineered seed varieties. Thus one might suspect that most agrochemical companies may not like crops being grown that overnight are immune to insect attack and so render the companies' pesticides obsolete. That can make one skeptical of the motives behind the sudden furor over GM foods.

If on the other hand a GM plant reduces the use of agrochemicals and increases the richness and fertility of world soils, it would then be substantially contributing to global climatic and oceanographic stability. Currently, and until global warming effects are returned to normal, I believe all other considerations pale in comparison. There will always be differences of opinion on the use of genetic engineering to modify plant characteristics. That's perfectly reasonable. I would presume that if a GM product is legal then maybe it should simply be labelled as GM.

With genetic engineering there will always be serious issues that have to be considered, as has often been the case with technological advances. The invention and development of the spinning jenny in 1764 caused a furor.

GM foods may or may not be in the same class.

Unfortunately the use of animal manures, so beneficial in the production of fertile soil, can often legally disqualify a product from being labelled organic simply because the diet of the animal supplying the manure was not absolutely free of agricultural chemicals. Likewise, the agricultural use of city sewage is not permitted. This is most especially at odds with our objective of combating global warming. That is why I argue the term is too restrictive to combat global warming.

"Priority one" for a broader term specific to global warming

We need a new name to label food, products and services that significantly contribute to the reduction of atmospheric greenhouse gases. Wherever soil is significantly increasing in fertility, by whatever means, produce from that soil could be labelled with the logo. The term would be used to describe produce where the growing process specifically increases soil fertility and thereby combats global warming, and that should be its only defining requirement for agricultural products.

The name or logo needs to be simple, indicative and recognizable. It should also indicate the relative importance of the objectives we intend to achieve. The prime, the number one environmental threat to this very Earth, and all who live on it, is the climatic change being generated by rising world temperatures. Climate change is destroying whole societies. In the Pacific, nations that are members of the United Nations are ceasing to exist because of rising sea levels and climate change. It is killing people in previously unimaginable numbers and in unforeseen ways. Climate change is an ecological disaster. Preventing climate change must be our number one ecological priority. In any country, in any locality the first and major priority for the next quarter century must be the world's climate. It is Priority One.

With that principle in mind and to be able to easily recognize goods and products that help prevent global warming and climate change, I suggest *Priority One* as an appropriate label or logo. That is why this book is called *Priority One*.

Among other things the label should be used to describe any produce grown in any manner, or in any system that progressively increases the fertility, the stable organic matter content, and the humic acid content of soil.

Specifically I suggest the term be used to label any farm produce where the farm's soil humic acid content, as tested at some initiating time, increases by a nominated percentage per year. Such tests are readily available and inexpensive. I would argue that the figure be 6% increase per year in the actual quantity of stable organic matter present. That means if a soil contains 10% organic matter, that 10% should rise by 6% to give 10.6%

organic matter content in the first year. (Not 16% as that would mean the organic matter rose by 60%). The following year it must reach 11.4%.

I think this is a sensible and easily achievable improvement percentage and should not be lowered. At 6% per year the fertility of a soil would double in twelve years. Some farmers will progress slowly, but others with very little more effort will far exceed those figures. Their certification should apply as long as the fertility stays in excess of the calculated percentages based on the original readings.

Once a farmer started on a program of soil-fertility enhancement, his soil would only need subsequent testing every few years to confirm the soil building process and average improvements were being maintained. We consumers would then be assured that the farmer was contributing to the reduction in greenhouse gases and we in turn should support those farmers by buying their produce.

Such a labelling system should also be used to indicate or nominate any produce, product or system, the alteration of which has contributed to the normalization of world temperatures.

For example, in the production of aluminium approximately one third of the cost is electricity. If that electricity is generated without using fossil fuels, the aluminium should carry the logo; buyers of aluminium and aluminium products would thus know. Aluminium foil made from that aluminium would qualify, and that is the aluminium foil we should buy in the supermarket. The same applies to magnesium. It too is a metal that uses huge quantities of electricity in its production. Magnesium is also used in the manufacture of a wide range of consumer products, cars for example.

Automotive fuel made from sugar cane or maize can also be so labelled, and the same for diesel produced from vegetable oils.

If the soil in the fairways on a golf course are tested to determine humus levels and then the golf course is managed so as to constantly increase those levels, the golf course could become a Priority One rated course. Local, state or federal tax breaks could be given to such golf courses. The conversion of any entity combating global warming must be encouraged.

Currently most town sewage systems in their operations actually convert the effluent into atmospheric carbon dioxide, and so increase global warming. That is ridiculous. The effluent should be used to increase soil fertility. Even if timber were the only product allowed to be produced on the areas involved, we would have achieved the objective. Then the sewage system could be rated as a Priority One installation and receive tax breaks, or some other meaningful and applicable encouragement.

Here and throughout the world, we want businesses that reduce global warming to be more profitable than those that don't. By our selective spending, a Priority One label allows us to ensure that happens.

We start locally. Then we make it national. Then, by what imported goods we select at supermarkets we force it to become international. We do that and global warming starts being controllable.

If we apply such principles for the next few years and have them spread internationally, we would achieve total control over global overheating and that has never before been thought possible. It has also not been encouraged to be thought possible. Fossil carbon-based industries want global warming to be thought of as an inevitable result of rising living standards.

It would give us ample time to restructure our energy systems to maintain climate stabilization, and we can do it (see chapter 11).

As individuals, how do we change world agriculture?

The beauty is it's so easy. The problem is we don't have much time.

For an immediate start, demand organic labelled foods. Then we insist that farm subsidies are only paid on produce complying with the organic certification requirements, or labels indicating the fertility enhancement practices are being applied. This will automatically apply a brake on global warming.

Then we do more. As has been pointed out, the legally defined term *organic* is unnecessarily restrictive. A broader but legally defined term such as *Priority One*, specifically related to global warming, is essential to allow us consumers to choose selectively. Also such a label or product indication is necessary to more easily allow for the structuring of a range of tax incentives designed to combat global warming. This is where people in the legal and accounting professions are essential in the war against global warming.

But for now, buy "organic" whenever possible.

Never forget that while we are not all farmers, we most definitely are all consumers, and we are all voters. That gives us tremendous power. And that is our weapon to change world agriculture. We must recognize and really appreciate that farms prosper only if they supply the goods we decide to buy. So with as many of us as possible buying selectively we have an extremely effective system for controlling and manipulating farm practices. We know that without chemical stimulants, crops will only produce voluminous and profitable yields on rich fertile soil. Our action therefore is to foster and encourage a market for organic type food, and also for organically grown cotton, wool and timber.

If consumer demand is overwhelming for organic, or at least chemical-free produce, then suddenly farmers will have a big incentive to enrich their soil, and that, in the final analysis is only achieved by removing carbon dioxide from the atmosphere and converting it into soil humus. For the farmer, improving soil fertility must become a financial essential. That's how we make things happen.

How we consumers make agriculture beat global warming—in summary

The required national change to organically grown foods doesn't start with governments. It starts with us the consumers. The power is in our own hands, so let's use and keep using it. Don't stop using it. It's like a consumer referendum on calling a halt to global warming. And it's a vote we exercise every time we walk into a shop. Each dollar spent the right way is an action that reverses global warming. Each dollar spent wrongly or carelessly increases the frequency and severity of weather disasters.

We must change agricultural subsidy systems—from ones based on land areas farmed, to ones based on quantity of produce harvested. To make that happen, we must lobby our members of governments. We must write to our papers. We must call our radio stations. And we have to do it ourselves. We can't expect our neighbours to do it for us. Our neighbours might be waiting for us and it will never happen. We must now demand changes be put in place to modify all agricultural subsidy systems, so money is paid only when the farm produce is grown using farming systems that enhance soil fertility.

We must recognize the fiction that scrubland clearing increases global warming. That concept is false. It is a total factual distortion. It is a manipulated public relations exercise to restrict farmland areas to force the adoption of intensive chemical-based agriculture. It also generates an explosion in the tax-funded waste and extravagance that is the burgeoning biodiversity industries (see Strategy 50).

Tax deduction regulations must be corrected. Taxation laws that allow agricultural chemicals and pesticides, fungicides and herbicides to be claimed as a tax deduction simply means that taxation laws are structured to actually increase global warming. While being ever mindful of the opposition such tax law changes will receive from sales-oriented agrochemical companies, we must steadfastly press on to terminate these dangerous, insane and irresponsible tax laws.

When farmers know they will be rewarded for increasing their soil fertility it will undoubtedly happen. When farm subsidies are only paid when soil-fertility-enhancing practices are used, when farmers find the market is demanding organically grown food, it will all happen. And that is where we, "the average citizens" come in, for ultimately it all depends on us acting wisely. It depends on us demanding organic type produce in our retail shops, and us demanding the necessary tax, subsidy and legislation changes—the changes that make converting atmospheric carbon dioxide into soil organic matter good business for the farming community.

By making these things happen, we are going to halt global warming.

9

Strategies, guidelines, tactics and ploys for marketing and promoting fossil fuels and petrochemical products

THERE are two serious threats facing the fossil carbon industries. One relates to energy and that threat is the development and expansion of non-fossil-carbon energy supply systems. The other relates to agriculture. That threat is the development and expansion of soil-fertility-enhancing agriculture coupled with the expanded use of timber and natural fibres.

People in the oil and fossil carbon industries are very aware of these threats and they are totally aware that for their own survival they need to minimize such threats as much as is possible.

There are no mysterious conspiracies. There are just logical marketing tactics, just strategies of clever manipulative marketing, clever manipulative advertising, and clever manipulative public relations. And of course hand in hand with this, persistent, adept and manipulative lobbying.

A warning from President Eisenhower

President Eisenhower, in his Farewell Address to the Nation in January 1961, lamented and warned Americans about the power of the military-industrial complex. He was extremely concerned. So too must we be extremely concerned; but for us the complex is slightly different. Our concern has to be the power and undue influence of the agrochemical/fossil-fuel complex. Both the farming community and city dwellers have to concern themselves with the power of that alliance. For on this planet, at this time, global

239

warming poses a bigger threat to mankind than any current foreseeable military war. The stark reality is, the only significant causes of global warming derive from our use of the products of the agrochemical/fossil-fuel complex.

Over time, within the military-industrial complex, a huge web of common interest was generated with such political power that the democratic process was and is often suborned in order to inappropriately divert government funds to the complex. This is not wild-eyed conspiracy theory; it is but a matter of simple record in American politics, and to some extent, also Australian.

The large petrochemical industries are automatically part of this complex. In consequence the self-generation of an agrochemical/fossil-fuel complex was inevitable. Their requirements would not be for governments to buy the products they make, but to have governments and government agencies legislate and regulate so as to make the sale of their products to others, such as farmers, almost as inevitable as taxes. In this they have been frighteningly successful.

At least with the military-industrial complex the hope is that their products are created to ensure their general non-use, to guarantee peace. This is not so with fossil fuels and agrochemicals. The ongoing promotion and the subsequent establishment of excessive use has made fossil fuels and agrochemicals more deadly and more threatening to a far greater number of people than war and the chemicals of war. Today we must recognize the new relevance of those warnings from President Eisenhower. We must recognize that a powerful web of interests have been woven to ensure that as much collected taxes and as much consumer money as possible is ferried to the fossil carbon conglomerates. We must also recognize that policies and opinions are constantly being groomed and shaped to convince us that there are no viable options. We must also understand that to the people involved, it is no more than astute marketing.

We must now ask ourselves, are we really being influenced to such a degree? Are our opinions really being changed and modified so constantly without us being particularly aware of it? It's now time to urgently reassess, for it is happening. Every year billions of dollars are spent on advertising by all sectors of industry and government. Why? Because advertising does work! A dollar doesn't go into advertising unless many more dollars come back. Most of us realize that unless we consciously stop and question our decisions and actions, the subtle effects of advertising have real effects. Generally we don't mind too much. But the immense issue of global warming means the stakes are too high to continue to be complacent.

How well are the public-relations organizations, the advertising agencies and the lobby groups employed by the fossil carbon companies doing their job of selling us fossil carbon fuels and products? Are they utilizing their clients' billions effectively? Are they instilling in us beliefs that the massive use of fossil carbon fuels and products is safe or if not totally safe, then certainly safe enough? Think about it for a few seconds. Could there really be any doubt?

Petroleum and petrochemical products are promoted and marketed with brilliance and talent. Attractive, clever advertising is used to create images implying responsibility and desirability. Well-oiled public-relations machines ensure that educational institutions, governments and government agencies all look excessively favourably on the industries involved.

Of course within those industries any other approach would have to be considered as utterly incompetent, unrealistic or stupidly naïve. Tobacco companies market nicotine. Beer, wine and whisky brewers market alcohol. What else do we expect the oil and coal and petrochemical companies to do? Take note when you next see a rural newspaper, and you will find they are full of agrochemical advertisements and agrochemical "advice".

Good marketing means it is logical to sell to the world such premises that "chemically based agriculture is the way to go" and "organic agriculture can never ever feed a hungry world".

The same logic applies with wood. Wood is the only construction material not derived from oil or coal, and wood doesn't even require any significant quantity of fuel or petrochemical products to produce. Therefore the fossil carbon industries must instill in us psychological responses that suggest that the use of timber is somehow socially irresponsible and possibly even quite unacceptable.

It is a necessity for the fossil fuel industries to convince us that fossil fuel energy cannot be replaced in any immediate future and to have us believe that alternative energy systems are a pipe dream not really to be taken too seriously. They must also instill in as many people as possible a fear, disgust, or at least a vague dislike of any form of nuclear energy. Their job is to condition us to believe that nuclear energy is synonymous with nuclear bombs, that nuclear waste is a dangerous and impossible problem, and nuclear energy will never be a safe option for mankind in any immediate foreseeable future.

These are all logical ploys if your job is to convince the world to buy more oil and simultaneously to shun alternatives. The campaign to remove legislation requiring at least some electric cars be used in California is an example of how alternative initiatives are crippled, and how a potential threat is astutely nipped in the bud.

It is apparent that a brilliant ploy, in the fossil carbon industries' strategies to further their marketing plans, has been the creation and manipulation of a whole range of environmental movements and environmental issues. It is ironic that so many environmental movements have been so successfully seconded to become insidious weapons to actually promote concepts and products that destroy the environment. Environmental movements now too often contribute to the destabilization of climatic stability by consistently adhering to the dictates of the fossil carbon lobby. They don't seem to appreciate that climatic instability is biodiversity's single greatest threat.

It's all so very well done. Creating false images has become an art form. Environmental arguments are kept tightly focused to exclude any possible broad outlook but still make sense to too many unsuspecting yet sympathetic people. Today, so many single-issue environmental concerns conflict with each other that it becomes a confused lament to the responsible members of so many environmental organizations. Global warming is lost in the mélange and oil sales boom.

Once upon a time, who would have suspected the motivations or the integrity of environmental movements? But things have changed. *Australasian Science* in its Volume 19, Number 1 issue commented "Perhaps the most common strategy of corporate front groups is to portray themselves as environmentalists", along with the "corporate views they are promoting". Using, creating and fostering environmental groups have become very effective marketing tactics.

In the past, environmental issues have, almost by definition, been unarguable. Now the manipulations of emotions and beliefs have become the norm. Opinions have been manufactured. Stop anybody on the street. Ask them if they believe that wind turbines are noisy and ugly and responsible for killing large numbers of birds. Ask them if they think that solar energy uses up valuable land and is hopelessly intermittent and ridiculously expensive. Ask them if they believe that plutonium is the most dangerous, most poisonous substance known to man and is a totally man-made poison that never previously existed on the planet. Ask them if they believe nuclear reactors can turn into nuclear bombs and explode, destroying millions. Ask them if a nuclear meltdown will cause thousands to die. Ask if they believe the death toll from Chernobyl is not 48 but at least many thousands, etc.

Unfortunately and incorrectly, most people will say that all the above is true.

Millions of high-energy particles and supposedly deadly rays produced by naturally occurring radioactivity pass through our bodies every second of every day of our entire lives. Ask them if they know that. Ask them if they know that all life on earth has evolved in, and adapted to, this constant level of natural background radiation over the billions of years since life first began. Ask them if they know that the human immune system is designed to comfortably handle radiation levels way in excess of the low background levels common anywhere on the planet.

You can be sure that the vast majority of people are totally unaware that undisputed evidence has already accumulated that shows that having considerably higher levels of background nuclear radiation than is prevalent is healthier and increases longevity. The oil-created images of nuclear radiation hazards totally bury these facts. For more, see chapter 10.

The manipulation of perceived images is very insidious. Test yourself. What do you tend to believe? Do you believe that man-made lakes and hydroelectric power stations are ecological disasters? Do you believe it is impossible to feed the world without fertilizers and agricultural chemicals? Did you think that drastically restricting the area of the world's farmlands and creating wilderness parks made good ecological sense? And did you believe that rainforest trees should be left standing and never harvested, and not just the rare or ancient or exceptional ones, but all of them?

The list of questions can go on and on. And you'll find they all seem to have the same inevitable stock answers. Answers that are now all too readily accepted. Stock answers that are promoted by one or more professed "environmental" organizations. Stock answers that never get challenged. Answers that subtly just sneak in to become preconceived opinions. Stock answers that, as we will see throughout this chapter, actually ensure the sale of more natural gas, more oil, more coal, more plastics and an incredible quantity of agricultural chemicals. Stock answers that are just plain wrong.

The cliché answers and opinions didn't come about by accident. They are the result of broad-based and sustained public relations campaigns, and the media help it along. The media were, and still are, "encouraged" to write "the right copy". They are of course encouraged to do so by their own advertising departments. Advertising departments whose job it is to chase the advertising dollar. Executives who don't want to lose those big oil company accounts—ever. The general public has now been conditioned to accept, without question, too many "environmental" beliefs that ensure fossil carbon industries survive and prosper.

Are your own opinions on environmental issues based on genuine factual knowledge? Are they based on your own thoughtful information gathering and your own intelligent reasoning, or are they just part of the "common knowledge" we all now tend to accept?

It was only when I asked myself these very questions that I slowly realized much of what I presumed so glibly to be true, was simply not true. There were just too many lies. There were just too many distortions in matters of fact. I started to feel cheated and manipulated. I didn't like the feeling, and neither should you.

When we are fed a constant stream of slightly distorted facts, and a constant stream of slightly biased stories, we inevitably form opinions that we eventually begin to hold as accepted fact. But when you carefully re-read through all the articles, all the periodicals, all the newspapers, you see what they really say. You see how every single item of evidence, every concept that does not serve the acceptance of the required dogma, has been changed or defused. You see how evidence contrary to the oil-selling cause is so consistently disputed, distorted, ridiculed or clouded in confusion. And when that doesn't work, note how unpleasant truths are channelled into information quagmires where in time they are conveniently forgotten.

You also see how so many government decisions favour the fossil carbon industries. Decisions that all contribute inevitably to the unpredictably chaotic world climate that is beginning to swamp us all.

Yet, at the same time you see the instigators of this never-ending dirge of information manipulation, demand and gain credibility by deliberately and systematically posing as environmental benefactors.

I think the evidence is overwhelming and it says, "We are being manipulated". And the evidence also says, "The fossil carbon industries are the manipulators".

It may seem unlikely on first look, but as the facts are untangled and the biases are stripped away, the distinct and somewhat unpleasant picture clearly emerges. Without realizing it, so much of the green movement, so many environmental movements, and many of those protectors of esoteric biodiversity threats have been seconded to sell oil. They are unwittingly manipulated and manoeuvered to effectively support and protect the coal, oil and petrochemical industries.

For example: the very noble-sounding Washington, DC–based Global Climate Coalition (GCC) is a group reported by the American Association for the Advancement of Science to be supported by oil and coal producers and utilities. The World Wide Fund for Nature (WWF) is also typical of organizations with fossil-fuel interests at heart. Green movements all over the world are either well supported or seem actually created by the fossil carbon industries. They simply manipulated or seconded the environmental movements to their marketing aims. They effectively took them over. Unthinking members of environmental movements became their foot soldiers, their "green pawns" in their campaign to sell more oil, more coal, more natural gas and more petrochemical products. Green movements and fossil fuel interests are now so often so happily in bed together.

The World Conservation Union (IUCN, formerly the International Union for the Conservation of Nature) is an international umbrella association of the world's major environmental organizations. The IUCN is the primary environmental advisory organisation to the United Nations. It must be significant that all references to global warming and climate change are absent from the Prime Mission Statement of the IUCN.

Whenever you see or hear a statement from green movements or environmental movements always ask yourself the question, "Does their position on the particular issue directly or indirectly support the sale of fossil carbon fuels, derivatives or products?" Remembering while you ponder that destabilizing world climate is precipitating the greatest human and environmental disasters since the end of Neanderthal man.

At face value this all could sound somewhat unbelievable but there are many parallels with other global industry ploys. For example: the tobacco industries secretly funded many previously and ostensibly hostile businesses and universities to argue that no links could be made between smoking and ill health. Remember the stories constantly circulating. There was always the story of somebody's grandmother, reported to be very healthy and still smoking at ninety-five. How many lives did these subtle, pro-smoking campaigns cost?

Another example: Officials in the old USSR, after the collapse of that totalitarian regime, described how funds had been pumped into pacifist organizations and antinuclear groups in the West. They were selling communism with the same tactical marketing systems employed by PR companies to sell tobacco. See chapter 10; see also Strategy 32.

More recently in Australia, talkback radio personalities were criticized for allegedly accepting funding to bias supposedly unbiased editorial material about some major banks. Several irate phone-in listeners stated they were shocked and disgusted that such a practice was then apparently defended as "accepted procedure". It was about banks and banks are always fair game for criticism. Oil companies are smarter. They never let things get so far out of hand and are much more careful and professional in their manipulative practices.

When any large business is being subjected to public criticism, or is likely to be, it is understandable that it activates its public relations gurus to stall, defuse and distract adverse criticism, whether valid or not. Such advertising gurus have become expert in the dissemination of disinformation.

It's all standard practice and now, sadly, much of the environmental movement has become green pawns in the ongoing game of promoting fossil carbon materials.

It's time we all did some reevaluation. It's time for second thoughts; it's time we questioned the very existence of many environmental issues. It is time we weighed the relative importance of dozens of minor red-herring environmental issues against the destruction of our world's climate, and what such destabilization means. It's time to wake up to the fact that even those of us not affected by weather-inspired catastrophic events are now paying the price. Skyrocketing insurance premiums are just one example. In many areas premiums, in real terms, have risen 400% since the 1960s. Many of us know from experience that insurance is often only partially effective. Most of have learnt that in real life, so much of what can be lost is just not insurable.

There is no need to believe that somewhere, at some time, a select group of evil men sat around in an oak-panelled boardroom and planned the destruction of the world climate. But they might just as well have. For destruction of the world's climate is exactly what's happening.

No, it is more likely that the top executives in the big oil and petrochemical companies were simply justifying the continuation of their very enjoyable salaries. In consequence they single-mindedly and often fanatically promoted their companies' products to the absolute best of their ability. They may have even originally been oblivious to the ultimate earth-heating results, or at least they claim to be.

It is the game plan of big business and it's also the game plan for small business. It's part of the system that has created a rich and vibrant standard of living in all those free countries where personal enterprise is rewarded. But every system requires some checks and balances, and for the fossil carbon and agrochemical industries' effects on world weather, there were none, and there still are none. And that can't continue.

Unfortunately there is an upper limit on the quantities of greenhouse gases the atmosphere, and indeed the whole biosphere, can cater for. If Earth's human population was under a few million, we could quite comfortably operate an advanced civilization based entirely on fossil carbon products. With a world population exceeding even one billion, we can't. For marketing considerations the oil companies and the oil countries cannot afford to accept this premise. Their business is selling oil. Their lifeblood is oil.

Fossil carbon companies have been at the game for a long time, and they have not always been too subtle in their endeavours to promote their products as the following example illustrates.

Los Angeles wasn't always the way it is today. Prior to 1936 Los Angeles was smog free. In those days the City of Angels was serviced by the largest interurban surface electric train system in the whole United States. There were 1,100 miles (1,775 km) of rail lines linking the three counties in the Los Angeles area. (More correctly it should be described as Greater Los Angeles.) The whole system was owned and operated by private companies. The biggest company in the group was the Pacific Electric Railway Company. The popular name for the system was "Red Cars". In LA, if you wanted to go some place, you took a Red Car.

In 1936 General Motors formed a company called National City Lines. National City Lines was formed then it systematically acquired and dismantled the Los Angeles interurban electric rail transit system. The rail lines were to be replaced with diesel buses, manufactured of course by General Motors.

Firestone Tire, a major supplier of tyres to General Motors, and Standard Oil of California joined the General Motors marketing conspiracy. Once the rail lines had been physically removed, the diesel bus system that replaced it was itself then phased down. The smoky, smelly bus system was so decidedly unpopular that Los Angeles commuters bought automobiles by the thousands. Finally the last of the original patrons of the rail transit system, in desperation, also switched to automobiles.

Chrysler and Ford must have been impressed, for they joined in and began eliminating more of the state's electric rail systems. By the end of the Second World War the entire interurban rail transit system of Southern California was gone. Before General Motors started to disband the system there were also 3,000 electric trolley cars. They too went the same way.

They discovered or created a marketing bonanza. The same thing then happened in over forty cities across the United States. Electric trains were replaced with General Motors' buses. In total, over 100 electric rail transit systems were dismantled. And in consequence, as planned, sales of automobiles, tyres and gasoline boomed.

This was a momentous change in direction for urban transport, and as we now appreciate, a disastrous one. It also illustrates the ways in which these industries gained their wealth and strength in the early twentieth century. More recently in Brisbane, Australia, a long-term plan to install light rail transit systems through the city was replaced with a bus-way system without any significant public debate. Does that sound like the Los Angeles strategy? But there is hope; Queensland is starting to rebuild its interurban rail system.

Just like the automobile and tyre companies, the fossil carbon companies have been a little too successful in their marketing and their lobbying. Their efforts to manipulate public opinion and community understanding has been so successful that they have created a nightmare for the entire world, and now for themselves. They may have been oblivious to the consequences initially, but by now they must surely realize what they have created. They are at the helm of an enormously successful economic juggernaut that, having created the era of chemical agriculture and the era of fossil fuel derived energy, is now taking us down the road to an era of endless worldwide catastrophes.

People are getting sick of it. Half a century later, after Los Angelenos got totally disgusted with their petroleum-generated smog and atmospheric pollution, the citizens actually voted to increase the taxes they pay. But the money had to be used to rebuild a rail system. So finally, sixty years after the dismantling program, the first trolley cars (trams) and the first underground or subway trains began to roll once again. The people got a chance to vote and they made a wise decision. The people themselves, not government and not corporations, got mass transit moving again in Los Angeles.

To save the planetary environment, to stop mad climatic changes, to save billions of people from never-ending "natural" disasters, it becomes absolutely necessary that we all recognize the factual distortions deliberately heaped upon us. We have to recognize the subtle tricks and techniques used by the marketing people to create their false images. We must recognize the almost subliminal messages that are now moving us to a fatalistic acceptance of our world being in a process of slow self-destruction.

When we recognize and understand what is actually going on, we will realize that global warming is not necessary, global warming is not inevitable, and we, the people, can stop it happening. However we have to realize that governments, if un-prodded, won't stop it. Executives of fossil carbon companies won't stop it. It is up to us, the consumers and the voters; we are the ones that have to make things happen to halt global warming. No longer can fossil fuel corporations and fossil fuel countries count on us being the silent majority. It is time to be heard.

First, we need to know the enemy and learn how he operates. This chapter spells out what must be the probably unwritten, but obviously well-used tactics and guidelines that the fossil carbon companies and their associates employ. The guidelines their public relations and marketing people must live by. If in the following there are some concepts that are not being used it would have to imply marketing incompetence. And I don't think that marketing incompetence is among their faults. While all those involved would vehemently deny the very existence of the following marketing strategies, they are without doubt slavishly followed and rigorously adhered to.

Over time, marketing principles and guidelines have been developed for almost all possibilities. The strategies are subtle, well thought out, and are readily adapted if genuine environmental arguments arise, or when non-fossil-fuel systems are proposed.

There are two simple rules that apply to all marketing operations, and in the case of the marketers of fossil carbon, those rules have been honed to a knife-edge.

First, concepts and actions that increase sales must be encouraged.

Second, concepts and actions that decrease sales, or could have the potential to decrease sales, must be "handled" or "spun". As part of this second rule it seems mandatory that genuine facts and straight honesty should never be allowed to cloud a fossil-fuel or petrochemical marketing issue that might hinder the application of these rules and threaten sales!

In the rest of this chapter, some strategies and ploys covering the marketing of oil and coal, natural gas and petrochemical products are considered in detail. A summary list is included for easy reference. The reasoning behind their existence, the methods and techniques, and consequences of their use are discussed. Fossil carbon advocates will argue that a few of the following strategies are not yet used and never will be. That may well be, but if it is so argued then you alone must be the wise and observant judge. Of course the techniques and wording used by individual fossil carbon marketing organizations and the particular emphasis they push will vary from time to time. However, the motivation behind these strategies and guidelines is to sell fossil-carbon-based fuels and products, and that fundamental requirement will not vary from one fossil carbon company, or country, to another.

Many of these strategies you will be familiar with. Many you may not previously have considered as planned marketing strategies or ploys. This only highlights their effectiveness. But be assured, they are proven and successful promotional strategies and they are proven and successful marketing ploys.

One topic, the prevention of the development of nuclear energy, is extremely important in relation to the prevention of world climatic instability. Therefore a full chapter has been devoted to that subject (chapter 10).

In reading this book, you may only want to look at those strategies that are of particular interest, or that seem pertinent at the time and skip the others. Generally the strategies are fairly specific and so need not necessarily be read in sequence. Strategies can thus be perused at any time they seem relevant.

What will be of interest I'm sure, is whether the fossil carbon lobby and their green pawns in environmental movements dispute that these strategies even exist, or dispute that they are used, or used partially, or not at all. Some may even acknowledge that it is the way things work, and may ask, "Why not"? Then again in politics, a well-used tactic is to simply not answer questions nor dispute anything that might possibly generate unwanted attention.

But no matter what happens, we all must develop a deep and healthy skepticism and even cynicism for this current multiplicity of green causes and their oil-funded and their tax-supported organizations.

And we must all realize that no environmental issue exists today that is even remotely as significant as the destabilization of this Earth's total climate.

STRATEGY 1
Oil companies and countries lobby to influence world decisions, intergovernmental panels and international treaties

In the arena of international politics, intergovernmental and international agreements are dreamed up and signed. Those decisions profoundly influence world fossil carbon industries and the people who use their products. It is one of the most important facets in the ongoing marketing and sales expansion of fossil fuels and fossil-carbon-related products.

In this arena, policies are made, guidelines are established, procedures are determined and priorities are set. Big oil, naturally, must not allow any of these decisions to conflict with their own interest.

The world's scientists may well agree on the world's ecological problems, but if those scientists determine guidelines and suggest international policies that are in conflict with various sectional interests, then those sectional interests will lobby hard to protect their interests. Although that is to be expected, we, the citizens of this world, must not allow them to succeed when their success threatens the stability of the total world environment.

The big oil companies are more wealthy, more powerful, and have more influence than many individual nations in this world of ours. The big oil companies are also the single biggest sectional interest group on the planet.

We can be sure they do not plan to lose their wealth, nor their power, nor their influence. The countries that have the oil wells and the mines will also want to protect their interests. Mostly, all the manoeuverings are kept well out of the public gaze and we can only ever see the tip of the iceberg of this influence on decision-making worldwide.

In 1972 there was a conference in Stockholm, Sweden, the first world conference on the global environment ever held. It was titled the United Nations Conference on the Human Environment. The Secretary General was Maurice Strong. At the conference many views were expressed and many speeches were made. But only one really significant item resulted. That item was the formation of the U.N. Environment Programme.

The Stockholm conference was the stimulus for the United Nations General Assembly to establish, in 1983, the World Commission on Environment and Development. Its chairwoman was the then Prime Minister of Norway, Ms Gro Harlem Brundtland. It became known as the Brundtland Commission.

In 1987 Brundtland published a report entitled "Our Common Future". In her report she established the concept of "sustainable development". She called for a "marriage of economy and ecology", so that governments and their people could take responsibility, not just for environmental damage, but also for the policies that cause the damage. Some of these policies, she warned, threatened the survival of the human race.

The Brundtland Commission, realizing the seriousness of the threat posed by global warming to the world environment, called for an even grander conference that would involve all the nations of the world.

As a result, and at the urging of climatologists worldwide, the United Nations established the Intergovernmental Panel on Climate Change, the IPCC. It was also decided that IPCC meetings should be held on a regular basis. As a result the first meeting was held in Sundsvall, Sweden in 1990.

At the meeting, the meteorologists and all the other learned scientists present were overwhelmingly in agreement on two important issues. Their meetings established these two important facts. The first was that the rapid rise in carbon dioxide and other anthropogenic gases was definitely causing massive world climatic changes. The second was that the politicians and their bureaucrats would not yet agree that major efforts should be made to prevent it.

At this first meeting Brazil objected that extreme overemphasis was placed on deforestation. The Japanese, who have no deposits of fossilized carbon, stated that they would only raise their emissions by negligible amounts. The Japanese also stated, justifiably, that they were already the most energy efficient of all the industrialized nations.

The Japanese then presented their own action plan. A U.S. pressure group, with a clever and very placating name, the Environmental Defense Fund, immediately claimed that the Japanese concern about greenhouse gases was only motivated by their desire to sell their environmental technology, which mainly involved improving energy efficiencies. Why that would be such a disaster was not asked. Their implied insistence that from a moral standpoint, the attainment of environmental objectives must never be financially successful, would more likely only ensure that the objectives were never attained.

Alden Meyer of the U.S. Union Of Concerned Scientists was obviously disappointed at the IPCC report. He described it as just plain "wishy-washy". It was obvious to him that nothing decisive was allowed to happen. And nothing did. The conference became a pointless exercise for environmentally concerned people and a total victory for the astute marketers of fossil carbon products.

The IPCC organized another World Global Warming Conference in February 1991. One hundred and one nations sent delegates to that conference. The venue was Chantilly, Virginia, near Washington, DC. Many subsequently claimed the fourteen-day conference was a total waste of time. It was felt by many that this was due to well-orchestrated delays. An influential United States–based environmental organization, the Sierra Club, had a representative at the conference. The representative, Dan Baker, summarized the general frustration when he claimed, "We've just wasted two weeks arguing over the shape of the table." Unfortunately too many in the Sierra Club with influence would have preferred arguing whether the table should have been made from plastics and not rainforest timber.

The powerful U.S. government delegation moved at a snail's pace. They insisted on getting approval for even the most minor change in the U.S. position. The U.S. delegation initially would not even concede that carbon dioxide was a greenhouse gas. In long telephone calls, John Sununu, Chief of Staff at the White House, had to be convinced before the United States could allow even that fact into the discussion. The only things of remote significance that happened at the conference were that two more committees were formed and that negotiations to limit greenhouse emissions should start.

The first committee would "consider" and "propose" methods of limiting greenhouse gas emissions.

The second committee would advise developing nations that they should not cut down their forests and should not use the wood. It would advise them to switch to (oil-based) Western technology. And, magnanimously, this committee would also teach backward nations how to "preserve and conserve" the tiny per capita energy they used for their very survival. It was hypocritical.

The petrochemical industry must have immense lobbying power in world politics. These are typical examples of its extent.

Following the meetings in Sundsvall, Sweden in 1990 and Chantilly, Virginia in 1991 came the world conference in Rio de Janeiro in June of 1992. It was given the high-sounding title of the Earth Summit. The Secretary

General of the United Nations Conference on Environment and Development was the same Maurice Strong who had been the Secretary General of the original Conference on the Human Environment in Stockholm exactly twenty years earlier.

It was a very big affair indeed and was attended by over 100 heads of government. They came from all the major world powers and they came from tiny Pacific island states.

So what happened down there in Rio?

It can only be described as another "snow job" on global warming. Although this time it might better be described as a blinding blizzard.

One of the major objectives of the Earth Summit set by the IPCC was to have all participating countries sign a charter recognizing the all-encompassing threat of global warming to the planet, and then agree on procedures to minimize it.

But it didn't happen that way.

It seems that well before the conference, steps were taken and procedures were established to ensure the total failure of the conference. Several of the more thoughtful and concerned environmental groups were realizing, even before it started, that the conference could well be—to quote one—"a failure of historic proportions".

The United States was already being blamed for what amounted to a guarantee of automatic failure. It was claimed that the White House had laid out a series of recommendations dubbed the "ten commandments" as guidelines for its negotiators attending the 1992 Rio conference.

The guidelines included a stance that all military matters be avoided, that America accept no liability for the environmental problems of backward countries, that all aid requests should be avoided, that overconsumption by developed nations must not be discussed and that even mechanisms for settling disputes could not be created.

Policies to frustrate the implementation of greenhouse prevention measures became well known prior to the meetings. Some of the U.S. obstructionist tactics were reported in *New Scientist* in their April 1992 issue, and that was two months before the conference even got started.

As the conference time approached more public relations manipulations became apparent. Underdeveloped nations that now contain much of the world's remaining cheap raw materials and natural resources were complaining bitterly that the Western press and Western governments were dominating and manipulating the conference agenda. Need we ask whose interests were being served by these manipulations?

The founder of the Indian Center for Science and the Environment and a former advisor to President Rajiv Gandhi spelled it out clearly. He said, "every element of the global environment agenda is being chosen by the Western world. It is pushing a new ecological order down the throats of a hapless Third World".

It is often stated that 80% of the world's resources are consumed, and 80% of the world's pollution is produced, by the 20% of the world's population living in rich countries. To avoid these simple and relevant facts all the emphasis in pre-discussions and agenda structuring at the Rio de Janeiro conference was centred on sustainable development for Third World countries. The environmental mistakes of the Third World were to receive, and did receive top billing.

By contrast, the only mistakes the Third World countries themselves claim they were guilty of was in simply supplying the needs, and the demands, of the Western economies. If the West ordered tropical timber, they argued, then they supplied it. And that is after all, what one might expect.

The Third World Network, whose headquarters are in Malaysia, represented some Third World countries. Their director at the conference was Martin Khor Kok Peng and he warned the Western world of the suspicions and fears Third World countries had, that "environmental protection will become another Western instrument to dictate to them".

At the time, it had already been happening. Two years earlier in August 1990 a forty-day-long march of 6,000 forest-dwelling Bolivian Indians had marched 400 miles to their capital, La Paz to protest a "debt swap" organized by American conservationists. Conservationists, who the Bolivian Indians insisted, sat at home back in their U.S. of A. while supposedly "protecting the Amazon's rainforest".

The concept of "debt swap" is best explained by considering a hypothetical situation. If the banks in a country, or the government of a country such as Bolivia or Paraguay or Ecuador, owe a few hundred million dollars to the U.S. government, or to U.S. banks, a debt swap might be proposed. Green movements and wilderness societies in the United States guarantee funds to the U.S. banks if they write off the debt in the targeted country. In exchange for this, the government of the target country agrees to partition off enormous areas of their country and legislates to prevent any form of development in the nominated areas.

Generally speaking, to write off the debts the wilderness societies prefer to lobby the U.S. government direct, while in turn they nominate and influence the areas restricted. Wilderness societies must get quite intoxicated by controlling and experiencing such power.

In most cases, debt swaps ideally dovetail the long-term strategies of the oil and natural-gas industries. Large chunks of a country are prevented from ever becoming cheap agricultural land, and the vast timber resources of the target countries are prevented from competing with plastics, or any of the broad range of energy-based structural materials.

Debt swap becomes a system where inane and bigoted decisions are forced on underdeveloped countries to the detriment of their future development and to the hindrance of their quest for a reasonable standard of living. In essence, in these Third World countries their "wealth of nations" is being cruelly manipulated by self-righteous, patronizing, self-proclaimed do-gooders.

The La Paz debt swap took 120 million hectares of their land, that's over a quarter of a billion acres, and locked it up as an inaccessible "scientific research and nature reserve". This was despite the obvious reality that these people had lived on that land for possibly a thousand years. The natives couldn't even utilize their own timber. The timber harvesting that was permitted was allocated to a group of foreign logging companies.

It had become obvious, even before the 1992 Earth Summit had started, that climatic destabilization from fossil-fuel use was being orchestrated into a minor item on the agenda.

Up until just prior to the Earth Summit in Rio de Janeiro, the U.S. government had always argued that a simple reduction in their use of chlorofluorocarbons, or CFCs, would be a sufficient contribution from the United States to the cause of reducing global warming. The United States argued that this proposed CFC reduction should mean that no limit on its carbon dioxide emissions would be required. We could ask: is it just a coincidence that at that time there were thirty-four U.S. senators in office—that's one third of all United States Senators—who represented states that were major producers of oil and coal? For them to be reelected, they reason that global warming has to stay a non-issue. Likewise in Australia where every state has large fossil carbon deposits, mainly coal and natural gas, so the political reality is that continued global warming is also almost an Australian imperative. Of course the Middle East states have the same imperative.

The European Commission had been deciding their own carbon dioxide emission policies prior to the Earth Summit, and obviously the European Commission was already being "handled" by the oil-coal power brokers. The EC had initially pledged to bring CO_2 emissions back to 1990 levels by the year 2000. Unfortunately the proposed methods to do so were being vigorously blocked by interested parties. It was claimed by some Europeans that the methods "threatened industrial growth". Then strangely in a total about-face the EC eventually admitted that their CO_2 emissions would actually increase 14% by the year 2000 and not decrease at all. As time showed, there most certainly was no decrease.

As the new millennium got under way the EU (European Union) decided to opt for an 8% reduction in greenhouse gas emissions by 2008. But of course there is no way this will occur while European cars run on petroleum fuels and electricity comes from fossil carbon sources. It's simply another delaying tactic.

To reduce the emissions of carbon dioxide into the atmosphere, it is often proposed that a tax, or some other form of levy, be imposed on the producers or suppliers of fossil carbon fuels and products. This discussed levy has become known as a carbon tax.

Even before the Rio conference the EC had decided to impose a type of distorted carbon tax but to collect it by an additional electricity charge, not a charge on coal or oil or fossil-carbon-based fuels. This insane energy tax would therefore also be levied on wind, wave or any other alternative-energy-generated electricity. Britain had previously agreed to the format prior to the conference but then announced that it was "having problems with the text".

Even moves on energy efficiency were slashed from the EC agenda.

The European Commission, with much fanfare, decided that its policy should only be to "aim for improvements" at the coming Rio conference. In consequence they set no goals for their submission to the conference. Even reporting requirements were not considered necessary. No time limits were decided. No standards were set. Finally, and still before the Earth Summit, the EC ministers weren't absolutely sure whether they would even send that final, very watered-down submission to the Earth Summit conference at all.

At the same time on the other side of the Atlantic, it was suggested that to prepare the conference for the worst, it was leaked that President George Bush (the elder) wouldn't even make a token visit. Also a coalition of U.S. industrialists were reported to be preparing suitable documentation to counter the growing awareness of carbon dioxide emissions and other gases' contribution to global warming. One action that resulted was headed by Don Pearlman, a former advisor to President Reagan, who wrote to the IPCC rebuffing the threat of greenhouse gas emissions. The letter was under the banner of the Climate Council, a Washington lobby organization. Don Pearlman just happened to be also working for the U.S. National Coal Association at the time.

The Earth Summit in Rio de Janeiro finally got under way.

Prime Minister John Major of the United Kingdom scheduled himself to arrive towards the end of the conference. To set the scene Major had already given advance warning that the UK had no money for any environmental aid.

At the summit, Germany suggested a more definitive declaration on carbon dioxide emission limitations. Britain and the United States vigor-ously opposed this concept. Ultimately Britain did agree to a watered-down version. Today one must wonder if the German position was as noble as would be presumed, for in 2003 Germany renewed legislation to continue the subsidization of their coal-fired power stations and had, almost simultaneously, closed down all but one of their nuclear power stations.

Although the Pacific island states were bitter, the Climate Change Con-vention agreement, hopelessly watered down by the United States and others, was eventually signed. It effectively confirmed that nothing was mandatory on participating nations to reduce carbon dioxide emissions at all.

Coincidentally on that very same day of signing, a different and totally unrelated group of U.S. government scientists finalized a politically unrelated report. It was produced by the United States National Oceanic and Atmospheric Administration. This report related to the Marshall Islands, a group of islands halfway between Australia and Hawaii, concluded that rising seawater levels and resulting flooding would cause devastation to the Pacific island group. So in Rio, the United States was categorically and emphatically denying their own meticulous, well-funded research. It was double-think at its worst.

The foreign minister for the Islands, Tom Kijiner, speaking back in Rio, said that the rising seawaters from global warming could destroy the Marshall Islands "as effectively as a nuclear bomb".

The Vanuatu U.N. Ambassador Robert van Lieerp expected similar devastation on his South Pacific island chain. He also reported that many islands in the Maldives, a group in the Indian Ocean, had already been evacuated and abandoned because of sea-level changes.

Ten billion dollars in pledges for assistance had been assembled, before and at the convention. It was felt by the Western nations that such pledges would surely signify the success of the Rio de Janeiro conference and then things could again continue undaunted. It was probably reasoned correctly that the Western donor nations and their lobby groups would control the money.

Much of the money had already been earmarked for squandering on the much touted "Threat to Biodiversity" and in consequence more tropical timbers wouldn't be harvested, and an ever-booming market for oil-derived plastics would be assured.

About a hundred nations had their bureaucrats and their officials there to sign the Earth Summit Declarations, and it all meant nothing. However that conference was useful in one important respect. It was indeed educational. The Earth Summit in Rio de Janeiro in June of 1992 clearly demonstrated the lobbying ability, the immense power and the marketing and public relations skills of the world's fossil-fuel producers. It showed clearly how and how much they could influence governmental and intergovernmental decisions. And to all thinking people, this has to be frightening.

Then there was to be another IPCC conference. Would the same thing happen?

Berlin April 1995: Another conference on global warming was convened. Leaders from 120 countries and their 2,000 delegates attended to either lament the destabilization of world weather, or to protect and pursue their markets for oil or coal.

The first world conference in Rio de Janeiro in 1992 had proved an almost futile exercise benefiting and protecting only the oil and coal producers. Was the Berlin conference handled and manipulated the same way?

It certainly seemed so.

This time finally even the energy power brokers almost conceded that global warming was really happening. Their attack then switched from denying its very existence, to blaming everything except the fossil carbon industries for its creation. They blamed sunspots. They blamed land clearing and deforestation. They blamed pig and cattle flatulence, and anything else they could think of.

In addition they switched to another, totally new line of attack. This was structured on endeavouring to establish the concept that it was more economical for the world to let it just happen.

Paul Ekins, an economist of Birkbeck College, London, who attended the conference, was hugely critical of this public relations ploy. He was vociferous in his attacks on the Intergovernmental Panel on Climate Change's emphasis on the cost of global warming compared with the cost of preventing it. The "preventing systems" he said, are never defined and in consequence the hypothetical costs are a dreamed up fiction. He described these "red herring" arguments as "the economics of the mad house" and added, "I did not become an economist to produce figures of this kind".

The IPCC preliminary report, being drafted at the time, stated that the damage cost of a massive doubling of atmospheric carbon dioxide levels would only reduce world Gross Domestic Product (GDP) by between 1 and 3%, and even this would take until the middle of the next century to happen. Ekins pointed out that these results appear to "suggest that very little abatement of carbon emissions is justified, because the costs exceed the benefits". A conclusion that would be extremely acceptable to the powerful oil lobby, and obviously one it would plug for.

A very dubious, and one might suspect highly biased, U.S. study put the cost of preventing global warming at an incredible US$3.6 trillion, suggesting it was more economical to ignore it. The study blithely presumed that the necessary relocating of people resulting from the loss of their land from permanent flooding or permanent drought would only cost a mere $1,000 per head. Apparently the almost unbelievable objective is to prove that ignoring global warming is somehow "cost effective".

We should ponder, "How was this $1,000 determined?" Is it the cost to build railroads out of global warming devastated land, plus the cost of cattle trucks to transport the people to some new Utopia? One would suspect it would not be much of a Utopia as there would be no roads in their Utopia, no fences, no infrastructure and probably not much left from the $1,000 to build them. That particular study did magnanimously indicate that the US$3.6 trillion would be spread over 110 years. Of course by then most of the refugees would have died from (if nothing else) old age.

Paul Ekins has done some quick sums on that U.S. study. He was able to point out that even this fanciful sum, spread over that 110 years, would only reduce the average 3% annual growth in the Gross Domestic Product of the

United States by a minuscule 0.074%. He commented, "They wouldn't even know they had made the sacrifice". And that is only if the $3.6 trillion was actually true.

Carbon dioxide levels, Ekins calculated, could easily be cut by 20% in Western industrialized countries. They could be cut with little effort and quite comfortably in ten years and "at practically no cost". These figures are more in line with what is generally considered as current unbiased reasoning. The 20% could be accomplished quite easily by simply minimizing energy waste.

A lot of figures emerged before, during, and after the Berlin conference. A lot of attitudes hardened. Some of the industrialized countries, notably the United States, were most reluctant to commit themselves to any reductions in their greenhouse gas emissions at all. They still doggedly argue that scientists have yet to come up with conclusive answers as to the reality or not of global warming.

Kuwait and Saudi Arabia strenuously opposed even the thought of a reduction in the world use of oil. The powerful U.S. oil lobbies were determined that the United States should do the same.

The IPCC expects doubling of world carbon dioxide levels to increase average global temperature between 1.5°C and 4.5°C (probably during your children's lifetime). Wild climatic fluctuations ranging from new ice formations with freezing weather, through flooding to the formation of new and scorching deserts, are now predicted by most meteorological climate modelling. And the new climate patterns can never really stabilize as long as CO_2 continues to be added to the biosphere.

We can ask: "What finally was allowed to emerge from the Intergovernmental Panel on Climate Change Conference in Berlin in April 1995?"

The countries all agreed to the "Berlin Mandate". This is a document "of principle". It contained less than 1,000 words—that would be about three pages. That's just half a word for every delegate attending the conference. The main principle that all agreed to was that another meeting be called. At this next meeting it was hoped that some international legal commitment by the attending nations could be formulated.

At least something happened. The Berlin Mandate meant that most of the governments of the world's nations, now finally accepted the words of their scientific advisors. They now actually agreed that something should be done. It seems that buried in the typically verbose wording of the other many documents produced, genuine commitments were not only agreed to but also actually made. Of course all this may have been just a ploy by the string pullers to give people time to "accept" that global warming was inevitable, and therefore should be accepted.

John Gummer, Britain's Minister for the Environment at the time, said enthusiastically "It means we have a real chance (but only a chance) of avoiding the worst of climate change". Venezuela and Nigeria are major oil producers, but they, nevertheless argued for curbs on CO_2 emissions, a policy more in line with other developing nations and not the oil producers. This apparently forestalled an expected combined veto from Saudi Arabia and Kuwait designed to protect their oil sales.

Australia, the world's greatest exporter of coal, which is the world's worst fossil-fuel atmospheric polluter, sided with Canada, another large fossil-fuel producer, and with the United States to play a very low-profile role. Apparently the Clinton Administration needed to play this low-profile role to appease the Republican-dominated Congress. Republicans are notoriously friendly to their oil lobby. And with its massive income of export dollars, both sides of Australian politics are notoriously friendly to their coal lobby .

Al Gore, the Clinton Administration's proclaimed green Vice President did not attend, thus ensuring little U.S. media coverage.

Kamal Nath, the environmental minister of India, pointed out that the carbon dioxide discharged into the air from the Western industrialized nations, in the time between the Rio de Janeiro conference and the Berlin conference, would be more than enough to "suffice India's development needs (for discharging additional CO_2 into the atmosphere) for the next 50 years".

It put some perspective on emission levels.

It was agreed at the conference that undeveloped nations need not accept limits on their carbon dioxide emissions as their per capita CO_2 emissions were negligible compared to the developed countries. This would have pleased the oil companies as it gave them open slather, effectively a no-holds-barred opportunity to structure new markets.

There were some sources of atmospheric pollution that were almost conspicuous by their obviously contrived absence in discussion. This is one. The fastest-expanding source of atmospheric carbon dioxide in the world comes from bulk international air transport. It was conveniently agreed at the meeting that the use of oil as the power source for bulk air transport would not be targeted.

Also totally missing from the Berlin conference was any mention of the expanding use of agricultural chemicals for the production of the world's food. We have seen that the use of these chemicals and the resulting destruction and breakdown of soil organic matter releases carbon dioxide into the air at a rate comparable with that of burning fossil fuels. Yet this never got a mention. That it didn't get a mention, one might presume, was not just some simply foolish oversight.

The Global Climate Coalition, one of the U.S. organizations funded by the fossil carbon industries, attended the conference, so naturally they kept hammering the "uncertainty of global warming predictions". Maurice Strong, an avowed proponent of hydroelectricity and sustainable development, had been Director General at the Rio de Janeiro conference; he in turn became chairman of Ontario Hydro. Strong, most assuredly, would have had his finger on the pulse of world opinion. The Global Climate Coalition must have gloated on hearing Maurice Strong's lament that since Rio "there is no question that there has been a recession of political will" on countering global warming and also his summary of the Berlin conference that: "For all the talk, evidence of major decisions promoting sustainability, is hard to find."

The periodical *Scientific American* in their June 1995 issue penned a very astute and succinct summary of the events. The article first mentioned the lofty principles propounded in Rio de Janeiro in 1992 and then went on to say, "Fast-forward to 1995. Just as St. Augustine prayed for chastity—'but not yet'—parties at the climate convention meeting in Berlin in April expressed an earnest desire to do something about the release of greenhouse gases, chiefly carbon dioxide—but not yet".

At the conference, the upper limit of global temperature warming of 5°C by the year 2100 was reassessed, and lowered to 3.5°C. This figure was included in the IPCC report. But as we shall see later, the reassessment should have gone up, not down.

Ironically the slight reduction in forecast temperatures is now attributed to the cooling effect of aerosols, i.e. fossil carbon pollutants. But these are surely "snake oil" cures, wherein the medicine is often more deadly than the disease.

Truth however did manifest itself to some extent towards the end of the Berlin conference. Global warming and its horrendous consequences, they concluded, are happening right now. Unfortunately and sadly, the information and the warnings were difficult to find in subsequent media reports.

In October 1995, the IPCC released its global warming report in Washington, DC. The report was 1,800 pages long. It took two full years to compile and assemble. It involved something like 500 scientists and hundreds of submitted scientific papers. There were 500 reviewers scrutinizing the papers and the reports. They came from 70 countries. Strangely, it was released too late to be used at the conference.

The report emphatically declared and confirmed that global warming was happening. It considered that global warming could be expected to affect just about everything we do, human health, world agriculture and food production, ocean fisheries, the spread of tropical diseases, and generally and unhappily for us, all for the worse. And this report was released just a little too late for the Berlin Conference. Search the Web for "IPCC Second Assessment Synthesis of Scientific-Technical Information relevant to Interpreting Article 2 of the U.N. Framework Convention on Climate Change".

The report also declared that the effects, and the warming itself, could quite possibly be dramatically reduced at surprisingly low cost.

This enormously detailed report, this report of world significance, this report warning of a plague of human disasters unparalleled in recorded history, received minute world media coverage. Why was that? One has to again ask, who orchestrated that particular giant cover-up? Surely, one might think such a report was scary enough to be seen as news.

Even as late as December 1995 when global warming reports in general were being submitted to an IPCC governmental meeting in Rome, there were loud objections. And the loudest, to quote *New Scientist*, came from, of all people, Saudi Arabia, Kuwait and Dow Chemicals.

One small item in the report discussed the expansion, resulting from global warming, of areas defined as tropical or subtropical. With clinical detachment it pointed out that the inevitable concurrent spread of malaria-transmitting mosquitoes would ultimately result in an additional 50 million to 80 million cases of malaria every year. Other unrelated studies show that new drug-resistant malaria strains, carried by pesticide-resistant mosquitoes, are spreading rapidly in tropical areas. This spread alone is already of grave and mounting concern to anybody who knows.

Various lobby groups still found the report threatening enough to warrant repudiation. For example: John Shales, the Executive Director of the coal- and oil-funded Washington-based Global Climate Coalition, described suggestions and proposals in the report, designed to mitigate global warming, as "speculative technologies and wishful thinking".

In New York there is a structure called the Environmental Defense Fund (don't they have such beautifully marketable titles?). Michael Oppenheimer from the fund suggested that only "at the high end of projected warming (do) all societies face substantial disarray." How nice. Are we to presume that "general" disarray is to be taken as quite acceptable? And if so, by whom? Certainly not by those facing the disarray. Incidentally, one group of those facing the disarray includes residents living all along the U.S. Atlantic coast, both north and south of New York City.

Robert Watson was in the Clinton Administration's White House's Office of Science and Technology as the Associate Director for Environment. He also co-chaired the IPCC study group. Watson magnanimously concedes, "The message of this report, from these 500 scientists, is that we all must be concerned about climate." Again, how nice!

Then in December 1997 came Kyoto. Over 160 countries sent their representatives to an International Conference on global warming in Kyoto, Japan. The conference was held to hopefully ratify some form of international treaty on greenhouse-gas emissions.

Prior to the conference, the U.S. President's Committee of Advisors on Science and Technology had proposed that the United States spend $1.1 billion on energy research to develop more efficient and renewable technologies. Britain's Prime Minister Tony Blair supported the view of his science advisor Sir Robert May that carbon-based emissions worldwide had to be reduced.

It sounded great, but then the lobbyists made their presence felt. Well before the conference date approached, U.S. "environmental" officials had already described as "unrealistic and unachievable" a European commission proposal that emissions should be reduced by 15% of 1990 levels and this should occur by 2010.

Prior to the Kyoto conference a 600-page "special" report on global warming and carbon-dioxide emissions was completed. The IPCC released an executive summary of this report at a meeting they held in the Maldives in the Indian Ocean. It was based on an expected doubling of carbon dioxide levels by 2100. It predicted a 2.25°C plus or minus 1.25°C rise. The worldwide minimum sea-level rise was predicted to be between six inches and three feet (150 mm to 950 mm).

The report suggested that entire forest types would disappear. It considered that two thirds of the American tundra would thaw, releasing additional huge quantities of carbon dioxide, and 60% of the world's population would become affected by malaria. There was little encouragement in this IPCC report.

Well, with everyone totally aware of the increasing disasters likely to result from global warming, what happened in Kyoto? It has to be said yet again the whole conference was an exercise in utter futility. The year 1990 itself was a dreadful year for carbon dioxide emissions. Yet 1990 had and has somehow become the "base" year. The level of a country's greenhouse gas emissions is based on whether they have increased, or decreased from those already huge 1990 emission rates. Even throughout the 1960s, the 1970s and the 1980s, greenhouse gas emissions were too high and constantly rising. Selecting 1920 or 1930 as a base year would have made real sense. But they didn't—they selected 1990.

There were 8,000 delegates at this United Nations Framework Convention on Climate Change in Kyoto. After it finally got started the delegates settled down into a never-ending argument as to what levels a country's greenhouse gas emissions would be reduced to by the year 2010.

One report summed it up beautifully. It said that by the end of the two-week conference everybody was so bored and so fatigued that they ended up agreeing (for want of something to agree on), that all countries should reduce their greenhouse gas emissions from their 1990 levels by "something". They even agreed that Australia, Iceland and Norway could increase their emissions by 8%, 10% and 1% respectively. This was considered an achievement as these countries wanted to increase their emissions by even greater amounts. Not one country agreed to reduce their levels by more than 8%.

Then again, exceptions were allowed for "countries in transition". They were conveniently absolved from any meaningful future responsible action. These were the East European countries undergoing a transition process to a market economy. These countries were allowed to actually increase their emissions from between 22% and 30%. This of course would undoubtedly firmly establish that a fossil-fuel-reliant industrial base would become well established. It was also agreed that "Developing Countries" didn't have to make any commitment about anything at all. It was also agreed that the signed protocol would not be a legally binding document until at least 55% of the parties to the convention had ratified it. Ratification approval invariably is dependent on back-home, domestic, political issues and systems. After they occurred there was still another 90 days before it could ever become enforceable.

The publication *Science*, the official journal of the American Association of the Advancement of Science, said in its January 1998 issue, commenting on the outcome of the Kyoto conference, "If no further steps [beyond what was agreed at Kyoto] are taken during the next 10 years, CO_2 will increase in the atmosphere during the first decade of the next century essentially as it has done during the past few decades".

And yet Kyoto was hailed by our puppet-like politicians, and by the vast majority of the media, as a great success story.

Quite a few delegates considered that it would probably be necessary to have another world conference before 2010. It seems that many of the delegates at the Kyoto conference were happy to put global warming on the back burner indefinitely. But they also seemed to agree that another world trip would be nice!

This conference in Kyoto of 160 countries and 8,000 delegates, discussing the massive deterioration in the stability of world weather and the resultant deaths and devastation and loss to our communal assets, was a failure before it started. It did not discuss the elimination of oil and coal and natural gas to power our cities and our transport systems and our lifestyles. It simply argued that some countries in the world should not contribute to this constantly emerging disaster at quite the same rate.

The Kyoto International Conference On global warming was a total win! win! win! for the oil and the coal and the natural gas lobbies.

Let us look at the realities of the Kyoto "achievements" and consider some determinations. Mike Hume, a Senior Research Associate in the Climate Research Unit, University of East Anglia, Norwich, and Martin Parry, the Director of the Jackson Environment Institute at University College, London put things in simple terms. They reported in the December 1997 issue of *New Scientist*, that if you run the scenarios through standard IPCC climate modelling (current at that time and it's gotten worse) it is obvious that if we do nothing the entire atmosphere of planet Earth will warm by 1.6°C by 2050; and it will happen along with all the associated weather and climatic changes. It is now generally conceded that compliance to all the Kyoto protocols by everybody will delay the 2050 date by just six months.

There were several proposals suggested by various countries. There was a call from the small island states, especially the Pacific island states, for a

20% reduction of CO_2 levels by 2005. That was actually considered laughable by most delegates. The United States suggested that world global emissions be "stabilized" by the year 2012. That is increasing levels but not reducing them. The European Union suggested a 15% reduction in greenhouse gases by 2010. The United Kingdom suggested a 20% reduction by the same date.

It was all pointless. Application of the most possible of these suggestions indicate that global warming would be at best slightly altered from a rise of 1.6°C by 2050 to a rise of 1.5°C by 2050.

Brazil proposed a 30% reduction in greenhouse gas emissions by the year 2020. That proposal would have the effect of reducing global warming to 1.4°C by 2050.

Among the vast majority of world's meteorologists and climatologists, you will find little argument against Hume and Parry's figures. Their figures are typical and undoubtedly conservative (as time has shown).

It is obvious that Kyoto was orchestrated to become a verbose argument over insignificant percentages. Kyoto was never allowed to even consider the elimination of fossil fuels nor how this elimination might be achieved.

Time has also shown the fossil fuel lobby was totally successful at Kyoto.

Then there was another IPCC conference three years later, this time in The Hague, in November 2000. In the time between Kyoto and The Hague, the U.S. legislature had totally rejected the Kyoto mandates. This was mainly because of the ridiculous Kyoto concept that developing countries could do whatever they liked about global warming and could add carbon dioxide to the atmosphere with absolutely no restriction whatever.

At The Hague, the discussions soon degenerated into arguments such as whether fossil-fuel consuming countries could grow trees in undeveloped countries and thereby meet their Kyoto "obligations". The Kyoto obligations remember, have only ever amounted to a minuscule few percentage points reduction on the frightening 1990 carbon-dioxide emissions. The obligations, it's been argued, could be met by financial trading in the conveniently invented market of carbon credits.

Other issues were argued and debated until everybody got disgusted and went home. The whole thing was a joke, and cost us taxpayers millions. The only agreement reached by the delegates was that they would all get together and have another debate in six months. At The Hague the fossil-fuel countries and the fossil-fuel companies had another brilliant win; just like at Kyoto.

At least the delegates at The Hague did finally agree that world temperature rises are caused by the burning of fossil fuels. This was actually very significant as it finally ended any argument that global warming was a myth and it also ended any argument that it could be blamed on unknown or undiscovered phenomena. Also at the conference the forecast maximum world temperature rise by 2100 was increased from 3.5°C to a possibly utterly catastrophic 6°C. As previously mentioned, that temperature rise is more than enough to induce an irreversible Greenland meltdown and guarantee world sea-level rises of at least 20 feet (6 metres).

And another meeting was scheduled by the Intergovernmental Panel on Climate Change, for Amsterdam in July 2001. This time 1,800 climate scientists from 100 countries met, yet again to discuss global warming. The conclusion was that it is definitely happening, and this time it was agreed that the consequences would be a lot worse for the world and its people than ever previously imagined. Again the scientists agreed, and this time emphasized, that politicians have to do something about it, and very soon. At the Amsterdam meeting the Kyoto Protocol, which was obviously a complete farce, was ratified by almost all countries. (Legal and binding ratification had still to come.) As a result the media happily reported success at Amsterdam. People at home could therefore relax.

Also as a result of the ratification of the Kyoto Protocol, oil sales will continue virtually unabated.

The United States was one of a few notable exceptions in not ratifying the totally inane Kyoto Protocol. President George W. Bush, like his father, has a background involving Texas oil. But the U.S. decision not to ratify the protocol could well have been based as much on the utter pointlessness of what was proposed as much as on a possible bias in favour of hometown oil interests. I personally believe that as long as the United States remains oil-fuel dependent it should source that oil from Alaska, or from anywhere else within its own borders, despite the hugely exaggerated environmental protestations. For the United States, sourcing the oil and protecting and guaranteeing those sources, whether they be internal or external, is a national and international security issue. Most advisors to the president unfortunately would endeavour to have him believe that global warming was of minor consequence. The creation and establishment of any practical alternative fuel systems is not on their agenda.

The U.S. oil lobby surrounds him with a smoke screen too thick for common sense to be even vaguely visible. As a result global warming is seen as something "put out by bureaucrats" and only maybe needing "clarifying research". It seems the only picture the U.S. President is shown is one that depicts global warming as somehow quite tolerable, at least for the United States of America; and apparently then only if it really does exist.

The President's bias against global warming considerations and illustrated by his belief that human-induced fossil-fuel-related planetary warming is merely something "put out by the bureaucrats" was reported in *New Scientist*, January 2003.

However, to be seen politically as environmentally responsible, billions of dollars were allocated, and thus potentially squandered, on the two most unrealistic, hypothetical, Alice in Wonderland concepts in the entire energy debate, fusion energy and the mystical "hydrogen economy". See "Strategy 32: Destroy the nuclear energy industry", and in particular chapter 10.

The reality is that whether a U.S. President ratifies any global warming treaty or not, it still has to be ratified by their Senate. And Senate members recognize and have stated that "Developing Countries Parties are rapidly increasing and are expected to surpass emissions of the United States and other OECD [Organisation for Economic Co-operation and Development] countries as early as 2015". The U.S. Senate therefore appreciated the stupidity in committing their country to an internationally binding agreement that limited their own production of greenhouse gases and placed no limits whatever on developing countries. Incidentally the developing countries included Mexico, Brazil, South Korea, China and India.

The United States, like most Western countries, is currently hooked on oil, especially to run self-contained transport systems such as trucks and cars. To legally ratify the Kyoto Protocol, which developed from the Berlin Mandate, would guarantee that all developing countries would inevitably also become hooked on oil. With no restrictions whatever placed on their use of fossil fuels, what would anyone expect? As a result in 1997 the following resolution was passed 95 to 0 by the U.S. Senate.

> 1. The United States should not be a signatory to any protocol to, or other agreement regarding, the United Nations Framework on Climate Change of 1992, at negotiations in Kyoto in December 1997, or thereafter, which would—(A) mandate new commitments to limit or reduce greenhouse gas emissions for the Annex 1 Parties, unless the protocol or other agreement also mandates new specific scheduled commitments to limit or reduce greenhouse gas emissions for Developing Country Parties within the same compliance period, or (B) would result in serious harm to the economy of the United States; and
>
> 2. Any such protocol or other agreement which would require the advice and consent of the Senate to ratification should be accompanied by a detailed explanation of any legislation or regulatory actions that may be required to implement the protocol or other agreement and should also be accompanied by an analysis of the detailed financial costs and other impacts on the economy of the United States which would be incurred by the implementation of the protocol or other agreement. (United States Senate Resolution 98)

Yet greenhouse warming has to stop. Therefore it has to be the voice of the American people demanding a supply of non-fossil fuels. A supply funded by the subsidies now going to fund fossil fuels and the high cost of fossil-fuel-related climate damage and human suffering. In the meantime a U.S. President will do more to mitigate global warming by embracing and promoting nuclear energy than by promoting the signing of some hamstringing and naïve protocol.

Yet another conference was called. In early September 2002 the United Nations World Summit on Sustainability was held in Johannesburg, South Africa. It was hailed as a followup to the Earth Summit in Rio de Janeiro in 1992. Again like all previous environmental world conferences it was a hugely expensive whitewash. The main beneficiary was undoubtedly South Africa, whose "tourism" revenue increased by hundreds of millions of dollars by hosting this gigantic party.

Finally, after much argument and discussion, more than 100 national delegations agreed to a 65-page Plan of Implementation. This document was really a feel-good bundle of platitudes in which nobody actually agreed to do anything.

The executive director of Oxfam in Australia, Andrew Hewett, lampooned the Johannesburg conference as "a triumph for greed and self interest, a tragedy for poor people and the environment". Even the British representative of Friends of the Earth, Charles Secrett, labelled it "the worst political sellout in decades", which of course did nothing, but did make Friends of the Earth sound responsible.

The public relations people from the oil/fossil-fuel lobby obviously did a brilliant job at Johannesburg for the conference to be so described. Although no delegates formally agreed how anything could happen, or would happen, they did finally agree on some things they thought should happen. They agreed that somehow fish stocks in the world's oceans should be restored. They agreed that half a billion more people should have access to fresh water and that one billion more toilets should be built, and both these things should happen by 2015. They agreed that it was a good thing to minimize the health and environmental impact of chemicals. But this, it was agreed, could wait until 2020. Also included in the noble Plan of Implementation was that consumers in rich countries should consume less. The concept of promoting corporate responsibility was another less than momentous decision agreed at Johannesburg.

Increasing the use of renewable energy managed to get included in the Plan. *New Scientist* considered however, that as no targets whatsoever were set, "negotiators from the U.S., Japan and the Organization of Petroleum Exporting Countries (OPEC), led by Saudi Arabia could go home claiming a victory". *New Scientist* also reported with disappointment, that the final agreement completely endorsed the use and development of "cleaner fossil fuel technologies". In the same issue *New Scientist* showed a photo of a wind farm with a caption "Some of the summit's losers". That caption probably said it all!

At the conference the United States committed a minimum of $36 million "to protect the Congo rainforest". Read "to keep huge quantities of timber out of the market". The World Wide Fund for Nature (WWF) along with several supposedly "green" donors announced a contribution of $81 million to, in effect, prevent the utilization of Brazil's rainforest timbers. Mahogany is a beautiful and useful timber, so the International Trade in Endangered Species group got mahogany trees added to their never-ending list of supposedly endangered species. But they are not in the least endangered. Brooks Yeager, vice president of the WWF, therefore maintained that the delegates at the conference made "progress on some new sustainable issues, which is great". Oil sales and sales of petrochemical products were most certainly assured sustainability. The WWF's opinion seems in complete contrast to how Andrew Hewett and Charles Secrett described this giant multinational nonevent. (See "Strategy 43: Stopping timber as a threat to oil and petrochemicals".)

Then in the first two weeks of December 2003, another international meeting of the signatories to the 1992 Framework Convention on Climate Change was held. It's been dubbed COP-9, being the ninth of these annual meetings. It was held in Milan, Italy. This time it was admitted by most that the Kyoto resolutions were a waste of time. The EU (European Union) was a prime promoter of the Kyoto conference but their delegates conceded that most of the EU member countries themselves are not meeting their Kyoto treaty carbon dioxide reduction obligations. It was however generally agreed by all that anything over a 2°C rise in global temperatures was "dangerous".

A new fix-it slogan emerged at COP-9 called "contraction and convergence" or C&C. The contraction means the total volume of greenhouse gases should be reduced. (Which had been decided almost a decade previously.) The convergence however is a new concept. The idea is that all countries should reduce their emissions proportional to their use. To quote *New Scientist* December 2003, the idea is that by 2050 "every citizen of the world would have an equal right to pollute". It seems the fossil fuel interests managed to again score a triumph at an international conference on global warming.

The British government, after much prodding by concerned scientists and meteorologists, must have decided that global warming and climate change were becoming too serious to wait on never-ending IPCC conferences. As current chair of the G8 group of rich nations they decided to call a meeting where the focus would be on the possible hazards and possible dangers of global warming and climate change. This time opinions were not watered down to suit the always-present influential parties. For the first time estimates of possible extreme scenarios were not dismissed out of hand. This time it was appreciated that runaway global warming with world temperature rises as high as 11°C were very much on the cards. It was also considered that we might have less than a decade to prevent such irreversible global overheating.

Many considered sea-level rises that will be seen by people living today, could easily drown a two story building, along with all the streets and parks around it. *New Scientist* reported the details in their 12 February 2005 edition. Four pages were devoted to what scientists and meteorologists at the conference were reporting. It was like being told the earth had cancer.

Further on in that issue of *New Scientist*, six pages were devoted to skeptical reviews of what the scientists said. *New Scientist* did note that the George C. Marshall Institute (Washington, DC), one of the skeptics, "receives money from ExxonMobil". There were five major skeptics making the case against the scientists at the conference. Four receive money from ExxonMobil. The fifth was an oil exploration consultant. *New Scientist* did point out that "Most of the prominent organizations making the case against mainstream climate science often accept funding from the fossil-fuel industry." And noted that a characteristic of these organizations was that "Few employ climate scientists."

The Kyoto Protocol, although already ratified, did not become a legally binding instrument on the signatories until Russia recognized its worth as a requirement to maintain the growth in its oil sales, and duly signed up. It became binding on its members on 15 February 2005. Australia, the biggest coal-exporting country on earth, would not sign up. The U.S. Senate had wisely already vetoed the United States from becoming a signatory to such a farcical agreement. The Kyoto Protocol, as an instrument to reduce global warming, is worse than worthless, as it will be used to placate responsible people genuinely concerned about our destabilizing world weather.

STRATEGY 2
Lobbying to influence federal, state and local governmental decisions and official statements

Ultimately, in a free society, a nation's decisions are made by congressmen, parliamentarians, senators and sometimes just by the president or prime minister. These people can all be influenced. But that's the nature of the democratic system. They are there, after all, to represent the perceived needs of their constituencies. They then in turn influence, or control, the official statements and actions of their own departments. This is where government policy and government action is decided. Therefore, this is where the fossil carbon industries will devote their greatest efforts.

Does it really happen? Of course it does. The fossil-fuel people are not fools. Their plans never include losing sales and losing business.

Here are some examples of governmental decisions favourable to the fossil carbon industries, although often disguised behind environmentally friendly facades.

United States car fuel efficiency requirements were scrapped

In the early 1970s, following the Middle East "oil threat", and the subsequent oil price hike, legislation was introduced in the United States to improve the fuel efficiency of automobiles. The average fuel efficiency of the complete range of cars made by each individual manufacturer had to exceed 27.5 miles per U.S. gallon by 1985 (33 miles per imperial gallon or about 8.6 litres per 100 klicks). These efficiency standards proved surprisingly easy to meet. The Reagan administration, for reasons we can only suspect, extended the time limit to 1990 and then in addition relaxed various efficiency require-ments. The result was that in 1989 average fuel consumption per vehicle ceased declining. Fuel consumption per vehicle in the United States then began to rise for the first time in almost 15 years.

To make it worse, from the point of view of global warming, in the 10-year period from 1980 to 1990 funding for research on alternative energy in the United States was progressively reduced until it hit just 10% of its 1980 expenditure. And who, other than oil companies are the beneficiary of such policies? No one.

Following the Amsterdam world climate conference, the U.S. federal government paradoxically decided to shelve a newly proposed upgrading of mandatory motor vehicle fuel-efficiency requirements. The proposed requirements would have resulted in a general decrease in vehicle size. The new four-wheel-drive, chromium tractors or suburban tanks, so common on today's roads, were of particular concern. Gasoline sales would obviously have decreased had the requirements been introduced. It appears the oil companies' public-relations machinery fought hard and long and success-fully. They yet again prevented increasing the fuel efficiency of U.S. motor vehicles. The U.S. motor-vehicle market is the key trendsetter for vehicle manufactures worldwide, so where it moves, most will follow.

No holds were barred in the oil companies' fight. Among other things a hypothetical concept was promoted that jobs would be lost if automobiles became more efficient. The unions actually swallowed this argument hook, line, and sinker and actively opposed the efficiency upgrade. Then the even more spurious argument that bigger and less efficient vehicles would save lives was promoted. A very worthy proposal that would have resulted in decreased fuel consumption and decreased global warming and slowed the insidious and cancerous growth of climate change was conveniently lost.

United States citizens never voted on the issue. The elected representa-tives of the people voted on the issue, and they voted, not for what was best for the people, not for what was best for the country, and certainly not for what was best for the world. They voted for those corporations who they believed would fund their next campaign.

UK governments are effectively sabotaging alternative energy initiatives

Governments invariably proclaim they are staunch environmentalists. This keeps the voters happy. What they actually do is often quite different, and usually carefully orchestrated. Power stations are expensive things to build, irrespective of the nature of the energy supply to drive them. To fund their construction, financiers must be assured that the power generated has a reasonably guaranteed market. Prior to proceeding with the construction of a power station, long-term contracts to purchase a substantial amount of the power generated are usually a prerequisite. Twenty-year contract periods for power sales remove much of the gamble in the decision to proceed or not.

In the United Kingdom in 1990, their Department of Energy informed the new and developing alternative energy industries that future guaranteed contracts to purchase electricity from the department would be assured, but the assurance would be limited to a maximum of just eight years. When no charge is levied for using the atmosphere as a carbon dioxide disposal dump, coal, gas or oil-fired power stations can usually produce cheaper energy than the sustainable alternatives. Thus the alternative energy producers can easily be forced out of business at the end of the eight-year period.

Thus the UK Government could blithely claim it was supporting the development of alternative energy. At the same time, mindful of powerful fossil-fuel lobby groups, they could feel assured that large-scale development of alternative energy sources will remain an impractical dream.

Would any judicious person seriously consider investing in, for example, a 100-million-pound project, that may easily take three years to complete but with assured sales limited to a short eight-year period? Unlikely, especially when they are aware that revenue in the remaining five years from commencement of construction would be at the whim of politicians. Politicians that are too easily influenced by the wealth and the handouts from the fossil-fuel industries.

The European Commission also imposed the throat-cutting eight-year limit in which renewable energy could receive any premium price. Whose side are these people on?

The very imposingly titled, "UK Non Fossil Fuel Obligation" (NFFO) was dreamed up by the UK Government supposedly to ensure the development of alternative energy sources to curtail greenhouse gas emissions. Strangely, this NFFO was also structured in such a manner that wind energy projects would not be assisted. Non-assistance for wind energy for Scotland was particularly interesting as wind speeds and wind consistency in Scotland are the highest in all of Europe. Scotland is therefore a perfect location for wind turbines.

Wind power was eventually subsidized, often up to around 4.5 pence per kilowatt-hour. Unfortunately the contracts were so short-term that wind power prices needed to recoup capital investment were so high that wind power developed a high cost image.

The Non Fossil Fuel Obligation was also structured to include nuclear energy, along with wind, wave, solar and tidal energy, as a renewable energy source. This is valid but the specific inclusion is a double-edged sword. The anti-nuclear-weapons, anti-nuclear-energy, anti-nuclear-anything protesters automatically became an anti-renewable-energy lobby.

The British House of Commons set up an independent Energy Committee to look at the nation's renewable energy options. The Energy Committee found that almost three-quarters of all government-funded research on renewable energy was, somehow, funnelled into exotic and unnecessary nuclear research, usually fusion energy. Fusion research is a never-ending money sink and had then (and still has) negligible prospects of producing usable anything in any foreseeable future. Fusion research is undoubtedly the least cost effective of all nuclear energy research and therefore produces a minimal threat to fossil fuel. Was research into conventional and practical nuclear fission energy and non-controversial alternative energy sources deliberately starved of taxpayer's funds, or is that just another convenient coincidence that again suited the fossil fuel lobby?

Europeans actually created laws that compel fossil fuel use

Biofuels are fuels made by producing high-energy liquid fuels from farm-grown crops. Biofuels are hydrocarbons and so produce carbon dioxide when they burn. However this is merely returning to the atmosphere the carbon dioxide originally consumed by the plant as it grew. It's a safe, carbon-dioxide-neutral, closed cycle.

Methanol, ethanol, biodiesel, bagasse and of course wood are biofuels. Biodiesel is produced by chemically combining ethanol with a vegetable oil such as palm oil. Biodiesel is a significantly better fuel than petroleum-based diesel. Bagasse is the fibrous material waste remaining after crushing sugar cane. The total quantity of carbon and carbon dioxide in the earth's biosphere is unchanged by the burning of biofuels. See chapter 11, and also Strategy 29: "Biofuels are a major threat to oil, coal, and gas".

The EU obviously should support the large-scale introduction of such fuels to stop global warming. However, it is obvious that the European Commission can hardly be described as magnanimous in their support for energy alternatives. By 1992, the EC had "allowed" ethanol derived from wheat, maize, beets or potatoes to be added to fossil fuels to power motor vehicles. But only 5% of ethanol was allowed to be added to conventional oil derived fuels. So in effect the European Commission insisted and mandated that 95% of fuel for spark ignition engines (petrol engines) had to be fossil-fuel based. This is despite the fact that ordinary motorcars run fine on blends containing up to 25% ethanol, as in Brazil. This again illustrates the frightening power of the oil lobby.

Australia is a major sugar producing country. One might presume that ethanol would be a significant component of motor fuel in this country, but it's not. When this was recently proposed The Australian Labor Party—the major left-wing party in this country—coerced the ruling right-wing party to nationally legally limit the ethanol content in petrol to a maximum of 10%.

The much-publicized argument being that ethanol was somehow harmful to car engines. Its catch-all suggestion was that more research was needed. Today almost every major automobile manufacturer in the world—and at no extra cost—produces motor vehicles tuned to run on either straight ethanol or ethanol blends—some even on both. What further research is needed? See "Strategy 29, Biofuels are a major threat to oil and gas" and chapter 11.

The French, in isolation, and to their great credit, had already exempted biofuels from fuel taxes until 1996. It was expected at the time that after 1996 the tax break would be structured to continue indefinitely. But oil companies always fight such incursions on their domain, and invariably win. In 2000 British Petroleum (BP) took legal action against the French claiming French subsidies for biofuels were damaging their business. BP won. The case was re-argued on technical grounds and the French won. So some French subsidies on biofuels still exist. The message is clear; in general the Europe Union does not encourage biofuel use. True, sometimes the EU will "allow" their member states to assist biofuel production. But any claim that EU governments are genuinely concerned about global warming is a joke.

The Environmental Energy Agency of France, the ADEME, was enthusiastic about the use of biofuels, including the use of canola oil (rapeseed oil) to produce the biofuel RME (rape methyl ester). Actually ethanol-derived rape ethyl ester or REE is preferred as ethanol is easily obtained from distillation of sugars and carbohydrates. The ADEME fell within the influence of the European Union, so a German group from their Federal Environment Office, the UBA in Berlin, tried to convince people that biofuels are somehow pointless. They made irrational and irrelevant claims that burning biofuel, particularly RME, produces as much greenhouse gas emissions as burning fossil fuels. Of course it does, and of course it goes into the atmosphere, but the next crop to make the next batch of biofuel extracts it all back out again. This childish argument made the German Federal Environment Office, the UBA, look either just a little corrupt, or stupid.

The German team at the time also gave the dire warning that the growing of crops to produce biofuels, and the widespread use of biofuels, would dramatically increase the use of agricultural chemicals, namely pesticides, herbicides and fertilizers. This additional piece of monumental nonsense had to have been based on the agrochemical industry's own much-proclaimed rhetoric, that commercial crops are impossible to grow without the widespread use of agrochemicals.

A push for baby power stations

Nuclear energy power stations of course do not use fossil fuels and they are sizeable complexes. To beat them the fossil fuel lobby uses their antinuclear movements, their green pawns, to do the job of prevention. But in case that might fail, as the public begins to realize how insanely exaggerated are the relative dangers of nuclear energy, other ploys might be needed. It would be clever policy for the oil lobby to actively encourage a fundamental switch from large power stations to a conglomeration of small independent fossil-fuel powered electric generating facilities to augment the nation's power supply.

Being small, these independent power companies could be located in local counties or shires, and even in or near towns with minimal justifiable opposition from the local citizenry. The very valid argument being that if they want electric power in their town they should be prepared to accept a small measure of local pollution. And for the PR exercise it would be best if the stations were locally owned.

For the fossil-fuel lobby it is a pleasant and very saleable concept with many advantages. Dozens of small independent fossil-fuelled power stations could be set up across the country, and they would be very hard to close down. The small stations would have the argument that they only established themselves in the neighbourhood to help keep the electricity flowing. The fossil-fuel lobby, in the "defence of free enterprise", could then rally behind the "independents" to fight any suggestion of possible removal. The political and media influence the fossil-fuel lobby has, could then make the removal of the independents a politically and financially expensive nightmare.

For the fossil-fuel suppliers it is clever marketing to make small independent power stations the flavour of the month, and thereby keep oil and gas sales bubbling. A move to mini-power stations has already commenced in the United States. All are oil or gas fuelled.

We should not forget that smaller power stations are generally less efficient so ultimately more fuel, either oil or gas will be needed. Oil and gas are about equal as producers of greenhouse gases. Supporting the concept of the introduction of a multiplicity of small independent fossil-fuel power stations is logical, astute and far-sighted marketing by the fossil-fuel establishment.

The great Australian river scam

The Australian Great Dividing Range separates the narrow eastern coastal belt from the vastness of the Australian inland. The range is rarely more than 4,000 feet (1,200 m) high. Between this range and the central Australian deserts is an area defined as the Murray-Darling Basin. It is a catchment area the size of Alaska, or Mexico, or Central Europe.

All running water in the area ultimately drains into the Darling River, the Murrumbidgee River and Murray River systems. The water then exits via the Murray to the Southern Ocean just east of the city of Adelaide. Rainfall throughout the whole region ranges from below 10 inches up to 30 inches per year in places (250 mm and 750 mm). From an agricultural perspective

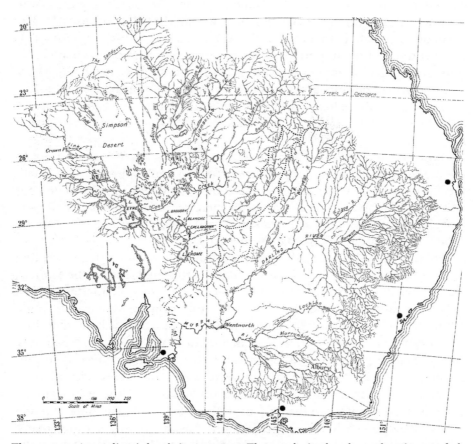

The eastern Australian inland river system. The creeks in the above drawing are fed by thousands of primary valleys. The area contains thousand of individual farms. A monstrous, all-pervading, relentlessly expanding carefully structured bureaucracy will control and limit the storage and use of rainwater falling on every single farm in that vast area. Today, in "a land of droughts and flooding rains", that bureaucracy is hopelessly frustrating the improvement of soil fertility in an area bigger than France, Germany and Italy combined.

the rainfall is not particularly low, but it is frustratingly irregular.

It is a huge farming area and is already a big market for the agrochemical industries, and they are positive that sales could be increased manyfold.

Apart from during the rare storms and floods, most of the maze of inland rivers are never more than a series of water holes and billabongs. Few flow consistently. It has been like that, on and off, for thousands of years. Over the last century, hundreds of earth wall farm dams have been constructed in small on-farm valleys to augment the water holes and billabongs for stock water through drought periods. This has been a serendipitous benefit for thirsty native fauna whose populations in many cases have exploded. Many of these farm dams and larger water holes are used for on-farm irrigation.

Through all those long ages of droughts and floods, the water holes and billabongs and later the new farm dams, stayed fresh and healthy, and were full of fish.

Typical of most of Australia, the soils in the eastern half of the continent are predominately phosphorus deficient. Small applications of phosphate fertilizers corrected this and the soil biology and soil fertility benefited. Soil organic matter content started to increase following Australia's general abandonment of the soil-inverting mouldboard plow beginning in the 1950s. This is discussed in detail in chapter 8.

Following World War II, the agrochemical companies started marketing their products in earnest and sales boomed. Crop yields rose in the Murray-Darling Basin for a period and simultaneously, soil organic matter content fell. Unfortunately, most agrochemicals and fertilizers dissolve in water. Ultimately and inevitably in inland Australia, the chemicals migrate into the intermittent, low-flow river system and the water holes and billabongs. Many became polluted by the excess nitrates and phosphates often poisonously coupled with pesticides, herbicides and fungicides. Phosphorus-dependent poisonous blue-green algae proliferated. During low-rainfall periods dead fish float to the surface in the thousands. The phenomenon is also becoming widespread in Western Australian streams and rivers. For the agrochemical companies the pollution problem became no more than a marketing problem and as such, an exercise in public relations manipulations.

How did it work? First the misnomer "agricultural nutrients" is used to describe agrochemical pollutants. The PR gurus then systematically attribute the poisoning and the algae growth to the accumulation of these "agricultural nutrients" in the river water. To these effects are added the vision of discharge into the rivers of sewage from inland towns. The message becomes: firstly it's not the fault of agrochemicals and secondly, it's unavoidable anyway.

But that is all fiction. The agrochemicals are not nutrients, and town sewage is never dumped into rivers. In all Western societies sewage is always treated, and although it is not used in food or other plant production it is very rarely dumped into rivers. Inland shire councilors are generally responsible people and invariably go to a great deal of trouble to ensure town sewage waste is released as far away as possible from their local rivers, not into them.

In any case, treated or untreated sewage, spread onto or into the soil, is a fabulous soil fertilizer. If sewage was the cause, or a major contributor to the formation of blue-green algae, then the crowded paddy fields of China and Vietnam and most of Southeast Asia could not have lasted a thousand years or more. No way! It is also quite ridiculous to consider agricultural chemicals as nutrients. They are either stimulants, or they are poisons. They are never nutrients.

Wise and concerned people have lamented the deterioration in water quality many of us had seen in our own lifetime, and justifiably—there is genuine concern. The reality is that the massive and continuing use of agrochemicals is the root cause of river water quality deterioration in all Western nations. Of course this, as you might have noted, is never publicized.

The logical answer to stop the poisoning of Australia's inland waters is to stop using agricultural chemicals and fertilizers. Or at least, massively minimize their use.

This solution does not suit the agrochemical industries at all. So they dreamed up another answer. The agrochemical industries realized they needed to turn the entire Australian inland river system into a fast-flowing sewer to dispose of the agricultural chemicals. Flush the poisons away into distant Southern Ocean. It is therefore necessary to boost river flow rates as much as humanly possible. If not, the accumulation of agricultural chemicals will cause an unwanted embarrassment and that would restrict agrochemical sales.

Could all this really be true? Well let's see what has happened.

For some apparently unknown reason, some "green advocates" and their organizations in the late 1990s, suddenly decided that Australia's inland rivers had to be "saved". The rivers had to be "cleaned up". They had to "run free". Funds to back the cause and support the publicity just as suddenly became available. Protesters waved their banners. Governments were lobbied. It was made to sound like such a worthy cause, and it all sounded so plausible and so noble. Signatures were collected from the concerned (but obviously unwary citizens). Petitions were submitted to state and federal governments.

The result of all this is that, although Australia is the driest continent on earth, laws have now been enacted to prevent farmers building simple earth dams on their own land and using the water to grow grasses and crops and improve the quality of their soils. As an example, in the central eastern state of New South Wales a new law decrees that 90% of the rain that falls on a farm and forms visible runoff has to go into flushing the river

Author (right) with Rob Borbidge (former Premier of Queensland) inspecting our solar thermal project. Rob Borbidge did not believe in imposing dictatorial regulations on the farming community, as has happened with the Australian river scam.

system. It is the new "Farm Dam Policy", as laid down by the New South Wales Department of Land and Water Conservation. This piece of crazy government irresponsibility became enforceable on 1 January 1999. The farmer is allowed to keep a tiny 10% of runoff rain, even when that rain falls on his own land!

The "Catch 22" is that decent runoff only occurs when rainfall is so high as to be near flood proportions and then there is a consequent massive excess of water flow. But the farmer is still not allowed to store and use these rare storm rains and floods.

It is endlessly promoted by powerful lobby groups and many government bureaucrats, that farmers are so irresponsible that they cannot be trusted to manage the rain that falls on their own farms. With this madness Australia's rare and valuable rainfall is effectively mandated to escape to the sea, and as quickly as possible. The only beneficiary to all this madness is the agrochemical companies, whose poisonous accumulations are hopefully flushed away.

North of New South Wales in the semi-tropical state of Queensland, there are new laws just as conniving. Much of the southern area of Queensland also drains into the Murray-Darling Basin. The Queensland Government decided that the rain that falls on that State, anywhere in the State, belongs to the State. At this time of writing, legislation to this effect has been enacted. If the rain actually soaks into the soil the farmer is allowed to keep it. Otherwise it is the property of the State and will be allocated by the State, undoubtedly through their entourage of bureaucrats and administrators.

Farmers can request, by suitable procedures, and using the nominated forms, and if they pay an additional tax, farmers are permitted to keep more than the 10% of what is in reality their own water. The tax is charged in the form of an extra water allocation licence, which of course, can be controlled by those with influence over governments. In Queensland it's called the Water Allocation Management Program or WAMP. Could we say it's therefore administered by "wampers"?

The legislative structures are such that these same insidious restrictions apply to the short, faster flowing rivers on the narrow eastern Australian coastal belt. The wetter coastal belt farms can afford more chemicals, so the only possible benefit for this inclusion is so even more agrochemical runoff can be flushed out to sea. And most of Queensland's eastern rivers flow into the waters of the Australian Great Barrier Reef.

It is incongruous. An Australian farmer is legally allowed to poison his soil and the nation's rivers and even the Great Barrier Reef by spreading absolutely unlimited quantities of chemicals over the whole farm, but he is forbidden to store and spread life-giving water. Surely this is shades of George Orwell's *1984*.

When the British controlled India they imposed a salt tax. So the ludicrous inevitability was that Indian citizens were not allowed to drink or taste seawater. They were not even allowed to go swimming in case they drank some. So now, in Australia, when "raindrops keep falling on my head" and those raindrops don't manage to soak in, they are subject to an inane and unjust state water tax. It seems that Australian farmers now need their own Gandhi.

Even the Federal Government has become party to the scam. It is now a Federal initiative that the Murray-Darling River system, the system that drains the majority of the eastern half of the Australian continent, is going to be "managed". The declared objective is to increase the flow rate in these two river systems in an endeavour to improve "water quality". This is insane. Australia does not need this stupidity. The buildup of agricultural chemicals and the release of salt from poisoned soils are the problems. Problems that are the inevitable result of the destruction of soil fertility caused predominately by the expansion of high levels of chemical-based agriculture.

"There's none so blind as they that won't see." Jonathan Swift 1667–1745, Anglo-Irish satirist and author of *Gulliver's Travels*.

STRATEGY 3
Selecting noble but irrelevant environmental issues and being seen to be green

As false as it is, whenever and wherever possible the companies in the fossil carbon industry must, and will always portray themselves as the epitome of, and the guiding light for, environmental responsibility. They must create an image that "big oil" and "little people" are united and together in a quest for a cleaner world. What a fiction! Read the fine print in their advertisements. Read the fine print in their press releases and recognize the real motives. With almost criminal cynicism they are trying to engender in us a belief that, as far as this planet and its climate are concerned, they are on our side.

The fossil fuel/petrochemical industries manufacture and produce the majority of the products and commodities that are destabilizing this world's climates. They know full well that unless extreme care is taken, a public image of their industries will develop that could prove quite disastrous in the marketing of oil and natural gas and all the products derived from them. For them it is absolutely essential that this disastrous image is averted for as long a time as is possible. The fossil carbon lobbyists know the consensus of public opinion must be continuously shifted in directions that assist their marketing requirements. They also know that individuals have different opinions and different beliefs, so promotional material must be broad based and have wide and unarguable appeal.

Solar-powered motor vehicles are a perfect concept to use to create such a risk-free and desirable image. Onboard solar power systems can never power the family car. It's totally impossible. So the oil companies give full support to solar-powered vehicles. In this way the big oil companies appear to foster some "new and friendly environmental age". A race on a good road, across the dry desert centre of Australia, in a solar powered vehicle, with winning speeds of 60 miles per hour or 100 klicks, gets great and controllable publicity. These races are now a regular occurrence. Supporting such events is designed to indicate a high degree of responsibility and environmental concern. And that's just what the oil companies want and need.

Public opinion polls show most people think solar-powered motor vehicles are a great idea and viable. That's good. A consensus will also show that many believe solar vehicles are not only desirable, but also inevitable. That's even better. Such imaginings beautifully defuse unwanted concern over the ultimate inevitability of global warming with its horrendous climate changes.

However, let's be sensible and not blinded by media hogwash. A lightweight standard sized motor vehicle would have a total surface area of about 100 square feet. That's about 9.5 square metres. Let's consider the entire area being completely covered in solar cells. Let's assume all those cells have the maximum theoretical efficiency possible, about 36%. The practical maximum is actually around 25%. Let us also assume that the cells are swivel mounted so they always face into the direct sun. Let's also assume that our solar vehicle is being used in the tropics, at midday, with no clouds and no passengers and just a lightweight driver. Under those sunlight conditions the peak power output of the solar vehicle will be four and a half horsepower, or 3.5 kW. If you get hot driving this car, that's too bad, you can't turn on the air conditioner. Turning on an air conditioner would leave no power to run the car. It would stop, so no air conditioner.

If this ultra lightweight, pancake-shaped vehicle contained a huge bank of batteries, power could be saved up to boost performance for short periods of needed acceleration. The gadgetry would require about 10 hours in the tropical midday sun for one hour of non-air-conditioned driving.

A typical small four-cylinder automotive petrol or ethanol-powered engine produces a maximum of about 50 horsepower or 38 kW. Less power available and the vehicle becomes impractical. Of course it can be argued that you don't need the maximum output of the engine all the time you're driving but sometimes you do. With a solar-powered car it is very difficult to have the entire surface area of the car constantly facing a tropical midday sun. In the early morning or late afternoon the solar array would act like a sail and in a strong wind the car would blow over. The solar car will never happen. The concept is a PR production. It's utterly unrealistic.

The big market in automobiles at the moment is for overpowered, four-wheel drive, quasi off-road vehicles weighing several tons. Immense machines designed to travel for hours, carrying the dog, or the whole family, or the shopping and the toys, all as advertised in comfortable, air-conditioned, protective custody.

Ask any marketing person in General Motors, Toyota, Mercedes Benz or any other motor vehicle manufacturer if they think the general public will be happy to buy a 4.5 horsepower family car that can't even carry the smallest family. Especially when their potential buyers understand that 4.5 horsepower is about what is needed to run the car's air conditioner.

The oil companies are not fools, they are well aware that solar-powered vehicles are totally impractical and no viable market for them could ever exist. A motor vehicle has simply too little surface area to be able to run on sunlight. It is easy and eminently practical to replace petrol and diesel fuels with non-fossil fuels. Spending time and money on solar vehicle concepts is clever and logical oil marketing. It is not practical and logical research. It's simply a continuous distraction (see chapter 11).

The oil companies' predisposition to solar-powered motor vehicles and the publicity they direct towards them must be seen for what it obviously is, nothing more than an exercise in "green" image building and public relations.

The oil companies are well aware that a continuous preoccupation by the media, by academia, and in consequence the general public in solar-powered motor vehicles happily ensures a continuing market for gasoline. Additionally, it also ensures a supposedly responsible image for the whole oil industry.

STRATEGY 4
Using advertising expenditure to obtain suitable editorial

In the oil industry, a huge amount of money is spent on advertising. They blatantly use the power of this money to influence relevant editorial and the message in reported news. It's all to encourage the sale of oil and petrochemicals, and to ridicule and deride alternative concepts. Usually a very minor change in editorial material can achieve the oil lobbyists' desired results, and in general, editors are prepared to accept these minor but meaningful changes.

The advertising manager in any media organization is a powerful person. Many of them will do almost anything to sell advertising space and they are the ones that most influence the editors. Look at any newspaper report and look at the wording. By changing just a few words it is so very easy to alter the meaning without changing the broad nature of the article. Sometimes something as minor as a comma can change praise for an alternative energy system to ridicule.

I know this interrelationship between advertising and editorial from experience. In manufacturing it is common to receive notification from newspaper and magazine publishers informing you that by buying suffi-cient advertising space, comparable editorial space will be made available. And that editorial you can generally write yourself. What you write is printed up as a news item. What is in that space is read as reported news—but it's not. Imagine a scenario when huge advertising dollars are involved. Imagine the "news" space the oil and petrochemical industries can demand.

A friend of mine kept an article he personally thought was a typical example of how editorial can be used to knowingly or even unwittingly to placate fears of global warming. It was a newspaper clipping from the Victorian *Herald Sun* newspaper of 4 July 2001. The large headlines at the top of the page read, "OCEANS CAN SLOW WARMING". The byline told us the writer was an "environmental reporter." The article stated that "coral reefs may not be degraded by increasing atmospheric carbon dioxide levels as previously believed" and it might actually be "creating more reefs". At the very tail end of the article it reported that the scientist being quoted also "warned that his findings provided no good reason to continue filling the atmosphere with large amounts of carbon dioxide". The message in the headline was clear and would surely placate anybody's fear of rising seawater temperatures damaging coral reefs. But for a correct interpretation the article had to be read in its entirety. The grim reality is that the Global Coral Reef Monitoring Network based here in Australia estimates that 25% of the world's coral reefs died in the past few decades and it's obvious when you swim over them. Another 25% are expected to die over the next 20 years. The worldwide collapse of coral reef structures is attributed to both rising seawater temperatures and agrochemical overload from adjacent river systems.

STRATEGY 5
Using the threat of potential job losses to support the status quo

Towns and cities and even entire national economies have become established around fossil fuel mining operations. The fossil fuel industries always endeavour to stop or slow the growth of alternative energy systems. If all else fails, then local politicians can often be manipulated into endeavouring to protect mining jobs in their area.

The fossil carbon companies often have their minions imply and argue that any rapid global change away from fossil fuels to sustainable energy and sustainable agriculture might cause a "devastating world depression". You may have noticed, that phrase is often used.

An ongoing theme, also constantly promoted, is that higher oil prices will cause a world depression. Why do that? The subtle message is that low oil prices are the foundation stones of a thriving world economy. The perceived implication being actively generated is that a switch to any slightly higher cost and non-fossil derived energy system will therefore plunge the world into a depression. This is nonsense. Oil prices have not been low for a quarter of a century, and for all that time they have been way above actual production costs. A rise to US$57 for a period during 2004 had almost negligible effect on the world's average income. Most economists think it's ludicrous to suggest that an oil price could cause a world depression.

Oil pricing policy will always be structured to guarantee both an assured and a monstrous income to oil producers. Nevertheless there is an upper limit. It is set by the threat of competition. Oil prices are therefore structured to be just below those of non-fossil-fuel alternatives, whatever those alternatives might be. Their policy must be to constantly discourage any threat from alternative fuel and energy systems.

But sensible, practical alternative energy systems are here now, so the oil producers need and utilize their financial muscle and market manipulations to keep the expansion of alternative energy systems to an absolute minimum.

It is often claimed or even stated categorically in structured editorial and news reports that even a minimal switch to alternative energy systems will cause catastrophic job losses, especially in coal mining towns. The resulting generated fear can be used to create confusion and force major delays. In some areas it could curtail any progress whatsoever towards a sustainable environment.

The reality is that mining towns are established because a commercial geological deposit of—whatever—has been located in the area. When mining operations commence, a work force is needed. People move into the area. A new town booms. But no matter what happens, the town only lasts as long as the mine lasts. It is the same whether it's a silver mine, or a coal mine, a gas field or an opal deposit. Look at history. In Australia today there are many small towns with just a few thousand population. In their boom, at the height of the gold rush periods in the mid to late 1800s, often as many as a hundred hotels or saloons would exist in the town and they would operate twenty-four hours a day.

The Australian gold rush started when gold mining was finally legalized in an effort to slow the 1849 mass migration across the Pacific from Australia to California. Australians were joining the "forty-niners". Gold was "officially" discovered in Australia in February 1851. The unbelievably rich deposits unearthed on both sides of the Pacific generated a constant each-way flood across the ocean of hopeful diggers chasing every new field discovered.

Wherever it might be, when the ore body runs out, the miners abandon the town in droves. Often only a ghost town remains. That is the end reality of all mining operations and it will always be so. But not so with non-fossil-fuel facilities, with non-fossil-fuel energy systems the likelihood is that jobs will be created, not lost and those jobs are likely to be much more permanent.

STRATEGY 6
The ploy of inferring global warming is not happening at all

This ploy was used extensively through the 1980s and 1990s, but now, visible and active promotion of the argument that global warming does not exist is beginning to look foolish or naïve. However, some people still like to believe global warming is a fiction. Therefore, any statement to support the fiction, especially by somebody newsworthy, will be quoted by the fossil carbon companies' public relations people whenever and wherever possible. This can "justify" such beliefs and help create doubt and confusion.

Speculation about some hypothetical imminent ice age is great anti-greenhouse public relations material. The oil sales people will always endeavour to give such speculation prominence. It justifies the "not happening" concept and further helps promote feelings of confusion and uncertainty and consequential disinterest. Being cynical, one might ask, who suggested that the themes of the latest crop of disaster movies be centred on global freezing? No matter where you look, suppressing proof of dangerous and insidious climate change and global warming seems to be an ongoing exercise in public disinformation.

The cold hard fact is that ice volumes around the world have dramatically declined since the mid 1950s. As an example: over the last two decades there has been severe thinning in the Arctic ice layers and in just in one ten-year period—1977 to 1987—20-foot thick ice (6 m) had thinned to about 13 feet (4 m). United States Navy submarines have for years collected invaluable data on the deterioration in Arctic ice. It was never published. That data clearly shows the frightening effects of global warming. No national security was involved (at least militarily) so for what reason was the information restricted? U.S. military policy simply mandated that such information should not be released. Who benefited from that policy? Fortunately the policy has now mellowed and the unpleasant facts are now more readily available.

When the first George Bush was President of the United States, he made far-reaching decisions constantly in accord with the wishes of the big oil companies. Like Margaret Thatcher in the United Kingdom, President Bush invariably quoted the George C. Marshall Institute in Washington, DC to validate U.S. policy on global warming. This pro-oil organization has always been vociferously opposed to the whole concept of global warming and dangers associated with it. For a period they seemed to claim both that global warming didn't exist and that global warming dangers were exaggerated—an interesting piece of doublethink.

A notorious report, often cited to erase greenhouse fears in anybody becoming concerned, is one co-authored by William Nierenberg, Director Emeritus of the Scripps Institution of Oceanography at La Jolla, California. This 1989 report was entitled "Scientific Perspectives on the Greenhouse Problem". Surely it's not a coincidence that this report minimizing global greenhouse concern apparently was written for the George C. Marshall Institute. Surprisingly in this report, Nierenberg concedes that he does "believe that there is a Greenhouse Effect due to anthropogenic emissions of carbon dioxide".

The Intergovernmental Panel on Climatic Change presented a range of theoretical global temperature rises based on a doubling of atmospheric carbon dioxide levels. Nierenberg reviewed this report and admitted his "preferred estimates" are very much "near the bottom" of the IPCC range. He suggested (possibly to take the heat off carbon dioxide emissions) it was more logical to worry about cutting CFC emissions first. Concentrating on CFC reduction is certainly more "logical" for the oil companies, as whatever is done with CFCs it can never decrease oil sales.

Nierenberg hammered his point with phrases like "there are no valid results on changes in probability of extreme climatic events". In other words, "let's pigeonhole the problem for a few more years and see what happens".

Those few years have now long since passed and the existence and severity of global warming is almost becoming generally acknowledged.

STRATEGY 7
Claiming there are no significant overall changes in world weather patterns

The majority of informed people are now beginning to accept that global warming is a reality and is causing climate change. The fossil fuel lobby counter in several ways.   One is by publicizing old historical weather disasters, with associated editorial to make it dramatic and frightening. The logical public relations objective is to create in the public mind the feeling that "it's all happened before and despite it all, we still survived". It's promoting the Australian expression "She'll be right mate".

I grew up believing that in general the world was a fairly benign place, where, omitting politics, human beings could live just about anywhere on the whole planet in reasonable comfort and security. True, there was always a measure of risk, some places worse than others. There was the odd volcanic eruption, there was the odd earthquake, and of course the possibility of a tsunami. These things were sometimes very deadly and almost always totally unpredictable in the short term. But living in such areas is often a matter of choice. We knew where we lived. We knew the local conditions and we knew local weather. And we could plan for, or ignore both.

Sure, there were a few places where the environment was not at all friendly. We accepted that. At the North Pole and South Pole it was extremely cold and most inhospitable. You couldn't grow any food there, and it was night-time the whole winter through. There were also a few deserts, the Sahara Desert, the Gobi Desert, Death Valley, parts of central Australia, which were most inhospitable. However, you could still build railways, build roads and lay oil pipelines across them if necessary. Then there were jungles. Jungles were hot, wet and stagnant, smelly and timeless, especially timeless. But we understood all that.

That's how it was.

But things have changed. The weather and the climates across the world are suddenly becoming inconsistent, and frightening, and unpredictable. Now we can no longer plan for the seasons ahead. We can no longer rely on the harvest.

It's going to be very costly and very time-consuming to cater for this new and never-ending unpredictability. All of us will pay for it. We will pay in increased insurance premiums, in reduced standards of living and many by increased illness and premature death. And some want us to believe it's all not happening. They want us to believe things are normal.

The producers and marketers of fossil carbon materials don't want us to appreciate the real costs of our current dependence on extracting ancient buried waste. They don't want us to even suspect that world climate is massively destabilizing.

How do they manage to confuse and defuse the issues? What games are they playing? What are their ploys? One way of doing this is to convince us that we are not destroying stable weather patterns at all. The ploy is to convince us that stable weather patterns never existed in the first place. In that way global warming becomes just another one of the natural events that periodically plague our planet, like earthquakes, tidal waves and volcanoes.

The problem for us, and therefore for our world, is that with many of us, they are succeeding. We are all being herded like sheep into a new attitude, into a new belief. The image being created is that the world is actually a very unstable place, a place of constant change. An image is being established that it has always been like that, and always will be. True, our Earth is constantly changing but major changes result from slow geological movements. Those changes were generally so slow that natural evolution could handle the changes. Species had time to evolve and survive.

But sudden changes, species can't handle. The dinosaurs proved that by their demise. Sadly global warming is creating the worst possible scenario for life on this planet; not just a sudden change, but centuries of endless change, a future of endless instability.

We are being conditioned. Many young adults are now growing up with an intrinsic conviction that this current deluge of droughts, fires, floods, tornadoes, hurricanes and typhoons is the norm.

True, such events have always been with us, but not as now in deluge proportions. There has always been the freak statistical event, the hundred-year flood or whatever. That was the norm. It is the savagely increased frequency and intensity of such events that is now, so definitely, not the norm. Insurance companies are very aware of the changes. They have their statistics. They know what is going on and adjust premiums to suit. Then soon they readjust, for insurance companies work on pure numbers and pure probabilities, and from counting the actual events and the actual payouts they are anticipating bigger claims, accelerating in size and number.

Sometimes some oil and petrochemical companies do concede that there "might" be a few more "natural" disasters nowadays. And if (and they emphasize the "if") there are a few more natural disasters, it just possibly may have something to do with the "slight" increase in world temperatures. Temperature rises that some people (whom the oil companies always imply are of doubtful reputation) label "global warming". That's been their line for the last three decades.

It is now time we cease being fooled by such blatant image manipulations and start looking at reality.

STRATEGY 8
Promote global warming as either beyond our control, or a natural phenomenon

Ultimately, when it becomes totally accepted that global warming from anthropogenic factors is indeed a reality, people might decide to act. Good marketing strategy is then to have people believe it is such a huge problem that it simply cannot be prevented. Have people accept that they have to learn to live with it. Oil sales can then continue almost unabated.

Some slight short-term abatement is necessary as a PR exercise. It's astute marketing. It's good politics. It's to have people believe genuine efforts to prevent climate destabilization are actually underway. Responsibility is thus being demonstrated. We can relax.

Are we to believe the big oil conglomerates are endeavouring to help protect the planet from themselves? Not bloody likely!

Since we are at the tail end of an ice age the argument often takes the form that the rising temperatures we are seeing are just a normal part of ice age cycles. This is somewhat similar to the previous strategy, and they like to work them in concert. This concept promotes either a fatalistic acceptance, or alternatively, a "wait and see" attitude. It also endeavours to divorce responsible people from their own sense of responsibility. The oil and coal companies have to foster such concepts, for as far as they are concerned the greater the confusion, the better for continued world fossil-fuel dependency.

The facts are: What we are experiencing now and what we have been experiencing over just these last few decades, has not occurred ever during any of the previous ice age cycles. Nor has it occurred at any time in the last one million years. That is the reality. The information is there to see. Researchers have techniques now that can determine conditions back a million years. The information shows the warming the earth is now experiencing is not part of any previously known, or even suspected long-term pattern. It's not a natural phenomenon at all. It's our fault. We made these happen and we can stop them happening. Don't ever believe we can't. See chapter 3.

STRATEGY 9
Claiming El Niños are the problem, not global warming

It is a sensible objective for fossil carbon public relations organizations to dissociate carbon dioxide buildup from climate change. For the fossil-fuel industries, the El Niño phenomenon becomes a wonderful scapegoat. All they have to do is make the El Niño phenomenon the culprit and blame El Niño events for the way world weather is destabilizing. Additionally, it must be inferred that El Niño events are unrelated and unaffected by global warming.

The fact that El Niños have occurred for centuries and sporadically for millennia makes it easier to dissociate the two phenomena. El Niños occurred before we started burning fossil fuels. It is therefore both easy and correct to associate El Niños with climate irregularities. There is abundant scientific data on the structure, the behavior, and the results of El Niño events. El Niños also occur over short enough periods for people to be aware of them, to observe their effects and to have them as a topic of conversation. El Niños have been around for a long time and therefore unrelated to global warming. This all sounds OK but what is never mentioned is the pattern and the frequency of recent El Niños, and they have changed dramatically. What is never mentioned is that El Niños have taken on a totally different form and life cycle. We can no longer predict when they will happen. It is now impossible to predict what the next one is going to be like.

We could once.

But if those inconsistencies are put aside then an El Niño can be blamed for anything. The fossil carbon public relations organizations have built the El Niño phenomenon into an overfed red herring in global warming discussions.

The reality is that the changing cycles of El Niño events are not a cause of climate changes. They are a result of climate change. The changing patterns and intensities of El Niño events are a direct result of altering the temperatures of the surface meteorological environment of the planet. The fossil fuel and petrochemical suppliers want this basic reality to remain esoteric and obscure for as long as possible.

If that is their objective then what should we expect the PR people do to image-build a disassociation between El Niños and global temperature increases? There are a few things that come to mind, and most seem to have happened. It would be logical to encourage detailed research on the El Niño phenomenon and its widespread consequences and logical to publicly foster and insist on the importance of such studies. Then argue that more detailed research, always over extended periods, is a "responsible" necessity and demand that research funds be allocated to study "the urgent and complex problems". It's best if the general public see things as a bit too confusing and best left to the experts (unfortunately too many of whom can be bought).

Reality is not so confusing. The information is there. As far back as 1895 Svante August Arrhenius accurately calculated world temperatures rises resulting from increases in atmospheric carbon dioxide levels. We have also known and become familiar with El Niño events for almost as long as fishermen have been catching anchovies off Peru. We have known for a long time the general mechanism of an El Niño event and how it's related to, and dependent on, the water temperatures in the tropical Western Pacific Ocean. Global warming is heating this water and El Niños are changing.

The first time I really noticed this dissociation of global warming from El Niño effects was in an editorial in *New Scientist* in September 1992. The article was captioned "Drought hits Brazil as climate chaos spreads". It described forecasts of disasters predicted by the Meteorological Office in the United Kingdom. The article first explained that El Niños are changes in wind and ocean currents across the Pacific. It described how El Niños seem to affect weather patterns from South Africa through Australia to South America and even up into the Great Plains of the United States. It then went on to report consequences. It reported on grain crops destroyed in Zambia and Zimbabwe, on millions of sheep dying in the resulting Australian droughts, how the parched rainforest of Indonesia got devastated by raging forest fires. It reported on horrendous flooding in Peru and how drought ravaged the Rio Grande do Norte in Brazil.

Yet nowhere in this succinct and detailed chronology of earth-spanning disasters is global warming, or rising world temperatures, or even atmospheric carbon dioxide levels given a single mention. This may have been just an oversight, but the implication, or at least the impressions one would receive, was that El Niños are powerful events unto themselves and unrelated to concepts of global warming. One might wonder was the non-mention of carbon dioxide buildup and global warming a coincidental omission that just happened to suit the public relations strategies of the fossil carbon industries?

From reading articles and editorials in all manner of publications it is easy to get an unnerving impression that the separation of destabilized climatic events from global temperature rise is a deliberate and cynically manipulated bias in media editorial. A bias created to sell fossil fuels and petrochemicals and to keep managers in advertising departments and their clients happy. This type of manipulation creates editorial bias that we must be constantly prepared for and to recognize.

STRATEGY 10
In the media, droughts and floods should never be reported as being related to global warming

Floods, droughts, hurricanes and all the disasters related to these phenomena are immensely newsworthy. They receive enormous publicity and no amount of influence can suppress the stories. However, for the oil lobby it's necessary and not too difficult to suppress the otherwise inevitable speculation on their relationship to atmospheric change.

The petrochemical-fossil fuel industries have enormous influence on the media, so it is not too difficult to have the media advertising people lean on the media editorial people to have just a few little things omitted or adjusted.

This is where the advertising dollar can push an editor to subtly change the emphasis in a story and muddy the connection between global warming and so-called natural disasters.

Of course to justify the omission of facts from a story, it can always be pointed out to the editors that any relationship is "still hypothetical". The oil lobby would naturally insist that it is "only speculation" that a newsworthy natural disaster is the result of some chemicals used in agriculture, or the result of coal used to fire some power stations remote from the disaster.

If such speculation is avoided then the advertising manager's very powerful client will be most appreciative. The general public, it seems, must never be allowed to drift towards believing that urgency exists for genuine and practical solutions to global warming.

How many times, when a weather-related disaster is reported, has global warming and spiralling atmospheric carbon dioxide levels been mentioned in the copy, let alone the headline? Almost never! Watch for this ploy when you read about natural weather-related disasters. Examples of this selective reporting practice in the various media are everywhere.

You might have noticed that up to recently, floods, storms, droughts and other weather-related disasters were often described as the worst, the biggest, or the longest ever recorded. This is no longer the case. Saying something is the biggest ever, confirms the weather is changing and the PR people don't want that message to come across. Comparisons are now only made from history when history records a similarly sized event. The message then becomes: it's all happened before, nothing is new. When events surpass all previous historical levels, this is now, most notably, no longer noted. The event is simply described by size but no longer by comparison.

The oil and petrochemical industries' influence goes right to the top. One incident: the previous United States Vice President Al Gore, in his book *Earth in the Balance*, reports how Ed Rogers (senior assistant to John Sununu, who at the time was U.S. Presidential Chief of Staff) contacted a TV network, reporting on the seriousness of global warming, and "helped persuade" them to "downplay its significance". Apparently it was part of Rogers' job to cajole "news organizations to downplay the global warming issue"—Al Gore's words.

It has now become standard practice for oil industry public relations. It will stay standard practice for them until we all become conscious and aware of the manipulation behind this form of reporting.

STRATEGY 11
Promoting global warming as beneficial and claiming excess carbon dioxide will stimulate plant growth

When sunlight is present, vegetation breathes in carbon dioxide and, with the aid of the chlorophyll molecule, breathes out oxygen. The carbon is converted into plant matter. The concept being promoted by the PR organizations is that increasing carbon dioxide levels in the atmosphere will stimulate plant growth and therefore reduce the rate of carbon dioxide buildup. The implication being that CO_2 buildup will be self-correcting. Television advertisements in the United States funded by the beautifully named Committee for a Greener Earth have extolled the supposed virtues of an atmosphere containing CO_2 levels of 540 ppm (parts per million). Remember that preindustrial levels, prior to World War II were 280 ppm.

We have already increased the CO_2 levels in the atmosphere by 30% to 365 ppm, thus creating excess planetary heating and ever-increasing climatic instability. If our excess atmospheric CO_2 could significantly increase the volume or mass of the world's plants, then logically it would already be happening. It's not. The life cycle of plants is generally not particularly long, so generations of plants have already grown, reproduced and died in this current elevated CO_2 atmosphere, yet tree and plant sizes remain the same. If extra plant growth soaked up the excess we should not be registering any CO_2 buildup, and world temperatures would not be continually rising as they are.

Even if the effect was notable; it wouldn't help. Weather pattern changes are turning the rain off in too many of the world's forests and turning the forests into carbon-dioxide-belching firetraps.

Unfortunately increasing carbon dioxide levels will not somehow correct global warming. They won't even slow the heating. The concept is invalid. But for the fossil fuel companies that doesn't matter. Who cares about facts? For them it is only what people believe that is important. The fossil carbon industries therefore have to ensure that any statement, by anybody, anywhere, that implies these concepts could be significant, must get widespread media coverage. A sense of confusion must be fostered in communities to cloud and confuse the issues. Doubt must be created. Complacency must be fostered.

If it could be established even to some minute degree that higher levels of carbon dioxide could act as a fertilizer and stimulate extra plant growth, then deep concern on global warming by thinking people might be significantly averted or delayed. For the fossil carbon industries, a global warming self-correcting image with a widespread belief would be ideal. People's concerns would be delayed for another decade or so.

All the oil and coal producers need is to prove the stimulating effect does exist. Then headlines can be made to read "Greenhouse Gases Could Solve World Food Shortage" or some such similar fiction.

Exaggerated and colourful newspaper stories can do the rest.

Typical: a headline in a widely read and respected periodical stated that one Soviet climatologist predicted a "Global Paradise" resulting from greenhouse warming (*New Scientist*, Vol. 123 No. 1679). If the reader is not overly interested, then only the headline is seen. In this article, the fine copy right at the end did add that virtually all Western climatologists disputed his claim.

Mikhail Budyko, the Russian climatologist named, proclaimed that the weather would be warmer and more pleasant in Siberia. Greenhouse warming should therefore be appreciated and stimulated. Budyko also disputed the general prediction that rainfall in the centre of continents would decrease. He also argued that even if it did decline in the continents the rainfall would re-establish itself in no more than "sixty or seventy years". Yet sixty- or seventy-hour forecasts from most weather forecasters are still not particularly reliable!

The author's wife, Chris, at the park named in her honour by the City of the Gold Coast, in company with grandchildren Keturah and Rhiannon. We must not have our grandchildren inherit a world in climatic chaos.

The grain growers of the vast northeastern Australian state of Queensland, after almost a decade of crippling droughts in the 1990s and the early 2000s, would not be very happy with Mr Budyko's predictions. By the latter half of the 1990s, drought conditions had affected the entire Australian continent. This had never happened since records began. (I was very aware of the farming communities' hardships. My wife Chris set up an organization she named Save the Farm Fund of Queensland. Her fund collected and distributed over $14,000,000 worth of food and clothing and other essential items to over 20,000 farms throughout the Queensland and New South Wales drought areas. Chris was named Queenslander of The Year for 1996 and was awarded an Order of Australia Medal for her work. A park in Gold Coast City has been named the Chris Yeomans Park.)

At the 28th National Geological Congress in Washington, DC, Bill Fyfe of the University of Western Ontario rightly disputed an argument that says with greenhouse warming we will simply grow our grain in new "bread basket areas"; bread baskets that supposedly would simply be further from the equator and therefore cooler. He maintains that the infertile and undeveloped soils of these higher latitudes could not support the prodigious yields of the existing prairie and savanna lands of the world. Agriculture, he maintains, simply cannot re-establish itself that quickly.

Even if the soils were developed cheaply and rapidly, the immense infrastructure required to support new grain-producing locations would be expensive and slow to establish. And to compound the problem, would those new locations themselves be permanent? Would yet another move be required in another decade or so?

Quite a number of tests have now been conducted to determine if high levels of atmospheric carbon dioxide will stimulate specific plant growth, and indeed the effect has been detected. High CO_2 levels can stimulate some plant varieties. However in order to see the effects, carbon dioxide levels much higher than exist, or could exist in the real world, are utilized.

Higher levels of carbon dioxide than humans can breathe are often used in controlled laboratory atmospheres. Some plants exhibit slightly accelerated growth in these high-carbon-dioxide atmospheres. The effect, although slight, appears somewhat similar to that produced by nitrogen-based chemical fertilizers. The similarity being, that while the weight and bulk of the plant can show a detectable increase, the nutrient levels do not.

The claimed beneficial effects of high carbon dioxide levels are also doubted by Fakhri Bazzaz of Harvard University in the United States, as reported in *New Scientist* 2 June 1990. He considers that species could vary dramatically in their response. Unfortunately for agriculture, Bazzaz's own results indicate that plants such as sugar cane and corn are not improved, but weeds are stimulated.

Other results vary slightly. Christian Korner and John A. Arnone, both of the Department of Botany, University of Basel, Switzerland also set out to test these hypotheses. They constructed a humid tropical ecosystem typical of 40% of the earth's biomass locations. The control rooms had CO_2 levels maintained at earth's then current elevated level of 340 ppm. In the test room CO_2 levels were almost doubled to 610 ppm. A detailed report and analysis of these experiments showed a surprising lack of response to the elevated CO_2 levels. Their conclusion: global warming will not self-correct, nor will it produce any significant or meaningful enhanced plant growth.

Apart from the above, the lowest carbon dioxide level used in any of these types of tests, that I am aware of, was 500 ppm. That's almost double the preindustrial levels of 280 ppm.

To summarize: the growth-stimulating effect on some plant species in atmospheres with artificially high carbon dioxide levels has been definitely detected. Also, after considering the test results we can say with absolute certainty that it will have negligible effects on reducing, or even slowing global warming.

The oil companies' public relations people would like a different image to be accepted. They need confusion to be created and in consequence we are force-fed false and misleading statements about the growth benefits of elevated atmospheric levels of carbon dioxide.

The way we are being directed and brainwashed needs to become obvious to every thinking person. It becomes very apparent that thoughtful and responsible action by all of us, as individuals and collectively, is the only true defence against world climatic disaster.

STRATEGY 12
Suggesting fossil fuels are only a minor contributor to global warming

The fossil carbon companies and the oil-rich nations must always imply or suggest that the major causes of global warming are not the result of burning fossil fuels. This is not an easy task, but they have to keep saying it. So they blame burning or clearing of remote tropical rainforests. They blame methane produced in Asian rice fields, they blame methane released in the flatulence of farmed livestock, they blame land clearing and blame sunspots. They blame the unpredictable and uncontrollable discharges of carbon dioxide from volcanic eruptions. Everything is loudly touted as being at least a "highly significant factor" in global warming. They blame anything that can take the heat off the simple fact that fossil carbon fuels and petrochemical products are by far the prime cause of our current global warming and its cancerous climatic change.

Most of the volcanoes in the world are actually in the oceans. They occur between continental masses in places like the Mid-Atlantic Ridge that runs north-south up the centre of the Atlantic oceans. The fossil carbon lobbies' advertising and public relations people have not yet (at this time of writing) discovered these undersea volcanoes. But rest assured, very soon they will, and then promote them as a "very significant source" of carbon dioxide.

How often do you see stories in your local media about "pristine" rainforests being destroyed by supposedly new "slash and burn" agricultural concepts? One wonders what advertising agency dreamed up that beautifully emotive description of an agricultural practice that has been totally sustainable for several thousand years. Unnumbered examples of jungle land clearing by burning, subsequent farming for various periods and subsequent regrowth of the jungle, can be seen in places as far apart as the Amazon basin in South America and Borneo in Southeast Asia.

Methane is a powerful greenhouse gas and the fossil fuel industry ensures that all non-petroleum sources receive excessive blame. Flatulence from cattle receives a ridiculous amount of attention, but did the herds of bison that roamed the American west have better table manners or maybe a different digestive system than modern cows? They had neither. New Zealand recently tried to impose a "flatulence tax" on livestock to demonstrate the government's "seriousness" in combating global warming! New Zealand's leaders have taken virtually no other steps to control CO_2 emissions whatever, other than signing the hamstrung and meaningless Kyoto Protocol.

The media and the green advocates blame rice fields for producing methane. Yet swamps (that we must now call "wetlands" so they have a more acceptable image) are constantly producing enormous quantities of methane from rotting, oxygen-starved vegetation. The wet tropical rainforests of the world produce and discharge into the atmosphere an estimated 55,000,000 tons of methane gas per year. Almost as much again is produced in the northern latitude wetlands. This dwarfs methane from rice production tenfold (NASA Goddard Institute for Space Studies).

All these stories and claims are designed to instill a widespread feeling that global warming just cannot be stopped. It cannot be stopped by the efforts of nations, and definitely not by the efforts of individuals. If the public relations people can have us resigned to a belief that global warming is inevitable, they have won. People will then relegate global warming and endless and erratic climatic changes into some "too-hard basket".

STRATEGY 13
Claim electric cars result in more carbon dioxide from the extra power stations

For individual mobile transport, modifying them to operate on biofuels is the easiest and quickest conversion possible to cut greenhouse gas production. The other option is to build electrically powered vehicles and carry the stored electricity in some form of battery. The essential proviso is that the batteries must be charged from power that is not generated at fossil-fuel-burning power stations.

Electrically driven motor vehicles in particular have all the advantages and none of the disadvantages of petrol and diesel systems. Their problem is how to store the electrical energy needed to run them. There is as yet no practical answer to this problem, and when and if it is solved there is absolutely no distribution system in place, or close to being in place, to fill up when a vehicle gets low on this "fuel". Such a system can't even be thought of until a viable battery or a battery equivalent has been invented. These are probably the only real downsides. But they are extreme hurdles and not easy to overcome.

Electric-powered vehicles produce no pollution of any kind—just none. And if it's wanted, they can be made to beat almost any car off at the lights. The General Motors' electrically powered "Impact" sport car is mentioned further on. Electric motor vehicles present a difficult public relations problem for the oil companies, and oil people don't like to give in. Downsides just have to be invented and promoted.

Claim electric cars produce greenhouse gases

This is the major "downside" peddled.

Electric cars run on electricity. The electricity has first to be generated. The electricity is then sent down the wire from the power station, fed into the car and stored in some sort of battery. Coal is the traditional power source for large central power stations. Neglecting minor pollutants, coal is almost pure carbon. Petrol on the other hand contains carbon atoms and hydrogen atoms. Burning coal produces carbon dioxide. Burning petrol produces a mix of burnt carbon as CO_2 (and some CO—carbon monoxide) and burnt hydrogen as H_2O. So in terms of released energy, petrol produces less carbon dioxide. The argument therefore states: it is better to burn petrol in the car than coal at the power station.

Another part of the argument is that sending the electricity down the power lines and storing it in batteries is not 100% efficient. Therefore we need to produce more power at the power station to cover this added waste. This argument always avoids mentioning the higher efficiency of the electric motor at all speeds compared to the intermittently loaded petrol or diesel engine. The internal combustion engines used in motor vehicles also produce other nasties, various nitrogen oxides, sulphur compounds and carbon monoxide. Nevertheless the claim is made that electrically powered cars in the final analysis cause more pollution than petrol driven cars. This marketing ploy studiously avoids the reality that power stations don't necessarily have to run on coal or other fossil fuels.

To prevent the possible general adoption of the electric motor vehicle, the oil lobby group's obvious ploy has to be, "stop hydroelectricity, stop wave energy, stop wind, stop solar and tidal power generation, and especially stop nuclear energy". Their unavoidable and perfectly natural plan is that petrol, diesel, and natural gas must remain the inevitable choice for transport.

Claim electric cars simply move pollution out of town

By ignoring non-fossil fuel power stations and assuming the power comes from coal, the argument is made that the site of production of the greenhouse gases is simply moved from the car exhaust pipe to the power station smokestack. The problem is stated as having simply been moved out of town and the problem has been relocated into somebody else's backyard. Unjustly and ignobly the pollution is swept under somebody else's carpet. Guilt and animosity can thus be fostered.

The objective in these arguments is to establish a general feeling and belief in the community that electrically powered cars cannot and will not solve the problem, not now and not ever. An image can then be fostered that advocates and promoters of electric vehicles are undoubtedly fools and false prophets.

In the eyes of the oil lobby's image-makers, the general public can be so conditioned that they accept the totally false premise that electrically powered vehicles are an irresponsible answer. They can be conditioned to "know" that the adoption of these electric powered vehicles, simply and selfishly, forces the pollution problem onto somebody else's shoulders.

But the arguments are wrong. Electric powered motor vehicles will help reverse global overheating. If all our vehicles suddenly and miraculously became electric, then all we would need is a lot more power stations to provide the electricity. We just have to make sure these new power stations don't run on fossil fuels. If it means we have to pay a couple of cents a kilowatt-hour more for our power it would most certainly be worth it.

Electric vehicles are practical and versatile. They are out there in the marketplace and being used now. The General Motors "Impact" is one at the high-powered top end of the market. Most are smaller, more compact and designed for urban use. Wherever and whenever we can, we have to support their development and use, for eventually power for them will come from non-fossil-fuel sources.

The relative importance of various energy systems and the most practical of the alternate transport fuels is covered in chapter 11.

STRATEGY 14
Smearing the image of electric power in motor vehicles

Sometimes the articles published in science journals could be considered laughable if they were not so frighteningly insidious. This is one they didn't get away with. It asks, "What's wrong with electric cars?" and then supplies some strange answers. This is what happened.

We have three professors from the Carnegie Mellon University of Pittsburgh, Pennsylvania: a professor of economics, a professor of engineering and a professor of environmental engineering. In a combined authoritative article, they explain their version of the truth about electric cars. It was entitled "Environmental Implications of Electric Cars" and was published in *Science*, Vol. 268.

In a broad claim, the article makes wide criticisms. It argues that electric cars may produce no pollution at their point of use but everywhere else they do. It states categorically that the power generation required in the first place must come from a remote fossil-fuel run power station and therefore "electric cars are a means of switching the location of environmental discharges". As always, it is blithely presumed in the article that all power stations burn, and always will burn, fossil carbon as their energy source. Again, nuclear energy, solar, hydro, wave, geothermal and wind energy are presumed not even to exist. It then states that, "The environmental effects of internal combustion engines are well known", and therefore, it seems we are to presume, perfectly acceptable. It goes on with an unusual claim that "Pollution controls (on motor vehicles) have lowered emissions by 98%" compared to a "control car". That statement is standard statistical gobbledygook. Carbon dioxide is simply not considered as an atmospheric pollutant in such statements. They seem to be minimizing the description of pollutants down to sulphur compounds, nitrogen compounds, and maybe soot.

The main thrust of this report however, is to establish that the lead in the batteries of the electric vehicles will somehow get into the atmosphere. By using a series of somewhat unusual presumptions, they managed to conclude, "an electric car using batteries with newly mined lead releases sixty times the peak fraction released by combustion of leaded gasoline". However, this supposedly authoritative report does generously state that if "recycled lead, and 'technology goal' batteries are used, only five times as much lead would be released into the atmosphere". Technology goal, meaning that the ultimately ideal design for batteries is still apparently a lead battery.

They finally conclude, and expect people to believe that "Electric vehicles will not be in the public interest until they pose no greater threat to public health and the environment than do alternative technologies, such as vehicles using low-emissions gasoline."

The report was published in *Science*, the journal of American Association for the Advancement of Science. There would have been a lot of people that just read that one issue of *Science* or just the article, and not have seen the deluge of follow-up letters denouncing these irrational oil-biased claims.

The report received serious criticism in the subsequent issue of the United Kingdom publication *New Scientist*. It headed its article, "Fears over lead from electric cars unfounded". The *New Scientist* article cited criticisms of the Carnegie Mellon University report from innumerable sources. It stated that both industrial and environmental groups were vociferous in their claims that the report contains "grave flaws". The "researchers have used unrealistic assumptions", *New Scientist* maintained. John Rodman of the Massachusetts Executive Office of Environmental Affairs stated that "The benefits of reducing pollution from traffic in cities (by using electric vehicles) will far exceed the risks of small increases in lead releases".

Michael Weinstein of ElectroSource from Austin, Texas, a producer of advanced lead-acid batteries, was probably totally correct when he complained of "misleading scare tactics" in the Carnegie Mellon study.

Critics also complained that the Carnegie Mellon's claim that $1\frac{1}{3}$ tons of batteries were needed to run a zero-emission vehicle (ZEV) was a "serious over estimate". At that time General Motors had already produced their electric sports car, the Impact, for trial runs. This car contained 522 kilos (1,150 lbs.) of batteries and demonstrated a very zippy performance even on its conventional lead-acid batteries. The Carnegie Mellon team, for good measure, also let it be known that they were "skeptical" of the General Motors endurance figures for the Impact.

Incidentally, two U.S. power supply companies in Los Angeles conducted a survey on 79 drivers who were each given Impacts to use for 4-week trial periods. All the drivers were pleased with their vehicles and were impressed with the "Impact's quietness and smooth acceleration". Their major complaint was that recharging could only be done at their homes. To solve this problem, Californian power companies are now installing recharging stations in car parks and shopping centres around Los Angeles to cater for the expected expanding demand.

The Carnegie Mellon report received a wave of ridicule and criticism from competent scientists all over the United States. Finally, four months later in August 1995, *Science* finally printed a few letters criticizing the report. It admitted that the journal had received "an unusual number of letters" and that "most criticized the thesis that electric cars would be more polluting than leaded petrol". Comments included in the letters received by *Science* included words and statements like "absurd", "misleading" and "the analysis does not appropriately support its conclusions". Other statements included "These amazing conclusions result from errors of fact and incorrect assumptions regarding current and future EVs (electrical vehicles)". Other comments on the Carnegie Mellon studies included "the conclusions are over statements based on obsolete data and extremely pessimistic technology assumptions".

Some letters pointed out that lead-acid batteries are already in every car on every road in the United States, about 100 million of them. Other letters also suggested that undoubtedly superior batteries will come on line much faster as a result of the development of electric vehicles.

The published letters most definitely were not from irresponsible and ill-informed people and there were too many to suggest that the criticism was an orchestrated public relations exercise. Letters questioning facets and conclusions of the Carnegie Mellon study came from such people as Roland J. Hwang of the Union of Concerned Scientists, Berkeley, California, Gary Rubenstein and Thomas C. Austin of Sierra Research, Sacramento, California. Linda Gaines and Michael Wang of the Energy System Division, Argonne National Laboratories, Argonne, Illinois, Clark W. Gellings and Stephen C. Peck of Electric Power Research, Palo Alto, California, and David Allen of Department of Chemical Engineering, University of California, Los Angeles. The editors of *Science* received so many letters that they ultimately had to cap off the criticism.

It was certainly refreshing to see so many responsible people speaking out. Still one has to wonder how many times the original Carnegie Mellon report has been used by the oil lobby, and quoted as "published scientific facts" (that is, outside of scientific circles).

The invented dangers of EMF, a giant confidence trick

Electric vehicles are being linked in an incredibly sinister and irresponsible manner to cancer. This totally hypothetical link relies on some very nebulous and dubious "scientific studies". You be the judge.

Epidemiologists study epidemics and the occurrence and distribution of diseases in populations. In 1979 two epidemiologists, Nancy Wertheimer and Ed Leeper, of the University of Colorado Health Center in Denver, published a study suggesting a statistical link between the occurrence of leukaemia in children and their exposure to EMF or electromagnetic fields (confusingly, EMF is also used as an abbreviation for electromagnetic force). An unbelievable series of media reports and claims followed the publication of their paper in a science journal. This was unusual as such research papers on uninteresting statistical analysis rarely receive so much coverage.

An electromagnetic field, an EMF, is created around a wire when an electric current moves along it. You learn this in school physics. Every wire in your house, when carrying an electric current, produces a small electromagnetic field. Electric currents even flow in our own bodies and we produce our own EMFs. An electrocardiogram simply measures the EMF generated by the heart muscle as it beats. The strength of the EMF depends on the strength of the current in the wire, but more importantly on the distance from the wire carrying the current; it drops very rapidly as the distance away from the wire increases. It's the same reason why radio signals quickly become weaker as the receiver moves further away from the transmitter.

It should be pointed out that, totally unrelated to the EMF health debate, small quantities of ozone are sometimes generated around high-tension power cables. Very high levels of ozone are always produced during electrical storms. Ozone generators are actually used in hospitals to refresh the air as ozone is known to be beneficial at certain levels. In the case of power lines, and because the quantities are so small, it is virtually impossible to predict whether the ozone produced is a theoretical health benefit or a theoretical health hazard. So it wasn't an ozone issue.

Following Wertheimer's and Leeper's paper there was an incredible explosion in research to determine whether their nebulous link between exposure to EMF and childhood leukaemia really did exist. And if it existed, was it in any way meaningful? Could it be a significant health hazard? Was it simply a phenomenon of purely academic importance? Or was it imagined? Subsequent researches claimed they detected a statistical link. Others said their statistics proved that no links existed.

Other researchers claimed they detected beneficial effects. Some noted enhanced bone healing and bone regeneration after exposure to much higher levels of EMFs. Bone breaks were healing quicker. Other research suggested a statistical reduction in the occurrence of cancer in people exposed to high level EMF radiation.

The media seemed to have had a field day, but the reporting indicated a widespread and systematic bias. Virtually every caption, in every head-line, in every media report, highlighted the dangers. Rarely, if ever, were beneficial effects mentioned. Nor were we informed that a lot of the studies failed to find any link whatsoever. Despite the media headlines, absolutely no evidence was found to warrant concern for low-level electromagnetic fields. The research was extensive. In 1990, the Committee on Interagency Radiation Research and Policy Coordination, part of the White House Office of Science and Technology Policy, published a report concluding, "there is no convincing evidence in the published literature to support the contention that exposures to extremely low frequency electric and magnetic fields generated by sources such as household appliances, video display terminals, and local power lines are demonstrable health hazards".

Nevertheless, the fears that power lines were a health hazard continued to be promoted.

Then in 1992, a researcher, Robert P. Liburdy, published two papers that considered a mechanism for a possible link between electromagnetic field exposure and cancer—a connection that additionally would link EMF exposure to a host of other diseases. His research indicated EMFs increased the flow of calcium into lymphocytes. This increase in calcium flow could then conceivably lead to cancer because of the interrelation between calcium and cell division. Thus the plot thickened. A supposedly plausible, and very easily marketable link was thus finally established.

But who was Liburdy? Seven years later, in June 1999, the United States watchdog on scientific honesty, the U.S. Office of Research Integrity, stated that Robert P. Liburdy had "engaged in scientific misconduct by intentionally falsifying and fabricating data and claims". Relating to the EMF-cancer link, Liburdy had also "deliberately created artificial data where no such data existed". Before these findings, between 1992 and 1999, Liburdy had received federal research grants totalling almost US$6 million! The Office of Research Integrity's findings were reported in both the October 1999 issue of *Scientific American* and the 2 July 1999 issue of *Science*.

But that was in 1999. In 1992, the United States National Institute of Environmental Health Sciences spent US$66 million on a study concluding that the "possible" dangers of EMF radiation were "based on limited evidence". In 1995, the British National Radiological Protection Board's Advisory Group on Non-Ionizing Radiation, after a comprehensive review, reported that there was no persuasive biological evidence to link normal everyday EMF levels with the incidence of cancer of any form. In 1996, the United States National Research Council concluded yet another exhaustive three-year study on whether EMFs from power lines or household appliances posed a threat to human health. Their sixteen-member panel stated that there is "no conclusive and consistent evidence" that EMFs, at anything except possibly extreme levels, pose any threat to human health.

A large-scale study on EMFs was completed in July 1997. A team of epidemiologists led by Martha Linet of the U.S. National Cancer Institute and Leslie Robison of the University of Minnesota, Minneapolis completed what *Science* described as the most carefully controlled study yet. This was a five-year, US$5 million study on the possible link between EMFs and childhood leukaemia. "The results are very clear," Robison summarized at the conclusion of the study, "They're negative." There is no link.

Edward Champion, the deputy editor of *The New England Journal of Medicine*, on reviewing the 1997 study, suggested it was time to "stop wasting our research resources" on the EMF/cancer hypothesis. After spending almost US$100 million at a variety of universities and research establishments, that summation is now near everybody's opinion.

Who is it, or what organizations are they, that constantly fuel this hypothetical threat that EMFs cause cancer? And why do they do it? It would seem that if any risk factor did exist, the risk is obviously so low that avoiding it is vastly more life-threatening than living with it. Imagine eliminating electricity from our households, no electric lights, no refrigerators. How many people would die in fires caused by accidents with candles and kerosene lanterns, or suffer food poisoning from poorly kept food? So again, who benefits from constantly rejuvenating an esoteric debate about a nonexistent medical phenomenon?

In October 1995, Peter Wright of Cambridge UK, in a letter to the editor of *New Scientist*, pointed out some interesting concepts. California, along with twelve other U.S. states, were introducing legislation to enforce the introduction of ZEVs (zero-emission vehicles). The legislators were endeavouring to have 10% of the registered vehicles in each of their states as zero-emission vehicles by 2003. (It never actually happened.)

Wright reminded us that ZEVs run on electricity. The ongoing controversy over the apparent danger of EMFs in the United States appeared to be leading to the imposition of a federally enforced "safety limit" for human exposure to EMFs. A tesla is a measure of magnetic field strength. A proposed limit of 0.2 microteslas had been suggested. This is an exceedingly small amount. That law would then have automatically made zero-emission vehicles totally illegal in the United States, and if this were the case then no other country would ever have bothered producing them. The electric motor vehicle would have been finished. Incidentally the law would have also made it illegal to operate every vacuum cleaner ever made, along with almost every other electric appliance used in the home. That's what would have resulted had these irresponsible and idiotic "safety measures" been adopted.

The significant result would have been the creation of a U.S. federal law effectively mandating that all vehicles in the United States would be built to run on gasoline or diesel.

In the media the EMF argument still goes on. Despite all the research to the contrary, the media have kept hammering the supposed dangers of electromagnetic fields. What has been the effects of this long drawn out, extravagant, and wasteful debate? Although it is not necessarily wasteful to the objectives of the oil companies. Much of the development of ZEVs must have gone on hold "awaiting developments". In 1993, over 40% of the American population were convinced that exposure to EMFs from power lines was a serious health hazard. Four years after in 1997, a survey by The Edison Electric Institute showed that 33% of Americans still viewed EMFs as a serious health threat.

And what was the price paid? *Scientific American* reported on what appeared to be the only factual survey conducted on the cost to the U.S. economy of the EMF scare campaign. The estimate was around one billion U.S. dollars. The costs were mainly attributed to massive modifications and rerouting of new power lines. This incredible waste is now ongoing. The lies, the stupidity and the waste have spread across the world. We are all paying for this incredible mass of scare mongering.

The one really bright side to it all is that in the end and to their credit, the U.S. federal government did not make zero-emission vehicles illegal. This time the oil companies didn't win, it's just that everybody else lost.

STRATEGY 15
Claiming removing lead from petrol makes it safe to burn

The chemicals tetraethyl lead and tetramethyl lead, when added to petrol, greatly increases its octane rating. (See "CFCs and the story of a brilliant chemist" in chapter 4. The octane rating of a fuel is a measure of its anti-knocking properties. Knocking occurs when fuel-air mixtures pre-ignite from compression heating in the engine cylinder. The resulting overly rapid ignition produces a sharp rise in pressure that produces the "knock".

Older vehicles produced before about 1970 had engines with relatively high compression ratios, often around 10:1, and knocking was a problem unless tetraethyl lead was added to the fuel. Modern petrol engines typically use lower compression ratios around 8:1. The compression ratio is the ratio of the volume of the air in the cylinder when the piston is at the bottom, divided by the volume when it is at the top.

Less nitrous oxides are produced in petrol engines with lower compression ratios. Higher compression ratio engines are in general more efficient, but many factors influence overall efficiency. Today, well-designed modern engines are often more efficient, despite their reduced compression ratios, than the older higher-compression ratio engines.

The amount of lead added to some fuel categories has been kept high to cater for older vehicles, and also for a few "high performance" engines produced by companies like Ferrari.

When burning so-called leaded petrol, that is petrol containing tetraethyl lead in an engine, the exhaust gases do contain small quantities of metallic lead. Leaded petrol actually incorporates other additives that purposely ensure the lead is exhausted rather than deposited in the engine. With excessive contact lead accumulates in the human body and ultimately lead poisoning can occur. In ancient Rome, lead drinking vessels and dinnerware were common items on a meal table, making lead poisoning a common occurrence in those times. Entirely for health reasons, tetraethyl lead has been removed from most petrol grades and the petrol is less poisonous and less dangerous. Or so we are led to believe.

There are other anti-knocking compounds that can be added to petrol. Lead-replacement petrols often contain compounds like highly poisonous aniline ($C_6H_5NH_2$) although tetraethyl lead is probably still the most effective of the minor additives.

It has to be understood that ethanol, which is not derived from fossil fuels, is also an excellent anti-knocking agent, but you do need more of it—

up to about 25% suits well. This would be instead of half a gram of tetraethyl lead per litre, or a like quantity of some other additive to get the same anti-knocking effect. Brazil uses 25% ethanol blends so their cars can be built with more efficient higher compression engines.

The reduction in compression ratios that has been designed into current model cars used elsewhere has meant that tetraethyl lead can be eliminated from petrol, but most significantly for the oil industry, the addition of ethanol to boost petrol's octane rating is no longer a meaningful advantage.

Having sugar cane farmers or corn farmers produce 25% of the fuel for spark ignition engines in any nation will always to be strenuously resisted by oil interests. The resultant 25% decrease in oil sales if it happened would be a massive sales reduction in anybody's books.

Oil companies promote the introduction of unleaded petrol as a great environmental win for the people. Oil companies now advertise their fuel as environmentally friendly. The fact that from every kilogram of petrol used in a car almost three kilograms of carbon dioxide comes out the exhaust pipe is never mentioned. It has to be stretching the imagination to the extreme to believe petrol is in any way environmentally friendly. But we are encouraged to believe so. Beautiful images are used. Advertisements show children playing in a clean green forest. Sunlight filters through the sparkling canopy. The impression to be created in the public mind is that a great environmental breakthrough has been achieved. A caring sense of responsibility has been envisaged. Petrol or gasoline can be seen as a wonderful, environmentally safe product.

Drought, hurricane destruction, starvation, catastrophic flooding, malaria, the list goes on, are all becoming much more common because carbon dioxide buildup is destabilizing world climates. Car exhausts discharge carbon dioxide, carbon monoxide, nitrous oxides and sulphur compounds into the atmosphere, even if the lead is taken out. Removing lead from petrol has removed one toxin, but concurrently it usually decreases the engine efficiency so more petrol is used on a trip—bigger fuel sales, and more CO_2 is produced.

STRATEGY 16
Promoting petrol motor vehicles over diesel

This is on manipulating public opinion to increase the cash value of sales. With few exceptions, all motor vehicles are powered by internal combustion engines. There are two different types, one runs on petrol (gasoline), the other runs on diesel. The real difference is in how the fuel is ignited within the engine cylinder. Petrol engines use a spark to initiate combustion. Diesel engines use the heat of compression for ignition. The same heat you feel when using a hand-operated bicycle air pump.

In a common four-stroke petrol engine, a mixture of air and fuel is drawn into the cylinder as the piston descends on the "intake stroke". The fuel is mixed with the air either in an external carburetor or by "injecting" the fuel into the air just before it enters the cylinder. The piston then ascends on the "compression stroke". At the end of the compression stroke the spark plug ignites the fuel-air mixture. The burning fuel produces both a lot of additional gases and a lot of heat, which expands the gas mixture. The pressure in the cylinder increases, driving the piston down on the "power stroke". Finally, the piston ascends again on the "exhaust stroke", pushing the gases out and into the exhaust pipe. It then descends ready to start the sequence all over again.

A four-stroke diesel engine operates in much the same manner except for the essential difference that only air is drawn into the cylinder on the intake stroke. At the top of the compression stroke, the fuel is sprayed or "injected" at very high pressure into the cylinder. As the air is rapidly compressed in the cylinder it becomes very hot; hot enough that the injected fuel ignites spontaneously. That's the compression ignition. The difference in the method of ignition has some important consequences for petrol and diesel engines, mostly related to the compression ratio. In the case of petrol engines the compression ratio cannot be too high or the heat generated during compression will be enough to prematurely ignite the fuel-air mixture; if this happens, the engine "knocks" and doesn't run efficiently. The practical limit on the compression ratio for petrol engines is about 10:1, but most engines today operate at about 8:1 as noted. Knocking is prevented by the addition of special agents to the fuel as discussed in Strategy 15.

In contrast the compression ratio in a diesel engine must be high so that the temperature produced during compression is high enough to ensure ignition of the injected fuel. Compression ratios in diesels can be as high as 22:1 but more commonly are around 18:1.

There is a popular belief that diesel engines are much more efficient than petrol engines because of their higher compression ratio. That is true, but only in part. Today's diesel and petrol engines convert fuel to useful work with almost equal efficiencies. However, diesel engines do achieve better "fuel economies" measured in miles per gallon or litres per hundred kilometres.

There are two reasons for this. The first is there is simply more energy in a gallon of diesel than there is in the same quantity of petrol—about 10% more. The second reason for a diesel engine's better fuel economy comes from the fact that, for a given size, diesel engines do not provide as high a power output as petrol engines. This is in contrast to some vehicle manufacture's advertisements that proclaim the "power" of diesel engines. But anybody who has driven the same model vehicle, powered by petrol and diesel engines of similar capacity, will tell you that the petrol engine provides much better "performance". This is one reason why turbochargers are popular on diesel power vehicles—they provide more power and more rapid acceleration. This of course is at the expense of fuel economy.

If there is one enemy of good fuel economy, it is high performance. The more acceleration we demand, the more fuel we use. So it's sensible marketing to sell us "performance" vehicles.

Diesel engines are universally used in heavy haulage industries for a number of reasons. The higher fuel economy is more important because of the huge amounts of fuel being used, but also because the engines are more reliable and longer lasting.

Oil companies naturally prefer us driving high-performance petrol-engined cars as we must buy more fuel. Diesel is relatively simple to produce from crude oil. Petrol production requires more effort and is therefore inherently more expensive. Petrol therefore is a "value added" product. For the same distance travelled, oil companies make more profit out of petrol than diesel. If we do select a diesel car, the oil companies love it to be turbocharged at least, so it guzzles more fuel.

It is the obvious business plan of the petroleum companies to have everybody driving petrol-powered cars.

More frightening for the oil industry is the fact that replacing diesel with renewable biodiesel is amazingly simple, only the fuel is changed. No engine modifications are required as is the case in changing a current petrol engine to run on ethanol. A few farmers are already making their own biodiesel. It can be produced from any vegetable oils, even waste oils. It's very simple and recipes are readily available. (For both ethanol and biodiesel information, see chapter 11.)

With the generally poor acceleration of normally aspirated diesel engines and the fact that, as they age they often produce black smoke, it is not difficult for the oil companies to steer us from diesel cars to petrol cars. Although the black smoke that can come from old diesels looks bad, the actual chemical mix is nowhere near as toxic as that from petrol engines. The discharge of both poisonous carbon monoxide and various nitrogen oxides in the exhaust of petrol engines is far higher than in diesel engines. Of course they both produce huge quantities of carbon dioxide, which the oil companies like us to consider as a harmless byproduct.

The smoke produced by diesels gives the oil companies another angle to convince us to use petrol. Some of the very fine smoke particles are harmful. Others are not. Particles smaller than ten microns (ten millionth of a metre) are now generally referred to as PM10s. Two and a half PM10s, side by side, would be 0.001 of an inch across. The inhalation of these particles has the most effect on the elderly, but inhalation of PM10s is harmful to all. Because the smoke is very visible, it's relatively easy to get research funding to study its effect. The report from the United Kingdom's Royal Commission on Environmental Pollution insisted that atmospheric levels of PM10s have to drop. However the end results are not as bad as it first sounds, for the black smoke from diesels, including the PM10s, is solid carbon—it's soot, and so is easily washed out of the air by rain.

It may be a deliberate muddying of the waters, but it is extremely difficult to come up with death rate figures solely attributable to the poisons in petrol exhausts. The figures would certainly be many times higher than figures for PM10 deaths and just in Britain alone 10,000 people die every year from PM10 inhalation. That's Britain's estimate. An estimate for the United States suggested 60,000 deaths per year from PM10s from petroleum diesel but many times more deaths from petrol engine exhaust.

Biodiesel is far safer. Biodiesel is slightly more expensive than petroleum-based diesel but is totally biodegradable. It is also nontoxic and sulphur-free. The U.S. Department of Energy reports that there is a 47.4% reduction in the quantity of particles produced by using biodiesel in trucks. They also note that total exhaust-fume toxicity is reduced by between 60% and 90%. The U.S. Environmental Protection Agency, after rigorous testing, listed biodiesel as complying with the strict legislative requirements of their EPA Clean Air Act.

Therefore, in the UK alone, switching to biodiesel would save about 7,500 lives per year. In the United States, possibly 45,000 lives per year could be saved. Switching from petrol to diesel engines and then running them on biodiesel would save the lives of an incredible number of people.

STRATEGY 17
Promote fuel-guzzling vehicles and motor sports

In Western societies nearly everybody of any substance either owns a car or simply doesn't want to own a car. Selling more cars therefore does not sell more gasoline or diesel. It simply means older cars are junked quicker. So how do you sell more fuel? The only avenue is to have each individual vehicle consume more of it. Selling more fuel thus becomes a marketing problem.

Motorcar racing is exciting stuff—powerful engines, roaring exhausts, speed, danger and adrenalin. After watching a high-speed motor race it's almost impossible to get into the family car and not fantasize on having 500 horsepower under the bonnet. Motor racing makes it easy to sell powerful cars and powerful cars consume more fuel. Big oil companies support all motor sports. And as a bonus they acquire an image of cooperative community involvement. As the supporters of these sports they become the "good guys". Remember the cigarette companies, the advertisements on every flat surface? They did the same thing, and for similar reasons.

The marketing objective for the oil companies must always be to have excessively large engines that produce enormous acceleration and incredible top speeds. It's a wonderful objective. Such engines are gas-guzzlers just idling. The promotional literature discusses acceleration. It typically considers factors such as time taken to reach 60 mph or 100 klicks. The objective is firstly to have acceleration as a common topic of conversation, but more specifically to have people who currently own low-powered cars feel the need to "upgrade". It suits both the carmakers—they sell more expensive cars, and the oil companies—they sell more fuel.

Actively supporting all sports that use or rely on powerful engines is astute oil company marketing. It is wonderfully incongruous but rarely mentioned that actually most of these high performance race-cars run on methanol or ethanol. This is both to increase the efficiency of the engines and to eliminate the extreme pollution levels generated by using petrol. Levels that would almost asphyxiate the spectators, probably along with the host city. One important feature is that methanol and ethanol fires can be very easily extinguished with water. Those fuels mix and get diluted in water. Petrol and diesel don't. They just keep burning.

Both the methanol and ethanol can be made by fermentation processes. Ethanol always is. Both are therefore biofuels. This minor detail is never, never, highlighted in racecar promotional material.

Actually methanol can be produced more easily from oil, and generally is. Ethanol can't. So if a mention is made of the fuels being used and not the fuel company promoting the events, it is only ever of methanol. Methanol is generally the nominated fuel despite the fact that even in small doses, methanol is very poisonous, whereas humans drink ethanol. A good liqueur can contain 90% ethanol.

The other marketing ploy is simply to have cars made bigger and heavier. The end result of this concept is the two-ton, off-road, four-wheel drive, chromium tanks we now use to drive the kids to school. The automobile companies are very much on-side with big cars as the bigger margins are always in the bigger models; the bigger and more powerful the better. The silly thing is that there are so many gadgets and gizmos to go wrong in the modern four-wheel off-road vehicle, that it's almost madness to take it too far off-road.

These monsters are sold for their alleged safety. The reality is that they are often prone to roll over and kill the occupants, where a car wouldn't. Also, accidents involving such vehicles are much more likely to cause injuries and death to others. In accidents involving pedestrians, for example, for every single death from impact with ordinary cars, these macho machines will cause three deaths.

In many countries road and registration taxes on these fuel-hungry monsters are actually quite specifically reduced to help sales. Now that must have taken some astute and clever lobbying. If you don't own one, recognize the marketing hype, do the sums and don't buy one. Also help prevent global warming by reminding current owners of their gullibility so they don't buy another one.

STRATEGY 18
Promote walking and cycling to save the environment

This is a red herring that pretends that solutions are available to prevent global warming but people are too irresponsible to embrace them.

Walking or cycling to work or to the shopping centre is a nice, environmentally desirable concept. But the marketing people in the oil companies are very well aware that the concept is totally impractical and will never be widely accepted. Whether we like it or not, modern cities are designed to cater for cars, trucks, buses and trams. Or else cities have been changed and modified to cater for them.

In the old centre of many expanded cities, where streets are still narrow and four-wheel vehicular traffic is difficult, or even next to impossible, for short trips the bicycle can be a big part of a transport system. Of course weather is naturally a limiting factor, as few are prepared to venture out on bicycles if rain or rain showers are a regular feature of that city's weather. Bicycles don't take on in such towns and cities. Also if a city is not relatively flat, cycling won't ever be a preferred transport option. Nor will it be if distances are anything but tiny.

In underdeveloped countries, and especially in developing countries, the bicycle has become a major transport option. However this is probably because the only other option is to walk. When weather and topography allows, although slow, the bicycle is a very inexpensive means of transport. But as community wealth rises the small motorbike then become the preferred option. In developing countries it is common to see a whole family mounted up on a small motorbike. Such loading is relatively dangerous and of course would be totally illegal in a Western city.

Having experienced the freedom, the speed and the incredible convenience of totally personalized, individual and independent, self-contained transport, will you or the people you know, willingly go back to the bicycle, our childhood means of transport? What happens when it rains on the way home? How do you carry the shopping, and where do you put your personal laptop? Academic town planners have their lovely and impractical dreams, but observe them—they still drive their cars to their offices and universities!

The oil-marketing people aren't stupid. They support these hypothetical concepts with much fanfare. They know very well push-bikes will never be a serious threat to fossil fuel sales.

Walking is good exercise. Jogging and running are even better exercises. Riding a push-bike is good exercise. These activities undoubtedly will improve your general health; however to consider them as a viable means of modern day transport in our twenty-first century cities is ludicrous.

The standard of living of a society is fundamentally based on the efficiency of the members in the production of goods and services. In turn, the overall efficiency of the society is enhanced or depreciated, depending on

the efficiency with which commodities and services and the people themselves are able to be transported within that society and their communities.
Slow transport systems, such as walking and cycling, are good systems for
transporting people over very short distances. But that's all.

The expression "time is money" is a real truism. Wasting time reduces
the efficiency of a community and consequently reduces that community's
standard of living.

It is true that in flat country, with good road surfaces and consistently
pleasant weather, cycling can be a very practical means of transport to and
from a relatively close place of employment. It is also often the fastest short
distance intra-city parcel and document delivery system. Unfortunately as
a system for moving general goods and delivering services, it can't work. It's
also hopeless if you want to do any serious shopping, or pick up the kids
from school.

Mass transport systems, such as the London Underground, are extremely
practical and efficient people movers. Mass transit systems are a threat to
both the oil and the automotive industry. In consequence, have you noticed
how easy it seems to be to lobby successfully for funding for the construction
of dedicated cycling tracks. The tracks can be in towns or cities, or parks or
wherever you want. But it is almost impossible to obtain financial support
for the construction of mass transport systems. Why is this always so? Are
we in doubt as to who might benefit from such difficulties and obstructions,
and what industries always seem to win in the end?

It must be firmly understood that mass transport systems are an extremely dangerous threat to the petroleum fuel and automotive industries
and for them their adoption is a particularly nasty scenario. Remember how
General Motors, Firestone Tire and Standard Oil of California dismantled
the Los Angles urban transport system. But the threat of bicycles replacing
cars is not a worry. So if a transport system is not seen as any significant
threat, then the oil companies must of course support it, especially if they
achieve a "good image" bonus in the process. It is all just good marketing.
Big oil will always promote bicycles.

STRATEGY 19
Promoting energy conservation as achieving the best value for money

The fossil-fuel marketing gurus promote energy conservation. This seems
on face value to be the antithesis of what they should be arguing. But they
are not fools. The argument is that if we simply cut down on the energy
we use by being more responsible, we will achieve the greatest immediate
reduction in carbon dioxide emissions. And this argument is totally valid.
They endeavour to generate a feeling within us that if we have to, we can.
We can save the world for we always have the energy conservation option

up our sleeve.

By these means they instill in us a sense of complacency. Perfect. Then we will lose interest in other options and we won't have to concern ourselves with some esoteric non-fossil-carbon energy source that always seems to have some unfortunate and "well documented" downside. We can always conserve energy, they say. Sadly that's what too many people are currently believing.

A two-bar electric radiator consumes 2,000 watts. A 60-watt light globe consumes 60 watts. Household air conditioners are powered by between one and three horsepower electric motors. So they use up to 2,000 watts. In total, a civilized Western type society consumes, on average, between 500 and 1,000 watts of electricity per person per hour, twenty-four hours a day, seven days a week, fifty-two weeks a year. That's about equal to one horsepower per person, continuously.

With so much energy consumption it is not surprising that substantial savings should be possible by adopting energy conservation practices. Installing insulation in a house can achieve substantial heating and cooling power reductions, compared to uninsulated houses. Quite often new insulation can even pay for itself in twelve months. Better insulation in refrigerators can noticeably reduce the operating times of the power unit. Using fluorescent lighting instead of incandescent achieves significant power reductions. Turning lights off when you leave a room conserves power. Reducing the number of lights left on merely for decorative effects can achieve dramatic savings.

By adopting very simple energy conservation procedures, overall power reductions could be quite dramatic. It is technically quite easy for a household to reduce power requirements by as much as 50%. So a city of 2 million people being supplied power from coal-fired power stations by adopting sensible, practical, energy conservation practices can reduce its energy requirements to that of a city of only 1 million people. That 2-million-population city would then have reduced the carbon dioxide discharged into the atmosphere from its power station by half. They would be reduced from 24 million tons to 12 million tons a year. That is quite a substantial reduction, but it won't stop global warming.

For the media, promoting all these conservation concepts make good and responsible stories and editorial.

This concept of reducing energy use appears on face value to be such an easy solution. The fossil fuel companies must be seen to be responsible, and so they support it. In fact the fossil fuel companies support energy conservation concepts wholeheartedly. They promote it with very visible enthusiasm. Such action seems noble and very responsible. It would appear the companies are actually advocating a reduction in consumption of the very products they sell.

But is it that simple? Could there be a subtler, a more pragmatic action plan? The real question is: are people going to change? Are we going to change ourselves? It's not easy. And no matter how many conservation concepts are promoted and even adopted, reducing our fossil fuel consumption by these methods only means at best a temporary slowing in an inevitable, ever-increasing carbon dioxide buildup in the atmosphere. Expecting to save the world by the occurrence of a worldwide change in human nature is a risky bet.

The grim reality is that any promoted reduction in energy consumption on any meaningful and permanent scale has never happened. And it won't. The fact is that for the last almost ten years, in almost every major city in the world, we have been regularly requested to stop wasting power. But we don't. Of course in exceptional circumstances, it can work for short periods. Or it could if forced upon us, but neither can be sustained and for one good reason. Few of us will put up with a lack of some totally affordable practical convenience for any prolonged period. We would demand it be fixed. We don't need to nor do we have to put up with such things.

Fossil fuel producers know how we, their customers, behave.

New Zealand has a good example. In their winter of 2003, in the face of dire warnings, low hydroelectric lake levels and an uncommonly dry season, the authorities urgently requested a 13% reduction in power consumption. The reduction was suddenly and easily achieved. Then promptly at the end of the winter excess power was suddenly available. Advertising that promoted electricity consumption was recommenced. The irony is that one of the factors causing that original excess demand in hydroelectricity capacity during the winter was a massive sales promotion to use more power the previous summer.

Take the example of the fuel crisis of the 1970s. For a while cars were reduced in size and engine power. It didn't last long. It now has all been reversed. True, cars are no longer getting bigger and that's a conservation image being pandered. But fuel consumption and fuel sales are. Maybe cars are not getting bigger but the sales promotions and the sales are now for chrome plated, four-wheel or "all wheel" drive army trucks. The public relations people working for the fossil fuel industries made it happen, and they must love their success.

If everybody turned off all the extra lights in the evening, world carbon dioxide production would be reduced. If everybody switched to very small cars with tiny engines, even greater carbon dioxide reductions could be made. If houses were insulated better, still more reductions could be made. The figures prove all these scenarios would be valid. Energy conservation is without doubt the quickest method of rapidly reducing the levels of carbon dioxide emissions. Theoretically, yes, it would all work. Practically, no, it will never happen.

Actually, there is one really significant energy conservation concept that does work, and that is solar hot-water systems. Sunlight on a black pipe will raise the temperature of the circulating water to the point where it is more than ample for household use. There are surprisingly few areas around the world where solar hot-water systems are impractical. To get the water significantly hotter to suit other purposes, the sunlight has to be optically concentrated which is more tricky.

It is smart, and it creates a good public image for fossil fuel power companies to support energy conservation arguments. Concurrently, for their own survival and possible expansion, it is also necessary for them to adopt pricing structures and advertising gimmicks that actually, but subtly, encourage electricity consumption. You might notice that power company advertising always manages to feature well-lit rooms. It also hammers the reliability and convenience of electricity as a useful and versatile tool. Electricity is promoted very successfully as a wonderful and reliable energy source.

In Australia, despite (or perhaps because of) all the apparent efforts to promote energy efficient appliances and energy conservation, the average daily power consumption in houses has doubled over the last few decades. In all developed societies we buy more efficient appliances, but we buy more of them and use them more often. We often leave them turned on. We insulate our houses, then install power-hungry air conditioners. We buy "five star" rated refrigerators which use 20% less energy, but then we keep the old one in the garage as a "bar fridge" and it usually runs continuously as the automatic cutoff no longer works.

In general for meaningful energy conservation to occur, power companies would have to support government-run publicity campaigns advocating energy conservation. Of course, power companies may well see a genuine effort in this area as cutting their own collective throats.

The marketing gurus know we are only human. They wave big banners about energy conservation and how it might save the world. But with the other hand they promote the glamour of a life of high-energy consumption. The oil industries in their turn massively support images of fuel-guzzling car racing. They promote the "fun" of off-road, four-wheel drive, fuel-hungry behemoths that spend their lives on our freeways and suburban streets.

Maybe we can change ourselves a little and penny pinch our energy use and of course it will help—but not much.

Saving energy is not the problem. The real problem is that most of the electricity generated throughout the world comes from power stations that burn fossil fuel. It was always coal. Now they are switching to gas, which won't change things all that much despite the massive pro-gas marketing campaign.

STRATEGY 20

For the fossil fuel conglomerates, it is imperative that every threat to fossil carbon as the prime source of world energy must be fought and beaten

The majority of the countries of the world with a high standard of living support that standard of living by burning at least 5 tons of fossil carbon material annually for every man, woman and child in the country. That in turn produces between 10 and 15 tons of carbon dioxide for every man, woman and child in the country. The amount of money involved in the fossil carbon industries is obviously enormous. The mining companies and the distributing companies of those fossil materials have no intention of letting those numbers drop. As other countries become more productive and increase their standard of living, they too can consume 5 tons per year per person.

The fossil-fuel industries cannot tolerate the thought that this enormous potential market might be threatened by alternative energy. They can't let it. That's their business. Every viable, or even possibly viable alternative energy source must be fought. For all in the coal and oil and gas industries, alternative energy is the enemy.

Generally the terms "sustainable energy" and "alternative energy" are poorly defined despite their widespread use. Throughout this book, I am considering them to mean the following.

Alternative energy is any energy produced by not burning fossil carbon. Fossil carbon is oil, coal, natural gas or in some countries, peat—as peat is sometimes burnt as a fuel.

Sustainable energy is when the raw material for that energy is still there even after huge quantities of the energy have been used or extracted. The energy source is still there in virtually the same quantity.

Wind, ocean tides, hydroelectric, ocean waves, solar, geothermal, bio-fuels, ocean heat transfer, atmospheric heat transfer, nuclear—these are all alternative energy systems and they are also all effectively sustainable. To the oil and gas drillers and the coal miners, they are all the enemy. None of these alternative energy sources cause significant atmospheric pollution or add significant quantities of carbon dioxide to the atmosphere, so in consequence none of them contribute to global warming.

The production and use of nuclear energy does not add carbon dioxide to the atmosphere. Nuclear energy is totally sustainable. Its availability is unlimited especially when thorium reactors become available. That nuclear waste disposal is perceived as an unsolved and insurmountable problem is an example of hugely successful oil-marketing misinformation. The topic is discussed, and I think clarified, in chapter 10, which is devoted exclusively to nuclear energy.

Basic costs of most alternative energies are currently slightly higher than those of coal, and sometimes higher than oil and natural gas. For fossil fuel companies, the alternative energy threat is countered by advertising and editorial emphasizing these often-minimal extra costs. The fossil carbon lobby claim, or imply, that marked decreases in the general standard of living will follow widespread use of alternative energy. In contrast, the reality is that the general standard of living of all people is already reduced massively by their non-adoption and non-use. The costs to the world resulting from widespread weather pattern and general climate changes far exceed any extra cost per kilowatt-hour of alternative energy supplies.

The oil and coal powers are resolute. Alternative energy sources that even vaguely threaten to be cost competitive, or any systems using alternative energy that threaten to be in any way competitive, represent a risk. And that risk must be eliminated or, at the very least, it must be effectively minimized.

Every trick in the trade is used to the full. Environmental information is "rewritten" to denigrate the whole alternative energy concept. Public awareness is manipulated to delay progress and implementation. Government agencies are systematically influenced to obstruct and harass the new concepts and hinder their development. Pressure is brought to bear on the media to produce suitably biased and (for the oil lobby) acceptable editorial. Public officers and politicians are constantly being influenced and coerced into cooperation.

In Australia, in late 2003, a coalition of the World Wide Fund for Nature, Australia (WWF) and the Insurance Australia Group (IAG) was formed with an aim to "guide public opinion and government policy" in relation to global warming. The association describes themselves as The Australian Climate Group (ACG). They brought together "world-renowned scientists and experts from health, insurance and coal industries under the banner of the ACG". (To clear some confusion: The World Wide Fund for Nature, the WWF, was previously known as the World Wildlife Fund, also abbreviated to WWF. Obviously it was decided that a World Wide Fund for Nature is more marketable than merely a World Wildlife Fund.)

You will find the easiest way to access their information is now through the World Wide Fund for Nature. Their first report, released in 2004, *Climate Change—Solutions For Australia*, magnanimously suggested it would be a good idea to reduce greenhouse gas emissions (not levels) by 60% by 2050. That's almost half a century away!

Today, world oil reserves are still at about a 30-year level. (They seem always to be at 30-year levels.) So the Australian Climate Group, who are backed by the WWF, seems to advocate that first, we continue running on oil until all the known oil reserves run dry, and then we continue to run on oil from new oil field discoveries for a further 20 years. Maybe they figure that by then there won't be any oil left. In their plan, oil use will continue unabated, or at least until all current directors of oil companies are dead.

Then it seems we could rely on coal, and we can never really run out of coal as it's there in almost unlimited quantities and it's all easily accessible.

This is their strategy on how to "guide public opinion and government policy" in relation to global warming, all backed by their collection of "world-renowned scientists and experts from health, insurance and coal industries". Is the Insurance Australia Group serious in their supposed desire to reduce global warming? Maybe we should also wonder: did the IAG pick the World Wide Fund for Nature, or did the World Wide Fund for Nature pick the Insurance Australia Group?

Oil companies may compete with each other and oil companies may compete with coal miners and natural gas producers. But, they must all cooperate to downplay the resulting carbon dioxide effects on world climate, and they must all cooperate together to prevent different and threatening players coming into "their" market.

The campaign to distort the facts and confuse the public on the hideous dangers of cigarette smoking is a great role model for the oil-coal-gas lobby. There are more women smoking now than there were when anti-smoking campaigns began. Despite compulsory bans on a whole host of advertising procedures, the cigarette-marketing whiz kids have not given up. In many areas sales have turned and are now on the rise. But of course, the tobacco lobby must ensure such planning and strategic considerations never see the light of day. The fossil carbon lobby is no different.

For the fossil carbon suppliers, like the tobacco producers, it's a simple matter of business survival. To the producing countries it means national power and wealth. To the rest of us, it's the total destruction of the planet's environmental and ecological stability and the horrendous financial costs to us that result.

There are so many simple things the oil and coal people and their friends do to combat the threat of non-fossil-carbon energy. For example, the European Commission years ago established teams of scientists to study the most cost-effective means of stabilizing carbon dioxide emissions by the year 2010 while still maintaining living standards. They concluded that people shouldn't waste power and shouldn't use so much power. If people did that then carbon dioxide emissions could be stabilized. A child could have come up with the same answer at far less cost. However stabilizing is not the answer, emissions must now start decreasing not just levelling out. What is the point of stabilizing at some arbitrary and already guaranteed climate-destabilizing level?

It was even seriously pointed out in the study reported back in the January 1992 issue of *This Week* that Sweden could phase out all its nuclear power stations and generate all its power from oil. All their citizens had to do was turn off a few more lights, and become more diligent in their use of power. To any significant extent, in any modern developed society, that is most unlikely to happen for any prolonged time span. And it didn't.

Energy consumption rises with rising standards of living. With nuclear power manipulated out of the picture, where does the energy come from? The oil and gas companies win.

The same study showed that 22% of carbon dioxide emissions come from transport, but it was decided roads and road transport—not trains and rail transport—would receive the European Commission transport funding.

Also advocated was the concept of considerably more use of natural gas. Natural gas is a fossil fuel and therefore produces carbon dioxide. It just produces a bit less than coal and oil. It's the logical energy plan of the fossil carbon energy industries to eventually replace coal with natural gas.

The reports indicated that fusion energy generation could not be expected in less than fifty years and the European Commission then promptly allocated more than half of all energy research funding into this bottomless pit. Fusion energy is discussed in chapter 10.

The Europeans are simply refusing to develop energy systems and programs that don't destroy the climate. Do they expect the developing nations to develop the technology for them? What do the Europeans expect will happen if developing nations start pumping carbon dioxide into the air at the same per capita rate that the Europeans propose they themselves should stabilize at? The EU makes well-publicized efforts to decrease carbon dioxide emissions but it's all of little substance.

Alternative energy is claimed as "abominable for the landscape"

The oil tanker *Braer*, containing 84,000 tons of oil, hit the rocks off Garth's Ness in Scotland on 5 January 1993. All the oil ended up in the sea off the Shetland Islands. Coincidentally within days, the editorial in a prominent popular science magazine (*New Scientist*, 23 January 1993 issue) viciously lampooned and criticized alternative energy sources. That seemed like an effort to quell a public backlash against oil and fossil-fuel producers that the *Braer* disaster might generate.

In describing wind power efforts in the UK, the *New Scientist* editorial reminds readers that Californians already "know" that this energy source "has an appalling aesthetic impact on the environment". The article blithely states that the wind towers in Altamont Pass near San Francisco destroy the "natural rhythm of the hills" whereas a string of electricity pylons from British coal power stations "seem to lead the eye pleasantly across the British countryside."

It goes on to claim that the residents of Arizona and New Mexico "gripe about the damage done by solar power". It described a discontinued prototype solar energy system as "massed solar collectors mounted on rusting steel frameworks" and they are as "visually appealing as a junk yard". It even insists that the solar installation causes water erosion whenever it rains in the surrounding desert and that "helps scar the landscape further".

This type of hype is how they change our opinions without us being aware. It is time we stopped allowing ourselves to be so easily manipulated.

STRATEGY 21
Two fictions—clean coal and carbon dioxide sequestration

Firstly the "clean coal" sell:

A society supposedly hooked on cheap energy is like a society hooked on heroin. Promoting and marketing the fiction of clean coal is a little like promoting the concept of supplying clean needles. Clean needles might protect a user from some new infection but they don't remove the addiction problem. An addict can still die from the ill-timed injection or "overdose". In the same way, "clean" coal removes some unpleasant and visually noticeable effects but leaves the underlying problem unchanged. Clean needle advocates don't desire and plan for more heroin use. Clean coal advocates do desire and do plan for more coal use. Worldwide, coal kills more men, women and children by far then heroin ever does, and many times over. Coal-fired power stations are the most globally destructive energy system devised by man.

Coal is mainly carbon. The gases resulting from its combustion are therefore almost pure carbon dioxide. Coal is far worse than either oil or gas. Coal exhaust is our most dangerous anthropogenic atmospheric pollutant on the planet.

If your business is selling fossil fuels, or buried carbonaceous materials of any type, it is necessary that these facts be systematically confused, and then systematically defused.

It seems incongruous but it is totally logical for oil companies to support, albeit unobtrusively, the continuing operation and the continued construction of coal-fired power stations. It is very much in their interest. It must be understood that as long as electricity comes from coal it is easily and logically argued that electric motor vehicles can have no meaningful environmental advantage over gasoline- or diesel-powered vehicles.

In the Carboniferous era, 250 million years ago, enormous and prolific jungles and swamplands sucked the carbon dioxide out of an unbreathable atmosphere and buried it in the ground as coal. The released oxygen drifted into the air and the atmosphere slowly changed.

Over millions of years the oxygen levels built up while the forest litter and the humus accumulated, sometimes to immense thicknesses. Oxygen was unavailable at these depths and in consequence coal began to form. Later geological activity covered the material, sometimes with thousands of feet of earth. The high pressure and lack of oxygen finished the coal's creation.

Power stations that burn coal totally reverse this process. We are extracting the buried coal and by using our essential life-supporting atmospheric oxygen, turning it back into carbon dioxide. We are rapidly turning our atmosphere back towards a pre-carboniferous era mix that all modern mammals would find unbreathable.

The danger in exhuming and burning ancient rainforests, for that is exactly what coal is, is a far more deadly practice than burning existing rainforests. If the high rainfall doesn't stop, then rainforests are renewable. And they renew rapidly. If you know jungles, you will know that it is virtually impossible to prevent rapid regrowth. Such forests are, for the atmosphere, carbon dioxide neutral. Whereas when we burn a ton of coal, we add three tons of carbon dioxide to the atmosphere's and biosphere's total.

Coal is not entirely pure carbon. Being fossilized vegetation it contains many of the elements in that original vegetation. In turn, the combustion products contain more than straight carbon dioxide. A certain amount of ash is always produced; very similar to the ash you clean out after a log fire.

Sulphur is always present in coal and this produces sulphur dioxide in the exhaust gases. Sulphur dioxide is a highly toxic gas. There is always moisture in coal, which turns to steam as the coal burns and reduces the amount of heat that is obtained from the combustion. Worse, the sulphur compounds combine with the steam in the exhaust gases and produce sulphuric acid. It falls as acid rain. Combustion isn't always complete and so black soot is often produced in embarrassing quantities. The soot, the ash, the bad smells, the corrosive acids all comes out those high exhaust stacks and mix into the air.

In comparison to the quantity of carbon dioxide in the exhaust gases, the quantity of these pollutants is small. But you can't see carbon dioxide. You can't taste carbon dioxide. You can't smell carbon dioxide and you can't feel carbon dioxide. Carbon dioxide doesn't produce corrosive acid rain. It just controls the planet's weather. The minor pollutants however are very noticeable. Soot and ash covers everything. The thick smoke is very visible. Acid rain, now so common throughout Europe and the industrial world, comes down in every shower. The sulphur compounds often produce foul smells and everything feels dirty. But what you don't see, the effects of the carbon dioxide, is many times worse than what you do see.

If a coal-fired power station exhaust system is fitted with collectors, filters and scrubbers, these minor pollutants can be removed from the exhaust gases. It is planned so carbon dioxide and water vapour are all that is left. The minor pollutants may be dirty, corrosive and unpleasant, but it is the enormous quantities of invisible carbon dioxide that are changing the world's climate.

United states supports expansion of coal use

Just under 60% of the electric power generated in the United States is produced by burning coal. Still today 85% of the fossil fuel reserves of the United States is coal. It has been the deliberate policy of successive U.S. administrations to support and encourage the utilization of these reserves.

That policy keeps electric power generation a CO_2 producer and thus makes electric cars a pointless exercise.

The new Bush administration's National Energy Strategy is structured around the increasing exploitation of all local fossil fuel reserves. Global warming considerations are restricted to the PR agenda. The grim reality is that about 20 million tons of sulphuric acid are formed in the atmosphere in the United States every year from sulphur dioxide released by burning fossil fuels. That's about seventy litres or twenty U.S. gallons of undiluted sulphuric acid per person per year. Coal burning is responsible for 70% of that acid. Gas and motor fuel use make up the balance. On top of that, fossil fuel burning also adds about 15 million tons of nitrogen-based acids, such as nitric acid. That's about 50 litres or another 15 gallons each. The EU has similar figures and that's why their ancient buildings are suddenly all corroding away.

The removal of the sulphur dioxide by the use of "scrubbers" in coal-fired power stations is being made mandatory. The coal-fired power station then becomes describable as "clean". Unfortunately, the scrubbers them-selves require enormous amounts of power to operate and in consequence increase the coal usage. The total carbon dioxide discharge is increases by around 4%.

The waste product from the scrubbers themselves is itself an enormous problem. One large U.S. power plant is slowly building a waste dump of calcium sulphate from its scrubbers that, over its operating lifetime will cover a land area of 80 acres (30 ha) and will be a dump as high as an eight-storey apartment block.

This same power station needs 200 coal-filled railroad cars every day to fuel it. In consequence it pumps 60,000 tons of carbon dioxide into the atmosphere every day. And they try to tell us that "clean" coal is safe and clean to burn!

All coal-fired power stations produce radioactive waste

A quarter of a billion or so years ago, radioactive materials accumulated and concentrated in the coal then being formed. The radioactivity derived from the concentration of minerals and isotopes absorbed by the giant foliage, as over eons it grew and reproduced.

Coal also contains radioactivity from another source.

Carbon is used in many industrial applications as a filter to remove im-purities and poisons. It is used in gas masks. It is used as a filter on kitchen taps, and coal is nearly all carbon. Coal may look like solid black glass but it's not. Coal always contains a mass of fine hair-like fractures. A coal seam thus becomes a giant and very efficient filter. These massive filters have been entrapping all kinds of things, including heavy metals, radioactive isotopes and any number and variety of poisons and carcinogens for millions of years.

When the coal is burnt the materials are released en masse back into the environment. One result is that most coal-fired power stations actually produce similar quantities of low-level radioactive waste as is produced by an equivalent-sized nuclear power station. With a coal-fired power station the heavier materials usually end up as a component of the soupy fly ash slurry. The slurry is stored in enormous tailing dams that now surround most coal-fired power stations. Not all ends up in the slurry. Some of the very fine particles, radioactive ones included, miss the filters and get into the air we breathe.

Of course these things are rarely mentioned in the media. If mentioned, the story is often confusing and convoluted. But generally such topics seem defined simply as "not newsworthy". Nobody is encouraged to complain.

Coal industries claim "clean" strategy

Jim Harrison was chairman of the Environmental Committee of the Association of Coal Producers of the European Communities. In an early article in *New Scientist* (Vol. 127, No. 1732) he sought to remind us that British Coal is an industry "behaving responsibly from environmental, economic and social standpoints." He reviewed the work of the Intergovernmental Panel on Climate Change (IPCC) and pointed out that while its members are united about "certain aspects" of global warming they make no "confident statements about the magnitude of any effects".

Harrison inferred that the IPCC is downgrading previous high estimates on global warming and "perhaps reflects a current move away from past drastic estimates". He stated that the IPCC always "emphasizes their own uncertainty" on global warming therefore it is supposedly "poorly understood". Harrison stated the panel considered global warming was no more than, or at least well within, "natural climate variability". He suggested, "politicians should not launch draconian measures against greenhouse gas emissions with all the economic dislocation that could result."

Harrison advocates a "cautious approach" to global warming. He claims vaguely "an increasing number of scientists", especially those from the George C. Marshall Institute, are "disturbed by the hype being given to the greenhouse issue." He says the "debate" (which implies global warming is still very debatable) will continue. He recommends "further research" to "generate a better understanding" and to obtain "improved predictions".

But of course this is the coal industry talking.

In the same article Harrison also recommends increasing energy efficiency in power generation and end use, increased efficiency in transport, eliminating the production and use of CFCs, ending deforestation and moving towards the use of wood products from sustainable timber resources, and helping the developing Eastern European nations to achieve the efficiencies in production which have been achieved in the industrial nations. Finally, to ensure that the general public is totally placated, he infers that carbon dioxide released from coal-fired power stations is really only a temporary problem. It is a temporary problem, he tells us, because "British Coal has launched an international initiative under the auspices of the International Energy Agency to research the technical, economic and environmental feasibility of removing carbon dioxide from power station flue gases", a high-sounding but totally ridiculous suggestion.

A conventional coal-fired power station, supplying the needs of a city of a million people, burns about 4 million tons of coal a year. To suggest that we should wait for some highly imaginative scheme that will economically remove and bottle, or somehow store the resulting 12 or more million tons of carbon dioxide seems stupidly farfetched. And that quantity is from just one coal-fired power station. Anybody with a basic understanding of chemistry will realize that you cannot reverse the burning reaction and turn carbon dioxide back into carbon without consuming the energy released when you burnt it in the first place. Neither can you catch the gas and compress it into bottles without consuming vast amounts of energy (and bottles). Anybody who owns an air compressor would know that. See "Carbon dioxide sequestration" later in this Strategy.

Their name "Environmental Committee of the Association of Coal Producers of the European Communities" says who they are. Generally such organizations name themselves differently. Words like "Coal Producers" are omitted and more typically names adopted would read like the "Environmental Protection Committee of the European Communities".

Coal-fired power stations in Queensland claimed to be clean

Australian coal reserves are not the biggest in the world but Australia is the biggest coal-exporting country in the world. Queensland is the biggest coal-exporting state in Australia. Obviously a nice clean image for coal needs to be maintained in that state. The coal trains need to keep rolling to the overseas shipping terminals. The PR machinery also has to roll. The state's recently constructed Stanwell Power Station therefore becomes a new "environmentally friendly" and "beautifully clean" power station, all to help cultivate this image.

The plant was built for the Queensland State Electricity Commission. It's located seventeen miles (28 km) west of the Australian east coast city of Rockhampton on the Great Barrier Reef. The latitude line of the Tropic of Capricorn passes through the southern suburbs of the city. The station has a capacity of 1,400 megawatts. It can therefore supply enough power to cater for an industrial city of well over 1 million people. (For details on power stations and their size see "Total power use and the electricity grid system" in chapter 11, page 594.)

I recently flew a light plane over the complex and over the nearby coal mines that feed the plant. For a coal-fired electricity-generating facility this is as good as one could expect. It is typical of the newest and best of the "clean" coal-fired power stations around the world. The plant is located on a well-manicured 3,600-acre (1,450 ha) site. State government brochures proudly boast the environmental idealism of its construction, its filtration plants, and its locality.

The grim truth is that the power station puts 20 million tons of carbon dioxide into the air per year. That one single power station in tropical Queensland will add the equivalent of another warming blanket on 5 million acres (2,000,000 ha) of the earth's surface for every year it operates. Yet they like to call such power stations "clean".

The public relations exercise when building this plant was very good. It must have been good. It must have been very convincing, for hardly a murmur was heard from the conservation movement. No wilderness organization, nor any of the proclaimed "green" groups bothered. They seemed not very interested. They either believed the "clean green" propaganda or, maybe, nobody funded them to protest.

The Queensland state government, to start off the new millennium, approved the construction of three additional and similar coal-fired power stations in the southern part of the state. The same government vigorously supported a scheme to pipe natural gas from New Guinea, across the Torres Strait (through which Captain Bligh rowed to get help after the famous *Bounty* mutiny) to the tip of northern Australia, and on down the east coast to Brisbane, the state capital. In addition the same government, in a totally nonsensical and irresponsible move, gave massive financial assistance to shore up a shale oil extraction plant further north in the state. Even Greenpeace recognizes the extreme greenhouse dangers of shale oil systems.

Why is it that alternative power systems are never considered? Central Queensland is flat, dry, sun-drenched and hot. It is an enormous area considered by many to be perfect for the development of large-scale solar thermal power stations. And to make that concept even more feasible, much of the area is already connected to the national electricity grid. This ensures no possible interruption of power supply to consumers and allows excess solar-generated power to be delivered back to the coastal cities. Both the Queensland Government and the Australian Federal Government financially support photovoltaic cell applications in the outback. Photovoltaic cells in no way threatens the fossil fuel industries. Solar thermal power generation might.

U.S. fund-wasting research on another clean coal fiction

The United States has the second-largest coal reserves in the world. China has the largest. Over the last several years, the U.S. Department of Energy has handed out US$600 million in grants to fund research to produce another system of "clean" coal power generation. That's $600 million to produce a slightly cleaner poison.

A new process being examined is called magnetohydrodynamics or MHD. The process is advocated as a much more efficient system for extracting energy from coal. To be expected, it is described as "highly efficient and environmentally clean". The concept however still involves a coal burning process producing CO_2. In the case of MHD the coal is burnt at extremely high temperatures. The hot exhaust gases are ionized at these temperatures and in effect become a flowing electric current. It is proposed that giant magnets would surround the flowing gases and giant superconducting electrodes would collect the current. The whole configuration hopefully becomes one massive electricity-generating machine.

The main advantage with this MHD concept is that theoretically, 15% to 20% more electricity could be produced from the burning coal. Another presumed advantage is that the sulphur in the coal, a major contributor to the formation of acid rain, is easily removed during the process. A disadvantage however, is that as it operates at much higher temperatures it would produce larger amounts of nitrous oxides than does normal combustion. The nitrous oxides would not be visible but they would form nitric acid and thus increase acid rain. Australia, being the largest coal-exporting country in the world, has its CSIRO (Commonwealth Scientific Industrial Research Organisation) also conducting research on the MHD process.

One problem to be overcome is that the superconducting circuitry to produce the magnetic fields required to make it all work need to operate at -270°C which is very close to absolute zero. Near these magnets the operating temperatures of the burnt coal gases in the magnetohydrodynamic process are a scorching 2,000°C. Yet despite the ridiculous nature of this research, government funding is not lacking. (MHD is not supposed to be MAD, or Mutually Assured Destruction, but there do seem to be similarities.)

When these things are built, and that's happening now, are we expected to rejoice? Do they really expect us to feel thankful for being blessed with these new "clean" power sources? The grim reality is that a supposedly environmentally clean coal-fired power station is a marketing gimmick. The concept of benign coal-fired power stations on our overheating planet is both an actual and a theoretical impossibility. The concept is a total fallacy.

Carbon dioxide sequestration

Let's consider the concept of carbon dioxide sequestration directly from power-station exhausts. Many in the fossil fuel industries see the writing on the wall. They know they must do something, or be seen to be doing something about global warming, for they have to generate a clean image to maintain their sales. The concept of carbon dioxide sequestration might be the answer.

Sequestration is taking the CO_2 from the smoke stack and burying it "somewhere", or disposing of it "somehow".

For all in the fossil fuel industries, sequestration is a wonderful and fortuitous doubled-barrelled gun. They reason that if it works then fossil fuels can be sold almost forever, or at least into some far distant future. Fossil carbon fuels and products could be marketed and sold until the customers finally find the earth's air suddenly unbearably unbreathable.

Secondly, if it doesn't work, sales can at least continue unabated while people await the assured "final development of the successful research". The science involved in sequestration concepts is moderately tricky and therefore easily sold to the public. It is also more easily sold to their representative politicians.

It has certainly been sold well to the current politicians in power. In countries around the world incredible amounts of taxpayer's money have been spent on "developing the research". Grants are handed out to anybody proclaiming, "a solution is near".

How is sequestration supposed to work? As explained elsewhere, there are only two remotely feasible ways of extracting carbon dioxide from the smokestacks of power stations. One is to freeze the exhaust gases and the other is to collect the CO_2 by having it contact CO_2-absorbing chemicals after which the CO_2 is extracted from the chemicals.

In either system, after the CO_2 is collected it has to be compressed and then somehow disposed of. Disposal after collection is a somewhat hopelessly impractical concept as we will see further on. In public relation promotions it is always blithely ignored, or simply glossed over. Air is about one-fifth oxygen and four-fifths nitrogen. So in any imagined storage system the nitrogen has to be removed or it too would have to go into the storage system.

Let's consider refrigeration. In this scenario the gas mixture has to be cooled to a temperature where the CO_2 freezes solid. It's then easy to collect. Continuously refrigerating such an enormous quantity of flue gases is not easy, and it's an expensive process. It's also an energy-demanding process. Burning still more coal is therefore a requirement. However currently nowhere is this freezing concept, and the necessary extra energy required, factored in. At this time of writing vast sums of money are being spent, and more is being allocated to be spent, on the development of some futuristic and incredibly exotic coal-fired power station concept incorporating sequestration theories.

Although the concepts are utterly improbable, they are nevertheless brilliantly obtuse, and they are obviously kept obtuse for public relations and marketing reasons, and probably also for grant allocation motives.

One system being developed and promoted by Clean Energy Systems Inc. of California, and apparently under the auspices of the U.S. Department of Energy, argues the concept that the best way to separate the CO_2 from all the atmospheric nitrogen is to remove the nitrogen from the feed air first. They argue, burn the fuel in pure oxygen. The flue gases will then only contain carbon dioxide and probably some water vapour. The water vapour is first removed and the CO_2 can then be compressed to very high pressures again for "long-term storage or disposal". Where or how is not mentioned.

In this concept, air has to be reduced to extremely low temperatures (around $-200°C$) to separate out the oxygen. This incidentally is by far the cheapest way to obtain straight oxygen and is the current method used industrially.

Pulverized coal then has to be burnt in a specially designed high temperature combustion chamber using this pure oxygen. The quantity of oxygen is carefully restricted so that complete combustion does not occur. As a result, mainly carbon monoxide (CO) is produced, not carbon dioxide (CO_2). The process is called "gasification". Often steam is added during the combustion process. The final product is then a mixture of useful hydrogen gas and useful carbon monoxide, and useless carbon dioxide. The mix is called "syngas", for synthetic gas. Typically about 20% of the energy in the coal is effectively wasted in the formation of syngas.

The syngas is then required to be burnt, again with pure oxygen, but at very high temperatures and pressures. To compress the syngas mixture to the pressures required to feed the gas turbine combustion chambers uses additional energy. Also, burning any hydrocarbon fuel, whether it be syngas, kerosene or whatever, with pure oxygen at high pressures is a process currently possible only in exotic space-shuttle-type combustion chambers. Of course a space shuttle, or any other rocket combustion chamber, is not expected, nor designed to operate continuously for more than a few minutes at any one time. And certainly not for twenty-four hours a day, seven days a week, for decades.

The exhaust gases exiting the combustion chamber are too hot for even the best current gas turbines, so they have to be cooled. The idea is that this is done by spraying water into the combustion stream. It is envisaged that the cooled gases would then be used to drive standard turbine electric generators. Advocates of this system suggest that super-ceramic, extreme temperature turbine blades will soon be developed which would mean that the gases need only be cooled to around $800°C$ ($1,500°F$). Currently commercial maximum power turbine systems can't be made to operate above about $550°C$.

The exhaust gas from the process would predominantly be a mixture of carbon dioxide and water. The other pollutants, such as sulphuric acid and nitric acid, would need to have been removed beforehand.

Finally the exhaust gases, being relatively pure carbon dioxide, can be compressed in suitable compressors, or frozen solid, to be again delivered to some "designated final disposal system".

For reference on the above, there are two notable scientific papers that discuss the above carbon sequestration concept. One was compiled by Joel Martinez-Frias, Salvador M. Aceves, and J. Ray Smith, all of that most prestigious establishment, the Lawrence Livermore National Laboratory in

Southern California. The other author was Harry Brant, of Clean Energy Systems, Inc.

The second paper arguing the concept was a presentation to the Second Conference on Carbon Sequestration held in Virginia in May 2003. On face value the paper seems very convincing. There were four authors, all from Clean Energy Systems, Inc.; one was the same Harry Brant.

Both papers are surprisingly (or unsuspectingly) convoluted. The apparently reasonable costs they infer are definitely based on unrealistic assumptions, or at least very opportunistic presumptions. Our analysis indicates that at best, twice as much coal would be burnt and twice as much CO_2 would be produced as from any current state-of-the-art, run-of-the-mill power station. At the more probable, worst-case scenario, the proposed concept would burn four or more times as much coal and produce four or more times the quantity of CO_2. The only conceivable advantage would be that the CO_2 produced would not be diluted with nitrogen and therefore more convenient to compress.

There are other sequestration suggestions. They generally use various components of the above concepts. Mostly they are based on the use of pure oxygen. The general aim is to obtain relatively pure CO_2 in a nitrogen-free exhaust. But with all the proposals, energy is consumed and so more coal is burnt, and more CO_2 has then to be delivered to the "designated final disposal system", which incidentally is never designated.

One system that receives considerable government support is to use syngas in a system called an "Integrated Gasification and Combined Cycle" process, abbreviated to IGCC.

In the IGCC system the combustible gas mix is used to power a gas turbine, which powers electric generators. The waste heat from the gas turbines is then used to produce steam to power steam turbines to produce additional electricity. More fuel is used initially, but the extra efficiency of the gas turbine/steam turbine combination just about compensates by producing extra power. In most of the current natural-gas-fired power stations in operation today, this piggyback double turbine system is used, and is very effective.

Hydrogen gas can be produced from syngas. If super-heated steam is produced and then combined with syngas in a special reactor, the carbon monoxide (CO) in the syngas combines with the water (H_2O), and is converted into carbon dioxide (CO_2) and hydrogen gas. The hydrogen then has to be separated out from the CO_2. This incidentally is the process currently used commercially to produce industrial hydrogen. Syngas or natural gas can be used. It is unfortunate but the industrial-quality hydrogen gas produced cannot be used in hydrogen fuel cells. By their very nature fuel cells require an incredible pure gas supply to function for any length of time. The extreme purity is needed to slow down the buildup of contaminants on the catalytic surfaces.

The above system is the only viable process ever seriously considered to supply the raw base hydrogen for the much touted "hydrogen economy". In effect and in simple terms the "hydrogen economy" is already structured to be based on fossil fuels. The reality is that there is no sensible and viable alternative system for producing hydrogen gas in large quantities and the hydrogen produced can't be used in fuel cells. See item 16, "Fuel cells and the hydrogen economy dream" in chapter 11.

The second concept for the collection and ultimate sequestration of CO_2 involves solvents. Using solvents is currently the most common way of removing CO_2 from gas mixtures. The CO_2 used in industrial applications is almost universally produced by first entrapping the gas in a suitable solvent, and then extracting it from that solvent.

One of the most economical and safest industrial absorbers used to collect CO_2 for industrial use is an amine such as monoethanolamine. This particular amine fortunately is only moderately toxic. It causes eye, skin and mucous membrane irritation. Ingestion results in inflammation and bleeding in the intestines and digestive system. About four measures of amine are required to trap one measure of CO_2. The amine-carbon dioxide mixture is then heated to low superheat temperatures and the pure carbon dioxide is released. The amine is then available for reuse.

A joint project involving eight major energy companies in the European Union looked at the costs and practicality of sequestration of carbon dioxide from exhaust stacks from petrochemical and power station exhausts. It is called the CO_2 Capture Project and is designed to develop CO_2 capture technologies. A paper was presented at the September 2002 annual meeting of the Gas Producers Association of Europe.

In the paper a feasibility study "using today's best available technology" and using an amine-based CO_2 capture system was examined. The authors studied the fitting of an amine-based sequestration facility onto an existing European refining and petrochemical complex.

On the second last page of the report it was noted that the sequestration unit, considered capable of trapping the 2 million tons of CO_2 per year, required its own energy and boilers to operate. The report conceded that firing these additional boilers would produce another 600,000 tons of CO_2. The plant therefore wouldn't sequester 2 millions tons. It would only sequester 1.4 million tons of CO_2. The detailed cost analysis breakdown listed a total capital cost of US$476 million for sequestering what would amount to less than 1.4 million tons of carbon dioxide.

However, a coal-fired power station supplying a city of 1 million people would produce around 12 million tons of CO_2 per year. Our million-people city would thus require a plant costing US$4,080 million. That's 4 billion dollars. That's about four times the price of the actual power station. Also somewhere in such a system, in continuous circulation, there would have to be about a million litres of toxic monoethanolamine plus the extra needed for regular topping up.

The concept of using such processes and chemicals to remove CO_2 from power station exhaust gases is simply not feasible in any way, shape, or form. Don't believe it when they say: "The technology is just around the corner".

The list of schemes for sequestering carbon dioxide is only exceeded by the list of companies seeking government grants to study their own touted solutions. As far as the fossil-fuel producers are concerned, the more the merrier; it keeps people believing an answer is imminent. And when people feel that, global warming fears can again be put on hold. But no matter how good any carbon dioxide sequestration system might be (or how good they are claimed to be), we finally have to ask the obvious question; "What do we do with the carbon dioxide after it has been collected?"

Carbon dioxide by itself has a variety of industrial applications. When it is frozen it becomes the substance we know as dry ice. It is used to conveniently keep ice cream and similar products at low or below water-freezing temperatures. Carbon dioxide gas is used as a flux in electric welding. It is also a raw material in the chemical and pharmaceutical industries. And of course carbon dioxide is the gas in the bubbles in carbonated drinks. However, the worldwide industrial use of carbon dioxide for such applications would barely exceed the carbon dioxide discharged from a power station supplying one single world city. As a product in itself, the reality is that carbon dioxide does not have a big market. And after it is used in the market it does have, it still finally ends up in the atmosphere.

So where can it go? Consider our one million people coal-fired power station with its power output of 1,000 megawatts. Let's assume the coal is delivered to the power station by rail. That power station would need a rail train 6 kilometres, that's 4 miles long, full of coal and delivering twice a week. That's what they use.

Today the coal is more likely to come from an open cut mine than from an underground mine. Underground mining is more dangerous and more expensive. Digging holes underground is not cheap, which is in itself relevant to sequestration.

Now to simplify the carbon dioxide problem, let's imagine the carbon dioxide produced from the power station is compressed to the equivalent volume, or frozen to the volume of dry ice. Coal and the dry ice, roughly speaking, weigh about the same. Remember two trains a week brought the coal in. With carbon dioxide sequestration in operation, every day from our power station, including weekends and holidays, out comes a rail train, 5 miles long, with every freight truck filled to the rails with dry ice.

Is that right? Yes it is; coal is mostly pure carbon and carbon has an atomic weight of 12. So let's say we have 12 trainloads of coal coming in. Coal burns to become carbon dioxide or CO_2. Oxygen has an atomic weight of 16. So carbon dioxide weighs $12 + 16 + 16$. We therefore have 44 trainloads of dry ice coming out.

The next problem; all that dry ice has to be dumped somewhere. You can't sell the stuff. You can't even give it away. There is just too much of it. And it keeps coming. Pump it into old oil wells they say? That's no solution. The carbon dioxide produced from the world's power stations would fill all the world's empty oil wells in months.

Naturally, any future oil wells are most definitely not available, as every barrel of oil that comes from them also becomes another two and a half barrels of dry ice. Oil wells can't handle their own CO_2 waste. There are simply no holes, natural or man-made, anywhere in the world that could ever handle the quantities of dry ice or CO_2 involved.

Another suggestion is to pump it into underground sand beds and hope it won't ultimately seep back to the surface. Out of the question; power stations are built as near as practical to coal deposits. With all their tunnels, these are not even hypothetically leakproof carbon dioxide repositories.

The money involved in such schemes, were they possible, is so ludicrously high it would be cheaper to run a power station on sugar derived ethanol, or even peanut butter. Safe carbon dioxide disposal is a problem thousands of times more difficult than nuclear waste disposal. Carbon dioxide is a hard-to-contain gas and unlike nuclear waste, carbon dioxide lasts forever.

The concept of continuous carbon dioxide sequestration is pretence. The idea has only one plausible objective and that is to have us believe a technological solution is not only possible but also probable. It is simply a means to keep responsible people placated. It is to prevent people from acting decisively to halt global warming. It's simply to maintain sales of fossil fuels.

With global warming causing such havoc there is just no conceivable way that coal should ever be used as an industrial fuel in any human society, now or in the future.

STRATEGY 22
Establishing the myth that natural gas is environmentally friendly

Natural gas as an energy source is being sold the same way as "clean coal" is being sold. The marketing people utilize the principle that a lie is much easer to sell when it contains a small measure of truth.

Most of the compounds that form acid rain and the other impurities always found in coal and oil are almost nonexistent in natural gas. It is therefore marketed as an "exceptionally clean" fuel. In this respect, the waste from burning natural gas can be compared with that from burning coal where the coal exhaust gases are well filtered before being discharged into the atmosphere.

The impurities removed from coal-fired power station exhausts and the impurities that conveniently do or don't exist in natural gas have almost no relevance whatever in the destabilization of world weather patterns. Carbon dioxide discharge, as always, is the major villain behind global warming. Claiming that natural gas is a clean fuel is dangerously muddying the waters of truth.

Another major marketing ploy used in promoting sales of natural gas is to claim that the quantities of carbon dioxide discharged are significantly reduced while still producing the same power output. This is claimed for both motor vehicles and power stations. It is sad, for as a means of reducing global warming the reality is otherwise.

Of all the energy-producing compounds in natural gas, the highest proportion by far is that of methane at around 90%. Ethane generally makes up the rest. For the same energy output, burning pure methane gas does not produce as much carbon dioxide as burning oil or coal. Compared to a clean coal-fired power station, a natural-gas-fired power station, burning pure methane gas, would produce about 30% less carbon dioxide.

Unfortunately almost every known deposit of natural gas in the world already contains free carbon dioxide. Natural gas deposits in Indonesia for example often comprise 50% CO_2. That carbon dioxide is released into the atmosphere without the production of any energy whatever. Removing high levels of naturally occurring carbon dioxide is both a high-energy and carbon-dioxide-generating process. In most cases raw natural gas is burnt to produce the energy to remove the carbon dioxide from the remaining natural gas. Burning the Indonesian natural gas for power would produce more greenhouse gases than burning coal from the worst coal mines in the world.

In addition there are always significant losses from leakage when handling any gas. As none of the constituents of natural gas are overly toxic, natural gas losses are only minimized to commercially acceptable levels. Gas is constantly escaping to the air. As a greenhouse gas, methane is about twenty times as bad as carbon dioxide. With the CO_2 generated by its burning and with the leakages that occur in commercial gas handling from well to consumer, natural gas becomes no better and often far worse a fuel than oil, petrol or diesel. And it can often be worse than coal.

Using rare carbon-dioxide-free natural gas and being only slightly simplistic, the best we can say is that three natural-gas-fired power stations produce as much carbon dioxide as two coal-fired power stations.

U.S. worry over gas reserves

Natural gas reserves are only 10% of the domestic fossil fuel reserves in the United States, so the second Bush administration actually discouraged the utilization of natural gas. The fear being that encouraging its use could ultimately make the United States even more dependent on foreign oil and gas supplies than it already is. As has been noted, the United States has lots of coal.

STRATEGY 23
Claiming the world will run out of oil therefore global warming is temporary

A problem of supposed limited oil reserves is a marvelous public relations argument. The argument goes like this.

If the worst comes to the worst and we keep burning oil at our current rate we will rapidly and inevitably exhaust our already depleted reserves. Powering the world with alternative energy will by necessity automatically follow. The inventiveness of man, combined with simple market forces, will ultimately and unerringly lead us to a solution to all our global warming problems. We may have temporary climatic disasters but, *voila!* our grandchildren will be OK.

Utter nonsense, the facts don't support the argument. The fact is, there is more oil, more gas, and more coal under the ground than there is air above the ground to burn it and leave us with a breathable air mix.

All of the oxygen existing in our atmosphere today came originally from huge quantities of naturally occurring carbon dioxide spewing out of volcanoes. The carbon dioxide was split by plants using photosynthesis. The carbon ended up as dense fossilized materials, oil, coal or peat and a not inconsiderable quantity in enormous buried bubbles of methane and like gases. The oxygen went into the atmosphere. Some of it was consumed in oxidizing exposed rocks and minerals. Some combined with carbon and calcium to form the skeletal structures of living things. These ultimately became the world's limestone deposits. Some oxygen remained in the air, and that's what we breathe and what we have evolved to breathe.

The point is, to totally burn all the fossil fuels in the ground would require all the oxygen that exists in our atmosphere. Long before that could happen we would all die. Breathing as little as 1% carbon dioxide is uncomfortable and will give you a headache after a short time. Breathe much higher concentrations and your lungs will go into uncontrollable spasms and you die in a matter of minutes.

The scenario of ultimate fossil fuel depletion and therefore a termination in the expanding chaos of global warming and climate change suits the marketers of fossil-carbon-based fuels. For them it leads to a highly desirable sense of complacency in an otherwise thinking, worried, and concerned community. Responsible people are lulled into a false sense of security, and that suits the oil companies perfectly.

This whole concept of running out of oil and other fossil fuels is a fiction and the oil and gas people know it. However, strategically it would not be astute marketing to actually proclaim that running out of oil will save the planet. All too easily and quite correctly would geologists, environmentalists, and some wiser green movements dispute such claims and severely embarrass the oil companies' proclamations. So that would not be a good tactic.

Much more subtle types of campaign procedures are called for. A whisper campaign would be ideal—worth attempting but difficult. Media stories are better. A series of reports such as, "the results of some research conducted by some (unnamed) responsible organization" showed that global warming would self-correct as oil stocks were depleted, are perfect. Of course this type of copy must never be seen to have originated from its actual source.

Done well, this is an extremely effective procedure. Thinking citizens should watch for this ploy in action. We should recognize it and we should appreciate its insidious and powerful influence.

A much more subtle approach, and one that actually gets the same message across, is to loudly foster the totally impossible concept of having the country massively and radically reduce its use of energy, purely as a conservation measure. Advertising and editorial can then constantly warn the public of "our dwindling oil reserves". We are also warned that with our current rate of use, our current known reserves will be totally depleted within, generally, thirty years. Even in the early 1960s we were warned that the world will run out of oil within thirty years, so conservation was important. Noble, responsible, almost patriotic calls are made by green pawns for smaller and more efficient cars. Calls for the public to try and change their driving habits to get more miles per gallon and conserve "dwindling world fuel reserves" are a public relations tactic. It's never actually stated, but the perception, the understanding, is clear. "We must be running out of these fuel sources so, logically, global warming can't last".

Of course the oil companies recommend that everybody should show responsibility and walk, or ride a bike, or use public transport to further conserve oil reserves. But they know we won't.

A spin-off from these approaches is that the oil companies get a wonderful green image in the process, and for them that is a real bonus.

The often-used term "world oil reserves" needs examination. World oil reserves are only the known and actually proven reserves. They are also reserves held by or owned by somebody or some legal structure. They are nothing like the real total of extractable oil existing on the planet. Claimed oil reserves have never in the past ever exceeded about thirty years' supply. That's just practical common sense, for when easily accessible reserves are found that would suffice for thirty years or so, why would anybody spend huge sums drilling for more?

In addition, techniques are now perfected to enable oil producers to extract oil from old "exhausted" fields, such as exist in Texas and Pennsylvania and other places all over the world. Some of these newer techniques are expected to make possible the extraction of more oil than was the total take from the old, now supposedly exhausted, oil fields.

Total world oil reserves now remaining—and this is shown by almost every indicator—are actually considerably more than has ever been extracted since the first wells were drilled. We have our usual thirty-year supply. There is simply no shortage of oil. Global warming is only preventable by us switching to different energy systems. There is no way climate change will be halted because the world might run out of oil.

In addition, total world gas reserves exceed known oil reserves many times over.

In addition, total world coal reserves are so huge they make oil and gas reserves pale to insignificance.

In addition, methane deposits in ocean sediments far exceed all the above.

Whatever it is, be it coal, or oil, or natural gas, what comes out of the chimney is carbon dioxide and that carbon dioxide wasn't in our biosphere before we dug it out of its grave and released it by fire. The oil lobby doesn't want us to appreciate that simple reality.

STRATEGY 24
The delaying tactics of biodiversity studies, feasibility analyses and environmental reports

The fossil carbon industries use delaying tactics to prevent and forestall any substantial move towards alternative energy and chemical-free agricultural systems.

One technique that has proven most effective is to have green organizations do their work for them. Build a coal-fired power station, build an oil refinery, run an oil or gas pipeline across the country, there is never trouble. You want trouble: try building a hydroelectric power station, or construct wind turbine towers, or build a tidal power facility, or try building a geothermal power station. They're trouble. The green movement, along with a whole host of supposedly responsible organizations, will demand an "environmental report". When this is completed it will be disputed on an endless range of minor issues. Then the inevitable creation of a "biodiversity crisis" follows; at least some insect is sure to be threatened and this of course needs a separate and prolonged investigation. And on it goes.

Sadly it is always individuals with restricted access to funds that are the ones fighting to produce alternative power systems. Against them are governments with unlimited tax money, coerced by blind green pawns with petrodollars. These are the people so effectively preventing alternative energy development.

If done properly, demanding environmental reports, demanding more information and then demanding still more information, coupled with ethereal biodiversity investigations, not only creates never-ending delays, but also demonstrates an apparent, though false, display of noble responsibility by the oil interests and their bedfellows.

It is difficult to define an absolute truth in anything, so conflicting information can be fed into these expensive and time-consuming reports to create total confusion and uncertainty. A little lobbying can bury common sense for decades. A little negatively biased editorial, no doubt manipulated by corporations with advertising muscle who do not wish to see the expansion of alternative energy systems, and we see wise and sound projects sunk.

A green movement then claims very vocally a "victory for biodiversity". And quietly and behind closed boardroom doors the fossil carbon lobbyists laugh.

STRATEGY 25
Suppressing development of hydroelectric power

Electricity generated by letting water run downhill through a pipe and then into a turbine is the most sensible way to produce electricity known to man. There is no waste product, no soot, no carbon dioxide. Dams can be built in most areas of the world. In addition, once the hydroelectric power station is constructed, the energy is free. Hydroelectric power is a wonderful source of energy. As power demand fluctuates throughout the day, electricity output is controlled simply by adjusting a water tap.

Destroying the clean image of hydroelectric power was a real challenge for the public relations people that service the fossil fuel companies. On face value it must have seemed like an impossible task. In retrospect the brilliance and ingenuity of their campaign has been amazing. Against what must have appeared as impossible odds, they succeeded. They did it. Utterly clean, utterly green hydroelectric power now has a "bad name". A good image has been totally destroyed, and a bad one installed in its place.

How was this done? The fossil fuel public relations organizations fostered or created suitable green movements for the job, and then they moved them and manipulated them like pawns. They became their green pawns. They created what was in effect an anti-hydroelectric movement. That was the hidden agenda. What we saw in the media and on the streets were campaigns to save rivers, campaigns to save farmlands, campaigns to protect endangered species and campaigns to protect the wilderness.

What are never mentioned in all these image-modifying campaigns is global warming and the resultant destabilization of every weather system on the entire planet.

Tasmania is a good example. The Australian island state of Tasmania has the greatest potential for cheap efficient hydroelectric power of any state in the whole of Australia. Electric power could be fed north across the short intervening Bass Strait to power industry on the mainland.

The green movement stopped the hydroelectric dams. Now a gas pipeline has been constructed that feeds gaseous fossil fuel from the mainland, south across Bass Strait into Tasmania. Environmental organizations

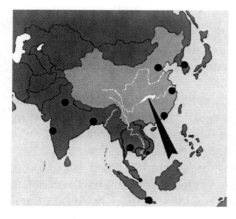

The Three Gorges Dam on the Yangtze River. The lake formed will be 600 kilometres long. The river to the north is the Huang He or Yellow River. The river to the south is the Mekong. All three are fed by snowfalls on the high Tibetan Plateau.

claim this as a victory.

The fossil fuel organizations run a never-ending war against hydroelectricity. In the past, as in the above case, they have usually won.

Giant Chinese hydroelectric scheme's constant criticism

But not always. Premier Li Peng turned the spade inaugurating the commencement of the world's biggest single hydroelectric project, the Three Gorges Dam on the Yangtze River in December 1994. The dam will be bigger but comparable with Hoover Dam on the Colorado River. The Yangtze discharges into the southern end of the Yellow Sea a few miles north of downtown Shanghai. The mighty Yangtze, with a length of 3,900 miles (6,300 km), is the third longest river in the world. It's only 260 miles shorter than the Nile.

Three hundred thousand people have died, in this century just ended, from floods on the Yangtze River. This terrible death toll will stop when the system is completed. The dam will create an inland lake 400 miles (600 km) long. It will become a marine superhighway servicing millions of people.

When the whole system is completed, and that should be by about 2010, it will generate 18,000 megawatts of power, enough to give electric power to 100 million Chinese workers. It will alleviate the discharge into the atmosphere of 200 million tons of carbon dioxide every year. That's like eliminating 20 major coal-fired power stations.

But hydroelectricity always has its well-paid critics.

American consultant Philip Williams, of Philip Williams Associates, was president of the International Rivers Network. This is a non-governmental organization that regularly campaigns against any large hydroelectric dams. He pronounced that the dam would not prevent flooding at all. Yet, one pet argument against the building of hydroelectric dams generally is that they do just that, and that is a supposed fault; they prevent downstream flooding. The argument is, if flooding is a regular occurrence on a river, the river ecology will have modified itself to survive the floods. So flooding is then an "ecological necessity" in this piece of prize ecological nonsense reasoning. On one hand hydroelectric dams are therefore an ecological disaster if they prevent flooding, but on the other hand, they should only be built if they do prevent flooding.

It seems that for green movements their criticism need not be consistent, and need not be logical, excepting their ongoing assistance in the marketing of fossil fuels. The criticism just needs to be very loud and very public.

Williams claims that large dams might encourage "undue confidence" downstream. He asserts that if the dam should not hold back some future flood, then "the loss of life would be greater than if the dam had never been built." He further argues that the "consequences of failure at Three Gorges Dam would rank as history's worst man-made disaster". It's argued that, if the dam broke, maybe 300,000 people would die. But we must not forget that 300,000 people have already died in the last hundred years because the dam was not there. The yearly loss of life would undoubtedly have continued if the dam was not built.

Then we have John Morris, a former chief of the U.S. Army Corps of Engineers, who stated authoritatively that landslides, earthquakes or especially military action, could all breach the dam wall. Presuming that to be the case, it might well be argued that the Chinese possession of such a dam as the Three Gorges could well discourage future Chinese leaders from military aspirations when they have such a supposedly vulnerable target sitting there.

Dam walls that are badly designed have been known to break, but it is extremely rare. Flooding from sudden massive rainfalls however is extremely common. Flooding is also getting progressively worse in our destabilizing world climate. It should be noted that flood rains cause more deaths and destruction than any other natural causes on the planet, tsunamis included.

Stopping alternative energy in Bulgaria

A typical, nonsensical attack on hydroelectric power occurred when an East-West environmental conference was held in Sofia in Bulgaria in 1989. It was a very important conference and was attended by 35 nations. At the conference, Ecoglasnost, Bulgaria's own proclaimed green movement, had collected 11,500 signatures before and at the conference demanding wider general public consultation on environmental issues. It would have been unlikely that many delegates would have refused to sign a petition put like that. It was also that sort of a conference.

Ecoglasnost asserted that this show of environmental interest supported one of their own pet causes, namely that a particular hydroelectric power station complex should not be built. The plan in question was the Rila and Mesta River development. This pollution-free, hydroelectric power that could have been generated from the Rila and the Mesta Rivers in Bulgaria was effectively put on hold. Coal thus became the assured energy source. Natural gas is now imported from the new Russia. Quite incongruously, about 40% of the electricity generated in Bulgaria is nuclear as Bulgaria was once a USSR satellite state. But installing more nuclear power stations is being vigorously resisted by other green movements.

Queensland hydro stopped

In Australia along the Queensland coast, near the mid-point of the Great Barrier Reef and just south of Cairns, lies the town of Tully. The nearby Tully-Millstream Hydro-Electric Scheme was to be expanded. The new scheme consisted of two dams and two small weirs. The water turbines were to be built deep underground and would have operated with 2,500 feet (700 m) head of water for maximum efficiency. The scheme would have created lakes with a total surface area of 10,600 acres (4,300 ha). Locally, there are 1,600,000 acres (650,000 ha) of tropical rainforests, of which a tiny 300 acres (120 ha) would have been "affected", not necessarily flooded, just affected by the dams. Our society seems to be becoming so stagnant that just affecting something becomes an environmental no-no if alternative energy is being contemplated? The output of the power station was to be 600 megawatts; that's enough power for a city of over 600,000 people. The generation of this power would emit zero tons of carbon dioxide a year.

The green pawns of the fossil fuel lobbies were called in to do their well-rehearsed rallies, ostensibly to "protect the environment", mainly the 300 acres of "threatened rainforest". In their small but well-filmed and well-documented numbers they protested against the construction of the complex. The media, obeying the dictates of their advertising customers, supported (they say "reported") the protesters and their rallies. The Tully-Millstream Hydro Scheme was stopped. The Queensland State Government thought they were obeying the wishes of the people. Or that's what they claimed. In the driest continent on earth, another freshwater storage system was stopped. Six hundred megawatts of pollution-free electric power will not be generated. Coal will produce the power.

Sabotaging the Hydro-Quebec power plan

The success of the oil, coal and natural gas lobbies in minimizing or eliminating any threat to their monopoly on world power is frightening. They are in a continuous process of sabotaging a giant project that will prevent 250 million tons of carbon dioxide per year being dumped into our atmosphere. To put things in perspective, we are discussing the carbon dioxide production from 20 million motor vehicles.

The project they are fighting is being undertaken by Hydro-Quebec in Canada and involves the creation of over 200 man-made lakes. These

Showing the location of James Bay in eastern Canada. The dots in the illustration show some of the larger lakes. There are over 2,000,000 lakes in Canada. They have never been counted. There are more lakes in Canada than the rest of the world combined. The larger dots are cities.

lakes would power hydroelectric turbines and produce enough pollution-free electricity to supply the needs of 30 million people in a Western society.

The project is the James Bay Power Project, located in the southeast corner of Canada's Hudson Bay. Hudson Bay is a subarctic region on about the same latitude as Denmark, Latvia and Moscow. Ireland is also on about the same latitude, but things are warmer there, as the Gulf Stream hasn't as yet stopped flowing.

The projected power output of a fully completed James Bay Power Project is more than ample to supply the needs of Quebec and all of eastern Canada. In addition, pollution-free power can be sold south, and flow into the grid system servicing the cities of Boston, New York, Philadelphia, Pittsburgh and Detroit. It could generate export income for Canada of at least a billion dollars a year.

For the oil and coal producers of North America, the James Bay Power Project is a major unwanted competitor—it would be better if it could be stopped.

The vast subarctic catchment area that would feed the new lakes and generating facilities has a total population of 15,000 people. That's the size of a small Australian country town or the size of a single city suburb. Obviously the fossil carbon energy people are recruiting all their naïve friends, those in "wilderness conservation" and "environmental protection", to ensure that as much as possible of this project is stopped. The public relations people and the lobbyists come out in force and have a field day. Most of the local inhabitants around James Bay are of Cree and Inuit Indian extraction and this provides plenty of fuel to generate emotive arguments, which is done. But all angles, especially emotive ones, however farcical, are always explored and exploited.

For example, trace quantities of mercury occur in many geological structures, and the geology of this part of Quebec is no different. Concentrations
between 20 ppb and 6,000 ppb of mercury occur in soils in North America.
The environmentalists claim that the mercury gets slightly concentrated in
vegetation. Mercury does not accumulate readily in plants and is typically
less than 20% of the concentration found in surrounding soil. (Although
some edible mushrooms, such as *Pleuritus ostreatus,* can increase mercury
concentrations massively.) It is argued that when the dams are finished and
filled, mercury will be released into the water from the flooded decomposing
trees. It is further claimed that it will then contaminate the millions of fish
that will ultimately colonize the new waterways.

But the arguments don't make sense.

If the country to be flooded after the construction work is completed is
heavily timbered, it could be typically covered with 100 tons of trees per acre
(250 tonnes per hectare). So the total mercury content in the trees on one
acre of ground would be 3.5 ounces (300 grams per hectare). When the dams
are flooded, they'll probably easily average in excess of 30 feet (10 m) deep.
So an acre of land would be covered by possibly 50,000 tons of water (125,000
tonnes per hectare). So the final concentration of mercury in the water
would be 3.5 ounces per 50,000 tons or 2.4 parts per billion. And that's if all
the trees rotted instantly and the water sat there totally stagnant indefinitely!
Of course it isn't going to sit there stagnant, as it's a hydroelectric project
and hydroelectric power only works when water flows downhill so mercury
levels will naturally be much lower.

The United States Environmental Protection Agency, their EPA, sets a
limit of 2 ppb of mercury in U.S. drinking water, although in truth some
drinking water gets as high as 10 ppb. So those fish are going to be swimming
in water that the United States' own EPA says is perfectly safe to drink. That's
when it first fills with water and the timber somehow instantly all rots. After
that mercury levels will rapidly decline.

The environmentalists' arguments are totally meaningless. That's possibly why the public relations people fighting hydroelectric schemes never
quote actual numbers.

In this day and age, modern scientific equipment can detect just about
anything and in just about everything, right down to detecting individual
molecules. "Scientific tests" can therefore be quoted to "prove their claims"
of mercury "contamination". There is enough mercury right now in your
little finger for these instruments to detect.

Of course, it is more logical to harvest the timber before the lakes fill
than to leave them to rot, so then even this hypothetical mercury problem
wouldn't exist. But then of course if that happened, the green-trained "hug
a tree" troupe would be called in to perform their unique padlock and chain
dance.

As some of the electricity is being exported to another country (over the fence into the United States) the Canadians have been manoeuvred into accepting that the Canadian Federal Government has ultimate control and responsibility. Compliance with all the irrational political environmental arguments and regulations that the Canadian government, like other federal governments around the world, is prone to imposing has become an additional obstacle in this project's life.

The project will affect the hunting lifestyles of some of the local Indians. It is argued by the oil companies' green movements that this should not happen. The lifestyles of the local Indians, that Canadians are being coerced into protecting, depend for their existence on trapping and killing wildlife, not to eat but for their skins. These skins will end up in a store near you. It seems somewhat irrational for a so-called green movement to support such a cause. The concept is apparently justified by green movements on the basis that early man has traditionally wiped out wildlife and thus has a right to continue.

The fossil carbon lobby and their stooges are having some success in preventing the James Bay Hydro-Electric Project from proceeding. The project has been put behind schedule while "environmental impact" studies are being undertaken. These delays have threatened contracts with major utility companies in the northeastern United States, who are naturally wary of the distorted influence of the so-called environmental movements.

The James Bay Hydroelectric Project would be a significant contributing factor to safeguarding our planet's atmosphere and climate. The objectors to the James Bay Hydroelectric Project are displaying a degree of vandalism almost unparalleled in the environmental history of man.

Mercury dangers from hydroelectric projects are an incredibly exaggerated nonsense. It's a public relations fiction. But mercury pollution from coal burnt in power stations is a very different, and very frightening story. It's also a story rarely told.

So what is that reality? Mercury is very poisonous and most poisonous when inhaled. As a comparison, injected poison from a diamondback rattlesnake is about 200 times more deadly. Inhaling the nerve gas sarin is only about 30 times worse than mercury vapour. Over 90% of the mercury entering the environment worldwide comes out the exhaust stacks of coal-fired power stations. And it's virtually impossible to remove. It becomes part of the air we breathe. For energy, the world burns about 4 billion tons of coal a year. Depending on the source, some coal-fired power stations spew half a ton of mercury vapour into their local atmosphere every year. Then it starts to circulate.

The high mercury levels in fish caught in the open ocean, hundreds of miles from any land, in the main comes from coal-fired power stations. No ocean in the world, no lake in the world is immune. No fish is safe from this form of mercury pollution. One estimate claims one drop of mercury in a 25-acre lake would make the fish unsafe for pregnant women to eat. This is possibly overly cautious but an eggcup full would make the water itself undrinkable. That's omitting any ongoing biological concentration. Every year, so the U.S. Environmental Protection Agency reports, their coal-fired power stations discharge over 19 tons of mercury vapour into the air.

For mercury pollution, coal is the villain, not hydroelectric power stations. Don't let people claim it's otherwise.

Stopping dams in India

In India, in Madhra Pradesh, a series of irrigation and hydroelectric dams are planned for construction on the Narmada River in central India. When completed they would supply clean water and power to an estimated 30,000,000 people. A well-publicized environmental report, typical of many, discussed these dams and the Narmada River Development Project. The whole concept that pollution-free hydroelectricity could be produced in huge quantities is not mentioned in the report. The prevention of downstream flooding is not given one line. The supply of reliable irrigation water to produce food for an overpopulated and undernourished nation is never mentioned.

What is mentioned is that 40,000 hectares of "prime wildlife habitat" will be submerged. What is mentioned is that 100,000 hectares of forest and agricultural land will be submerged. In India, with a population of a billion people, if it's still "prime wild habitat" it could not have been worth farming. What is also mentioned is that possibly 160,000 people will be "displaced". The wording is always "displaced" which is obviously more emotive than simply "resettled".

There are reportedly 369 species of plants that will be "drowned" by the Narmada Sagar Dam alone. The way the report is worded implies that it would be an horrendous annihilation of species. The copy however does go on to say that there are really only 31 species that are "rare in the area and could become extinct locally". The same argument applies to kangaroos in downtown Sydney. It is also valid to rephrase it and say that not one single species is in any way threatened by actual extinction.

Another survey in the area suddenly discovered 53 plants with "medicinal use" that, it is conceded, "may not disappear, nevertheless local knowledge on how to use these plants is at risk of being lost". The survey further claims that there are 209 species of birds that live in the areas to be flooded and these will have to move away from "their preferred feeding and nesting sites". It can be expected that millions of water birds would flock to the area, but this also is not mentioned in the reports.

Fish species are also supposedly threatened by the construction of the dams. Again, it is conceded in the reports that there are 440 species of freshwater fish in all of India. Of this 440 only 25 are considered as endangered, 20 are considered vulnerable and really only 14 of the 440 are rare and in need of "urgent attention", but no one is too sure where in India these 14 species actually survive best.

The report does mention that the loss of these rare species cannot justly be blamed entirely on the construction of storage dams. The report points out that industrial pollution, the introduction of "exotic species", i.e. fish from some place else, and (surprisingly) indiscriminate fishing using dynamite, also have had an effect on local fish species.

There was a gold- and black-striped Indian freshwater fish called *Etroplus canarensis*. The last recorded sighting was in 1878 by a surgeon, Francis Day, employed by the government of Madras. More recently it became "officially" extinct. But this fish, it now seems, is not extinct at all, and obviously never was. They have been "rediscovered", and there are plenty of them not far from the city of Bangalore, in south central India.

Possibly the gold and black *Etroplus canarensis* could live very happily, and multiply, in the new dams on the Narmada River.

Every hydroelectric project, anywhere, anytime, reduces the sale of coal or oil. If you are in the oil or coal business such projects must be stopped, or reversed, or at the very least they must be incessantly criticized. The image of hydroelectricity must be under constant attack. One report criticizing the Narmada River Development Project actually and blatantly argues that oil would be a better and cheaper option for power generation in central India.

It was reported in the Vol. 290 issue of *Science* that a commission sponsored by the World Conservation Union and the World Bank released a report in 2000 in which it was claimed that, for the most part, the cost of the world's major dams have outweighed their benefits. The report stated that "in too many cases" benefits have been gained at an "unacceptable and often unnecessary price". The price always being totally undocumented and unproven but taken to mean "irreversible loss of species, populations and ecosystems". The report also blithely suggested that hydroelectric power was not necessarily cleaner than burning fossil fuels. The report called for (time-consuming) halts for more research to be undertaken on the "environmental impact" of hydroelectric projects anywhere. Was it because hydroelectric power competes with fossil fuels that the World Bank also reduced funding for dam construction by two thirds?

A few years ago, creating a bad image for man-made lakes and at the same time attributing mystical properties to rivers would have sounded idiotic and downright impossible. But it's been achieved. Today the emotional response by much of the population to rivers and man-made lakes is in accord with the fossil fuel lobbies' desired reaction.

There are a whole variety of geological occurrences that form lakes. A big cliff can collapse and block a canyon. An earth tremor can cause a hill to slide down into an adjacent valley. A small climate change can make the foot of a glacier suddenly move upstream and form a wall. Water then backs up behind these obstructions and lakes are formed.

Lakes are beautiful. But to sell fossil carbon fuel it is promoted that if they are man-made they cannot be thought beautiful. When lakes are created by man's enterprise, they are supposedly ugly and always environmental mistakes. In addition a "free, wild, happy, beautiful, sparkling, mischievous", etc., etc. river has been, "drowned, murdered, killed, buried", etc., etc. forever. These dreadful ecological disasters are then always attributed to the greedy, profit motivated, callous, uncaring, etc., etc. scoundrels that work for the mining, business, power generating, etc., etc. multinationals.

What a sad thing that these lakes that are the very brilliance of man's creations can come to be so scorned and denigrated.

Glaciers can build dams and bulldozers can build dams. There is no difference. In colder ages past, or even now in cold climates, glaciers— giant rivers of ice—grind and gouge their way down valleys, polishing and cleaning the valley floor and sides. The material is carried in the ice down to the end or tail of the glacier. The ice river melts when it reaches the glacial equivalent of the "snow line" and a giant heap of broken and shattered rock pieces accumulates. Over many thousands of years, a rock-debris wall is formed across the valley to the height of the trapped ice.

A warmer climatic shift starts the ice melting progressively up the valley. It may retreat several miles before it stabilizes to the new climate. Another wall starts to form at the new position. Downstream behind the first wall, water backs up, creating a lake. The walls of these glacial lakes are often incredibly even and regular as if designed in a civil engineering office.

The walls of man-made lakes can be of earth and rock constructions, the same as glacial lake walls. Otherwise they are concrete structures or combinations of both, depending on the engineering and economics.

The water in the lake, and the fish in the lake, are the same whether the wall came into being due to a climate shift, or an earthquake, or due simply to man's ingenuity and engineering skills.

Many countries with an abundance of natural lakes consider themselves truly blessed. Yet we are being systematically brainwashed to believe that lakes, when man-made, are a curse. It is interesting to note that there is no dam constructed anywhere in the world that receives any criticism whatsoever, provided only that the construction of the dam wall was a random geological occurrence. The lake was formed "naturally".

Of course the local environment changes whatever way a dam is constructed. Water birds don't inhabit dry creek beds, but if there is a lake there, they move in. Creek bed life moves upstream or they move out as they do every time seasonal flooding occurs.

Land dwelling life on our planet is totally dependent on the availability of fresh water. Any means that slows the inevitable movement of fresh water to the ocean is a bonus for all land dwellers. The eventual result of constructing lakes, either by accident or by design, is usually a rapid expansion and proliferation of wildlife. It is most definitely not the other way round. People should become aware of this, but to again quote Jonathan Swift: "There's none so blind as they that won't see."

The supposed ecological damage caused by mankind suddenly building ten million dams to produce hydroelectric power would be as nothing compared to what we are now doing by burning fossil fuels.

Even the Aswan High Dam is constantly criticized by the pro-oil anti-hydroelectric fraternity. The Aswan High Dam stores the waters of the Nile. The wall is built as far upstream—that is as far south—as possible and still have the water stored within the national borders of Egypt. A good quarter of that portion of the Nile that lies within the Arab Republic of Egypt is now part of the Aswan High Dam.

The Nile is the longest river in the world. It is also the only river that takes the immense rainfall of the planet's equatorial regions and transports the water right through the desert latitudes to its receiving ocean. (See the map of Africa on page 43.)

The desert latitudes in both the earth's hemispheres are between approximately thirty degrees and forty degrees of latitude, where lie the immense subtropical deserts of the globe. The Aswan High Dam is in a desert that can now be irrigated.

For Australians it would be like a river fed with the tropical rainfalls of Malaya, Borneo and Indonesia, a river which then meandered south through the Australian central deserts to finally discharge its water into the Great Southern Ocean near the city of Adelaide. What a blessing such a river would be. What an asset it would be to have a freshwater lake in dry central Australia.

Sun-parched Mexico lies in the dry latitudes between twenty degrees north and thirty degrees north. A Nile River in the Americas would be like the Amazon River turning north and doing its meander through the North American deserts. A giant river running through the Mexican desert through Nevada, through Death Valley and discharging into the North Pacific Ocean at, say, Long Beach, California. Again, what a blessing such a river would be. That is what the Nile with its Aswan Dam is to North Africa.

Should we just dump fresh water of these immense quantities in the ocean when the supply of natural fresh water in the world is so limited? That is exactly what the critics of the Aswan High Dam wanted.

When river water flows into the sea it becomes salt water and useless. But when a river is dammed, once the dam is paid for, the fresh water is free and very, very useful. The hydroelectric power produced is also free. No wonder it is so important to the marketers of oil and coal and gas that an image is created, albeit a totally false image, that there is something environmentally sinful involved in the construction of water storage dams. In reality, it is gross environmental negligence not to build water storage dams and equip them with hydroelectric generators wherever they can be built.

There is no shortage of salt water. The oceans are full of it. In many parts of the world, oil is burnt to produce fresh water from salt water. An enormous market therefore exists for the use of oil to produce fresh water—for the oil companies that is another reason to oppose dam construction.

Part of the anti-dam marketing misinformation is that dams rapidly silt up. It is almost always a proclamation that in thirty years the whole exercise will prove to be a total waste of money, and thus an environmental disaster. The life of any dam, on any river, in any country, somehow has been arbitrarily nominated as thirty years; when thirty years specifically is quoted enough times it becomes another manufactured folklore myth. Such statements are made to distort and diminish the real value of dams. It's quite ridiculous; three hundred years would be nearer the mark.

Of course some silting does occur. Most major cities use man-made dams to supply the city with water. Many of those dams have been in place for generations and will be there for generations to come. They haven't silted up. Many naturally formed lakes have been there for thousands of years. Is it that man-made lakes silt up faster than lakes formed by geological accidents? Most unlikely.

The Nile carries more silt than any other river in the world. In the past, the silt that didn't end up in the Nile Delta ended up in the Mediterranean Sea. That tremendous quantity of silt is now being deposited in the silt traps constructed at the inflow end of Aswan High Dam and thereby creating new farmland.

If, in the dim distant future, the Aswan High Dam did ultimately become silted up, it would only mean a new rich "Nile Delta" created deep inland in southern Egypt, and surely that would be no disaster. The existing Nile Delta has to feed all of Egypt and yet it is no more than 3% of the land area of that country. Another Nile Delta, if it ever did occur, would not be a bad thing at all, but a great blessing. The population of Egypt has now grown to 55 million people. Without the Aswan High Dam, millions would be dying of starvation and malnutrition. The dam was essential.

The ecological disaster occurring in Egypt is not the Aswan High Dam. It is the rapid destruction of the fertility of the soil of the Nile Delta by the catastrophic increase in the use of chemical fertilizers. Per acre or per hectare, they now use twice as much chemical fertilizer on their soil as is used in the United States or Europe. In consequence, the soil is rapidly deteriorating. This soil collapse has occurred in the short lifetime of one average fertilizer salesman.

The oil companies are well aware that humans really do like lakes, and have since the dawn of humankind. Near lakes there has always been good hunting. People like to live on the shores of lakes. People like to fish in lakes. People like to sail on lakes. Lakes are invariably beautiful and surrounded by greenery, shrubs and grasses, trees and flowers. Lakes are a home for a huge variety of wildlife and lakes can supply us with cheap clean power.

But to sell more oil, the construction of new lakes must be stopped.

Somehow man-made lakes had to be seen by the general public as totally different from lakes created by geological phenomena. So the geological ones became "natural" lakes. Man-made lakes therefore became "unnatural", or as they are so often labelled, "artificial". They are not even allowed to be called lakes at all. They are dams. If dams can be sufficiently divorced from lakes in the public mind, then dams can be attacked selectively. Dams can be damned.

The possible "environmental impact" of a new lake can be made the subject of protracted and heated debate. Studies can be undertaken "in the public interest". The oil companies can, indirectly or even directly, fund a couple of university graduates (in some obscure biological field) to study a proposed dam site. If they do, then it is a guaranteed certainty that some unique habitat, some supposedly rare animal or some obscure variety of ferns, or anything, can be found, and it can become a "cause célbre". And whatever it is, it will be put at "grave risk" if a dam is built. The media, posturing civic responsibility and acutely aware of who buys their advertising space, naturally will produce copious quantities of supposedly responsible editorial damning the dam.

To prevent the construction of a dam, editorial is used to exaggerate and highlight the "environmental virtues" of the existing creek or river. Campaigns are promoted to protect the river. For this ploy to work more effectively, rivers must be given a suitable marketing image. So rivers are personified. We are brainwashed into feeling that the river itself has intelligent life, and should be treated as if they have emotional responses.

Said like that it sounds ridiculous, but it's not. Advertising works. Creating false images has worked for thousands of years. Modern advertising gurus have it down to a fine art. So we now have "wild" rivers. We have rivers "running free" and "rivers should be unhindered". Rivers can be "starved". Rivers can "whimper" and they can "sigh". They can be "turbulent" (both an engineering description and a lifestyle description so simultaneously correct and emotive). Rivers can also be "exciting". They can be "mysterious". But above all else rivers must be "uninhibited" by walls.

In other words no dams!

I am sure you have all seen words like these used to describe the river whenever a hydroelectric system is proposed. When words like these are used common sense goes out the window and emotive irrationalism comes up through the floorboards. As an exercise right now, think of a river for a few seconds. Use the above words to describe the river. You will soon realize how easy it is to have your emotions and judgment manipulated. You can do it yourself, to yourself. Try it.

That's why advertising gurus are paid so well.

In an example of ultimate idiocy, it is being proposed that existing lakes (of course exclusively with man-made walls) should be drained to "release" the "soul" and the "beauty of the cruelly drowned rivers". Where then is the energy supposed to come from?

Have you ever heard of a proposal to drain a naturally formed lake to "release" the river that lies beneath? Of course not. That would be excessively idiotic and much too hard to sell.

Rivers are indeed often very beautiful. But in reality, what is beautiful is usually the shoreline. What is beautiful is the sides of the river, the contact area of the water and the land. An expanse of water by itself is not particularly beautiful. It is always the shoreline. It is the lake front. It is the ocean beach. It is the rocky headland. If we lose the sides of a river we gain a much larger lake side. It's different, but it's also nonsense to pretend it's wrong and ugly.

Those in the oil business and those who support the widespread use of fossil fuels will always plug for the river. They will never plug for the lake. And they will use their advertising dollars and their emotive propaganda to short circuit this threat of cheap clean hydroelectric power to their markets.

STRATEGY 26
Hindering the harnessing of ocean tides for power generation

The gravitational force of the moon has a considerable affect on our planet's environment. The distortion of the solid planet is very tiny but readily detectable with the right instruments. However, the effect on the liquid oceans is significant. We see this effect as ocean tides. The sun's gravitational effect also creates tides although they are small compared to lunar tides. The sun's ultimate effect is to slightly exaggerate, or to slightly diminish lunar tides.

Exaggerated tidal phenomena are quite dramatic in parts of the world. Some coastal areas constantly experience amazing tides, often over 40 feet (12 m) from high to low. The water rushes in and out of the local bays and estuaries, twice a day, as regular as clockwork. Harness that massive flow and you have tidal energy. In some areas of the world, tidal power could present a real threat to local coal-, oil- or gas-powered generating systems.

Tidal power is very similar to hydroelectric power in that both rely on controlling water flow with man-made walls. With hydroelectric systems, wonderful sites, sites that are practical and economical, can always be found upstream on rivers that are usually hundreds of miles long. Sites that often create hundreds of feet of water fall are not too hard to find. Trapping useful water in a river is generally easier and cheaper than in a bay, as is needed for tidal power.

There are rarely a great number of bays on most coastlines, and there are even fewer shallow enough to economically dam. And still fewer where tidal heights are large.

Sometimes however a city, a nation or a state may have few alternatives. Tidal power generating stations are unlikely to present any serious threat to the fossil carbon fuel suppliers, as there are few areas in the world where extreme tides and suitable bays are common.

But nevertheless the fossil fuel people will quite naturally, but never obviously, want them stopped. It is inevitable that no matter where a tidal power station is built, a bay or an estuary has to be walled off. This almost certainly will modify the local ecology in some way. Whether it is more pleasant the way it was, or the way it will be, is irrelevant. Any modification to the ecology is enough for a green organization to latch onto, or more likely to be steered towards.

Most "conservation" and "wilderness" and "biodiversity" organizations in reality support stagnation ecology concepts. Which is, don't touch anything, and stop touching anything if you have ever been touching it. Members may even live near a proposed tidal power facility, and using them is cheaper than bussing in the necessary protesters. They can also be more easily harnessed. The relevant conservation and wilderness industries are then funded and supported to destroy any chance that a tidal power station could be built.

Worldwide, these efforts have been very successful. Tidal power generating facilities are exceptionally rare. They are now considerably rarer than are economically and viable sites where they could be installed.

Unfortunately tidal power can never be a meaningful energy source. If the entire Mediterranean was somehow converted into a giant tidal pond, it couldn't power the countries along its own shoreline.

STRATEGY 27
Stopping wave energy from being a serious competitor

Wave energy sounds like a hypothetical dream, but it's not. Several coastlines dotted around the world experience almost constant and large ocean waves. As a wave moves past a point, the immediate water level can change by 10 or 12 feet (3 or 4 m), several times a minute. This is like a complete tidal system change, not twice a day, but maybe 3,000 times a day. Tidal systems need a bay with a large surface area, whereas an ocean wave system to produce commercial power needs a long coastline.

Wave energy may be tricky to harness, but the energy supply is large. Parts of the coastline of Western Europe, Ireland and the United Kingdom experience an almost constant impact of wave energy delivered by the North Atlantic swells. The European power grid, as a potential customer, is also just across the narrow English Channel.

There is a huge amount of free energy in waves. The coal, oil and gas suppliers to Western Europe would not want wave energy ever to get off the ground, or maybe out of the sea.

How would the fossil fuel lobby handle the problem of wave power? It would appear that one way to prevent its development might be to influence the people and the politicians making the decisions on wave technology research funding.

In a very controversial decision, wave technology research was virtually abandoned in the UK in the early 1980s. Funding was almost totally curtailed. Why, we will probably never know exactly, but we should worry. These are some of the things that happened.

UK bureaucracy sinks wave power

Professor Trevor Whittaker and his team in the coastal engineering department of Queens University of Belfast developed an excellent wave power generation machine. They had started research on wave power back in 1975. The machine was considered by many to be one of the world's most successful designs. A test machine continually pumped 75 kilowatts of electric power into the UK power grid.

It used an ingenious method of harnessing the wave energy. In their case waves funnelled into a man-made "blow hole", just like in a normal blow hole common along rocky cliffs. In the system, trapped air surges in and out of a formed cavity at a high velocity. Instead of seawater driving the turbines, the high velocity air did the job. Clever little turbines called Well's turbines were used that always spin in the same direction regardless of the direction of flow. The high air speed means high-speed turbines could be used, and these are easier and more efficient to couple to electricity generators.

It worked so well that the British Department of Trade and Industry decided it would not fund a bigger 600-kilowatt system. The installation they refused to fund would have supplied the electricity needs of a town of 1,000 people.

Also in the United Kingdom, a Stephen Salter invented another ingenious system for harnessing wave power, again in the early 1980s. The device, dubbed Salter's Duck, bobs up and down on each wave and the energy is extracted to generate electricity. The Energy Technology Support Unit, part of the UK Department of Energy, passed on critical loading factors that were actually incorrect to an independent consulting body investigating the invention's feasibility. The consulting body was commissioned by the UK Department of Energy. Much later the UK Department of Energy, to do it justice, did recall these false reports from libraries and institutions across the country. But the harm had been done.

The European Parliament received the false information and passed it on to the European Commission. The erroneous reports were then used to calculate the cost of electricity generated by wave power. In consequence a $20 million research program on the general feasibility of all forms of wave-generated electricity was stopped.

It seems that at the same time a parallel study was carried out by Professor Tony Lewis of Cork University. This study also appears to have been fed the false information. The vice president of the commission at the time, Filipo Pandolfi, claimed that EC funding was withheld from the research because of the cost factors and it was therefore "premature to start demonstration in this field".

Lewis' study actually recommended that research should go ahead. The study also showed that Europe's western coastline could produce 110 gigawatts of electric power. (Although this figure is probably overly optimistic and unlikely.)

Salter himself has queried "why are there some people in official circles who are worried about wave energy? Could it be that this is the one that might actually be a threat to certain established technologies?" An astute question.

The UK House of Commons Select Committee on Energy called for an "independent investigation" on the affair. Shades of "Yes, Minister". But who ultimately won? Sixteen years later the United Kingdom Department of Trade had decided that recommencing funding on wave power generation might be a good idea after all.

Private industries' efforts and research organizations' efforts to develop alternative energy systems are so easily thwarted by bureaucratic stop-start sabotage. Such counterproductive techniques are beautifully inconspicuous to the general public. Governments can appear to display responsibility for the environment while still jumping to the requirements of the fossil fuel industry.

The reality is that large-scale wave power generation is unlikely to be of any grave concern to the fossil fuel establishment until offshore installations become considerably more viable. A coastal wave power station capable of powering a city of one million people might have to be 200 or 300 kilometres long. Often-quoted ballpark figures are that 1 metre of coastline is required to generate enough power for each person in an affluent Western society. That's about 1 kilowatt 24 hours a day.

STRATEGY 28
Geothermal is a viable but limited threat to oil

When the earth's unlimited geothermal heat is near the surface and economically accessible, electric power can be generated. Geothermal power is environmentally immaculate. It is as clean as wave, wind, hydro or solar power, and no large-scale structures, which are claimed to "spoil the landscape", are required.

For the marketing and image creating people working for the fossil carbon industries, geothermal power is another big problem to be handled. Creating pseudo-environmental issues and influencing policy makers in government seem the only options available to suppress this extremely economical but unfortunately limited source of free energy.

Geothermal phenomena are somewhat mysterious and often awe-inspiring so the PR gurus figure fear is the best image to hammer. It is not difficult to make people uneasy and fearful simply by suggesting the possibility of some sort of man-made earthquakes, or of triggering volcanic eruptions. It is no more logical than suggesting throwing a pebble in the ocean could cause a tsunami. Of course it can't. But their hope must be that if common sense and logic are carefully avoided then sufficient fear and doubt and general confusion might be generated that could effectively stifle geothermal power generation.

Stopping the Hawaiian geothermal initiative

Geothermal power uses the earth's own heat to produce steam for steam turbines. There are two main systems for extracting the heat energy. In the first system holes are drilled and water is pumped down into the hot zone. The water turns to steam, and the steam is collected from another hole. In the second system which, when possible is far more practical and economical, the hole is drilled into high-temperature geological structures already containing vast quantities of superheated water. The released steam comes up the pipes and again drives the turbines.

The Hawaiian Islands result from shallow volcanic material oozing up through cracks in the earth's crust and forming islands. The earth's crust in that area is moving west-northwest in relation to the deep underlying magma. Over a few million years, the original island moves off a few miles in this west-northwest direction. Eventually the original hot spot becomes reactivated. Magma oozes up. Volcanic eruptions occur and a new island is formed. The new island again drifts off in an arc to the west-northwest. Eventually an island "chain" is born. Many of the Pacific island chains have this characteristic west-northwest layout. No oil or coal is formed in these relatively rapid geological processes.

The U.S. State of Hawaii has to rely on the importation of vast quantities of oil for its power. The bill for this oil is a constant drain on the economy of the islands. One or two nuclear power stations would easily solve their electricity supply problem on the more densely populated islands. The Hawaiian economy depends heavily on the tourist trade and large-scale guided tours of usually secretive nuclear power stations might be a world first and prove a major tourist attraction. The antinuclear environmentalists however have firmly closed the door on this option.

One would then imagine that geothermal power would be the perfect choice for this central Pacific group of islands. But that would interfere with the sale of oil. Geothermal power is constantly being suggested but always the well-trained environmental movement is called in to alleviate this perceived threat to the oil suppliers.

So the ever reliable "save the rainforest" and the "threatened biodiversity" banners are brought out of the toolbox. Of course members of environmental movements are constantly and invariably re-encouraged to trust and believe that nobler motives are the inspiration and it's not just to sell more oil.

One piece of nonsense claimed by Hawaiian green groups is that drilling a hole to tap artesian steam may put at risk downstream, lowland rainforest from possible escaping steam. There are incredible quantities of steam constantly being released from volcanic activity throughout these islands. Are people expected to believe that maybe the steam is somehow different? Hogwash, the two are the same. Geothermal steam released after being used in a turbine is even safer. It's cooler and it's controlled. When steam exits a turbine, it contains a lot less heat energy than when it entered. It's random and furious volcanic events that the locals have to worry about.

The natural steam from geothermal vents often contains small and harmless quantities of radioactive radon. If that steam is used, or not used, for power generation it contains the radon. Nevertheless the U.S. Federal Court ruled that federally funded geothermal research could not be supported in Hawaii until a "full environmental impact statement" had been prepared. Such environmental impact statements are easily manipulated into never-ending delays. Studies like this go on for years. One wonders just who went to the federal court to get such a ruling in the first place. But again, isn't the answer obvious?

In 1991, what was described as a "blow-out" happened on a drill site on the Big Island of Hawaii, not far from the Kilauea Crater. A previous geothermal hole drilled at Kahauale, much closer to Kilauea, had been buried in material from a nearby lava flow. Kilauea is the most continuously active volcano on the planet. The city of Honolulu is on the smaller island of Oahu.

The blowout on 13 June 1991 resulted in what was dutifully described as an "uncontrolled release" of steam. It took about half a day to cap it. Two workmen received minor injuries. This is probably about as bad as it can ever get at a geothermal plant. The blowout occurred because huge quantities of steam were encountered at considerably less depth than was expected, which is actually a bonus. A piece of equipment prevented the automatic shutoff from operating and it had to be removed. Technically, it wasn't even a blowout; a blowout is actually a release that can't be easily capped. And the supposed blowout was water. However six households were near the area were told to evacuate "as a precaution". One wonders why it got so much media attention. One wonders why it got any. On the other hand, a blowout at an oil or gas field or an "uncontrolled release" of oil or gas can be very dangerous.

Oil-inspired environmentalists inflate such incidents out of all proportion and in so doing initiate irrational and prohibitive safety and environmental regulations hindering geothermal power. And the oil companies win again.

A rainforest action group and an organization called the Pele Defense Fund oppose the whole concept of such geothermal power generation in

Hawaii. They claimed geothermal energy anywhere on the Big Island is not safe. They have two additional, almost amusing claims. One is that a geothermal power plant will destroy the adjacent rainforest. The second is that the power-generating unit itself will inevitably be buried in lava from the Kilauea Crater. How the rainforest and its biodiversity survive the expected lava flow is apparently irrelevant.

Members of the wealthy Greenpeace organization have boasted that Greenpeace is not interested in the facts when they decide to object to something, and neither it seems is the Pele Defense Fund.

At the time, a 500-megawatt geothermal plant was being proposed. That's enough generating capacity for 750,000 people. As most of the people on the Hawaiian Islands live in and around Honolulu, on the island of Oahu, it would be necessary to connect that island with a 200-mile (300 km) submarine power cable. A U.S.-government-funded feasibility study showed that such a cable could be laid and would be economically viable.

The design of the actual cable itself included an oil lining. This lining was a suitable and sufficient excuse for Greenpeace to oppose the whole concept. It claimed the cable might be cut by earthquakes or ocean currents and some oil might leak out. The hundreds of tanker loads of oil, constantly crossing the tropical Pacific to feed the oil-burning power stations of Hawaii, Greenpeace never mentioned.

Submarine "power lines" are now regularly laid. These are not to supply electric power but to pipe millions of tons of oil and petroleum products across hundreds of miles of the sea floor. There is now a proposal to run a flexible submarine oil pipeline from Oman in the Middle East across the Northern Indian Ocean to India itself. This isn't a cable with an oil-impregnated sheathing. This is a cable that will contain millions of barrels of oil and present a genuine risk of major spillage. Protesters have been deafening in their silence on the environmental risks of this little exercise.

Greenpeace and the Pele Defense Fund seem to have been successful. All the power still comes from imported oil. It seems incredible that geothermal power generation is not the major electricity production system in the Hawaiian Islands.

For the oil industries, the objective must always be to hinder, frustrate, and so delay the planning process to the point where the whole geothermal scheme is stopped. And stopped well before it can even get started. As soon as large power plants are built and prove themselves both economically and environmentally, a major switch to extensive use of geothermal power will occur. Of course such a switch would have drastic effects on oil sales. And incidentally, it would massively reduce carbon dioxide emissions from the fiftieth state.

STRATEGY 29
Biofuels are a major threat to oil and gas

Biofuel production is really a solar energy collection system. Solar energy is harvested by growing plants. The light energy is converted to chemical energy in the process. The chemicals formed are large complex carbon-based molecules. We either burn the plant material to produce usable heat, or we process the plants to extract oils, sugars or starches. We then convert these extracts into a variety of liquid or gaseous fuels. Biofuel production is a grow, burn and regrow process. It is therefore carbon dioxide neutral.

Ethanol is the biofuel that soon must replace petrol (gasoline). It is already added to petrol in many states and territories around the world both to reduce pollution and to reduce critical dependency on oil. It must, and it will eventually be used as straight ethanol to completely eliminate petrol's massive contribution to global warming.

Ethanol has had a long association with petrol. Boeing B-17 Flying Fortress bombers, fuelled with gasohol (a mixture of gasoline and ethanol) operated very successfully out of North Queensland during World War II, as noted in chapter 11. The big aircraft engines ran cooler and their performance was enhanced.

Petrol sold in Queensland between 1929 and 1957 contained 10% ethanol. After that, almost inexplicably some might feel, the production of ethanol for motor vehicles from Queensland sugar cane stopped. For a hundred years the oil companies have recognized the threat of ethanol as an automotive fuel and lobbied against it. Henry Ford spelled it out for them in 1906 when he said, "The fuel of the future is going to come from fruit like that sumac out by the road, or from apples, weeds, sawdust— almost anything. There is fuel in every bit of vegetable matter that can be fermented. There's enough alcohol in an acre of potatoes to drive the machinery necessary to cultivate the field for a hundred years." Just recently the production of ethanol blends containing less than 10% ethanol has ceased being a crime in Australia. Selling petrol with above 10% ethanol content however is.

To produce one barrel of petrol requires about 1.2 barrels of crude oil. At times the Middle East nations manipulate the price of crude, forcing it up to well over US$40 a barrel. If we add to this the 20% excess needed to convert the crude to petrol, and not include any manufacturing or production costs, the raw material cost for petrol becomes US$48 a barrel. There are 160 litres in a standard barrel, so $48 a barrel is $0.30 per litre of crude, which is marginally more expensive than ethanol produced by an efficient fermentation facility. To the price of petrol must be added manufacturing, shipping and production costs. What also should be added, but never are, are the political and military costs to protect the oil-supply systems.

It is not a coincidence that the world price of oil never seems to rise

In 1952 the author established an Australian water ski jump record. Here shown practicing on the Hawkesbury River near Sydney. Ski boats can happily run on ethanol or ethanol blends and be safer to operate. The ski boat (now just out of the above picture) ran on petrol. At the time the cancerous spread of destabilized climates around the world resulting from fossil fuel use was never even imagined.

permanently above a price where ethanol from sugar would be comfortably cost competitive. World oil prices are periodically adjusted and keep this situation permanent. Petrol and ethanol are therefore both produced at a cost of around 30 U.S. cents per litre. But unlike oil, ethanol costs can't be manipulated so as to destroy the competition and put them out of business.

Ultimately however, the biggest difference between cost of production and retail price is invariably due to national and local taxes. As a result there are few countries in the world where petrol is retailed for much less than 70 or 80 U.S. cents per litre or about US$2.80 a U.S. gallon.

The reality is that ethanol could easily be made cheaper than petrol at the service station and it could be accomplished with negligible modification to state or federal fuel taxes. Governments should not find it difficult to accept or even mandate a national switch to ethanol. But as we so often see, governments can be influenced, and sadly, too easily.

In Australia a new anti-biofuel tactic has emerged. Here, an image is being created that endeavours to portray ethanol as some form of pollution risk and as an engine-damaging substance. It is a subtle public relations and marketing campaign. Grave risks are carefully and subtly implied: an image is being sold that there is something "wrong" with ethanol as a motor vehicle fuel (in reality it's a better and safer fuel than gasoline). To this end a massive campaign was waged suggesting that ethanol will damage car engines. Senators and government ministers were coerced into legislating actual limits on the amount of ethanol that can be added to a fossil fuel. It was touted as a move to protect the engines in the family car. Utter rubbish. Legislation should have been introduced the other way round: limiting the amount of petrol that could be added to ethanol.

To illustrate how strongly these issue are forced into our thinking by the oil lobby consider the comparison with LPG (liquefied petroleum gas). Fuel companies often add special lubricants and additives to petrol to "prevent wear and enhance engine performance". This is easy with both petrol and ethanol, as both are liquids. With LPG, a fossil fuel product, this is not so easy. LPG becomes a gas before entering the engine and these previously much-publicized special lubricants cannot be incorporated into a gas. Politicians were conspicuous by their absence in any endeavour to protect the family car from wear caused by switching to LPG. This moralistic juggling and behind-the-scenes influence of the fossil fuel lobby on government is frightening.

Also in Australia, an interesting situation arose at the beginning of the millennium. The federal government was not applying a fuel excise to ethanol. Consequently fuel vendors would buy ethanol and add it to their petrol, thus avoiding a proportion of the fuel excise and so increasing their margins. They couldn't advertise, because if caught, they could be prosecuted for avoiding fuel excise taxes. The cars still ran fine, the vendor made more money and the environment benefited. The oil companies didn't like it at all—but so convenient for them, it was against the law. The Australian Government was made to dutifully crack down on such "tax cheats". But who won? Certainly not the environment. It was the oil producers as always who really benefited by the crackdowns.

Some of the ethanol was being imported from Brazil. The Australian Federal Government was coerced into imposing a tariff on imported ethanol. The so nobly stated intention was to assist Australian sugar-ethanol production. This new tariff should never have happened. A subsidy should have been paid to local sugar producers instead. This would have encouraged, and not discouraged, a change to ethanol-based motor vehicle fuels. Australia and the world would have benefited.

Then two years later the world price of sugar collapsed. (I know of no investigation as to how or why this happened, but surely it should be worthy of some investigation.) Australian sugar farmers are efficient and internationally competitive in a free market situation. Nevertheless they were hit hard. The Australian Federal Government then, in an incredible display of either naïveté, gullibility or blatant cronyism, stepped in and decided to "assist" Australian sugar farmers to vacate the industry and stop producing sugar. They would give them an assistance bonus to sell up and go. To fund this so-called assistance package a levy was dreamed up and applied as a tax on the price of sugar at consumer outlets. The benefit of all this to the oil companies was remarkable. The final effect is that the Australian consumer is paying a tax at the supermarket to assist Australian sugar and ethanol producers to self-destruct.

It is accepted by all that petrol use increases the net carbon dioxide level in the atmosphere and ethanol use doesn't. Yet the environmental protection bureaucracies and the industries that so often support them, call for further "studies" on ethanol use in motor vehicles. Simultaneously they both studiously avoid realistic global warming considerations. These people are dangerously clever and frighteningly manipulative. They must somehow imagine that ethanol-fuelled Brazil doesn't exist. Brazil runs on ethanol. Brazil is the biggest producers of sugar cane and ethanol of any nation in the world. All the major car companies with branches in Brazil manufacture cars that run perfectly on straight ethanol and or ethanol blends. By the 1990s there were over 4 million cars in Brazil operating on straight ethanol (see chapter 11).

Ethanol blends are now almost universally available in the United States. Ethanol blends are promoted there by the fuel companies because of their better performance characteristics—most definitely not for their greenhouse-reducing characteristics. Undoubtedly, to the unwitting chagrin of the U.S. oil lobby, the United States Clean Air Amendment Bill of 1990, actually nominated ethanol as a "clean fuel".

There is a twist however. Ethanol in the United States is made from corn and this is encouraged. The much cheaper production of ethanol from sugar cane is not encouraged.

Biodiesel gets the same treatment. It is the obvious objective of the fossil fuel interests to avert the commercialization of biofuels anywhere it might occur. Biodiesel was trialled in the UK. The fuel quality proved to be excellent, but not so the politics. For example, rapeseed oil modified into its rape-methyl-ester form (RME) was given a comprehensive trial by Reading Bus, a local commuter transport company. Canola oil is another name for rapeseed oil and RME is the biodiesel produced from this oil.

The rapeseed oil was imported from Italy and so fuel duty was dutifully imposed on the imported oil. As a result, the biodiesel cost the company about twice the price of the diesel fuel it replaced. Unfortunately because of the colder UK weather the locally grown oil is more expensive. Technically it is true that much of the imposed duty could have been claimed back. But such claims involve compliance with tortuous government regulations that make claim processes almost hopeless.

The buses ran well on the biodiesel. Drivers reported they started well, had no breakdowns, and produced less smoke. The fuel was as good as, or better than diesel.

Because of the lack of government support, and what seems to have been actual government hindrance, and because of immense bureaucratic compliance requirements, the buses in Reading were forced back to operating on diesel.

The United Kingdom Department of Transport then decided to try for a win both ways. It offered large grants to local authorities to try various other fuels to reduce consumption and pollution. This initiative was obviously designed to appease concerned environmentalists. That sounded all right, but at almost the same time the department said that preferences for the allocation of grants would be directed to trials involving compressed natural gas, LPG and electrically powered vehicles. The use of biofuels would not be a preferred option as, "the role of alternative fuels has not been fully thought through."

This effective elimination of biofuels would naturally appease the fossil fuel lobby and give the Department of Transport a rather unsavoury and sick double win; certainly it was a win for the oil companies.

The whole range of biofuels pose a very significant threat to the sales of fossil carbon materials. They are a most competitive transport energy source, and the fossil fuel lobbies are understandably determined to ma-nipulate against them and suppress their general adoption.

STRATEGY 30
Wind energy as a threat to fossil fuels

Wind energy is a very viable source of commercial electricity and the cost of the electricity produced is reasonably competitive with that from fossil sources.

Wind energy is similar to tidal energy in that it is limited to quite unique geographical areas and localized topographical forms. Nevertheless, oil companies would be remiss if they did not treat wind energy as a significant threat deserving of well-planned public image manipulation. So a bad image of wind energy had to be created.

Wind energy has been utilized by man since well before the beginning of recorded history. Probably its first use was to power sailing vessels with sails of woven reeds. Millennia later, the water wheel and the windmill were invented. Rotary motion and primitive gear wheels meant man and beast were no longer the sole source of useful energy. Windmills and water wheels became part of the very fabric of man's history. The old windmills that ground, or milled our flour for bread making were colourful and attractive. They are part of the heritage of human society.

It is not easy to destroy such an image, but destroyed it must be. Otherwise, modern technologies could turn a new generation of the old windmills into a threat to the purveyors of fossil carbon.

There are many localities where the wind is consistently strong and blows in a reasonably constant direction for the greater part of the year. And these of course are the places where wind energy becomes most competitive. However, every pulse of electricity, every watt of power that comes from a wind turbine, represents a loss in sales of coal or oil or gas. When a wind turbine installation is being considered some place, inevitably some fossil fuel company or country, somewhere, is going to lose sales. The well-oiled public relations machinery is put into top gear.

For the fossil fuel lobby, combating wind energy becomes just another part of the ongoing war against alternative fuels. An article in a prestigious journal discusses wind farms and expresses doubt whether they should really be considered as a "green" alternative energy source at all. It blithely states that wind turbines are not compatible with many other land uses "such as housing or airports".

That's ridiculous. It could just as logically be rephrased, and argued that wind turbines are compatible with all forms of land use, and more so than airports and housing.

The article also states that wind turbines have an "impact on the environment" as they are "noisy and unsightly". (A current catch phrase that presumes any impact on any environment as being bad.) The same article does, incidentally, concede that at a distance greater than 1,000 feet (300 m) their noise level corresponds to that inside a public library.

However the message is forced through and a negative image for wind power slowly becomes established in the public mind.

I believe that wind generating towers and their turbines are wonderful examples of brilliant engineering with beautiful and functional design. If we are to judge wind turbines as ugly then we can never feel proud of any of our achievements. Invention, construction, and even artistic design will all be sacrificed on an altar of environmental stagnation.

The common claim that wind farms take up a lot of area uses some twisted logic to justify. The land area a turbine really uses is no more than the base on which it rests, and that's about the same as the base area of one conventional power transmission line tower, the same towers that crisscross and span our countries from end to end.

Wind energy, like solar energy, needs an area less than 1% of the land area we need to feed ourselves, and when all things are added they both invariably use less total land area than a conventional coal-fired power system of the same output.

We are also being conditioned to believe that wind turbine blades kill flocks of birds. Don't believe it. The Dutch Institute of Nature Conservation and the British Royal Society for the Protection of Birds both concede that wind turbines have little affect on bird life. Modern high-capacity wind turbines have blades that turn one complete revolution in about three seconds. The diameter of a large wind turbine might be 130 feet (40 m), which means the very outer tip of the blade travels at around 95 mph (150 kph). Birds can dodge such things quite well. If they are not birds of prey themselves then they have learnt how to dodge them. Birds are good pilots. I fly myself and birds easily dodge light aircraft that travel at similar speeds to wind turbine blades. The turbine blades are stuck on their tower in one fixed locality and even the silliest birds soon learn to avoid them.

California has the most wind turbines. Denmark, coming second, has about 3,000. This is encouraging. However like all renewable energy projects, Danish wind farms ran into tremendous problems from government and bureaucracy in getting them approved and having them built.

Many of the new wind turbines coming on line will be built in shallow water, one or two miles out to sea. This has several advantages. Wind speeds are higher and more consistent away from the coast, and the builders and operators are not subject to orchestrated complaints of being "unsightly and noisy".

Generating costs of these new turbines can be less than $0.10 per kilowatt-hour, a perfectly acceptable power cost for a modern industrial society and automatically a significant threat to the fossil fuel producers. Efficient installations in ideal locations can produce power at costs as low as $0.03 per kilowatt-hour.

STRATEGY 31
The handling of solar energy

There are two fundamentally different technologies for the production of electricity from sunlight. The first uses photovoltaic cells or solar cells that produce electricity direct from sunlight.

The second, called solar thermal, focuses concentrated sunlight onto a pipe target. By various means this concentrated heat is then used to produce superheated steam to drive conventional steam turbines.

We've all seen solar cells. They receive a lot of publicity. Solar cell systems are inherently expensive and are not currently seen as a serious threat to fossil fuel generated power. So it's OK for the oil companies to foster them, and in so doing be seen to be green. This they duly do.

Not so with the emerging variety of solar thermal concepts and designs that might come on line. These, the coal, oil and gas producers cannot ignore. To date the only image their PR people promote is to claim that solar power stations require enormous areas of valuable land. But this is nonsense. In any Western society, or in any other advanced affluent society, on average a citizen uses about an acre, say half a hectare of land, to grow their food. Using solar thermal technology, each would need just 275 sq ft or 25 sq m allocated to generate solar power. That area would be sufficient for 24-hour operation, with suitable energy storage.

Solar power stations also work best in dry cloudless conditions—not in good farming country where it is desired that rainfall be ample and regular. The land requirements argument is nonsense. The land area for solar power is less than 0.75% of the land area for food, cotton and wool.

The fossil carbon energy people with their current appreciation of the impracticality of solar voltaics have only recently begun to comprehend the potential of low cost solar thermal power. With the generation of electricity from nuclear energy being systematically turned into a socially unacceptable power alternative, solar thermal power begins to loom as the most likely major threat to fossil carbon fuels. It is in the best interests of the oil, coal and natural gas industries to try and stop solar thermal power from ever getting a free run. If a solar power station gets going they want it out of business as soon as possible.

In 1979 LUZ International Limited was formed to produce and operate commercial solar thermal power stations. The group built a series of power stations in the Mojave Desert in Southern California. The plants have a combined generating capacity of 354 megawatts, enough to supply the power requirements of a city of 400,000 people. The power is distributed through the utility company, Southern California Edison. The LUZ plants are also equipped with natural-gas-fired boosters to maintain optimum steam temperatures and efficiencies. By a considerable margin, these plants in California produce many times more solar thermal electricity than is produced in the rest of the world combined.

Californians know about smog and air pollution and are prepared to pay a little more for their energy to beat the problem. Los Angeles was once the smog capital of the world, but things are improving there. European cities on the other hand are deteriorating fast, with some areas in Western Europe now making Los Angeles look pristine by comparison. The LUZ plants in Southern California are helping.

A United States law, passed to assist alternative energy initiatives, required utility companies to buy electricity from nonpolluting alternative energy sources when available. In addition the Federal Energy Regulatory Commission (FERC), recognizing the necessity for supplementary heat input to cater for variations in solar flux, allows a 25% input of fossil-fuel energy while still qualifying all the output as alternative energy. Most of the generating equipment could thus be operated overnight and so reduce the cost of servicing the initial capital.

The law also said that the price the distributing companies buying the wholesale power must pay must equal the highest peak load price they paid to any conventional supplier they purchased power from. On face value the law was well designed and worked well for a period. But the concept had a flaw.

As the incentive started to take effect and alternative energy generation increased, the fossil fuel companies undoubtedly got nervous.

So what happened? The LUZ power station setup, with something like 180 acres of collecting mirrors, was selling its power at a price based on expensive natural-gas-fired generating facilities serving Southern California Edison. Solar power was thus starting to get a foothold in the marketplace. Then a weakness in the LUZ financial structure was discovered and utilized. The gas companies slashed the cost of their gas and the wholesale cost of electricity plummeted. In consequence the support price for alternative energy crashed and so did the alternative energy solar electric company. In consequence LUZ International Limited could not go ahead with their next project, listed as SEGS-10. SEGS-10 would have generated another 80 megawatts of power, sufficient for the daytime requirements of a city of more than 100,000 people.

The total land area of that proposed plant near Barstow was 416 acres (168 ha). That's only 180 square feet (17 square metres) per person. Western man uses at least 200 times as much land for food. So, contrary to what is always inferred, LUZ technology proved solar land area requirements are actually tiny.

Solar panels, solar cells or photovoltaic cells (the terms are interchangeable) are the solar systems that always manage to generate considerable publicity. The marketing by some oil companies of the, to them, totally unthreatening concept of solar cells is brilliant. The across Australia, long distance "solar race" is a good example of their well-structured support.

But the facts are that photovoltaics generate very little power per dollar spent. Photovoltaics also manages to get something like ten to twenty times the overall publicity and general media coverage as do solar thermal concepts, yet solar thermal is already vastly cheaper and more efficient. Government funding constantly and very selectively supports photovoltaics, not solar thermal. Funds and assistance packages are structured so that solar thermal power generating systems never qualify for anything. It is insane that photovoltaics consistently receive anything up to a thousand times more government funding and research backing than solar thermal concepts. Is that really just accidental?

Purely for political reasons, governments have to display an interest in alternative energy systems, but most government funding for alternative energy is conveniently channelled away from realistic solar thermal development into expensive and exotic projects like deuterium hot fusion research. For the fossil fuel industries, deuterium hot fusion research is undoubtedly the most unlikely to work and the least threatening alternative energy and nuclear energy system on anybody's horizon. For the grinning oil producers, these projects conveniently drain away alternative energy research dollars like water from a kitchen sink.

STRATEGY 32
Destroying the nuclear energy industry

The all-electric car and the high-output hydrogen fuel cell have to be based on non-fossil-fuel energy sources for them to be sensible concepts. The electricity will be either generated "on board" using hydrogen fuel cells or it will be stored in electrochemical batteries. In either case the original energy has to be produced at non-fossil-fuel power stations.

The stark reality is that nuclear energy is the only energy source that can supply the huge quantities of energy needed to power any self-contained electrical transport systems. The oil producers understand that, so they see nuclear energy as an enormous threat to their continuing sales of gasoline, diesel and LPG.

Surprisingly, the oil producers have actually brainwashed themselves into believing that sugar cane and oilseed production are absolutely reliant on the chemical fertilizers they themselves manufacture. Using petrochemical fertilizers to grow sugar or vegetable oils, they reason, inherently negates the zero emission advantage of biofuels. At least this is their argument. Therefore, to them, only nuclear generated electricity is left as an all-encompassing threat to petroleum-based fuels.

Therefore, for the fossil fuel industries, the objective has been and must be to generate in the minds of the general public intense fear of all forms of nuclear energy and nuclear radiation. They must constantly argue the nonsense that the natural background radiation that has bathed the planet since before life first formed, is deadly to the life that actually evolved in it. The fossil fuel lobby continue to claim that all forms of radiation in even the tiniest of doses will kill, and thus all radiation must be avoided.

The oil producers must also create a general belief that the disposal of nuclear waste is an actual problem. Then they must follow up with invented arguments against every proposed disposal system.

The oil producers must always link nuclear-generated electricity with nuclear weapons. They, of course, must keep under wraps the logical and parallel argument that all conventional explosives and all chemical weapons are petroleum based.

Understanding how the truth about nuclear energy has been manipulated by the fossil fuel industries is frightening. But such massive manipulations have been done before. Maybe they slavishly copied an evil teacher in an endeavour to prove again that:

> The great masses of the people ... will more easily fall victims to
> a big lie than to a small one. (Adolf Hitler, *Mein Kampf*, 1925)

The systematic destruction of the nuclear energy industry and the consequential ramifications are of vital concern in our efforts to prevent total climatic destabilization. Chapter 10 has been devoted entirely to this incredible story.

STRATEGY 33
Ridiculing the nuclear cold fusion concept

Cold fusion is one of those strange and incredible concepts that, just possibly, could put nuclear-powered engines under the bonnets of cars. On face value, how research on such an important issue could be stopped seems difficult to imagine. Research costs for cold fusion are not the billions involved in hot fusion energy research. They are way down in the millions or even thousands of dollars range.

What can the oil companies do? It might be possible to suggest the threat of atomic bombs in every car on the freeway. It might then be possible to put a blanket ban on all cold fusion research because of this hypothetical threat.

Unfortunately for the oil-marketing gurus this would be too difficult to implement globally. Many countries—Japan being typical—are frighteningly dependant on imported energy. If there is any chance of the process working, then these countries are not going to let cold fusion just go away. For oil marketing then, at least wherever possible, the concept should be ridiculed. It can possibly be portrayed as some giant scam. In this way, participating research personnel could be made to look ludicrous. All of the claims of successful cold fusion to date may well have been scams, for that is what we are consistently told. Maybe true, but more likely and more charitably they were sincere mistakes. But that's what research and development is all about.

There are theoretical bases for a variety of cold fusion concepts so at least we should keep an open mind and keep looking. Who knows? Perhaps the scams have been intentionally promoted to ensure that all forms of cold fusion research become tarred with the same brush.

The oil companies' public relations and advertising people have to carefully monitor their "problem" of cold fusion.

The whole concept of cold fusion however, is a big if. In the short-term we most certainly can't expect it to be a contributing factor in our immediate need to prevent runaway global warming.

Research on cold fusion is not inherently expensive whereas, in complete contrast, hot fusion is a bottomless money sinkhole. Hot fusion is the process used in the hydrogen bomb and a practical system for generating electricity using hot fusion energy is a long way off. Temperatures in the millions of degrees, and enormous pressures coupled in incredibly expensive and exotic configurations are required to produce a hot fusion effect even in laboratories. From the oil companies' point of view, if research money has to be spent on nuclear energy, then it should all be allocated to the most unlikely, impractical, and expensive branch of nuclear study possible. Which is of course hot fusion power generation.

Hydrogen bombs can be made thousands of times more deadly than atomic bombs. What happened to the antinuclear movement that made them so supportive of hot fusion? Should they not ponder the wisdom of spending billions researching a branch of science that may one day lead to super simple super bombs. Hot fusion research is a track leading to discoveries with utterly unknown and frightening consequences. And it's not needed.

STRATEGY 34
Supporting subsidized agriculture and reduced agricultural land area to sell agrochemicals

Reducing the quantity of available agricultural land results in higher land prices and more intensive farming. This makes chemically dependent agriculture very much more saleable, affordable and justifiable.

The food market is limited by the actual requirements of the consumers, whereas the agricultural chemical market is only limited by the skill and daring of the marketers themselves. Every season, every acre can receive either a spoonful or a truckload of such chemicals. Manipulated agricultural laws, juggled agricultural subsidies, the infusion of a pro-chemical bias into agricultural research, intense lobbying and misleading advertising, all determine whether it be a truckload or a spoonful. In consequence and to ensure the expanding sales of agricultural chemicals, the worldwide manipulation of agriculturally related laws has developed into an insidious art form.

An extremely favourable structure for the agrochemical companies has been established for limiting agricultural production in most Western nations. Artificially high prices for food, especially grain, are determined by individual national governments. Government agencies are then established and funded to purchase the inevitable overproduction that is in turn often dumped at artificially low prices on world markets.

In the United States, these high prices were established following World War II. Originally, the idea was to stimulate U.S. food production to feed and restore a battered world. The world recovered, but the subsidized pricing structures remained. An enormous sociological, agricultural mess was created. There are now thousands of U.S. farms that are simply too small to survive in any normal and sensible free market situation.

The concept and the cancer of subsidized agriculture spread, and the value of agricultural produce and agricultural land became progressively distorted throughout the world. Of course, all these additional farmers have their political influence, so artificially high prices became easy to maintain.

In Europe, non-viable farms, supported by artificially high prices for agricultural produce, eventually became the norm. The same huge food stockpiles grew and grew, until they finally became a huge embarrassment. What to do? If the food is allowed to simply deteriorate and rot, the issue becomes a public scandal. That is why oversupplies are sold, or "dumped", on international markets at artificially low prices.

The political reasons for distorting world markets in this manner vary according to the current political agenda and national interests. But mostly the relevant governments simply don't understand and don't appreciate that there may well be a rather unhealthy logic to such dumping. For it is automatic that such dumping puts pressure on unsubsidized, more efficient, non-chemical-using farmers in other countries and puts them out of business.

One solution. Huge quantities of overproduction food could simply be given to the millions of starving people throughout the world. This might ensure continuing and possibly increasing sales of agrochemical products. However, giving food away as a long-term option has never been particularly successful for any government. It was practiced in ancient Rome and it didn't succeed. It doesn't today. Won't we ever learn? Large-scale gifts of food create enormous moral, monetary, criminal and political repercussions. The food is inevitably acquired by the current local power junta and pseudo-legal black markets are soon established. Donating governments are also rarely benignly generous and their food aid is invariably linked to subsidized, chemically based home agricultural production.

Food self-sufficiency in Third World countries is best achieved by the progressive mechanization of independent, but initially only subsistence-level farms. It is also more efficient, more logical and more productive and therefore essential for farmers to have clear and legal title to their land. That is how they can finance their tractors.

These farms improve dramatically and prosper when their labour efficiency improves with mechanization. They also prosper dramatically as they work to increase the fertility of their soils. Such small farms cannot afford to waste money on agrochemicals, and don't. Especially if those chemicals destroy the very fertility they are trying to enhance.

Such concepts have negligible appeal for agrochemical sales people.

Agrochemical companies know that if aid is to be given to Third World countries it is in their interest to ensure that the aid be directed to some administrative government agency, or alternatively to large government controlled farms. They know that aid must never go to small independent free-thinking farmers. They know that administrations can be manipulated and "collective" farms can be coerced into becoming huge markets for agrochemical products. Of course part of this process is that "technical advisors" must always be part of the aid package. And for "technical advisors" always read "agrochemical salesmen".

The population of the world is now considered by many to be increasing faster than the increase in world food production. The Malthusian theory that predicts we will breed ourselves into international famine has strong support.

The believed perception that worldwide starvation is now inevitable was argued by Lester Brown back in 1990 in the "State of the World" report issued by the World Watch Institute in Washington, DC. Lester Brown, who headed up the institute, is an agronomist and his report noted that while food yields grew at a rate of 3% a year between 1950 and 1984, and thus increased average individual food availability, the trend has now reversed. At the end of the 1980s the rise in food production had dropped to 1% per year (possibly as soil fertility levels slowly declined). But population projections were 1.7% per year.

At the same time, Western nations always claim to have excess food production capacity as, it is argued, agricultural land, supposedly still usable for food production, has been "set aside". However, Brown states that the reality is that the land was taken out of production because of depletion in soil fertility, which is in turn causing widespread erosion. The 1985 United States Farm Bill and the 1985 Food Security Act legislated a reduction in available cropland area throughout the United States by a massive 11% over the following five years. Very conveniently for the agrochemical companies, the legislation placed no limits at all on actual volume of production. Later legislation consistently maintained these conveniently structured influences on U.S. agriculture.

The same fertilizer-induced agricultural mistakes are also being made in countries such as China and the old Soviet Union states, all with "copycat" agricultural administrators. The report from the World Watch Institute, almost by accident, highlighted frightening emerging world food production manipulations.

Today a well-managed, well-orchestrated script promotes production of food using massive quantities of agricultural chemicals. That same manipulative script also attacks organic food and organic food production techniques with never-ending criticism. This is usually in combination with the manipulative creation of frustrating and prohibitive legislation.

Western nations that subsidize food production eventually reach a point where total production has to be limited, or embarrassing surpluses develop. So, on one hand we have increasing world starvation and on the other artificially limited agricultural land areas.

Bizarre? Yes it is. But it gets even more bizarre.

As was pointed out in chapters 6 and 8, if government agencies imposed a limit on the actual quantity of food at the subsidized price, then total subsidized production could be easily and conveniently regulated. That makes sense. But it's not how it happens. For the agrochemical industry such a limitation would be most unfortunate. They need agricultural land area restricted. It is obvious that whatever form of limitation is imposed, farmers will adapt. But if food quantity is limited specifically and not land area, then farmers will, as always endeavour to produce food in the most cost-effective manner. Expensive chemical inputs would thus be the first thing to avoid. The totally beneficial and cost-free concept of increasing soil fertility would suddenly be a logical scenario. The scenario would be adopted by farmers everywhere. Wise crop rotation would also become the norm.

This is not the way to sell agricultural chemicals. Fertilizer sales would slump. Worse, healthy plants do not need pesticides. Crop rotation would negate the need for fungicides. It would be a disaster. For the agrochemical-petrochemical industries there had to be another way. So that is why a limit is never placed on the total quantity of food that can be produced and be eligible for a price subsidy. That is why the limit is placed instead on the specific area of land on which the legally subsidized crop can be grown.

Thus, within the food price procurement structure the limit on the quantity of chemical stimulants used in crop production is only reached when the cost of chemical inputs ultimately exceeds the increase in crop mass.

Of course, the concept requires an army of bureaucrats to enforce. This naturally suits the inevitable empire-building ethos within the particular government agencies intended to administer agriculture. They therefore become allies of the chemical industries. It is obviously a cumbersome and unwieldy system, but from the point of view of the petrochemical industry, the advantages are mind-boggling.

United States agricultural products and most European agricultural products are still subsidized in this manner. And the money paid out is still based on unlimited quantity of crop, produced off strictly limited areas of land. This form of subsidized agriculture does not subsidize the nation's farmers. It subsidizes the producers of agricultural chemicals. And in so doing, it actually funds the destruction of a nation's topsoil and effectively funds the escalation of global warming.

STRATEGY 35
Creating the impression of giant wilderness areas that never existed

Enforcing intensive agriculture is the agrochemical companies' most assured method of massively increasing the sales of their chemicals and fertilizers. They therefore support agricultural land being taken out of circulation. The creation of enormous wilderness areas, bigger than some individual nations, can tie up future agricultural land on a grander scale and with more assured permanence than almost any other process or ploy known to agrochemical companies and their public relations gurus.

All that is required is that somewhere, within these potential giant land grabs, some "prime example of the wonders of our planet" can be claimed to exist. The PR people then fund some suitably bankrupt green movement to supply protesters. Send a good camera crew out with them to shoot footage on some attractive and photogenic location, and with the help of suitably manipulated television coverage, a million acres can be tied up forever. In addition, if they so choose, the sponsoring oil company can be seen as displaying "commendable corporate responsibility".

Often these good photogenic locations are so hidden in the vastness of these immense land grabs that they are often impossible for a visitor to locate. Generally the tax-funded custodians of any beauty spots feel they have to keep them that way. They therefore want visitors to keep out. But if beauty is "in the eye of the beholder", where then is the beauty if there is no one permitted to behold it? Tomorrow's generation will themselves have another "tomorrow's generation" so they too must be kept out by another crop of custodians for distant "future generations".

We should also be aware that already more than two-thirds of the land area of this planet is either defined, or generally considered as wilderness. Why do we need more? We must also remember that over the last 50,000 years virtually all the habitable landmasses of this planet have been occupied by man. Every wilderness area on this planet over those 50,000 years is now man-made either by cultivation and animal management, but primarily by the use of fire. If any habitable area on this world is not already totally man-made, it is at least influenced in a major way by human habitation.

An entire ice age has come and gone during the long period of man's influence on the ecology of the planet. Some of man's influence has been good, some bad, but nowhere does true pre-human wilderness exist, except only in the deserts of never-ending wind and sand, and in the deserts of never-ending snow and ice.

What then are wilderness societies trying to preserve as they strive to lock up massive chunks of the planet's surface? Maybe they are just bored, looking for a new interest? Or are they just the nonthinking front line troops of the petrochemical industries, the green pawns of the fossil fuel lobbyists?

We obviously need intelligent decisions as to how much of our land surface needs to be preserved as wilderness parks, and where and what those areas should be. However it is silly to presume that a wilderness has unique value simply because it is currently defined as a wilderness. Look up wilderness in the dictionary—it does not say wilderness is in any way something special or worthwhile, and mostly it's not.

So maybe something could be unique? We should remember most things and most places anywhere are in some ways "unique"—or one of a kind. But something unique in my dictionary also means "very remarkable". If it is not very remarkable and we change it, in all probability it will be just a different "unique". But irrespective of such hypothetical considerations, right now, for better or for worse such decisions must be determined by their effect on global warming. We have very little time available.

Of course, prime examples of extremely unusual geological structures or biological strangeness often require government legislation to ensure their survival. And their survival we should ensure. We must preserve our awareness, our knowledge, and our potential knowledge of the wealth and fascination of unusual ecological systems and mystifying natural environments. However the weight of wisdom and fascination, not the volume of noise, should be the deciding factor in determining uniqueness.

Land is used by animals and man simply because it is usable. Land never stays vacant. Unless it's snow or ice or desert sand. Uninhabited land inevitably and quickly becomes inhabited by something. Good fertile land, good fertile soil, is only fertile because life moved there and made it so. And almost invariably man followed and became just another occupant. That's what the world's wilderness areas are, and have been for at least the last fifty millennia.

The often used manipulative ploy of justifying the establishment of outlandishly vast wilderness areas by promulgating the concept of some dangerous massive loss in world biodiversity is considered in Strategy 50.

STRATEGY 36
Claiming world agriculture cannot produce enough food without the use of fertilizers

There have been large increases in the weight of crops produced per acre in the last fifty years. Most farmers acknowledge that the majority of these increases result from the development of faster growing and more prolific plant varieties. The agrochemical companies have to confuse and convince government agencies and the consumers of agricultural products, that this is not so. They claim it's chemicals that are responsible, and the ploy is working. Agricultural chemicals have gotten the image as the saviour in solving world food shortages.

Among the nonfarming population it has now almost come to be "general knowledge" that increases in world food production result almost exclusively from vast increases in the use of chemical fertilizers and agro-chemical products. These established fictions then ensure receptive minds in legislators.

The ultimate object of the agrochemical industries must be to coat every agricultural acre of land on the planet with a dose of some agrochemical product. And do it at least once every year. Strawberries grown in California are an extreme example. A few years ago, my wife and I were talking to some strawberry farmers in Southern California. They told us two things. The first was that it is fairly common in the growing of strawberries to dose the plant and the soil with up to forty applications of a range of fertilizers, herbicides, pesticides and fungicides every year. The second thing these Californian strawberry farmers told us was that they would never eat strawberries grown commercially in California.

The agricultural chemical business is a very big business indeed; and it's the intention of the agrochemical companies to keep it that way.

The concept that the quantity of food produced from organic farms must always be less than that produced by chemical-based farming is totally false. Food production per acre from organic farms as often as not considerably exceeds food production from neighbouring conventional farms.

Admittedly, during the two or three year process of converting a farm

The Esalen Institute, Big Sur, California periodically donates its facilities and convenes conferences, or think tanks, of selected top people in particular fields. The objective is to have such people meet, intermingle, bounce ideas around and hopefully to generate new ideas and concepts. From time to time great good has come from these initiatives.

In 1989 the Institute was made available for a think tank on the future of sustainable agriculture in the United States. A small group of leading thinkers from all over the United States were invited to a five-day conference. The author was invited over from Australia. One of the outcomes was the formulation of a declaration on sustainable agriculture for the United States. Immediately following the Esalen get-together there was a large conference at the Asilomar Conference Center, Pacific Grove, Monterey Peninsula, California. This conference was organized by the Committee for Sustainable Agriculture (now the Ecological Farming Association) and was attended by over 1,000 people.

At the Asilomar conference the declaration on sustainable agriculture was presented, considered and subsequently adopted as the Asilomar Declaration On Sustainable Agriculture. The author's concept of stopping global warming by changing Western agricultural practices to systems based on a continuous increase in soil organic matter was the theme he advocated at Esalen and at his opening address at the Asilomar conference.

Attendees at the Esalen Institute conference. Front row, from left to right: **Amory Lovins**, Rocky Mountain Institute, Snowmass, Colorado; **Terry Gips**, International Alliance for Sustainable Agriculture, Minneapolis, Minnesota; **Richard Nilsen**, Whole Earth Review, Sausalito, California; **Bob Rodale**, Rodale Institute, Emmaus, Pennsylvania; **Kaye Thornely**, Molino Creek Farm, Davenport, California.

Second row, left to right: **Chris Yeomans, Allan Yeomans**, Gold Coast, Queensland. Australia; **Eliot Coleman**, Working Land Fund, Vershire, Vermont; **Steve Gliessman**, UCSC Agroecology Program, Santa Cruz, California; **Kevin Martin**, National Organically Grown Week, San Francisco, California.

Third row, left to right: **Steve Beck**, Esalen Institute, Big Sur, California; **Jane Mulder**, Organic Food Matters, Colfax, California; **Molly Penberth**, CSA Board President, Sacramento, California; **Diane Goodman**, Farallones Institute Occidental, San Francisco, California; **Wes Jackson**, The Land Institute, Salina, Kansas.

Back row, left to right: **John Reganold**, Washington State University, Dept. of Agronomy, Pullman, Washington; **James S. Turner**, Healthy Harvest, Washington, DC; **Bill Leibhart**, UCD Sustainable Agriculture and Research Program, Davis, California; **Steve Pavich**, Pavich Family Farms, Delano, California; **Conn Nugent**, Nathan Cummings Foundation, New York, New York; **Ron Kroese**, Land Stewardship Project, Marine, Minnesota.

from chemical-based agriculture to strict organic agriculture, total food production can fall, but falls are rarely more than 25%. This period of reduced income could easily be avoided if the excessively rigid definition of "organic" was tempered slightly making the produce more marketable. Or as a complete alternative, certification of food produce could be based on increasing carbon dioxide sequestration into the soil in which the produce is grown. Buyers would see a label that showed the product was combating global warming and make a purchase decision accordingly.

Changing to organic management allows previously used agricultural chemicals to be broken down or leach away within a couple of seasons. Vigorous soil biological activity will concurrently re-establish itself. Worm counts will begin to rise—often from zero. The soil remineralization process will commence. Generally within two to three years full productivity, usually higher than before, will become established. At that point a specifically "organic" certification can be applied for if desired. But certification and product labelling for changing to general global-warming-mitigating practices should be available immediately the switch is made.

Over the last few decades the agrochemical industry has been quite successful in hindering or limiting the number of studies on organic farming production. The information that is available does however, conclusively confirm the total viability and reliability of organic type farming as a food source system. The research and the published scientific papers relating to this research are usually confined to relatively obscure scientific publications. It is to the petrochemical industries' advantage to utilize their advertising and commercial influence on editorial to maintain this subtle form of censorship.

Almost unique in Western nations, Australian farmers since the late 1940s have on average increased their agricultural productivity most significantly. This increase in productivity has been achieved by the widespread adoption of crop and pasture rotation, coupled with a general switch to the use of non-inversion tillage practices that benefit soil biological activity. I am not alone in attributing much of this change to my father's work and discoveries. All his books on Keyline agricultural concepts were best sellers in this country. Coupled with the widespread adoption of the many facets of Keyline, the utilizing of new plant varieties and hybrids has also been a major factor. Most importantly the change has been achieved without any significant increase in the always relatively low use of agricultural chemicals.

No other Western nation uses so little chemicals to produce so much food. This is well documented in *World Resources*, a World Resources Institute report published in conjunction with the U.N. Environment Programme and the U.N. Development Programme. This productivity occurs despite the fact that Australian soils, on average, are the poorest natural soils occurring on any continent on the face of the earth.

Australian soils, on average, are constantly increasing in fertility, despite what the Australian academic bureaucracy claims. In many ways Australia is probably the only Western nation operating an entirely sustainable agricultural system. I am utterly certain that this in part resulted from a history of almost total lack of agricultural subsidization of, and bureaucratic interference in, Australian farming practices.

However, to sell agricultural chemicals the Australian experience must be derided. Australian farmers must be portrayed as irresponsible, negligent, and totally neglectful of the land and the soil they farm. Not so. The false and deliberately manufactured image that Australian farmers are irresponsible and destructive towards the land they own and farm, is regrettably becoming increasingly established in urban thinking. That is so very wrong. In general, Australian soils, managed by Australian farmers and graziers, are the only agricultural soils in the world being constantly improved en masse.

To gain increased agrochemical sales throughout the world, it is important that publicity must be channelled into the concept that only governments and government agencies are wise enough and responsible enough to care for and sustain agricultural land. Again this is total nonsense. We are talking about the very land and the very soil on which the farmer depends for his livelihood. This is the soil on which he lives and brings up his children. Are we to pretend that he is less responsible and less knowledgeable than some remote bureaucrat sitting at a desk in some federal capital? That is plain rubbish.

The argument the bureaucrats and the chemical companies make, in obvious collusion, supports demands that if individual farmers make decisions not to take the advice of their agricultural departments and not to constantly dose their land with agricultural chemicals, then the right to make those decisions should be taken from them. How else could agrochemicals actually be forcibly sold?

The PR gurus have to simultaneously promote two almost totally conflicting concepts, and that takes brilliant image juggling. One concept is that to produce sufficient food to feed the world there has to be a massive and continuous use of agricultural chemicals and only then will it all become possible. The other is to sell the concept that farmers should be funded to not produce food on much of their land. The employment of pseudo-environmental issues had to be the only way to handle this obvious inconsistency, but then advertising departments are absolute masters at inventing and promoting conflicting and often hypothetical issues.

STRATEGY 37
Promoting hydroponics and thereby promoting agricultural chemicals as safe

This is a strategy to create the fictional image of safe and healthy agricultural chemicals, despite the frightening and well-documented deaths and sicknesses from their use and handling.

Clinical tests on human males throughout the developed nations have highlighted a frightening drop in sperm counts. Research is being undertaken to determine the cause and to devise a "cure" for this quite startling decline. A recent analysis of sperm densities in Danish agricultural workers demonstrated markedly higher sperm counts in Danes working on organic farms. Chemical companies can never ever allow stories like this to receive wide publicity.

If the general public, as consumers of agricultural products, reject the use of chemical-based agriculture, then farmers, as suppliers, will be forced to stop using chemicals. Agrochemical companies must therefore create in the minds of the general public a perception that pesticides, herbicides, fungicides and fertilizers are safe to use, can be used everywhere, and have little or no effect on the environment and the ecology. And indeed that is happening. False images, totally misleading images, are being manufactured literally to order. Most people instinctively fear the addition of unnatural chemicals to their food, and with good reason. But the power of marketing imagery should not be underestimated; people's opinions are being altered.

Hydroponics is the process whereby plants are grown in vast chemical vats, and soil is totally eliminated from the growing process. It is the ultimate in chemical agriculture. In organic farming the chemical industry supplies nothing. In hydroponics the chemical industry supplies everything; except perhaps water. If hydroponically grown food is perceived as clean, fresh and healthy, the agrochemical companies have a double win. They win because a clean and safe image of food grown totally in chemical soups is also transferred to farming the soil. The result is more sales to conventional chemically based farmers. And they win because hydroponics is a whole new market for them. If hydroponics achieves a positive image in the public mind then an incredible expansion in agrochemical sales becomes possible.

Ultimately, the perfect scenario for the agricultural chemical companies and the marketers and producers of oil is a world where all food is grown in vast agrochemical factories, a world where the last farmer has moved to the city.

Already a surprisingly successful public relations exercise has created an acceptable image of hydroponics. To support this image reports on comparative food values are deliberately structured to favour hydroponics. For example, in production the essential mineral content of plants can be biased by adding an excess of appropriate chemicals containing that mineral to the brew in which the plant is grown. Nutritional analysis techniques are used to compare the levels of this one element. The hydroponically grown plant naturally wins such carefully structured comparisons. Press releases are worded accordingly. Some methods are not totally specific to particular nutrients. Combinations can be used in more carefully structured tests.

Hydroponically grown plants can thus be shown to have higher chemical nutrient levels than those produced in common farm soils. This can be achieved by a combination of choosing a favourable method of testing, dosing the hydroponic bath with the right chemicals and making predetermined selective comparisons between different tests. But the tests only test for specific elements. But a spoonful of chemicals won't keep you alive.

Good healthy food is rich in nutrient combinations, complex organic structures and enzymes, a whole range of constituents that biochemists have yet to discover and evaluate. We know virtually nothing about the complex biochemical influence and benefits of the many plants and fruits we eat daily. Millions of dollars are spent on studying human biology and food nutrition, and the things our bodies have evolved with, and in turn have learnt to rely and depend on. We still have a long way to go to fully develop such understanding. Promoters of hydroponics like to suggest it is all well studied and well understood, and the food they manufacture in their factories is more than sufficiently nutritious for good human health. The reality is, nobody knows. The reality is, common sense is more trustworthy, and so are your taste buds, which have after all, evolved for that purpose.

Hydroponics lends itself to good visual imagery. Plants can be produced that are large and impressive, albeit nutritionally poor, and lacking in taste. Plants are generally grown in enclosed and relatively sterile environments, so they always appear healthy and disease free. They are always displayed while they are still growing; a wonderful image of health and freshness is imparted to the unwary. From an agricultural chemical sales point of view, these images have to be fostered. Likewise all discussion on the enormous energy requirements to run the factories and to produce the chemicals used must be strenuously avoided.

As consumers, concerned about global warming and concerned about our individual health, we should where possible shun produce grown hydroponically.

STRATEGY 38
Organically grown food and soil fertility must never become accepted as viable concepts

The major threats to the agrochemical industries are organic food production and agricultural practices that enhance soil fertility. Organic agriculture uses almost no products manufactured by the petrochemical industries. If a widespread consumer demand for organic food is allowed to grow, then sales of agricultural chemicals and fertilizers will plummet. The oil and agrochemical companies must put all the brakes they can on the growth of the concept of soil fertility enhancement and organically grown food.

The National Standards Associations in most Western nations have now adopted and published standards for the growth and processing of organic foods. These standards are surprisingly uniform from country to country and are usually backed by legislation to ensure that food and products labelled or described as organic comply to strict minimum requirements.

Generally for compliance, the area being farmed or grazed must not have been sprayed or dosed with chemical fertilizers, fungicides or pesticides within the last three years. The periods vary slightly from country to country but the principle remains the same. Neither can the crop itself, during its growing cycle, be similarly dosed. The relevant published standards usually contain lists of natural products that may be used in the farming program.

Quite often, specific rules are established to handle the transition period from chemical agriculture to organic agriculture. These are short-term, practical considerations that are permitted so as to assist farm viability during the changeover process, but they are still very limiting.

For the agrochemical producers there is no choice. To them it is absolutely critical to hinder and hopefully stop the expansion of the organic agricultural movement. To achieve this, organic agriculture and all it implies, somehow, has to acquire a bad image. So, watch the press. The marketing people have started to come up with ideas. They always will.

Here is a frightening example of how agrochemicals are promoted as environmentally friendly. It also illustrates how agrochemical marketing people seem to scrape the bottom of the barrel in marshalling support for chemical sales. Apparently, in the Agronomy Department of Egerton University, in Njoro, Kenya, there is a soil scientist and lecturer whose name is Norman Adams. One must wonder why his statements were reported in such detail in such a popular and respected international journal as *New Scientist*.

Adams states, and one might presume this is what he teaches his students in Njoro, that while leguminous plants fix nitrogen in soils, better results are obtained with fertilizers. He blithely claims an organic farm would decrease, not increase soil fertility in endeavouring to sustain production. Adams says the importance of humus is grossly exaggerated and plants depend on simple chemicals to grow. He cites selected reports of high production from soils with low organic content to support his claims of chemical benefits. Also to support and encourage the widespread use of pesticides and fungicides, Adams dutifully reminds us of the Irish potato famine of 1845 and the locust plagues in biblical times. He blithely presumes that agrochemicals would have totally prevented these happenings.

"What about the claims that organic crops have more flavour, and are better for health?" he asks, and then demands that detailed tests should be done using organized "taste panels" before such statements should be given any credence. Adams also claims that it would be "difficult to prove" that organically grown food was more nutritious.

He suggests that the increase in life span of Western man proves the value of chemical agriculture, and by inference, is not related to increases in medical and human safety procedures. Whereas in reality, the major increase in average life span results from the almost total elimination of child mortality and vastly superior medical expertise. If medical expertise and accidental deaths are removed from the equation, then longevity is actually in decline. Today, on average, people live longer, but extreme age is becoming rarer.

Finally, Adams makes the totally misleading claim that more land is used in organic farming to produce the same weight of food as that produced by chemical agriculture. Even if this were true, bulk is not the only measure of a food's worth. It is often acknowledged that the additional nutritional value of organically grown food more than compensates for any reduction in weight. Most of the additional weight in chemically grown food is simply water in inflated plant cells. That, incidentally, is one of the reasons why they lack taste.

Adams also makes the incredible statement that organic farming's supposed increase in farm area would have a "serious impact" on wildlife numbers throughout the world. He wants us to believe that the wildlife would have no room left if organic farming became more common. In total contrast biologists, veterinarians and many in the animal welfare movements argue that it is agricultural chemicals themselves that pose the greatest threat to the world's wildlife.

All Adams's statements seem to religiously follow the very unsubtle standard oversimplification used by the agrochemical marketers. As you might gather from what has been said so far in this book, Adams's claims are either clearly biased, or just plain foolish.

Unfortunately for us all, it now seems necessary to seriously consider and query just who might be funding, and for what motive, the writing and publishing of articles and reports on the effects of agricultural chemicals on environments. It now seems that we must do this before we too readily accept such writings as honest and truly meaningful. Barely concealed bias is becoming the norm. We should also be cognizant of who must be suppressing the undoubted mass of critical reports we rarely get to see on the harm of chemically based farming.

STRATEGY 39
To sell agrochemicals, organically grown food must never be recognized as being more nutritious

This strategy indicates again how they try to achieve this aim.

There has always been a prevailing understanding that good food, grown on rich soil, tastes better and is more nutritious. This is something that most of us see as a logical and inevitable consequence of our long evolution. But that doesn't sell agrochemicals. So common sense, logic and useful facts have to be bypassed, or blatantly distorted.

This is achieved by supporting any study or research that supports overly simplified concepts of the chemical structures in living things. Food is an inherently complex mix of complex chemicals and our bodies utilize food in extremely complex, multilayered biological processes. Because of this complexity, our understanding of these chemicals and biological processes is relatively poor and it is easy to fall for oversimplified and invalid arguments. Agrochemical marketers will always vigorously call into question the additional nutritional value of organically grown food. They use invalid concepts and grossly simplified biochemistry to suggest that any additional food value is negligible.

Undoubtedly our taste buds are an evolutionary requirement to allow us to determine the nutritional value of what we put in our mouths. The reality is, to any animal, nutritious food has to taste better; any species with a taste system that led it to eat foods that made it sick would not survive long in the fiercely competitive evolutionary process. Animals often seek out particular foods to correct nutritional imbalances in their diets; they can only do this by taste, and/or smell. This is noticeably seen during pregnancy and in cases of severe illness. Unfortunately, in this age of highly processed food, taste is often confused by the addition of concentrated flavourings added during preparation. Supporting or promoting the consumption of highly processed and flavoured foods suits the agrochemical companies. But remember, in unprocessed foods, taste is invariably a measure of food value. Strong attractive flavours added to a food product are, in essence, false advertising.

Agrochemical marketers always avoid discussions and speculations on these concepts and always imply that taste differences are at most minute, and suggest that the handling and storage of fruit and vegetables, and the geographical area where the product is grown have a vastly more significant effect on taste than the type of agriculture involved. This is an ideal distraction as people can be inveigled into never-ending debate and confusion on essentially irrelevant issues.

STRATEGY 40
Agrochemical companies always will support wetland and ocean outfall sewage disposal

Sewage disposal hardly seems to be a subject that would interest the petrochemical industries, but it does and it must. The human population on the planet is 6 billion people. That is huge. The volume of human excreta produced is enormous. This human waste product makes wonderful organic fertilizer, and for thousands of years it has been used as such in almost every country in every civilization on the planet.

Sewage is a cheap waste product from towns and cities and is loaded with minerals and trace elements. So of course, the chemical fertilizer companies are interested. It's a very competitive product, so the best thing for the agricultural chemical companies is to have it dumped where it is totally wasted and completely out of the marketplace. The ocean is preferred, for there it is totally unrecoverable.

Provided sewage is dumped sufficiently far out to sea to avoid localized concentrations, the ocean can handle it with ease and quite logically will be able to do so for ever. Where are we supposed to imagine whales and dolphins go to the toilet? The millions upon millions of tons of sea creatures, squid, prawns, fish, octopus, lobsters, coral polyps, etc. all contribute to make the ocean one vast, super efficient, biological septic tank. If the Mediterranean can even remotely handle most of Europe, and it has for a long time, then the world's oceans will suffice humanity forever.

Over eons rain has washed everything possible, and everything imaginable, down the rivers and into the sea. Therefore the world's oceans are already immense repositories of every element known to man, from the most benign to the most toxic. To the oceans, the sewerage outlet from a city would be just another tiny source of nutrients. There have been problems but these have only ever arisen where large concentrations of sewage have been dumped directly into areas where seafood is harvested. Even then the problem is usually more political than real.

If, for geographical reasons sewage can't be dumped in the ocean then as an alternative, fertilizer companies will advocate and financially support the argument that it be dumped into some convenient swamp or wetland. In wetlands it can't damage the chemical fertilizer markets. Dumping sewage in swamps is the chemical companies' perfect alternative to ocean dumping. Swamps don't produce food and as the wetlands get smothered with excess nutrients the biological environment within them deteriorates opening up a possible new market for some new chemical fix. Also very little usable wood can be grown in swamps, and if it could it would be difficult to harvest.

Also, as the swamp gets bigger due to sewage overload, it reduces the area of usable neighbouring agricultural land, which tends to force more intensive farming. Better still.

To finally ensure that nutrients in the sewage are never ever used, the whole expanding swamp areas, renamed as wetlands, are hopefully turned into "national parks". The argument used in this ploy is that wetlands are the home of a whole variety of wildlife. Of course they are; every bit of land, anywhere on the planet, whether it be swamp land, crop land, range land, forest land or wilderness, is the perfect home for some or other forms of wildlife.

Also defining swamp areas as "wetlands", or redefining new areas as wetlands makes marketing sense to the agrochemical industries. For them the disposal of sewage into some nearby wetland is an ideal scenario. Yet for us it's idiotic. The logical reality is that wetlands should never be used for sewage disposal. The dead and dying vegetation in swamps and wetlands eventually sinks. The stagnant water in swamps is lacking in oxygen so the rotting vegetation cannot form true soil. The dead vegetation decomposes and putrefies in a process very different to that involved in the creation of humus. Under water it is anaerobic bacteria, that is non-oxygen-breathing bacteria, that digest the dead plant material. The byproducts of anaerobic decomposition are gases like hydrogen sulphide (rotten egg gas) and methane (marsh gas). That's why swamps smell. Methane is also twenty times more potent a greenhouse gas than carbon dioxide itself. After several thousand, or more like millions of years, the material finally left at the bottom in a swamp forms peat.

Because peat is formed in the absence of oxygen, if it ever dries out it's flammable. In Russia, millions of acres of ancient peat beds exist and are the "subsoil" of thousands of farms. The local farmers there don't have bushfire problems; they have something worse. In extremely dry conditions the very ground on which they live and build their houses and farm their farms can catch fire. These smoldering underground fires are often extremely difficult to control. Some can smolder for centuries.

It is quite impossible for the biological activity in a swamp or wetland to utilize the never-ending flow of super-rich nutrients delivered from sewage outfalls. Wetland biology did not evolve and develop under these conditions. Chemical nutrient levels therefore soon build up to where they become actual poisons; poisons that can never escape. The vegetation and the wildlife, all those things that were the professed motive to keep or pro-tect or create the wetland, all eventually die. Forms of algae take over that are often poisonous. Then chemists are called in to develop or recommend some new chemical additive to cure this "strange new problem".

That's what ultimately always happens with wetland sewage disposal. How could it be anything else?

To many people, using sewage as a fertilizer is an anathema. Yet animal excrement is used and its use is universally accepted. Such material is rapidly broken down and the minerals become available to plant growth in any soil that has a reasonably low content of agrochemicals. The breakdown process is totally biological and that is why most chemical fertilizers prevent it, as they kill soil bacteria and earthworms. These processes see no difference between the excrement of animals and that of humans. The only possible difference is that humans, being the top of the food chain, may have slightly higher concentrations of some toxic elements in their excreta. But these tiny traces (when they do exist) are easily chelated and locked safely away by humic acid molecules in the inevitably good healthy soil.

Neither are human pathogens in the sewage a problem. It's a general rule that harmful pathogens don't survive in fertile soil. *Homo sapiens* have had plenty of time to become immune to germs that do.

For the fertilizer producers there are several angles of attack that can and must be used to prevent sewage use in agriculture. Anti-social stigma is one that has to be fostered. Some hypothetical threat of spreading disease and plague must be given wide press. Yet this is easily fixed by simply exposing the treated sewage to either sunlight or by passing it by ultraviolet lamps. Both efficiently sterilize the material, if that is desired.

Fortunately for the petrochemical companies, in many cities industrial chemical waste is disposed of through the sewerage system. Even vaguely poisonous properties of any of these chemical wastes can be exaggerated. It can also be suggested that the poisons cannot ever be removed. In some rare situations where this actually might apply, the sewage should be used to grow timber, especially rainforest varieties. At worst, at some impossibly high concentration, it would merely pest-proof the timber produced.

The general population must be coerced into feeling threatened—feeling distrustful that poisons might get into the food chain. All this then vindicates the concept of locking sewage out of any recycling possibilities. It also, at least, defers decisions on possible reuse. Then long drawn out, self-righteous "safety checks" are always instigated.

All these ploys to stop the agricultural use of human sewage are conveniently and invariably claimed as "social responsibility".

From an environmental point of view, our current methods of sewage disposal defy logic. Sewage, treated or untreated, is extremely rich in soil nutrients. Sewage naturally contains every element required to produce life. After all that's where it comes from. We do not accumulate essential elements or minerals in our bodies; we require a constant intake because we are continually excreting them. Sewage also contains very large quantities of both nitrogen and phosphorus. Nitrogen is the element being sold in nitrogen-based fertilizers. Phosphorus is the element being sold in superphosphate.

The only logical, sensible, practical, inexpensive and environmentally perfect use for sewage is to grow plants. That's what excreta has been doing for a thousand million years and, logically, there is absolutely no reason why those plants can't constitute useful and valuable crops.

When human sewage becomes a socially acceptable fertilizer again, then the crops in turn will be acceptable for human consumption. But for now, the crops can be trees or grasses. I think the smartest thing to do at this stage, and to forestall green pawn protesters, is to plant and grow useful rainforest timber and fertilizer it with partially processed human excreta. This concept is the theme of my late father's book, *The City Forest*, P. A. Yeomans, 1971.

The economical and rapid growth of useful and valuable timber fertilized with organic human waste is the antithesis of everything the oil and agrochemicals industries advocate in their marketing of both agrochemicals and plastics.

STRATEGY 41
Destroying the asbestos, hemp and natural fibre industries

To sell petroleum based plastics, fibres and materials with high energy content, the image and market of already existing and established natural products has to be manipulated to destruction.

The structure of the natural fibres, cotton and wool etc., is such that garments made from these materials feel very comfortable against the skin. Cotton has marvelous "wicking" properties that rapidly absorbs moisture away from the skin. Wool has the wonderful property of effectively releasing heat when it absorbs moisture, so woollen garments keep you warm, even if you get wet.

When the plastics, nylon, rayon, terylene etc. were first developed, tremendous efforts were made to establish them as viable alternatives to natural fibres for the clothing industry. Despite all the efforts it was never dramatically successful. The synthetic materials had an unnatural and uncomfortable feel. There were two main faults. The materials when dry could often build up unpleasant static charges. Wet, they had another fault, they trapped moisture near the skin and ruined our natural ability to cool ourselves by sweating. Nylon stockings were about the only dramatic success story.

But soon clothing manufacturers found that blending natural fibres with synthetics produced attractive and practical combinations. This has been a major success story. Blended clothing materials are often superior to either the straight natural fibres or the synthetics.

In general, from a marketing point of view, old established natural fibres are hard to combat. But there are always possibilities that the petrochemical companies' marketing and public relations people can exploit to sell their products. Almost all plastics today are made from oil, and they require a lot of energy to produce, usually oil or coal derived power. The reality is that oil pulls the plastic-fibre strings.

Industrial hemp

Hemp is a classic example of such market manipulations. Hemp is best known for its use in making cordage, the familiar hemp rope. But that's only one use. The North American Industrial Hemp Council claims there are over 25,000 products that can be made from the industrial hemp plant. The list includes such items as paper, cloth, lubricating and edible oils, construction materials and varnishes. The oil produced from hemp can even be used to make biodiesel. The Kimberly-Clark Company mills industrial hemp in France to produce a high-quality paper. This paper is often preferred for the production of bibles as the hemp paper lasts longer and doesn't yellow with age.

It was a sad loss for the world, but a surprisingly easy task for the petrochemical industries, to virtually eliminate the world production and use of hemp. Or at least in their major market, the developed world.

To achieve this hemp was simply linked to the drug marijuana and legislators around the world were effectively coerced into banning it. It took some time, but for the petrochemical industries it was worth it. In the United States the Marijuana Tax Act of 1937 started hemp's demise. The end of hemp was effectively completed globally by the late 1950s.

Industrial hemp fibre comes from a shrub that belongs to the plant genus Cannabis and there are hundreds of varieties within the Cannabis genus. Sailcloth was originally commonly made from cannabis plants and the word *canvas* is derived from cannabis.

Cannabis plants produce chemical compounds know as cannabinoids of which two are important: delta-9-tetrahydrocannabinol (THC) and cannabidiol (CBD). THC is responsible for the narcotic effects associated with marijuana, while CBD actually inhibits the narcotic effects. At one end of the spectrum of cannabis varieties, there are plants which produce a lot of THC, up to as much as 6% by weight, but very little CBD. These plants, *Cannabis sativa*, are the ones classed as "marijuana". At the other end of the spectrum is "industrial hemp", which produces almost none of the narcotic THC, but does produce some inhibiting CBD, the contents of either chemical being usually less than 0.25%. The plants are similar in appearance, as is for example sweet corn and maize. It is however impossible to get "high" with industrial hemp plants. The THC levels are way too low, and the CBD levels guarantee a zero narcotic effect. The smoke from burning the industrial hemp plant would be no different to the smoke wafting off any backyard, wood-fired barbecue.

The plastic industry's natural duty to itself is always to resist, inhibit or thwart the use of any natural fibre or any naturally fibrous material. Confusion is one of their most favoured stock techniques and this was used very effectively with hemp. As a result industrial hemp has, to all intents and purposes, been abandoned and often effectively banned as a viable commercial crop for fifty years. Nevertheless there is hope; Denmark for example has recommenced cautious agricultural experimentation.

One must wonder how much of the anti-marijuana campaign is funded or otherwise supported by the fossil carbon industries. One might also wonder whether the tobacco and alcohol lobby actively and materially support the never-ending anti-marijuana campaign. It would certainly cut their sales drastically if it were ever to become legal in Western societies. Self interest always predominates: the anti-hemp campaign goes back to the 1930s when both the U.S. forestry industry, concerned about paper production, and the U.S. cotton growers, concerned about fibre production, both attacked hemp.

The use of heroin and its derivatives is legal in medicine. The use of the relatively harmless marijuana-derived THC in medicine is almost totally and violently prohibited. Why this should be seems to have only one sensible and logical answer: Hemp rope and hemp products might re-emerge to again compete in the marketplace.

To all in the petrochemical companies, it is surely obvious that the confusion between industrial hemp and marijuana is a confusion to be exploited. By promoting and supporting any groups campaigning against the legalization of marijuana, the petrochemical companies keep at bay a serious industrial threat. They also get a double win by also seeming to appear as responsible, caring and moral organizations. The tobacco and alcohol producers of course have to come on side with the petrochemical industries. It's like an unholy triumvirate.

Animal furs

Fashion is a tricky thing. Animal furs make comfortable, attractive and very warm coats. For a long time, the animal liberation movement has been endeavouring to make the fur coat a socially unacceptable garment. Why? Who beats their drum and pays their expenses. They are not all motivated by altruistic zeal.

In Australia, introduced foxes, feral rabbits and cats have spread throughout the country. Rabbits in particular have achieved disastrous plague proportions. The foxes and cats find the small, rare native marsupials and the flocks of native birds far easier game than the "street-wise" European rabbit.

The few large marsupials that survived the original human population influx into Australia, such as the Eastern Grey kangaroo and Western Grey, easily elude the smaller feral cats and dogs. In addition, outback farmers in Australia constructed dams to water their sheep and cattle. The kangaroos found the dams and so found an extremely reliable and plentiful supply of water. So in drought times the big kangaroos don't slowly die of thirst as they once did. Instead, their numbers regularly zoom to extreme plague proportions. Nowadays there are more kangaroos in Australia than people in Mexico City and New York City combined.

Kangaroos, like most marsupials, are not particularly intelligent, and so, although usually supported by animal liberationists, family planning clinics, contraception pills and sterilization, are a smidgen impracticable. It is a sad thing to contemplate that the skins of kangaroos and unwanted feral mammals are left to rot in the sun, while we are badgered by animal welfare groups to support oil-derived plastic fibre products as a substitute for their skins and leather.

The asbestos story

Asbestos is now probably one of the most feared contaminants in Western society. But is it as bad as we are all now conditioned to believe? Or are we all jumping, with knee-jerk reactions, to some blatant public relations orchestration? The truth is that now, and for the last thirty years, the only asbestos-type material mined anywhere in the world of any significance is as safe as rockwool (mineral wool), or fibreglass, or many of the plastic fibres manufactured to replace the "dreaded asbestos".

Normal industrial safety standards covering the manufacture of brake linings, fibre cement sheets and pipes, and other fibre composite materials are completely safe and satisfactory for the asbestos now mined. It is certainly as safe as the most of the materials promoted to replace it.

Asbestos once had a very big and constantly expanding market. It was a market obviously coveted by the petrochemical producers and their plastics industries. Just think for a second how big the asbestos cement pipe and the asbestos cement sheet business was. And they wanted it. Therefore they needed asbestos out of the picture. Asbestos is not a product of any petrochemical manufacturing facility, anywhere, anytime, anyhow, and not in any possible future. And they knew it. Asbestos is a naturally occurring fibrous rock. You simply dig it out of the ground. Then you weave it.

Minerals in the earth's surface come in all shapes and sizes and in a host of different forms. For example, mica and vermiculite are two other naturally occurring minerals with useful properties. Mica forms in flat, multi-layered, dark gold-coloured crystals; small particles of mica can be seen as the gold-coloured flakes in granite rock. Mica sometimes forms naturally in large sheets, and in this form was mined and used extensively as a flat electrical insulator capable of withstanding very high temperatures. Very little energy is required to mine and shape mica, yet oil-derived plastics have generally replaced it as an insulator.

The mineral vermiculite, like mica, exists in a flat crystalline form. Vermiculite has a similar gold color. When particles of vermiculite are rapidly heated tiny quantities of water in the structure turn into steam and the little particles puff up like concertina-shaped popcorn. This expanded vermiculite is an excellent thermal insulator. Vermiculite has generally been replaced by plastic fibre, aluminium foil, rock wool (mineral wool) and glass fibre, all of which require huge fossil carbon inputs either as raw materials for their manufacture or for energy to power the processes. Vermiculite has not as yet been targeted, but watch for media inferences that vermiculite somehow, has some yet to be invented "problems".

Mica and vermiculite form as flat crystalline sheets, but some minerals form fibrous strands. In some cases the fibres can be yards long. That's asbestos. In the ground, it looks like just another type of rock, but break the material up and it becomes like a natural bundle of fibreglass or rockwool material. Some forms have fibres as fine as threads of silk.

Being minerals formed in the cooling of molten magma, the fibres are utterly fireproof. When bundled together and soaked in oil or fat the fibres make a great torch. These were the torches that once carried the Olympic flame. A wick made from the fibres would last almost indefinitely and so the ancient Greeks named the material "asbestos" meaning "inextinguishable". Plutarch indicates that the "eternal flame of the Acropolis" had an asbestos wick.

Asbestos can be woven into cordage and a whole range of totally heat-resistant cloths. The fibres are actually stronger than steel. The cloth can be thrown into a fire to clean and sterilize. The Romans named it "amiantus" meaning unpolluted, because it came out of the fire whiter than it went in.

Under the heading of "asbestos" there are six main minerals, actinolite, anthophyllite, amosite, crocidolite, tremolite, and chrysotile. Three were used commercially. Of these three, amosite or "brown" asbestos, and crocidolite or "blue" asbestos are no longer in commercial use. The only mineral described as asbestos that is still in any commercial use is chrysotile or "white" asbestos.

Brown and blue asbestos fibres are known as amphiboles. Amphiboles are extremely strong, hard and straight and are highly resistant to most forms of chemical attack. These properties make them an ideal fibre for commercial use. Unfortunately, these very attributes ensured the amphiboles' own well-deserved demise.

If amphiboles, the brown and blue types, are inhaled or swallowed as dust, tiny pieces of the straight fibres can embed themselves in the lung tissue or gut lining. Being almost chemically inert, they can accumulate in tissue to reach dangerous levels.

The vast majority of asbestos used in industry was always chrysotile or white asbestos. Its characteristics are as different from brown and blue types as poisonous toadfish are from tasty tuna. Worldwide, chrysotile eventually accounted for more than 99.5% of total asbestos use. Chrysotile also goes under the name serpentine because its fibres are not straight, but twist and turn in a snake-like fashion. The ore too can display a distinctive mottled snakeskin-like appearance in the ground.

In absolute contrast to the dangerous forms of asbestos and glass fibre, chrysotile fibres, being curly, don't slither into flesh. Not only that, but being much softer than amphiboles they can be broken down relatively easily within the human body. They are thus like the common glass fibre used in boat building. They are like man-made mineral wool.

Constant inhalation, in high concentrations, of the dangerous straight amphibole fibres over long periods, ten years or more, will harden and damage the linings of the lungs. Shorter but very intense exposure can have the same effect. The ancient Greeks and Romans recorded a sickness of the lungs in the slaves who cut and wove these fibres into cloth. In more modern times, enormous quantities of the dangerous forms of asbestos were mined in remote locations in southern Africa. It is unlikely that health requirements in any of these mines received a priority any higher than those applying to the slaves of ancient times. Many mine workers died from the health condition that came to be called asbestosis.

Asbestosis is not lung cancer; it is a scarring of the lung tissues that ultimately restricts air flow and oxygen uptake. The occurrence of asbestosis in asbestos workers is somewhat similar to black lung disease in coal miners. Both are more debilitating than life-threatening but both can kill.

Mesothelioma is different. It is a cancer caused particularly by exposure to the dangerous amosite and crocidolite minerals, the brown and blue types of asbestos. It is a cancer of the cells that make up the lining around the lungs and sometimes around the abdominal organs.

Asbestosis was quite common in asbestos milling, weaving and process-ing plants in the United Kingdom in the early part of the 20th century. In 1931, to safeguard personnel working in the asbestos industries, the UK Asbestos Industry Regulations Enactment was enacted. However, at that time the relative dangers of the different types of asbestos was not appreciated.

Asbestosis may have been checked by these safety laws but mesothe-lioma was different. It was not until the 1960s that warnings about the risks of mesothelioma suddenly received wide publicity. Asbestos workers had an incidence of lung cancer as much as 8 or 10 times the national average. That meant that the risk of an asbestos worker developing lung cancer was as bad as that of a person smoking cigarettes.

All this makes the mining and milling of asbestos, and the production of components containing asbestos fibre, actually no worse and in many cases safer, than a host of other mining and industrial processes. So why was asbestos given such a hard time? Why is it still perceived as such an evil, dangerous and hazardous product?

The track record of the cigarette companies is not dissimilar to that of companies that produced asbestos; both seemed to be aware of the cancer risks associated with their product and both kept quiet about it. The cancer risks for tobacco and asbestos are about the same. Cigarettes manufacturers obviously ignored or "buried" details on the health risks of smoking. If the distributors of brown and blue asbestos knew of the cancer-causing consequences of working with their products, they too chose to do the same.

After all, sales volumes were at stake.

What was more deadly was that the two risks combined produced a murderous multiplying effect. If you smoke cigarettes and work in the asbestos production industry, then the likelihood of you contracting lung disease is high. The *Encyclopedia Britannica* claims a ninety-fold increase in the incidence of lung cancer for workers in the asbestos industry who smoke.

As a matter of interest to smokers, you might remember the much-promoted "Micronite" filter manufactured by Lorillard Tobacco. The filter was supposed to remove all those bad things from cigarette smoke. In his excellent book, *The Asbestos Racket*, published in 1991, Michael J. Bennett tells us that the "presumably secret element in the Micronite filter was blue asbestos." Thirty-three workers making these Micronite filters were studied. Bennett reported at the time that twenty-eight of these people had already died and only one death was not asbestos related. Blue asbestos can be very dangerous.

However, chrysotile or "white" asbestos compared to blue asbestos is like comparing chalk and cheese. Bennett's book warns us of the extreme dangers of both blue asbestos and brown asbestos, but expounds the considerable worth of the totally different chrysotile, or white asbestos.

The combined risk of smoking cigarettes and working with asbestos was too alarming to be glossed over. One of them had to go, asbestos or tobacco? The cigarette companies had the money. They also had the influence and the advertising dollars. In the United States the result was that their Environmental Protection Agency put a total ban on virtually all forms of asbestos in use, anywhere. In complete contrast, the EPA made the cigarette companies put a warning on their packets that cigarettes were a health hazard. A relatively small printed message at the bottom of the pack seemed to happily satisfy the United States Environmental Protection Agency for a statistically more deadly health risk.

The whole thing was so blatantly biased that finally in 1991 the Environmental Protection Agency's all-encompassing ban on all forms of asbestos fibres had to be slightly more logically modified to more fairly align with reality. Rules for asbestos use in the United States are now tempered with common sense. With current safety standards, mortality rates from active industrial exposure to asbestos fibre is now considered to be minuscule. When compared with such things as smoking or drinking alcohol, the modern asbestos industry is safer than any hospital.

The Royal Society of London, the World Health Organization and in Canada, The Ontario Royal Commission on Asbestos, and others, have stated most emphatically that air containing asbestos dust with concentrations as low as one asbestos fibre per litre are insignificant, that is about thirty fibres per cubic foot. A large study reported by the Canadian Asbestos Institute indicated that chrysotile workers breathing air containing 45,000 fibres per litre showed no statistical increase in the incidence of lung cancer.

Ordinary air, all over the world, contains small quantities of asbestos fibres in the form of airborne dust. These fibres don't come from man-made sources. They come from the geological decomposition and weathering of natural rock formations containing the various types of asbestos minerals. These fibres include the dangerous amphiboles of blue asbestos. The United States National Academy of Sciences and National Research Council concluded, in a 1984 study, that the average outside air concentration throughout the United States is 0.4 fibres per litre, while in major cities concentrations ranged up to 7 fibres per litre.

There is an often used anti-asbestos copy line that runs "one fibre can kill". It dramatically infers some extreme danger associated with asbestos. In medical documentation the cliché is described as being beyond the "bounds of scientific reality". United States citizens, breathing air containing an average of 0.4 fibres per litre, breathing about 10 litres per minute, 60 minutes per hour and 24 hours per day, would breathe in an average 5,760 fibres per day. If "one fibre can kill" then the entire population of the United States, every single human being in the country, would already be dead.

Asbestos cement sheets were once one of the most commonly used materials in building construction. Millions of houses and thousands of factories in just about every country on earth were walled in and roofed over with corrugated asbestos cement sheeting. We should all be dead.

While all the supposedly incredible dangers are in scientific circles recognized as fiction, the dreadful image of all forms of asbestos has been irrevocably established in the public mind.

As a result, and with government insistence, the asbestos used in the manufacture of fibre-reinforced sheets has now been replaced with a plethora of less worthy fibrous materials. And there seems to be no sane health reasons for the change.

One thing the substitutes all have in common—they are all either derived directly from oil or they use large quantities of oil in their manufacture.

To compound this waste and stupidity, demands are being made to remove all asbestos-based products from all buildings. The removal would start with public buildings. Such an action won't make one single person live one day longer. If anything the opposite will happen. Dust is created and stirred up when old brittle sheets are broken during removal. The cement becomes more brittle with age, not the fibres. This creates a hazard where none previously existed. We can be absolutely certain that hundreds of workers around the world, maybe thousands, will die from accidents, all totally unrelated to asbestos during such a ridiculous and insane process. The petrochemical and plastics industries will be their only beneficiaries.

Drinking water conveyed in asbestos cement pipes is safer than drinking water conveyed in PVC pipes or even steel pipes. Automobile brake pads made with asbestos fibres are far and away the safest brake pad now possible. On a steep decline asbestos won't break down if your brakes overheat. Good brakes save lives.

Asbestos fibre and the asbestos industry have been given the same vicious image-destroying treatment as nuclear energy and the nuclear energy industry. In the nuclear energy public-relations battle, plutonium has been particularly singled out as the epitome of all things dreadful, yet asbestos and plutonium are both about as safe and about as dangerous as thousands of other chemicals, products, and materials used in our modern day civilization. It is just that in the production, both are independent of fossil carbon materials, but both compete with fossil carbon materials.

Today, because of deliberate structured advertising and image manipulation, almost the whole of Western society now "knows", with absolute certainty, that asbestos is one of the greatest horror stories of modern civilization. The belief that asbestos is an horrific health hazard, anywhere and at any time, is now so ingrained in our minds that it's an eerily alien concept to believe or even suspect that much of it might be a marketing fiction.

STRATEGY 42
Implying disposable plastics are "greener" than wood, paper and ceramics

This illustrates how establishing ridiculous and illogical beliefs within the general public's overall awareness can be made to occur when we are not extremely watchful. From the oil producers' point of view, it is simply good marketing to keep the buying public uncertain, confused, and undecided. If comparisons can constantly be dreamed up that imply that oil-based products and oil-based energy sources are more environmentally desirable, public confusion can reign supreme. And, sadly, now mostly does.

References to happy, carefree, 85-year-old chain smokers have maintained a poisonous cloud of indecision over the health risks of cigarettes for over half a century. The big oil companies know that they must use the same tactics or they too will be brought eventually to bay. Confusing themes and red herrings must be used over and over again to confuse and confound.

Take plastic cups for example. It is being promoted by the petrochemical lobby that plastic disposable cups are more environmentally friendly than paper cups. It's even been suggested that plastic disposable cups are more environmentally friendly than nondisposable ceramic mugs. Now to most of us, these statements immediately appear ridiculous. Here the plastics advertisers had to create arguments and numbers to "disprove" common sense.

With paper cups one promotional line hammered that paper cups are made from trees. Oil company marketing always implies that trees are not a renewable resource. The fossil carbon industries' marketing tactic that trees should be constantly planted, but of course never ever harvested, is brought into play.

The energy required in the harvesting and transport of raw materials, and then in the manufacture of the paper cups is tallied, but always wildly exaggerated whenever possible. In contrast the energy inputs to manufacture the plastic are glossed over. So the logic is distorted and throwaway plastic cups appear to be the lesser of two evils.

The disposable plastic cup is a good heat insulator and this characteristic is inferred to have some significant environmental advantage. Why this should be so is not explained. It is a valid, marketable, convenience attribute, but has no environmental relevance whatever. Nevertheless the insulating properties are being carefully blurred with notions of environmental responsibility. Fossil carbon industries' PR people love to blur the picture.

But we can fight back. If we demand it, we can have it both ways. Plastic manufacturers rely on oil for their raw material but this is not at all essential. Algae and various plant materials can be just as good and just as cheap for raw materials. For example: the major byproduct in the totally environmentally friendly production of biodiesel is glycerol (glycerine). As a raw material in the production of plastics and other current petrochemical products, glycerol is excellent and the quantities are an excellent production match.

Arguments for plastics and against ceramics use the same energy-of-production factual distortions. It is presupposed that a ceramic coffee cup has only a very limited statistical lifetime. The argument then becomes: to "fire" ceramics uses a lot of heat energy and electrically heated kilns are common. So this energy use, divided by the statistical usage of the coffee cup, gives an energy requirement per use.

The energy used is first presumed to be derived from coal-fired power stations. Such arguments rely heavily on this presumption. Therefore ceramic cups result in the production of greenhouse gases and are therefore environmentally undesirable. They further argue that the ceramic cup is not thrown away and has to be washed. Energy is required to heat the washing-up water. It's the same argument used in Strategy 13 against electric cars. Electric cars, they argue, are pointless as power stations run on fossil fuels.

In this way, the ludicrous determination can then be made that the oil-derived, throwaway, plastic cup actually contributes to the environmental wellbeing of the planet, and reusable ceramics are a danger.

Not everyone blindly accepts the validity of these fairy-tale conclusions. However, a great deal of doubt can be insinuated into general public awareness. The objective, as always, is to have clear reasoning muddied.

STRATEGY 43
Stopping timber as a threat to oil and petrochemicals

To keep and to expand the sales of petrochemical products and to sell more fossil-fuel energy, the timber industry has to be attacked and destroyed.

The oil companies know this only too well. Enormous quantities of energy are consumed in the manufacture of virtually all construction materials. There is only one incredibly significant exception, and that is wood.

Items from toothpicks to apartment buildings are made, very satisfactorily and very successfully, from wood. Timber is a natural and innately beautiful material. So to sell petrochemical-dependent materials, wood has to be tainted. Wood has to acquire a bad image. It is important therefore that timber must be attacked on all fronts. Facts and truth must never hamstring the image-destroying process. Wood's competitors are either made out of oil or use massive amounts of fossil fuels in their manufacture. So naturally the fossil carbon industries must always support wood's competitors.

Every one of wood's competitors is a serious contributor to global warming. Aluminium is refined from the ore bauxite. Enormous amounts of electricity are used. It depends on all kinds of factors but as a rough approximation it takes about six tons of oil or nine tons of coal to produce one ton of aluminium. An aluminium refinery can use as much electricity as a medium-sized city. In the component costs of aluminium, electricity costs are by far the greatest. They easily exceed the costs of the bauxite ore. In Australia, as in many countries, the electricity to produce aluminium comes mainly from burning coal. If hydroelectricity is the planned power source for an aluminium smelter, instantly the save-the-river green pawns are called in to protect the fossil fuel interests. This happened in Tasmania and natural gas is now piped to the island. For such systems, if power is already hydroelectric, other green groups then demand the dams be removed. Always to supposedly save some special fish, or view, or whatever.

Iron is one of the most common elements on our planet. The inner core of the earth is composed almost entirely of iron; 35% of the whole planet is iron. However, in the earth's crust it amounts to no more than 5% of all materials. It is expensive to obtain metallic iron except when the iron is in the form of a couple of very specific ores, namely haematite and magnetite. Iron ore is placed in a blast furnace along with coke and limestone and heated. The limestone is used to scavenge silica and ash from the melt and so produces slag.

Initially the heat is provided by gas or oil-fired burners that is then delivered as a blast of hot air fed in at the bottom of the furnace. The coke ignites to provide more heat. Because it is burning in a carbon-rich oxygen-poor environment, and at high temperatures, it produces large quantities of carbon monoxide. The hot carbon monoxide and the coke in the furnace reduce (removes oxygen from) the iron ore to produce metallic pig iron and carbon dioxide. Only tiny amounts of carbon remain in the final pig iron. Some carbon remains in the furnace slag, but the vast majority is discharged into the atmosphere as carbon dioxide.

Coke is basically pure carbon, manufactured by heating bituminous coal in the absence of air. This process itself requires considerable energy input. Enormous quantities of coke are used in the production of iron and steel. In consequence enormous quantities of carbon dioxide are discharged into the air.

Steel is iron in which the carbon content has been carefully modified. Steel is formed by blowing oxygen through molten pig iron. This process removes more carbon that discharges to the atmosphere as carbon dioxide. Steel also contains small quantities of other added metals to improve its qualities and strength. But steel is the construction material on which we have built our civilization. Nothing beats steel in big construction projects so, like it or not, we have to stay with it. However from an environmental point of view, from the point of view of preventing global warming, if wood can be used to do the job, it should be. Using steel to frame a residential house must be recognized as a display of callous irresponsibility.

Plastics use a lot of energy in their manufacture, but more significantly, the actual raw material from which almost all plastics are derived is oil. Again if wood can be used to replace plastic it should be.

Cement is made from clay and limestone. The material has to be heated to 1,450°C and this takes massive amounts of energy. Again that heat energy comes from the burning of coal or oil. About 4.5% of the world's total carbon dioxide emissions come from the burning of fossil fuels to make cement. In addition, the chemical process itself, that is, the high temperature conversion of calcium carbonate (the limestone) to calcium oxide (the active ingredient in cement) contributes another 2.5% of carbon dioxide to the world's total emissions. The figures quoted here come from Joseph Davidovitz of the University of Picardy in France, and they are typical of carbon dioxide emissions from cement production throughout the world.

Stone has always been a common building material, yet even stone needs far more energy to prepare than wood. The raw cost of stone, as a construction material, is negligible. The world is made of it. Yet stone, when cut and prepared, is a very expensive item in construction. A lot of time and energy is consumed to saw up rocks and turn them into building blocks. Timber is easy to cut and the energy to mill timber is relatively minute.

Bricks are a much more common construction material than stone and much cheaper. But every brick in every house, in every city in the world was once clay. That shaped block of clay had to be heated to very high temperatures where finally the clay particles melt and fused together. To make bricks, you burn oil or you burn coal.

The one exception to this rule is sun-dried mud blocks. Unfortunately suitable mud is not often available. Also using often inane reasoning (which a cynic might suspect was supplied and fostered by fossil fuel interests), many local building ordinances have been modified to effectively ban mudbrick or adobe construction.

But all is not lost; the energy used in the production of all these various materials, apart from iron and steel, could come from sustainable-energy-derived electricity. Producing iron and steel will always produce large quantities of carbon dioxide. But we can never abandon the use of iron and steel, but neither is that necessary. The quantity of carbon dioxide generated in their production may be large but it pales to insignificance when compared to the quantity produced in the generation of electricity and in powering our transport systems. Fix those and we can have our steel. Of course where possible, timber should replace steel, but never should steel replace timber.

With cement a similar argument applies. Carbon dioxide is released in the chemical process, but the actual energy requirements could be derived from sustainable sources. Again however, where possible timber should be the preferred option.

As a material of construction, wood has excellent characteristics. There are dozens of varieties, each with its own unique properties. Bridges can be made out of timber. Salad bowls can be made out of it. We have been building houses out of wood for thousands of years. It also makes the best toothpicks. It comes in an infinite variety of patterns that can be polished to reveal stunning beauty. The fossil carbon people don't like wood because no oil, no coal, no gas, is consumed in the manufacture of wood—only sunlight. Describing wood as "God's own plastic" is apt.

Because of the wonderful and incredibly competitive properties of natural wood, it becomes the job of the advertising and public relations departments of the petrochemical companies to give the material a negative image. If they are not endeavouring to do just that, then they are not doing the job the oil companies pay them to do; heads would roll.

How are the marketing gurus of the fossil carbon lobbies achieving these aims? There are many marketing techniques and lobbying manipulations. The most obvious and significant of these are considered in the following strategies for they too need to be appreciated.

STRATEGY 44
Promoting the idea of trees as a carbon sink but not timber products

This is the ultimate mind-juggling act to establish a winning position for the fossil fuel and petrochemical industries.

For the oil companies, forests that tie up rural land are OK but wood, which competes with plastic and other oil-reliant materials, is not. This Orwellian doublespeak is not easy to sell. However, the oil-marketing gurus know that even the most rational and responsible lay person can be made totally confused when technicalities are deliberately made unnecessarily complicated. The actual numbers involved, the areas, the weights, the volumes, for carbon entrapment in carbon sinks are not easy to find and very time-consuming to analyse. And as always, a certain measure of truth is always conveniently stretched by the image-makers to cloud factual realities.

People are being brainwashed so effectively by the fossil carbon lobby that growing useless trees, on useful farmland, is accepted as responsible. At the same time, making useful products out of timber is becoming frowned upon. Resisting the harvesting of timber while simultaneously supporting the planting of trees is a brilliant public relations juggling act. But it is an act of almost criminal irresponsibility.

Timber is such an important enemy of the fossil carbon industries that they must constantly resist the establishment of huge plantations of good usable trees. Also, they want the harvesting of already existing, good quality, naturally sown timber to be stopped. At the same time, and as per their general marketing policy, good agricultural land has to be taken out of production to boost agrochemical sales. See Strategies 35 and 36.

The agrochemical marketing gurus support useless trees being planted in good food-producing cropland. It ensures the land will be unavailable for food production indefinitely. Both these objectives must be accomplished while simultaneously enhancing the public image of the fossil carbon industries.

Unfortunately these marketing strategies, if they continue to be successful, guarantee continuous and disastrous global warming. The concept of planting non-harvestable trees to combat global warming is an utter fiction.

In 1982, I planted 120 native Australian trees and shrubs, of various varieties, at our home in Forbes, in central New South Wales. Most of the plants survived. Many grew to maturity and died. A few of the larger trees are over 3 feet (1 metre) round at the base but most are much smaller. In 1995, 13 years after planting, I calculated the atmospheric carbon dioxide effects of those plantings and compared it to the emissions from the cars that my wife and I drive.

My rough back of the envelope calculations show that the wood in our garden had a total mass of only around 2 tons. At best trees absorb 2 tons of carbon dioxide from the atmosphere to produce 1 ton of wood. That means roughly 4 tons of atmospheric carbon dioxide have been absorbed. My wife and I are both low to average car users; our cars therefore release each year about 12 tons of carbon dioxide. So the carbon dioxide absorbed by our trees and shrubs, in that 13-year period, is less than that produced from the petrol burnt in our 2 cars in just 4 months of driving.

To absorb the carbon dioxide produced from just our two cars, we would need to grow enough vegetation, trees, shrubs and whatever, to absorb, not four months of car use, but thirteen full years of car use. That's 5,000 plantings. Alas, once the trees mature they reach an equilibrium where no more carbon dioxide is absorbed. In general our trees have been like that now since 1995.

The shrubs and trees we planted are typical native varieties for the area. We cared for and watered those plants to make sure they survived and thrived. Of course, if we had planted fast growing, forestry-type trees, a much larger amount of carbon dioxide would have been absorbed per tree. But we would not have been able to fit anywhere near as many on that quarter-acre block.

We would have needed about 10 acres and we would constantly be requiring yet another 10 acres every thirteen years. That's almost an acre per year per car. Growing sugar cane to produce ethanol would require 1 acre per car, so 2 acres of a sugar cane farm could run both our cars for ever.

But let's look at some researched documentation on tree growth. Dr Peter Attiwill of the University of Melbourne and the late Geofrey Leeper previously Professor of Agricultural Chemistry, University of Melbourne wrote *Forest Soils and Nutrient Cycles*. The book is an excellent analysis of forestry soils and timber growth. They report on growth rates of the relatively fast growing *Eucalyptus delegatensis*. Their figures show that an acre of forest containing young vigorous trees will absorb 10 tons of carbon dioxide per year for about 35 years. After which its absorption rate will then stop. Then another acre would be needed.

For every person in a Western society who drives a car we would need to plant 2 acres of trees tomorrow morning (0.8 ha). Maybe then we could continue to use fossil fuels at the Kyoto Protocol-recommended 1990 consumption rate. In addition, for every person in the society not even driving a motor vehicle we would need another 1 acre of trees also planted first thing tomorrow morning. Thus the world would need two billion acres or nearly one billion hectares of new trees to be planted tomorrow just to stay at current CO_2 levels. Remember CO_2 levels now well exceed even the high 1990 levels.

To continue to use fossil fuels at any of these rates, every farmer in the world would have to switch exclusively to using their tractors and trucks and all their equipment to planting useless trees until the world ran out of farmland and everybody starved to death.

Most of Australia is either outright desert or too dry to support forestry. Australia is about the same land area as the U.S. mainland with a population of just under twenty million. So Australia's population is a little less than that of Venezuela and about half that of Colombia.

An optimistic estimate of the area suitable for planting these trees would be about 5% of the national total. That's an area of just 85 million acres (39 million hectares). Most of this area is already used for agriculture, so we would need to tie up nearly a third of the nation's agricultural land to grow enough trees to continue to run just Australia on fossil fuels. Actually a lot more land would be required, for as the trees grow they need to be thinned out, this being essential forestry practice. All things being considered it makes fossil fuels an extremely expensive energy source.

To buy the seedlings, dig the hole, plant the tree and water each one several times is going to cost at least a few dollars per tree. Maybe $5, maybe $10, but certainly the cost will not be much less. Nationally, that would be between $75 billion and $150 billion for a population of less than twenty million people. It can never happen, and it will never happen, and of course it should never happen.

Most people I talk to who are familiar with tree planting and growth, say that without constant watering they would expect at least half of the trees to be dead within twelve months of planting. So we would need to double all those figures. Then of course we would have to repeat the whole exercise on new land every decade or so, and energy demand increases have still to be factored in.

Just to produce the seedlings would be a massive task. The entire output of all the forestry nurseries in the United States is only 850 million seedlings per year and the United States has a much bigger problem than we have in Australia.

A few years ago, a much publicized and incredibly expensive campaign was launched by the Australian Federal Government to plant one billion trees to "enhance the beauty of the country and to minimize the effect of our greenhouse gas emissions". It's a drop in the ocean of what is required, yet even this multibillion dollar political public relations fiasco is frightening in its useless enormity. The concept promoted seems almost deliberately structured to grow trees that are never expected to be harvested. The plan was definitely structured to avoid the production of useful forestry timber.

In this exercise, the Australian people were asked, or told, to fund a mad scheme designed to tie up valuable agricultural land forever, a scheme to produce an unharvestable and virtually useless product. In all of this fiasco, the fossil carbon companies must have been very proud of their lobbying efforts. Of course it is possible they had no part in, and no influence on this ludicrous government initiative. Maybe they were just plain lucky!

Planting such trees to solve the problem of global warming is utter nonsense. The concept is promoted to confuse and placate responsible and concerned citizens and further the interests of the oil and petrochemical producers. No matter how rough the calculations might be and how much the numbers are massaged, the concept of growing billions of trees is ludicrous.

STRATEGY 45
Claiming tree planting can prevent soil salination

An objective of the agrochemical industries has to be to have the public believe the myth that tree clearing causes salination. Trees are supposed to suck up water and thus keep salt water tables from rising. The corollary being that planting millions of worthless trees will fix the problem.

It is next to impossible to grow commercial timber in salt-laden soils. Any trees that grow are always next to worthless. Worthless or not they could never be harvested, for that would defeat their ostensible purpose. Therefore if we have thousands of acres of useless and unusable land and the tree-planting myth somehow worked, we would still end up with thousands of acres of now very costly, useless and unusable land. What is the point in spending the national wealth on changing land that is useless because of salt, into land useless because of trees?

What are the motives behind the salination fiction? The benefits to the agrochemical producers are twofold. It is wise for them to support the myth that tree clearing causes salination, and tree planting will cure it.

Firstly, what gets buried is the facts, and the truth and the reality that worldwide soil fertility is being destroyed by monocropping, incorrect cultivation practices and excessive use of agrochemicals. But the agrochemical companies want their sales to increase. The second reason to concentrate on the tree fiction is that if it is implemented, the excessive planting of useless trees will very significantly reduce farmland areas. This will force up land prices, and using "conventional agriculture", it will justify their marketing plan for ever-more-intensive agriculture and expanded use of agrochemicals.

Planting thousands of useless trees will waste our land, not save it. For as long as the sickly trees might stand, the land becomes locked away from any sane and sensible use. The details of deterioration of agricultural land by salt poisoning and its restoration are discussed in chapter 7. Here is a short summary.

Salt, which was once safely chelated within the subsoil, is released by the breakdown and destruction of soil humus.

Any rise in the water table, whether natural or irrigation-induced, carries the released salt upward to the root zone along with any salt occurring naturally in the groundwater. The salt kills the crop.

Salt, as a minor constituent within the usually excessive quantity of irrigation water required for crop growth in infertile soil, is progressively added to the soil and subsoil.

Trees cannot solve the problem in any way, shape or form.

Lowering the water table does not remove the salt—only restoring soil humus levels and gentle percolating water can do that.

Trees are of little value in increasing soil fertility. Their supposedly marvelous ability to drain away excess groundwater is a fiction, or at least a massive exaggeration. Many common crops have larger leaf areas and consume greater quantities of soil moisture than trees. A good healthy crop of lucerne (alfalfa) will consume many times more soil moisture and in consequence lower water tables more than will almost any permanent stand of trees. We should also realistically appreciate that neither trees, nor lucerne, like to partake of salt-rich water in a high water table. The limited number of plant species that will grow in salty soils are rarely of commercial value. Their one value is that they can produce the humus to commence soil regeneration and land value regeneration, but enormous quantities of chemical fertilizers are sold to farms in the world's irrigation areas.

The myth that trees can lower water tables and prevent salt buildup in agriculture benefits the agrochemical industry. The agrochemical industries know that this myth must be promulgated throughout society and hopefully even become one of those "known facts". And they seem to be definitely succeeding. It is part of their frighteningly logical and never-ending campaign to reduce available agricultural land areas. It is their marketing strategy to encourage ever-more-intensive farming practices that, they maintain, depend on ever-increasing chemical use, with of course hydroponics as their ultimate endgame.

Simple changes in farming techniques that increase soil fertility and soil organic matter, instead of techniques that decrease soil fertility and soil organic matter, will easily solve the majority of the world's soil salination problems. This is not the way the petrochemical companies want it portrayed.

STRATEGY 46
Claiming trees stop soil erosion

This ploy is to massively reduce agricultural land areas by promoting the idea that trees conserve soil.

The concept of tree planting conveniently dissociates declining soil fertility from increased soil erosion. By these means the idea of overuse of agrochemicals and their unfortunate results is removed in the public mind. Erosion is blamed on tree clearing rather than agrochemicals and reduction in soil fertility. By these means agrochemical sales are maintained and the concept of soil fertility loss is replaced by the concocted concept of tree coverage loss. In this way good agricultural land on which there are any visible examples of soil erosion can be fenced off and, as is often the misguided practice in Australia, planted with "native vegetation".

In inland Australia what has come to be called "native vegetation" is hardly worth replanting. The stark reality is that the native vegetation of most of Australia is the sorry result of 50,000 years of human intervention with fire. Native vegetation is what didn't become extinct during that period. If replanting is proposed then what should be replanted, unfortunately, no longer exists. What the country looked like 50,000 years ago is unknown, and obviously can never be reconstructed.

Unfortunately, once the scrub or bush or a few sorry trees do get established, the ideal opportunity for applying soil-enhancing agricultural techniques becomes unavailable. A farmer who even attempts to clear this useless regrowth to improve his soil and his land is loudly criticized and derided as being irresponsible. That farmer is actually improving the wealth of the nation and the environment of the planet and yet he is scorned. Manipulated government legislation is created to prevent tree and scrub clearing and this results in locking good land away forever; all for no sane nor sensible reason.

The end result of the "trees can stop erosion" concept, as always, is reduced agricultural land area. Chemical based agriculture, along with soil inversion tillage, is responsible for the erosion. It has nothing to do with trees. Trees don't produce rich soil. Trees don't manufacture soil, and they never have.

The richest natural soils in the world are invariably the soils produced and sustained by our planet's edible grasses. Grass makes soil. It is the grasslands of the world that nourish the vast majority of advanced life on our planet. The soils of the savannas, the steppes, the prairies are the world's richest soils, and they were created by grasses directly from decomposed rock.

Grassland soil constantly erodes but at a slow rate. A rate that over time constantly exposes a regular supply of mineral-rich subsoil to the plant roots. So the grasslands stay rich. Rapid and harmful erosion in these soils only occurs if they lose their rich organic matter content. The fibrous nature of soil organic matter is what binds soil material together and thus controls erosion rates. These materials give soil the texture and feel agronomists describe as good soil structure. That texture is the feel and the effect of decomposing grass roots. Trees don't have that effect on soil.

The truth is that trees, in isolation or semi-isolation, are worthless for erosion prevention. Even tree roots themselves on a farm often have to be protected from the very erosion they are claimed to prevent. A tree, newly planted in an eroding area, will have a poor chance of survival as continuing fast erosion exposes its roots and soon kills it.

In a forest it is the dense mat of dead and rotting tree litter found under the canopy that is the erosion preventer, not the trees. A good carpet of grass does a much better job, and a good carpet of grass is more useful than covering the earth with totally unpalatable, dead and rotting tree litter. The highly developed herbivores of the world rarely live in forests. They would starve.

Short grass growth cycles can also rapidly and dramatically increase soil humus levels and so combat global warming. Trees can't. Grass will always prevent soil erosion. Trees won't. If a land surface is seen to be eroding badly, it will be found to be in a condition created by deterioration of the soil structure, and this usually results from the deterioration in the nature of the grass cover, not the tree cover.

Trees very often produce natural poisons that kill nearby grass plants to prevent them competing for soil nutrients and water. Also simply by producing shade, trees will reduce the growth rate of any nearby grass plants. A tree planted in conditions where rapid soil degradation is established is more likely to exacerbate erosion problems. It won't fix it. Only grasses can fix it. Trees and grass are enemies and are forever in competition for resources.

Correct cultivation, and the introduction and management of suitable pasture grasses, will definitely re-establish high fertility levels and good soil structure. After the soil has improved then a planted tree will thrive. Although, unless its timber is required, or the tree is a convenient shade for animals, or it forms part of a windbreak, planting a tree is a totally pointless exercise.

There is one notable exception where trees do have a very useful and beneficial function in the prevention of an unusual type of land erosion. With some geological structures on steep hillsides, mud slides or slips can occur. The removal of large quantities of deep-rooted tree varieties can cause slips. A "slip" results when a fairly large area, often forming one large slab, on the side of a hill becomes dislodged and slides some distance downhill. Even small slips or mudslides may contain 10,000 tons of earth and move 100 yards (100 m) or more in a few minutes. Uncharacteristic prolonged heavy rain can initiate a slip. Recent rain-induced mudslides killed thousands of people in South America. Mudslides in Southern California are regular killers.

A small area near the town of Picton in New South Wales has a geological form susceptible to slips. The country is very steep with very deep soil occurring on the steep slopes. With excessive rain, the hillside soil can suddenly slip, and slide down the hill face in an enormous sheet. These slips near Picton are visible and quite noticeable from the main highway.

Deep tree roots can bind this soil material and minimize the slips. Slip country or country prone to mud slides is rare, but the slips and slides are always dramatic. The tree lovers like to use them to prove that the whole world should be planted with trees for erosion mitigation and ignore the fact that the unique geological formations necessary for slides are rare occurrences.

In photographs trees look better than grasses. It is only farmers that are aware of the pointless waste in planting huge quantities of useless trees. The agrochemical industries, helped by their save-the-tree pawns, use stunning photography and vague but emotive environmental claims to mask these inconvenient truths in their never-ending marketing campaigns.

STRATEGY 47
Making timber harvesting socially unacceptable

The fossil carbon advertising gurus love to take dramatic and emotive footage of trees crashing to the ground. The shots show native animals scampering for safety, or even crushed. They invariably depict timber workers as evil, uncaring and avaricious. Another gimmick they love is to attribute to trees qualities that render them somehow different to other plants. It suggests that trees have some magical sense of nobility about them. In effect they portray trees as having a living soul. And it's done well. It's all very powerful stuff, and it is often very hard for us to remain objective.

Man seems always to be in awe of anything that has a life span longer than his own, especially if it is more massive than himself. This very human characteristic is an excellent basis for manipulative emotionalism. Trees sometimes can be very big plants. In size and weight, they often totally dwarf human beings. These features, used carefully by the people in the advertising department, can be made to inspire awe, reverence, respect and concern for big trees. And so we are conditioned to almost love these "noble elephants of the vegetable kingdom" as one piece of well oiled copy described them.

Hugging a cabbage, or chaining oneself to a tomato plant, doesn't have the same impact. Although there is little difference in the logic.

Using these ploys means that the threat of wood to the whole range of energy-consuming alternatives is felled in one blow. The alternative argument becomes a complex and protracted debate over the pros and cons of timber versus other materials. The single-blow strategy is simple, more sweeping and less open to debate. By this means the incredibly competitive nature of timber never gets a mention. Timber harvesting is stopped with a very inexpensive marketing campaign.

The oil driller and the coal miner have, in comparison, a beautifully con-structed, very marketable, diligently manufactured image. Tough, strong, courageous workers they are. Combating desert heat, battling the ever-increasing ferocity of North Sea storms or combating the terrors of the deep underground, these men are bringing us the energy to create a bright new future.

The reality is that the oil-gas workers and the drillers are the conscripted front-runners in the fossil carbon lobbies's deadly hit squads. The compa-nies that by their very existence are killing our atmosphere, wreaking havoc with our weather, destabilizing world climates, destroying our crops and forcing millions of people into unprecedented drought and flood-initiated starvation.

The campaign to present the actual timber harvesting as evil and ungodlike is the other ploy. Creating the image of the timber cutters as a dying breed of uncaring, irresponsible villains is achieving remarkable success. Children's television is rampant with these brain-molding messages. Some Australians might remember such blatant image manipulation in the theme song from the Blinkey Bill television series. Similarly, the movie *Fern Gully* could well have been produced by the petrochemical industries. Listen to the words of the song "Toxic Waste" from its soundtrack, it could easily be an oil company anthem.

Such messages are so wrong. It's the timber getter, not the oil driller, who is the real hero in saving the planet.

STRATEGY 48
Establish wood as a socially unacceptable product

The appreciation of timber as a material of true worth and delightful beauty has to be destroyed. Rainforests produce some of the most beautiful timber in the world. If beautiful timber products that you have in your home can be insulted and criticized, portrayed as products of Western man's greed, products of the wanton destruction of "God's rainforests", then the petrochemical marketing people will have won. The use of plastics and other oil-dependent materials will dominate our civilization; the richness of human life will be poorer for it. If people can be made to somehow feel vaguely uncomfortable, or embarrassed, for owning or using timber and wooden products, then the fossil carbon industries will receive a tremendous marketing boost.

If wood is "God's own plastic", then making wood socially unacceptable is one of the greatest examples of orchestrated public opinion modifications of the twentieth century. It ranks alongside the creation of the negative images of nuclear energy and the created fear of white asbestos. Such blatant false image building should rankle in all of us.

When we are unaware of the facts and do not take the time to question what has become dogma, it becomes almost impossible for us not to be affected by the force and power of image-makers and their anti-timber campaigns. The manipulation of human attitudes towards timber and forests has been so successful that an environmental report published in the United Kingdom proudly claims that retailers and consumers are refusing to buy products made from tropical timbers. Thin veneers of teak and mahogany covering the bare plastic is portrayed as environmentally responsible. Many furniture manufacturers have switched entirely to plastic and aluminium to cater for this green absurdity in the marketplace.

STRATEGY 49
The slogan-dominated cult of rainforest protection

This is another ploy that illustrates how nonthinking environmentalists are manipulated and cajoled into fostering the aims of the oil-gas lobbyist. It has almost become a form of twisted "common knowledge" that the so-called destruction of tropical rainforests (or any rainforest for that matter, or even any forest), is the worst ecological disaster of the 20th and now the 21st century. It is happily claimed by the fossil carbon companies' public relations people to be a key factor in every serious environmental problem facing the planet: mass extinctions of species, shortages of "natural resources", poor air quality, global warming, massive human displacement and suffering, and anything else that comes to mind. It's all fiction; the facts don't support any of the claims.

The fossil carbon industries have two compelling motives for this campaign of disinformation. Of course one is to minimize the use of wood. The other is to minimize the availability of land to ultimately encourage intensive agricultural practices, but most importantly to hinder the production of sugar. Ethanol is the fuel that must and will ultimately replace petrol. Sugar cane is currently the best and cheapest raw material from which to produce ethanol. Sugar cane grows best in the tropics and semi-tropics—precisely where rainforests cover the land.

All these supposed "truths" about rainforests and deforestation, are in truth a pack of untruths. They are riddled with manipulated disinformation and wild and woolly exaggerations. It is carefully orchestrated public relations image building to sell more petrochemicals, more agrochemicals, more plastics and more fossil-based energy. For Big Oil, it is a fabulously successful marketing ploy to be fostered and encouraged ad nauseam.

What is never claimed, never mentioned, and never hinted at, is that tropical rainforests contain a huge quantity of beautiful and immensely versatile wood, and that wood, in so many cases, is plastic's greatest competitor.

It is never mentioned that tropical timbers regrow, and tropical forests regenerate faster than any other ecological system on the planet. It is never argued, never suggested, never promoted that the most responsible environmental thing to do with tropical rainforests is to periodically harvest the timber.

To waste the wood and to let it rot is environmental negligence of criminal magnitude. It is utterly illogical and sickening to imply that the key to preventing global warming is to prevent clearing of tropical rainforests, and to cease harvesting tropical rainforest timbers. It's a blatant public relations lie.

When trees die they decompose and turn into atmospheric carbon dioxide. This is true of all trees whether they be in boreal forests, temperate forests or tropical rainforests. Look at the logic: if they did not turn back into carbon dioxide then where is all the litter? After the thousands of years that many of these forests have existed, the litter would have to be hundreds of feet thick. But the ground litter in rainforests is only ever finger deep!

Can rainforests be useful to us as carbon sinks to mitigate global warming? No way.

A carbon sink, like any sink, like a kitchen sink, must absorb things and not return them. A tropical rainforest is certainly a storehouse of carbon, but the storehouse is full. It's been full since the first crop of trees grew to maturity in them many thousands of years past; probably many millions of years.

It is common knowledge that trees extract carbon dioxide from the air. What is not so commonly known is that overnight they feed carbon dioxide back into the air. Trees are living creatures; they metabolize sugars to stay alive—a process that requires oxygen. That's what they breathe in at night. They also live in symbiosis with mycorrhizal fungi, which live around their roots extracting minerals and nutrients from decomposing organic matter. Mycorrhizae breathe oxygen and expel carbon dioxide to perform their function. If you cover the soil around a tree with plastic or flood its roots for a long period the mycorrhizae will die and so will the tree.

Unlike us, plants and trees make their own food sugars from scratch using photosynthesis. It is this process which extracts carbon dioxide from the air and releases oxygen. Photosynthesis stops as soon as the sun goes down, or in the case of deciduous trees, whenever the tree loses its leaves. However the trees remain alive, consuming the sugars stored in the sap. Maple trees are an excellent example; they store large amounts of sugary sap to tide them over the long cold winters, and early Canadian settlers learnt to tap into this resource for the same purpose—hence maple syrup.

For a young vigorous tree, growing in plenty of sunlight, the amount of carbon dioxide absorbed is much higher than the amount released by the tree's metabolism, and the difference ends up stored as wood. But only while the tree is growing and enlarging. The actual heartwood of a tree is dead. As trees grow bigger and older, more often than not the heartwood begins to rot. Some big old rainforest trees are completely hollow. As the heartwood rots, stored carbon is released as carbon dioxide. The overall result is that a fully mature tree, in which the mass of wood is no longer increasing, releases as much carbon dioxide as it absorbs. If the heart is hollowing out the mass of wood will actually be decreasing. The tree then becomes an overall source of carbon dioxide, not a sink.

Measurements by Charles D. Keeling and Stephen C. Piper of the Scripps Institution of Oceanography in La Jolla, California and reported in the October 1998 issue of *Scientific American*, not only confirms the above but indicates that tropical rainforests are now tending to become a source of carbon dioxide, not a sink! The recent development of inconsistent rainfall patterns stops rainforests from being rainforests. The total mass of vegetation within them declines. That's global warming in action and feeding itself.

The only way a rainforest is of any use in the prevention of global warming is to harvest its timber before the trees die and rot. The carbon dioxide is then not discharged into the air but is locked away as beautiful timber furnishings. Those furnishings are an ideal, practical, man-made carbon sink.

It required great ingenuity for the fossil carbon lobby to forestall such a common-sense appreciation of the value of wood and timber. But they did it. The vast majority of people now really believe harvesting rainforest timber is gross irresponsibility.

Weather patterns in the tropics are not generally as vulnerable to shifts in ocean circulation patterns as those in the more temperate regions. Tropical jungles and rainforests have therefore developed into the most long-term stable terrestrial ecological systems on the planet. Most tropical jungles have been completely stable for tens of thousands of years. Many of these jungles would have been little affected by the ice ages that were felt so harshly in the higher latitudes. The evolutionary changes stimulated by climate changes in higher latitudes are significantly reduced in tropical rainforests. Relatively speaking, tropical rainforests are now evolutionarily stagnant.

The very stability of tropical rainforests has unfortunately ensured the destruction of the tropical soils by the one-way process of soil leaching. Leaching is the process where minerals are washed from the soil by an excess of water. Leaching occurs in all soils to some extent, generally the higher the rainfall, the higher the risk of leaching. At the same time, in all soils, a slight amount of erosion occurs. This constant gentle surface erosion ensures that an unending supply of mineral-rich subsoil is always becoming exposed to the biological activity stimulated by oxygen and powered by sunlight. Thus new mineral-rich topsoil is constantly being formed. The minerals thus exposed counteract the losses due to leaching. Slight soil erosion is therefore essential in sustaining healthy advanced terrestrial life. In the wet tropics and subtropics, sunlight is in abundance and rainfall is excessive. So soil leaching is inevitable due to the high rainfall, but unfortunately where the super-dense rainforests grow and litter covers the ground, soil erosion is near zero.

The deep litter covering the rainforest floor eliminates soil erosion so completely that the normal constant exposure of deep mineral-rich subsoil to the surface environment is totally prevented. The constant process of growth, decay and regrowth and the high rainfall gradually demineralize the soil. See chapter 6 for a more detailed discussion.

Rainforest soils are the poorest, most worthless soils anywhere on the face of the planet. They are portrayed as fragile but they are certainly not fragile. Quite the contrary, their very worthlessness makes them almost invulnerable to change. Only hot sandy deserts have more impoverished surface soil material. In many ways rainforests are simply huge green deserts.

The 21 September 1996 issue of *New Scientist* reported on the poor nature of rainforest soils resulting from this leaching process in a comprehensive cover of agriculture in the Amazon. It was pointed out that slash and burn, with its inherent slight erosion, is actually a sustainable agricultural practice for the Amazon and other tropical rainforests. The system has operated perfectly well for centuries, long before fossil fuels began to destabilize world climates. One of the articles was even captioned "Slash and Grow".

The pressure to prevent the use of high-rainfall tropical land is ongoing. To further prevent the concept of harvesting and regrowing boreal forest and rainforest trees, a new marketing buzzword was generated, "old growth forests". "Old growth" was an old and rarely used term, first seen in the late 19th century and then totally reinvented by the advertising copywriters. But "old growth forests" and their "protection" has certainly been processed into a new and cleverly emotive, although pointless cause.

The argument dreamed up to market the "old growth forests" concept says that when an old tree falls over and dies, it forms an important link in the chain of the forest ecology. The fallen tree clears the forest canopy for a short period and native animals are then supposed to move in and live under the fallen branches. One might ask, is there something different if the tree is chopped down? The canopy cover argument is no different, and surely the very few animals that do inhabit dense forests can take up residence under the smaller scattered branches. Or is that too simple?

Tropical jungles are a symphony of chirps, and whistles, and screeches, and haunting bird calls, a symphony of life—but only in the movies.

The reality is different. Jungles and tropical rainforests in the real world are silent, still, lifeless places, with a constant smell of rotting vegetation. There are few animals and most of these are small. Good nourishing food is difficult to obtain in an environment where the soil is so leached and depleted.

Walking over the ground in a tropical rainforest, the first thing you notice is the dark and eerie quietness. There are no sounds. Then you notice what else seems to be missing. There are no plants. There is no greenery. There are hardly any insects. You have to dig into the carpet of dead litter for termites and centipedes to find any of the tropical rainforest's much-publicized biodiversity. So little sunlight penetrates this dark cavernous interior that plants simply can't grow there. All the greenery, and any life in a rainforest, is in the dense canopy ten stories above your head. And even in the high canopy life is still sparse, for the green treetops contain few nutrients, few minerals and few proteins.

Birds are about the only common large life form that you will find, for they can range over a huge area to find enough food to survive. The so-called richness in tropical flora and fauna is always confined to areas where breaks occur in the monotony of the forest. Rich life only occurs along rivers or near cliffs, or in the rare grassy clearings, or in the flood-prone valleys where the smothering effects of the endless canopy is broken. That is the only place where nutrients and minerals can enter the biological cycle. That's where the monkeys live. We are fed a constant barrage of claims that clearing rainforests will lead to some horrendous "mass extinctions". We are fed suggestions, innuendos and suppositions but we are never let see the facts.

There is now a sizeable worldwide lobby demanding rainforests be placed out of bounds for all, and for ever. "Shortages of natural resources" is often vaguely thrown in by the oil-gas marketing gurus and their green pawns to somehow justify this fencing off and locking up of tropical rain-forest. The only significant "resource" is the timber the forest contains. If this timber, by political and environmental manipulation, is mandated or legislated to rot on the tropical floor, then by definition the tropical rainforest cannot in any way be described as a resource. By definition, a resource is something of use or of value. Locked up rainforests become nothing more than protected habitats for a great diversity of termites.

It is constantly argued by those who want rainforests locked away for-ever, that just possibly, somewhere in those endless green forests is some plant, some insect or some fungus that contains some magical drug, "a magic cure for cancer".

That is a twisted and sick scenario. The following is typical of what really happens. In the January 1998 issue of *Science*, Vol. 279, it was reported that John Daly, a chemist at the National Institute of Diabetes and Digestive and Kidney Diseases in the United States, made an incredible discovery in 1976. He isolated a chemical he called epibatidine. It came from the skin of a frog in Ecuador. Ecuador straddles the equator on the western coast of South America; it has a population of 12 million. The average annual rainfall in the northern Ecuadorian coastal areas is around 80 inches (2 metres). That's classic rainforest country. The frog was called *Epipedobates tricolor* and that is where Daly derived the name for this amazing chemical.

It seems epibatidine is an incredible painkiller. It is 200 times more effective in blocking pain than morphine. Epibatidine was found to work through a totally different set of receptors, and therefore it was unlikely to have the deadly addictive properties of morphine. When the frog was grown in laboratories, it didn't produce the miraculous painkilling chem-ical. More research was necessary. But now the almost out of control "save the rainforest" pawns decided their political domain was threatened by independent researchers. They reacted. To quell their protests and environmental screams, the frog was placed on the "endangered" species list. The chemical in the frog's skin could no longer be studied.

A few tiny, irreplaceable samples of the chemical were refrigerated and stored. Nothing happened for ten long wasteful years until techniques in nuclear magnetic resonance spectroscopy became available to determine the structure of the stored chemical. Finally, research in this substitute for morphine was able to recommence. Variations of the chemical were produced and tried on laboratory animals, and finally variant ABT-594 was selected for intensive study. Pain was stimulated in rats in a variety of ways, and the chemical's pain-relieving and suppressing characteristics were studied.

Spinal pain was reduced as dramatically and as effectively as with pure morphine. Even more startling, it was found that benign sensations such as touch and the feeling of warmth were unaffected. ABT-594 did not sedate test animals. They remained awake and alert. Normal respiration was not repressed as happens with morphine. Ten days of particularly high doses in test animals, when stopped, did not produce suppressed appetites and withdrawal symptoms. I believe it is currently ready for testing in humans.

Around the world, how much crime has been committed, how much suffering has been felt, how many of us have became drug addicts because a safe alternative to heroin and morphine, an alternative with great promise, was delayed for one entire human generation for no sane reason whatever. We still can't get supplies of the original secretions. We only have the synthetic versions.

If we can't use the forest, we won't go there. Why would we? And nothing will ever happen. And the oil companies will have won their battle. It is blatantly irrational to preserve millions of square miles of rainforests in the hope that they might contain some miraculous cure for cancer if research into that cure is not allowed.

"Deforestation" has been taken by the manipulators of human opinion, and turned into a dirty word everywhere. Yet deforestation was an essential part in the process of creating our rich and prosperous societies. We used the wood to make useful articles, houses, furniture and tools, and in the process we created agricultural land.

Most articles on tropical rainforests show consistent irrational bias. They are also pathetically emotive. It is always "timber companies" chasing "quick profits" by "mining" tropical timbers. "Swarms of people hungry for land" follow the bulldozers while they "rip and slash" their way through the "pristine" forest. The writings always reek of unfettered emotional manipulation.

It is also implied or presumed in these stories that the rich and developed nations of the world achieved their high standard of living by viciously exploiting and destroying the natural wealth of the poor nations of the world. Mostly this is rubbish. Hard work, mechanization, the right to own land, free enterprise and the constitutional right of a people to sack their own government—history shows that's how rich nations became rich.

The resources that were used to create rich nations came from within their own borders. There were simply not enough transportation and port facilities available to ship in from "poor countries" the raw materials needed to create their immense wealth. Nor did the world's developed nations receive one cent in foreign aid to help build their societies. They pulled themselves up by their own bootstraps and they should feel proud of their accomplishments.

The members of affluent societies must not allow themselves to be manipulated into feeling embarrassed because of their own accomplishments, as so many uninformed, self-righteous people would like us to feel. The self-righteous bigots of the world never created anything, neither good laws nor an affluent society. They nevertheless greedily, hypocritically, and invariably claim their share of the wealth and freedom others created.

Rainforests have their few native human inhabitants. It is therefore presumed by these self-righteous souls that regulations must be dreamed up to "manage" the jungle and to maintain the environment for the inhabitants. Environmental organizations then proclaim their particular form of rainforest management, and their form of local people management, all in their own particularly "enlightened" way.

That rainforests should be managed at all, or even conserved at all, is always just blithely assumed.

Other conservation groups argue that under the "stewardship" of the local natives, the forests have been "managed wisely". That the jungle is still there, I presume, is the evidence we are to accept for the presumption. Are we supposed to believe that without such "stewardship" the jungle would not survive? The reality is that jungles persist. Jungles survive despite the natives, not because of them. Jungles are almost impossible to remove and keep removed. And the few indigenous human inhabitants in these jungles have an indiscernible effect.

I know that when the jungle is cleared on tropical Pacific islands, and coconut plantations are established, it becomes a constant battle for the owner to prevent the regrowth of native vegetation. On the flat coastal strips where clearing can be achieved the increased sunlight reaching the ground ensures that plant growth is even more prolific. Constant maintenance and cleaning of regrowth is absolutely essential. I remember in the old New Hebrides (now Vanuatu) that if a copra (coconut) plantation was neglected for about ten years it became economically impossible to re-establish the plantation. The coconut trees would still be there and could be thirty years old—only half way through their useful production life—but selectively clearing the massive volume of jungle regrowth to allow the individual coconuts trees to produce properly would no longer be viable. It was more economical to start again from scratch. Usually after neglect for twenty years or so, it is generally no longer possible to even find the plantation. The coconut trees are possibly still there—somewhere in the impenetrable jungle.

Jungles always persist and will persist as long as the rains keep coming and persist even as the soils grow poor. Water, air and heat are all that is needed to nourish the never-ending jungle (or using its new title the never-ending "tropical rainforest"). As long as the rainfall is high and regular and the sun shines, rainforests will dominate totally. It is a cliché of those that know jungles that no matter what you try to build, no matter what you try to do, "the jungle always wins".

But probably not against the creeping cancer of climate change.

The reality in large tropical rainforests is that the local natives barely maintain more than a subsistence level. Life there is a constant struggle for survival. Any easily obtainable food supplies and edible game that did exist were long ago exploited to extinction. To the natives, "management" and "stewardship" is not some noble cause, as many proclaim. It is simply staying alive the easiest way possible.

Conservation groups always seem to presume that the natives live happy, healthy, contented lives in a green and bountiful world. It is apparently irrelevant why by our Western standards their life expectancy is always so amazingly short. Population densities without birth control, as always anywhere, are reduced to survival levels determined by food supplies. Apart from the supply of wood, rainforests really have never been a bountiful suppler of anything. In the jungle, animal or human population densities are always extremely low.

Whenever such natives receive a comprehensive Western education they do one of two things. They either do their very best to avoid going back to their supposed ideal existence, or they go back with the express desire to educate, modernize and change their supposedly happy and bountiful lifestyles to something better. However, the moment this happens, the conservation societies decide that no longer is the native's stewardship of their own jungle to be trusted. Yet surely if the land is to be managed, then with the recent demise of communism, it should be managed, and owned, by "them that live there". Not somebody in some high-rise city apartment.

This however does not suit the oil companies. If the natives owned and managed land, then the three most profitable products to concentrate on would be native timber, ethanol from sugar cane and natural rubber.

It is therefore apparent that "preservation of tropical rainforests" must seem a most worthy cause to foster in the calculating eyes of the petrochemical industries.

The reality of rainforest logging is that if we harvest and log rainforest timbers, the rainforest ecology may noticeably change. However there is a good argument that says that any change will be for the better. Of course this would be totally opposed by oil interests and proponents of stagnation ecology concepts. However to satisfy all it is now becoming obvious that it's surprisingly easy to selectively log rainforests with negligible shifts in a prevailing ecology.

That may be contrary to established dogma but the facts are there. As an example let's consider Borneo. It's a big island about the same size as Madagascar, New Guinea, or Texas. The equator runs right through the island of Borneo. The island is considered to contain the world's richest rainforest. Borneo is therefore a good place to investigate the effects of logging on tropical rainforest.

Britain's Royal Society has a field station in Sabah on the northern tip of the island. The field station is in the Danum Valley, just 6 kilometres north of the equator. In the late 1980s a team of scientists set out to observe the effects of various logging techniques on these tropical rainforest ecologies. The results were enlightening and quite fascinating.

The primary effect of selective logging in dense jungle is to change the quantity and nature of sunlight reaching the forest floor. The studies were designed, among other things, to determine how this change in light levels affected the forest flora and fauna.

Three of the principal researchers involved were rainforest ecologists. They were Tim Whitmore, from the University of Oxford, Malcolm Press, a plant physiologist and lecturer at the University of Manchester in the Department of Environmental Biology, and Nick Brown, a rainforest ecologist lecturing in the Department of Geography at the University of Manchester.

These people were astute researchers. The tests they designed were sensible and effective. Areas were cleared ranging in size from 30 feet (10 metres) square to 5,000 feet (1,500 metres) square. The regrowth patterns and species were observed over a five-year period that proved ample to draw meaningful conclusions.

What the research showed was that there are two fundamentally different types of rainforest timber. The first is a group generally described as climax species. These include most of the dense tropical hardwoods. Their seeds fall to the ground and immediately germinate. Most of them then die from lack of sunlight as only about 2% of the sunlight energy falling on dense tropical rainforests makes it through to the ground. Some of these seedlings, lucky enough to get a few flecks of sunlight, eventually become well-established mature seedlings. If a few branches fall from the overhead canopy or a mature tree topples, these mature seedlings rapidly develop in the sudden burst of additional sunlight. Even then it's not easy as too much sunlight on their dark-adapted photosynthesis system will kill the less hardy. So only the strongest seedlings survive to reach up and annex their own area in the high canopy's harsh and direct tropical sun.

Trees in the second group are generally known as pioneers. These trees grow very fast and produce a very soft lightweight wood. The balsa wood familiar to model aeroplane builders is a typical pioneer species.

Unlike the climax species, the seeds of pioneer species don't germinate immediately on contact with the ground. They lie dormant waiting for big openings in the overhead canopy. Also unlike climax seedlings, pioneer seedlings need, and thrive, in strong direct sunlight.

In the trials, it was obvious that the larger the area of canopy removed, the more dominant the pioneer species became. Fauna associated with the pioneer species also dominated.

As the canopy re-established itself, ground-level sunlight diminished; the sunlight flecked, semi-darkness returned and the balance shifted. The ground-level environment again favoured the development of the climax species and their dependent fauna. The pioneer species in turn languished.

The results of the research show that logging in tropical and subtropical rainforests, while changing the current ecological balance, almost instantly establishes the opposite balance. The removal of all timber coverage is described as clearfelling. The results also showed that, except for very small areas, clearfelling severely hinders regrowth of the more valuable tropical hardwoods of the climax species. Clearfelling exposes the vulnerable hardwood seedlings to direct sunlight which kills them. Since the climax species lifecycle does not include a dormant seed process, some mature climax species trees must be retained for seed and seedling production. Once the softwood pioneer species become well established, the hardwood trees then follow.

Thus total clearfelling of large areas of high rainfall tropical forests is counterproductive to timber production. A landowning timber producer would therefore retain some dispersed hardwood trees for this necessary seed production. This is exactly the same as grain farmers keeping seed for next year's planting. Unfortunately when the land is owned by the state, such simple practical responsibility soon becomes a bureaucratic quagmire.

In the trials in the Borneo rainforests, it was found that within six months, small cleared plots were well covered with pioneer species. Within two to three years a canopy of pioneer species shaded the ground so effectively that, provided there was a seed source close by, the hardwood climax seedlings dominated again.

Another report in an August 1998 issue of *Science*, Vol. 281 described more findings on the impact of logging in the Borneo rainforests. The report was detailed and well documented. The researchers observed and studied the effects of an actual logging operation that was described as haphazard and indiscriminate. Considerations of biodiversity did not appear to be an issue for these loggers. Yet within eight years, regrowth and reforestation was total. Biodiversity was unaffected.

Rainforests are great survivors and have been for millennia. Again, "the jungle always wins."

Logging is widely publicized as the "kiss of death" for rainforests. This is totally untrue. Maybe a common-sense proviso might be added that only useful and mature trees should be harvested or felled, or with clearfelling some climax species trees should be retained. Even with wildlife, fluctuations in population densities can be quite dramatic, but no studies support the much-touted concept of inevitable desolation.

Research on rainforest population and density changes, conducted by Andy Johns and Frank Lambert, both of the University of Aberdeen, showed that very few species of vertebrates are entirely lost in an area with even severe logging operations. Again, this is in complete contradiction to every media and public-relations pronouncement. Their studies showed that the large herbivores thrived in the pioneer species dominated regrowth. Populations of elephant and deer almost exploded. However bird species with highly selective food requirements often only survived well in small selected pockets untouched by the logging operations.

Jeremy Holloway of the Natural History Museum and Ashley Kirk-Spriggs of the National Museum of Wales are entomologists. (Entomologists study insects.) Their research on insects showed the same overall pattern.

It seems obvious that man can easily affect the ecological balance of a rainforest. It is also obvious that the result is simply the creation of a new ecological balance. There is change but no loss. Usually the balance swings back. At most it is a philosophical argument, whether the old ecological balance or the new ecological balance is more desirable. Also whose definition of desirability are we to pander to and why?

They are all strange arguments, for worldwide we are not actually losing forest density at all. Resources for the Future is a think tank in Washington, DC. Roger Sedjo of that institute has been studying the relationship between atmospheric carbon dioxide buildup and deforestation. His particular findings add a much needed influx of common sense and illumination to the esoteric "deforestation debate".

In the early 1980s anti-deforestation propaganda claimed 4 billion tons of carbon dioxide were released into the atmosphere by the destruction of the world's forests. Roger Sedjo conducted what is possibly the first global analysis of forest destruction and regrowth undertaken. Despite all the rhetoric, he shows that the truth is that since 1920 timber regrowth in the United States has substantially exceeded deforestation. In 2001, United States forestry nurseries produced 850 million seedlings per year; these seedlings are planted, grown and the survivors harvested to produce timber. All these trees sequestered carbon dioxide. Figures for Canada are similar. Even in the old Soviet Union, regrowth and replanting exceeded deforestation.

He points out that it is reasonable to presume that in the tropics, regrowth is already as high as 75% of deforestation. The very considerable forest regrowth and forest plantings in the temperate latitudes then almost exactly balances the remaining 25% of tropical deforestation. Sedjo draws the logical, unbiased and unemotional conclusion that "the global forest ecosystem is roughly balanced".

So it must surely follow that global warming can never be attributed to some fictitious massive global deforestation.

The horrendous fires now becoming a regular occurrence in the world's rainforests, caused by decreased rainfalls, are the only things that can significantly diminish world forest cover, and in so doing obviously contribute significantly to global warming. Lack of rain makes rainforests flammable and lack of rain is global warming in action. It becomes a vicious circle.

A stable rainforest requires a high stable rainfall. Periods of drought, now more severe due to global weather changes, often leave rainforests vulnerable to lightning-initiated forest fires. In the Great Borneo Fire of 1983, 15,000 square miles (40,000 square kilometres) of tropical rainforest were burnt out. Rainforests have to be wet places. Drought induced by global warming caused the fires, not some hypothetical mismanagement nor "indiscriminate logging".

The new regenerating rainforest in those burnt-out areas would be subject to rapidly changing local ecologies as the forests re-established themselves. And when that new "stability" does become established, it too will have its own uniqueness and its own vulnerability.

In Borneo, in 1997–98, it happened again. It is now accepted that the severity and the frequency of the fires in the Indonesian islands, especially the island of Borneo, is predominately determined by the severity and frequency of ENSO events. And ENSO events are increasing in frequency and severity as global temperatures climb. The 1997–98 fires spread smoke over the whole Southeast Asian region including Malaysia and Singapore. Damage estimates were in excess of US$1.5 billion. Twenty million people were breathing polluted air well above danger levels for months on end.

But again the jungle in Borneo regrows to burn yet again, so why waste the wood?

The Amazon is no different. If atmospheric carbon dioxide levels increase at current rates as will most certainly happen if we don't do something serious about it, then the Amazon basin will simply dry up. All those thousands of square miles of rainforests will die and then surely burn. That comes from a three-year in-depth study, concluded in 1999, by the British Meteorological Office, Hadley Centre. In the Amazon we are talking firestorms ten times worse than has ever happened in relatively tiny Borneo.

Rainforests and tropical jungles, when left alone, do not produce oxygen for the rest of the world to breathe. They are not carbon sinks; they do not absorb atmospheric carbon dioxide. They cannot reduce global warming at all. Harvesting rainforest timber, building things with the wood, and replanting or simply awaiting regrowth, creates a carbon sink that did not exist before. Additionally a huge quantity of plastic and other fossil-reliant materials won't get manufactured.

These actions can significantly reduce global warming. So that's what we must do.

If the demineralized soil in an area of cleared jungle was actually bulldozed away or allowed to erode away, this would I believe be an improvement. The combination of newly exposed, mineral rich subsoil, tropical heat, high rainfall and grass would very rapidly create incredibly rich and fertile soil. The soil would be better than has existed in those jungles for countless millennia. That new soil-fertility-building process would be a huge carbon sink, bigger even than any possible regrowth forest. The greenhouse carbon dioxide budget would come out way ahead. The tropical nations, owning the old jungles, would now have rich fertile soil on which to produce their crops and feed their people. And as has been noted: if the natives owned and managed the land themselves, then the three most profitable products to concentrate on would be native timber, ethanol from sugar cane and natural rubber.

There is a scenario the oil and petrochemical industries dread and with complete justification. But preventing world climatic chaos is more important.

Right now, for all of us, and for all things that live on this planet, global warming is the only environmental issue that has immense and overriding significance. It is the fossil carbon public relations people that have turned tropical rainforests into today's holy grails. And the fossil carbon industries are the only beneficiaries in this quixotic quest for the new holy grail.

STRATEGY 50
Invent a biodiversity crisis to stop timber harvesting, to support wilderness claims and to limit agricultural land

The energy that ultimately powers all living things on this planet of ours is the energy in sunlight. It all starts because some life forms here can manipulate very tricky photochemical effects and harness this energy to create energy-loaded complex chemical compounds. These then become both the building blocks and the energy packages for all the rest of life on earth. By bonding and modifying these building blocks, even more complex and versatile molecules are produced. These processes can only happen, as far as we know, within and as part of, a whole variety of strange watery soups.

In the sea, which was the primeval soup, all the elements needed to manufacture the needed complex and versatile molecules were there in abundance. On land it was different. Life forms there had to develop the ability to contain their own chemical soup in some sort of membrane, and at the same time to somehow break down and extract the needed elements from nearby hard rock particles. But they did it, and most successfully.

In the process of life, from there on in, all living things grow, thrive and reproduce by eating other living things, or the remains of other living things. These things are their building blocks. Thus more sophisticated creatures could evolve based on a copious supply of highly sophisticated building blocks, both to build with and to dismantle for needed energy.

The off-cuts or the scantlings in the building processes and the decom-posed ingredients after energy-extracting processes return to the soil. With these waste products is mixed some decomposed rock particles, then using the energy in sunlight the whole sequence endlessly repeats itself. Within this ongoing process individual life forms constantly change and evolve, or they perish.

The system forms a food chain.   Humans, along with a few other creatures live at the top of the chain.

On this planet life has invaded every nook and cranny where light and moisture can penetrate. More advanced life forms have moved in to every other dark or dryer nooks and crannies in search of shelter and safety.

Some very rare forms found energy and a suitable soup to develop in near hot volcanic vents at the bottom of deep oceans. On this planet these places are the rare exceptions where the energy to power life is not totally sun derived.

Today, every nook and cranny, every field, every hill, every puddle, every stream and every ocean is occupied by a variety of living things to the maximum extent possible under the given circumstances. All these localized conditions are in a state of constant change; some fast, most exceedingly slow. As they evolve, so the inhabitants evolve or perish. In consequence there is an immense and varying variety of life forms or species on earth.

Over the last 50,000 years Stone Age man hunted to extinction a host of these more fascinating and interesting species, especially the big ones. Now, in most affluent societies the extinction rate of such species has dropped to near zero.

Even so, I do not believe that mankind has some ordained moral re-sponsibility to maintain the exact number and variety of species currently existing on the planet. It just seems a sensible and wise philosophy to adopt for otherwise we might be burning bridges. Therefore, whenever it's reasonably possible we should prevent interesting species from becoming extinct.

I believe that if a species is happily living and breeding somewhere on the planet, although not necessarily where it might have lived in some time past, it cannot be catalogued as a "threatened species." To say that kangaroos are now extinct in downtown Sydney or some other suburban areas, is utter nonsense. Actually there are more kangaroos in Australia than people, and probably more than have existed for millennia.

In total contrast to statistical facts, we are constantly told that current extinction rates on the planet have reached some utterly undefined, and always suitably indefinable crisis point. This is simply not true. It is just that the rare exceptions receive exceptional publicity, and always to support some particular hidden agenda.

To say that because of these rare occurrences the world environment is at crisis point is simply not true. And if it is not true why are we being brainwashed into believing it is?

Again we should ponder what Sherlock Holmes said to Dr Watson, "To solve the mystery, first look for he who will benefit".

The industrial world's massive use of fossil fuels, petrochemicals and agrochemicals is putting the entire world on a road to global crisis. That crisis is global warming and radical and unpredictable climate change. Logical marketing for those industries most contributing to global warming is to defuse those issues, most effectively by creating some alternative "world crisis". An horrendous threat to world "biodiversity" became that theme.

The promotion of "biodiversity crises" as a concept was brilliant marketing. The concept is impossible to clearly define and can be specifically adapted to suit almost any situation. Biodiversity has systematically been structured to become the "in" word for the environmental crusaders. No matter what human beings wish to do, if it threatens the sale of petroleum or petrochemical products, a threatened biodiversity scenario can be dreamed up and used to prevent it.

The creation of the myth of some pending dreadful biodiversity crisis was marketing magic. It is used with reckless abandon to support the most impossible and impractical demands imaginable. It is used to imply that change in any direction that, in reality is generally no more than away from fossil carbon use, will always be seen in some way as almost criminally irresponsible. With this constant manufactured myth of threatened biodiversity, public opinion becomes controllable and capable of being manipulated almost at will.

It is worth noting that *Webster's Dictionary* notes no recorded use of the word "biodiversity" prior to 1986. Now the word has become a religion.

This carefully structured "crisis in biodiversity" implies that serious harm is, in some undisclosed way, going to befall the world. It is even suggested that there may be insufficient numbers and varieties of species to sustain a truly ongoing development of planetary life. That is plain ridiculous. It is conveniently forgotten in these arguments that 80% of the species on the planet—dinosaurs included—were wiped out before we got our own chance to evolve. Such wipeouts have happened several times in Earth's long history. The planet didn't stop.

We are told that the Panama Canal was a man-made ecological disaster. When the Chagres River, that flows north into the Caribbean, was joined by man-made lakes to the south-flowing Grande to form the canal, the two ecosystems came into sudden and total conflict. Biodiversity should plummet the pundits would claim. But it didn't. Ninety years after the canal was built a study shows biodiversity actually increased significantly. Eldridge Bermingham of the Smithsonian Tropical Research Unit in Ancon,

Panama says: "It flies in the face of what was ecological dogma". See *New Scientist*, 28 August 2004, reporting on *Proceedings of the Royal Society*.

The wonderful thing about biodiversity as a marketing tool is that usually very few of us can make any intelligent judgments as to its actual worth, if indeed there is any. We can't validate or invalidate the myriad of supposed threats. We can however, most certainly be made to feel guilty. And guilt feelings can be manipulated by the public relations gurus with consummate skill.

In an act of brilliant public relations, the marketers, the actual perpetrators of the greatest of all biodiversity threats, manage to portray themselves as warriors in a new "noble cause" to protect our planet's biodiversity. It is worth pondering the theme behind so many of the current oil companies' advertisements. And observe how they structure the themes to suit and manipulate public opinion.

The "cause" of biodiversity is twisted to enforce limitations on total areas of agricultural land with the object of forcing the general intensification of chemical-dependent agriculture.

Threats to biodiversity are constantly employed to forestall the adoption of all forms of alternative energy systems.

Promoting biodiversity issues so conveniently thwarts the production of sugar cane and the production and use of the ethanol derived from it. It is also used to effectively prevent the general expansion of sugar cane production.

Biodiversity issues are used to hinder and prevent the harvesting of timber.

One of the greatest advantages of creating and promoting a holy grail of biodiversity is that it supplies an unlimited array of minor "causes" to keep responsible and caring people from concerns of impending climatic chaos. It may well be a "just cause" to argue the maintenance of current numbers of some individual species on the planet. But supporting such causes must never, directly or even indirectly hasten the destabilization of world climates. Especially now when climate change itself has become recognized as the single greatest threat to all our world's total biodiversity.

The biodiversity juggernaut has been expanded to include a concept of the "richness of life on the planet". By so doing it has in too many ways acquired the trappings of a religion where so often faith is far more important than truth. The evidence is overwhelming that this adoption of religion-styled convictions is a deliberate and planned marketing ploy. By accident or by deliberation, it's what has happened. It is therefore important for us to assess the tenets of this new religion and recognize where truth ends and blind belief begins.

History of ecological theories

Arguments and discussions about environmental concepts started in the 1800s. The manipulation of environmental concepts to suit political and industrial motives came later. Unfortunately, with it came blinkered bigotry— the most vicious example being the adoption of concepts of ecological purity as a rallying tool by the Nazi party in the 1930s.

The general evolution of environmental movements into a money, industry and political power started to seriously self-generate from the 1960s on. It became well established by the mid to late 1970s. It continues to grow bigger in wealth and power—but often not in wisdom.

Ecological theories and ecological concepts, like everything, have their own interesting histories. That history is very relevant to our current thinking and understanding, and so must be understood so as to avoid any uses of it for propaganda and misinformation.

The presumption that variations in biodiversity, or even losses in any current level of biodiversity is in itself a threat, is heavily dependent on the concept of the actual existence of a meaningful "balance of nature". Is there really a balance of nature, or is the whole concept a fiction? Is the balance of nature really the way things actually work in the real world, or do things work otherwise? In many ways, and in many places, a belief in the balance of nature along with its holy grail of biodiversity has indeed become a quasi religion. The bright and harsh light of reason and understanding is always the enemy of propaganda and disinformation, so the history of the concepts should not be ignored.

Beginning in the eighteenth century, a theory developed in ecological philosophy that held that a closed independent environment will, over many thousands of years ultimately settle into a stable internally interacting equilibrium. And in consequence, a grand design will ultimately always emerge. In this concept each species is considered to be interdependent with all other species and all species then form part of some grand master plan. It is a tenet of these beliefs that man's involvement must inevitably alter and disrupt some delicate balance of interaction and thus destroy the equilibrium. Stability and harmony, it is further argued, can only be achieved by removing man (generally considered as modern civilized man) from the ordained ecological equation.

This belief in some pre-ordained balance of nature is a major cornerstone by which wilderness environmentalists demand that vast areas of our planet be excluded from all future human activity. It is the conveniently chosen doctrine of all wilderness environmentalists. The truth is the utter and total opposite. The whole concept is now no longer accepted nor believed by the majority of well-informed and observant biologists.

A succinct and well-respected analysis of present-day ecological thinking is clearly explained in the book *Chance and Change,* by the late William Holland Drury, University of California Press, Berkeley and Los Angeles,

California. William Drury was, until his death in 1992, Professor of Biology at the College of the Atlantic, Bay Harbor, Maine. Following Drury's death, *Chance and Change* was ultimately edited and completed by John G. T. Anderson, who also in turn became Professor of Biology at the College of the Atlantic.

Drury was an astute, very hands-on field observer. He was not only a botanist and a zoologist, he was also a competent geologist. These multiple disciplines ensured Drury a broad and balanced comprehension of the biological sciences. He was brilliant and insightful, and he could not at all hold with the concept of some supremely ordained ecological order governing biological systems. Nor was he alone in these (for the 1950s and 1960s) somewhat heretical opinions.

I believe we should all take heed of Professor Drury's and Professor Anderson's thoughts and opinions with trust and appreciation. It is refreshing to observe their insights. In *Chance and Change* we learn of some of the history of the concepts of equilibrium and balance of nature theories.

Way back in the mid 1700s, a collection of writings appeared called the *Linnaeus Essays*. These essays had a profound effect on zoological, botanical and biological thinking. That effect or influence has lasted through to this day.

Carolus Linnaeus, 1707–1778, was a religously devout Swedish naturalist who in 1767 also invented a system for classifying and cataloging living organisms. It was called *Systema Naturae*. This taxonomy is now the basis of all biological cataloguing around the world.

In 1749—totally unrelated to his *Systema Naturae*—Linnaeus wrote *The Economy of Nature*, in which he outlined the concept of an all-pervading natural equilibrium in nature. In so doing he established a conviction that an all-pervading balance of nature existed. His *Systema Naturae* for cataloguing was good, it was timely and was universally adopted. Unfortunately, carried on its coattails went his other concept of a supreme balance of nature as proposed in *The Economy of Nature*. Linnaeus's writings were penned well before Charles Darwin's time, and therefore well before it was finally realized that botanic and zoological organisms are actually in a constant state of evolutionary change. It is doubtful that Linnaeus ever considered that evolution was even a possibility. At that time the very concept of evolution would undoubtedly have been a sacrilege. (Even today some still see it as a sacrilege.)

Linnaeus in effect taught that a status quo of all living organisms existed. He believed that the status quo of life came into being at some original creation. He believed the status quo he saw around him would obviously last until the end of time. This belief, this concept, argued a divine equilibrium, a divine balance of nature. And this, we should appreciate, would most conveniently not in any way conflict with the theological convictions then current, but would reinforce them.

Unfortunately, equilibrium theory with, in effect, its concept of a super-organism is still the concept taught in many basic introductory textbooks on the natural sciences. Charles Darwin, in contrast to Linnaeus, emphasized the importance of individual organisms and emphasized the individual's inevitable contribution to continuous evolutionary change.

Darwin still seems to be studiously ignored by disciples of balance of nature concepts. Darwinism simply doesn't suit their political agenda.

In *Chance and Change*, Professor Drury categorically states that: "equilibrium theory, the characteristic ecology taught in introductory textbooks, clearly provides the intellectual foundation of politically active environmentalists."

Dating from the early 1900s, what became known as the Clements-Shelford school of community ecologists, believed that an ecological community existed as some form of superorganism. In consequence they believed that removing or interfering with any one particular species within the superorganism would irreversibly destabilize the biome. (Biome is a term to describe a major self-contained ecological community, such as some particular rainforest, desert or savanna.) At the time and by contrast, the more liberal Gleason school "contended that each species simply fills its own niche, and the coexistence of certain species in communities is simply the result of the similarity of their niche requirements". Drury also notes that in more modern analysis the "typological thinking of the Clements School has since been thoroughly refuted". The superorganism concept and the balance of nature concept have now become disproven theories.

It is presumed, quite erroneously, in balance of nature thinking that ecological systems, divorced from human influence, achieve a stability by a complex interwoven system of biological and ecological checks and balances. But it doesn't. And it can't. Even with all external (generally presumed to be man-made) influences absent, this still can't happen. For any dynamic system to achieve some form of statistical balance it is obviously necessary for correcting influences to come into play almost as soon as any imbalance occurs. For this to have any possibility of happening in a biological sense, it would logically be necessary for members of the various inhabiting species to all have approximately the same life span. This would seem essential to prevent wild fluctuations in the various population densities. It is exceptionally difficult for the population of a predator species with a life span of several years to attune to changes in the population of its prey when the prey has a life cycle of possibly just a few weeks. The other way around—with prey with a longer life cycle—would be less stable again. Balance doesn't occur. In the real world, feast or famine is always the norm. It is not benign stability.

Ecological systems, even simple ones, are composed of a myriad of life forms, all interacting, cooperating or competing. The destabilizing reality is that life cycles, from plant to plant, animal to animal, insect to insect, bacterium to bacterium, vary so widely, from a few minutes to a few hundred years, that ecological systems are fundamentally inherently chaotic.

Chaos theory therefore becomes the most applicable concept to describe ecological and biological behavior; this is made obvious in current mathematical, statistical and ecological investigations. One of the fundamental principles of chaos theory is that the detailed future behavior of a chaotic system cannot be predicted. Small changes to the starting conditions for a chaotic system lead to large differences in outcome. The first shot in a game of pool is a good visual illustration of chaos theory. Where the balls end up is anybody's guess.

By using reality stretched to extremes, chaos is sometimes explained as the "butterfly effect", wherein a butterfly beating its wings in South America can ultimately lead to a hurricane in Japan. It's just that the odds are against it.

Despite this apparent total lack of predictability, chaos theory nevertheless does have its own set of specific and definable rules, and from these, certain types of predictions can be made. Chaos theory generally applies where statistical rules cannot.

One rule in chaos theory is that the frequency of fluctuations in a chaotic system are scale dependent. That means that the size of a fluctuation determines the frequency with which it can be expected to occur. Applied to ecological systems it means that small fluctuations in populations will occur often and large fluctuations will be rarer, though even this rule itself is not always consistent. Except for very short time spans we have no way of predicting what new population densities will be. Most importantly we cannot predict how small changes in an ecosystem, such as climate variations, will affect future populations.

What global warming will do to the world is therefore anybody's guess. It is the first shot in the pool game. All we can say with certainty is that every complex ecological system will fluctuate within the confines of its geological and geographical location and the nature and consistency of its local weather patterns. Within the system, individual population numbers—and even their very survival—are inherently unpredictable. Chaos theory tells us that while we may well see a stable population in a variety of species for extended periods, this can suddenly change and produce inexplicable and unpredictable population changes. Populations go from borderline annihilation to plague proportions with seemingly tiny changes in the local environment.

Again, such wild fluctuations are usually interspersed with periods of apparently benign stability. On first glance, populations can thus appear stable. Occurrences of long periods of stability has led many to proclaim, and some to believe in the concept of a mystical "balance of nature" that regulates the world environment with some beautiful ordained "web of life" controlling all. When the sudden and inevitable large population shifts occur, the balance of nature adherents immediately presume someone is to blame. And that's always us, never the oil companies. They then presume firstly, that we are irresponsible, and secondly, that only they are responsible. Only they are sufficiently responsible to restore the mystical balance of nature they proclaim must exist.

Fly over any tropical jungle and there is really only one thing stable and consistent, and that's chlorophyll. Chlorophyll is endless. It's everywhere converting sunlight energy to plant growth. So with constant rain the hot humid jungle is always universally green. Within and beneath that endless green canopy it is not stability, it is instability that reigns supreme.

Even in established temperate forests wild fluctuations, not equilibrium, is the norm. The changes in the structure of an established forest is an exceedingly slow process. Just a few generations of tree reproduction might easily take a thousand years. It is probably inevitable that in the short life of an observing botanist, a forest would seem utterly stable and in perfect equilibrium. It's like the old story of a group of blind men feeling parts of an elephant and each in turn telling the world what an elephant is. The balance of nature hypothesis is nothing more than the claim that a snapshot in time is how the entire film should look.

For another clear and accurate overview, untainted by manipulative public relations and advertising, read *The Skeptical Environmentalist*, subtitled *Measuring the Real State of the World*. It was written by Bjorn Lomborg, who at the time of writing was an Associate Professor of Statistics at the department of Political Science, University of Aarhus, in Denmark. It's published by Cambridge University Press.

Lomborg is a statistician. He doesn't preach. He simply analyzes the known numbers and the published figures on species numbers around the world. He looks very critically at the mass of unsubstantiated utterances of the biodiversity "industry". He quotes their statements and clearly shows how incorrect the vast majority of their statements really are.

Lomborg uses a catalogued figure of 1,600,000 species for all the vertebrates (animal, birds etc.), mollusks (shellfish etc.), crustaceans (prawns, crabs etc.), insects, and vascular plants (all the plants with "pipes" with flowing sap). The number of non-insects are actual counts. The number of insect species is an approximation. The known, properly documented and recorded extinctions of all these known species, since the year 1600, totals 1,033. That's a rate of 2.6 extinctions per year. There are probably more actual extinctions as the 1,033 count excludes guesses. However, most of the world's significant species are now known. The discovery of a new species is newsworthy, so the 1,033 figure can't be wrong to any great degree.

Therefore, since the year 1600, less than three known species became extinct per year. That's a little less than 0.0002% per year. If these assumptions are badly out, if the rate is twice as much, it's still only 0.0004% a year.

Biodiversity issues are consistently and massively exaggerated and un-realistically and erroneously portrayed. The concept of a biodiversity crisis is used to hinder and prevent anything and everything that competes with fossil fuels and petrochemicals anywhere and any time, especially timber.

Let's look at what some of the foremost biodiversity axe-grinders have claimed.

The Sinking Ark by Norman Myers, published in 1979, told the world that we were losing species at the astonishing rate of 40,000 per year. *The Sinking Ark* sold well, and was believed by many.

The much-quoted environmentalist Professor Paul Ehrlich dreamed up his own figure of species loss in 1981. He nominated a loss of 250,000 species per year. That now appears to be an exaggeration of 249,997 species or an 80,000 times overstatement. Ehrlich also informed us that half of all species would be gone by the year 2000. It hasn't happened, and at this time of writing his deadline was over four years ago. An almost zero loss is more like reality. He also warned us that all species would be gone from the planet by 2010, or at least within the following fifteen years.

In the late 1980s Harvard biologist E. O. Wilson told us that he estimated we are losing between 27,000 and 100,000 species per year. Where do these figures come from? This is where Wilson got his. The 27,000 per year is derived by saying rainforests contain "conservatively" 10,000,000 species, and as we are losing rainforests we are therefore losing species. The estimated "conservative" loss of species is nominated by him at 0.27% per year. Multiply 0.27% by 10,000,000 and that's where the figure of 27,000 species lost per year comes from. The guess of 0.27% is 1,600 times bigger than any known actual documented percentage. It's a fifteen-year-old political "guesstimation" and it seems quite unrelated to reality. What is almost criminally irresponsible is that these fictions on diversity figures are taught as gospel in many environmental school and university courses. We allow our children to be taught these lies.

The ex-vice president of the United States, Al Gore, in his book *Earth In The Balance*, published by the Penguin Group in 1993, uncritically repeated the 40,000 per year figure from Norman Myers' 1979 book *The Sinking Ark*. Al Gore almost became president of the United States!

There has never ever been one shred of documented evidence to sub-stantiate these wild claims of massive species extinctions. Surely it's rea-sonable to assume that if 27,000 species per year have really been lost every year for the last fifteen years there would be a substantial amount of obvious evidence. But there is none!

It seems that environmental crusaders simply dream up these fictitious numbers to create an issue. They then happily quote each other's numbers to support their own hallucinations.

What has been the result of these number manipulations? Achim Steiner, director general of the World Conservation Union, proudly tells us in an article in *New Scientist,* October 2003 that there are now over 100,000 "permanently protected" areas on the planet. Their total area is 18.8 million square kilometres. That's 12% of the all the land surface of the planet. It's also an area bigger than the combined areas of Canada, the United States and Germany. But more significantly it's bigger than the total area of the world's croplands.

But Steiner still laments that it's not enough. His World Conservation Union (IUCN) "estimates that at least 11,000 known species are threatened with extinction, which is between 1,000 and 10,000 times the background or natural extinction rate". He also tells us that conservation organizations are pushing for more "managing" of all those massive areas of land. Undoubtedly, one might expect, that management would be by a huge army of bureaucratic experts, all tax funded to most specifically keep taxpayers out.

When *The Skeptical Environmentalist* first came out it was considered a brilliant analysis of environmental issues. However, in retrospect it was too brilliant and too lucid for some. The book was too factual and far too logical for what Lomborg calls the "biodiversity-environmental establishment". As soon as they realized it threatened their honey pot, they fought back.

Scientific American in its January 2002 issue says the book should be a welcome audit of environmental issues "yet it isn't". It goes on to say, "if its purpose was to describe the Real State of the World" then "the book is a failure." It relates how many scientists felt frustrated at Lomborg's "misrepresentation of their fields". Incredibly, *Scientific American* devoted eleven full pages to criticism of *The Skeptical Environmentalist.* The sheer volume and venom of the critics was itself astounding.

Three full pages are given to criticism by Stephen Schneider, a professor in the Department of Biological Sciences at Stanford University. Schneider is editor of *Climate Change* and the editor of the *Encyclopedia of Climate and Weather* and also the IPCC (Intergovernmental Panel on Climate Change) guidance paper on "uncertainties"! Schneider's specialty seems actually to be in doubting things.

Schneider wrote a testimony for the U.S. Senate on *Climate Change: Causes, Impacts and Uncertainties.* His paper commences by asking, "Does Natural Variability Explain All Climate Change?" It does seem to say in places within the voluminous text that global warming, caused by anthropogenic rises in atmospheric carbon dioxide levels, is actually happening. A huge concession for him, I feel.

For two more pages in *Scientific American* there is criticism of Lomborg by John P. Holdren. Holdren is noted as the Teresa and John Heinz Professor of Environmental Policy at the John F. Kennedy School of Government, as well as Professor of Environmental Science and Public Policy in the Department of Earth and Planetary Sciences at Harvard University. Holdren reminds us (as justification for his opinions?) that he was involved with Paul Ehrlich in the production of "our 1977 college textbook *Ecoscience*". We have already noted Paul Ehrlich's pronouncements on biodiversity arithmetic, so Holdren evidently concurs.

Holdren criticizes Lomborg's discussions on energy, complaining that the nineteen pages devoted to energy is insufficient. In Lomborg's defence it should be remembered that he is a statistician and getting sense out of the quagmire of misinformation on world energy reserves is extremely difficult. Holdren criticizes Lomborg's statements that the earth is running out of usable fossil fuels. In this respect, Holdren is right and Lomborg is wrong. Altering the optical characteristics of the atmosphere is the problem. We can never run out of fossil fuels.

Holdren claims we are "running out of environment" which is a good each way bet. Holdren also likes to tell us that "oil is the most versatile and currently the most valuable of the conventional fossil fuels" and it is so nobly supplying "civilization's energy". The rest of Holdren's criticism is, as one might now suspect, along the same lines.

Lomborg also considers a wide variety of grossly inaccurate environmental claims other than biodiversity. He discusses global warming and asks if this too is being exaggerated. If it is, he argues, should we not just get on with life and use some of our extra wealth to pay for any extra global warming costs? I maintain that the seriousness and the dangers of global warming are not exaggerated at all, but are deliberately and strenuously minimized. The minimized published effects and numbers are the ones Lomborg relies on in his book to justify, on a cost basis, the continued use of fossil fuels.

Lomborg also looks at the much-publicized "human population explosion" issue. He suggests that population is not the problem and argues the real problem is poverty and lack of productivity. (Add in entrenched and incompetent and corrupt bureaucrats and I would totally agree.) Lomborg points out that the most densely populated regions of Southeast Asia have the same population density as the United Kingdom. He also notes "The Netherlands, Belgium and Japan are far more densely populated than India, and Ohio and Denmark are more densely populated than Indonesia". He also notes that world food production is climbing more rapidly than is world population. These facts are also in complete contrast to what the environmental industry and fund collection organizations keep claiming and promoting on TV.

John Bongaarts is noted as vice president of the Policy Research Division of the Population Council in New York City, and he gets two pages to counter Lomborg. Bongaarts criticizes Lomborg's statements that food production per head has risen without acknowledging that some government-inspired "green revolution" was a major factor. Bongaarts argues for more government-controlled assistance. (Surely the underdeveloped world needs less bureaucratic interference, not more.) Bongaarts states that cheap food in Western countries is only possible with agricultural subsidies. That too ignores reality.

It certainly ignores Australia, an affluent Western nation that produces and markets extremely cheap food with zero subsidies. Food prices are low because now, with mechanization, one man can grow enough food to easily feed fifty people. Nevertheless, Bongaarts is allowed over two full pages in *Scientific American* to develop these flawed arguments.

Thomas Lovejoy also gets two full pages to criticize *The Skeptical Environmentalist*. Lovejoy is described as a chief biodiversity advisor to the World Bank. From 1973 to 1987 Lovejoy directed the World Wildlife Fund-US (WWF). His criticism is predictable, and especially so when one reads Lomborg's assessment of the World Wildlife Fund (now the World Wide Fund for Nature).

It must be noted that the World Wildlife Fund seems decidedly pro-oil. For example, the construction of a massive 1,050 km long oil pipeline through the rainforests of Cameroon in West Africa was supported by the WWF. The WWF refused to join environmental groups who were in strong opposition. British biologists claimed the huge pipeline "could wreck the coastal ecology of Cameroon and put thousands of fishermen out of work". The oil pipeline received US$220,000,000 in funding loans from the World Bank. An odd background for a biodiversity crusader, surely?

The WWF also seem very pro-plastic or at least anti-wood. In Europe they have been insisting that when trees fall over in a forest, for what ever reason, the trees should be left there to rot. They say it is to preserve the biodiversity of the termites or what ever it is that eats rotting wood. They believe the wood should not be collected. The WWF also seems a little careless with their own statistics. The WWF conducted a population survey of the pygmy chimpanzee or bonobo in the Democratic Republic of the Congo. Their conclusion, as reported in *New Scientist* 5 February 2005 was that there were so few of the chimps there any more that "it was impossible to work out how many were left". In contrast Jef Dupain of the African Wildlife Foundation reported that from their own observations of the chimps' nests and actual sightings of the animals themselves that there were approximately two beasts per square kilometre. Their area counts show population densities at pre-2002 levels.

The witch-hunt for Lomborg did not stop there. Others joined the hunt.

Peter H. Raven gets five pages in the August 2002 issue of *Science*, a lot of which is devoted to criticizing *The Skeptical Environmentalist*. Raven waxes poetic about "false prophets and charlatans" and includes Lomborg as one of them. Raven himself is described as the director of the Missouri Botanical Gardens. He sites Lester R. Brown's book *Eco-Economy* as a source for much of his information (read misinformation).

Eco-Economy could well have been written by the oil marketing public relations gurus. It certainly follows their marketing strategies. It's all standard stuff. It says the people of Copenhagen use a lot of bicycles (for short trips). Nuclear fuel has public safety issues (implying danger) but nuclear energy is also too expensive (not true—see chapter 10). He naïvely tells us that things are "driving the global transition to solar/hydrogen age" (simply ridiculous—see "Fuel cells and the hydrogen economy concept" in chapter 11).

Lester R. Brown sees natural gas as the clean fuel for the planet's immediate future (therefore ignoring global warming). Brown spiels the standard pat phrases of the environmental industries, "deforestation increases flooding, accelerates soil erosion, inhibits aquifer recharge, and decimates plant and animal life". Brown also claims forests are preferred as they add organic matter to soil. (Utterly and totally wrong—grasses do, forests don't.)

As noted in Strategy 34, Lester R. Brown was instrumental in the formation of the World Watch Institute of Washington, DC, and of course their policies and pronouncements are in line with those in his book *Eco-Economy*.

Science magazine kept up the criticism of Lomborg. It reported in its 17 January 2003 issue that a Danish scientific dishonesty panel decided that Lomborg's book is "scientifically dishonest". (Fortunately the Danish Research Agency, the DRA, decided to investigate the dishonesty of the dishonesty panel itself and to determine if it was being influenced.) Subsequently the Danish Prime Minister, Anders Fogh Rasmussen, told Danish TV audiences that he "has full confidence" in Bjorn Lomborg. The Danish Prime Minister publicly exonerated Lomborg.

Fred Pearce's Comment and Analysis editorial in the 18 January 2003 edition of *New Scientist* showed that decency and scientific fairness was not totally forgotten. Pearce heads the article "Call Off The Witch Hunt". He asks in the article, is Lomborg a "misguided maverick, or a victim of green McCarthyism?". Pearce comments "Lomborg got it in the neck for being unkind enough to declare the truth. For instant, his questioning the claim that the planet loses 40,000 species every year was criticized, not for being unjustified but for failing to acknowledge that Myers (author of *The Sinking Ark*) deserves credit for being the first to point out that the number was large". *New Scientist* goes on to quite correctly ask, "Who is upholding good scientific practice here, exactly?"

Then in January 2004, a year after Pearce's call for scientific justice, *Science* reported that the Danish Research Agency repudiated the Danish interrogatory panel's finding. Lomborg was finally found to be not dishonest. However the tiny half-page report (remember eleven pages of criticism) clearing Lomborg's name still had a sting. It was headed, "Charges Don't Stick to *The Skeptical Environmentalist*". Did that mean to imply Lomborg was slippery? Ask an advertising copywriter.

The fossil fuel industries must have seen *The Skeptical Environmentalist* by Bjorn Lomborg as a book worthy of their attention the moment it was first reported. Just about every environmental report and environmental impact study being demanded today somehow always manages to target competitors that threaten the fossil carbon industries. That must take some clever arranging.

You never see glaring headlines and full-page stories of world "biodiversity" being threatened by increased carbon dioxide levels in the atmosphere, or by global warming, or by massive world climatic changes. Of course not, those phenomena are all caused by the coal and oil producers and the petrochemical industries. These industries are not going to allow their own arguments to backfire.

There are other things that eliminate the species en masse. In Earth's past, massive and virtually instant loss of biodiversity mostly happened when extraterrestrial objects rocked our planetary boat.

Along with the planets, comets also orbit the sun. Comet orbits are giant ellipses with one end near the sun and the other extending sometimes far off into deep space, sometimes millions of miles beyond our solar system.

As comets pass rapidly round the sun they often put on spectacular displays. We often get showers of "shooting stars", as cometary debris graze our atmosphere and burn up. The display periods only ever last a few weeks as comets soon head off again on their long elliptical round trips. Halley's Comet is perhaps the most well known; it returns to us approximately every 76 years. Halley's Comet is estimated to be over 8 miles across. Fortunately close calls with comets are relatively rare.

Asteroids are more dangerous. Between the orbits of Mars and Jupiter there are millions of bits of cold lifeless rock, orbiting in a roughly circular path around the sun. They just never ever bunched together, or accreted, to form themselves into another planet. The collection is called the asteroid belt. The giant gravitational field of nearby Jupiter kept disrupting the accretion process and a planet was never able to coalesce from all the pieces. Those same gravitational forces will sometimes dislodge an asteroid out of its regular orbit and send it drifting off unpredictably—chaos theory in action again!

In the asteroid belt there are about one million individual asteroids bigger than a kilometre across. There are about 1,000 bigger than 30 kilometres across, 200 of which exceed 100 kilometres. The three biggest asteroids are Ceres, with a diameter of 933 kilometres (579 miles), Pallas at 523 km (325 miles) and Vesta at 501 km (311 miles).

There are also an uncountable number of small items floating about in our solar system. They range from specks of dust, grains of sand, small rocks, large boulders and on up. These objects are constantly bombarding the planets. The craters of the moon are not volcanoes, but impact craters. Earth has had more impacts in its history but weathering has eroded away most of the evidence.

When a small object hits the earth's atmosphere, we call it a meteor. We might see it burning up in the night sky as a "shooting star". Objects smaller than about 30 feet (10 m) across burn up in the outer atmosphere and rarely make it to the ground. When a small piece does get through to the earth's surface it's called a meteorite.

The frequency of collisions between the earth and these space rocks has been quite well studied and like many natural systems it follows a simple scaling law—collisions with small objects occur frequently, collisions with larger objects are rarer. The events occur statistically. The frequency for small particles is quite well determined from measurements on the density of dust particles made with instruments in spacecraft. Mid-sized impacts are studied from the ground by observing meteor trails in the night sky. Large impacts leave their mark in the geological record.

The assessed results show that on average a particle the size of a grain of sand hits our planet every 30 seconds. Boulders three feet, or about one metre across, hit us about once a year. Seriously big rocks, say 300 feet (100 m) in diameter and big enough to penetrate through the atmosphere and leave sizeable craters, strike about once every 10,000 years. Catastrophic events involving objects around 10 km in diameter occur statistically about every hundred million years.

When an object hits the earth, it's travelling at an incredible speed. A large asteroid may strike with a speed approaching 20 miles per second (30 kilometres per second). That's 100 times faster than a supersonic rifle bullet. On impact an enormous amount of energy is released. At these speeds every ton of rock will release more energy than 100 tons of TNT. An asteroid 10 kilometres in diameter (6 miles) could weigh in at over a trillion tons. It would explode like ten billion Hiroshima bombs. Life certainly could not evolve and survive on any of the solar system planets back in the time when these collisions were more frequent.

There is a theory that the planet Jupiter with its enormous gravitational pull has sucked in millions of these rocks and effectively vacuum cleaned all the rogue debris from the inner solar system. This theory says that without this cleaning process life would never have had a long enough innings to evolve creatures as complex as us.

In July 1994, comet Shoemaker-Levy 9 was sucked in by Jupiter and provided direct evidence of these collisions and their spectacular energy releases. The comet was named in part after one of its discoverers, Eugene Shoemaker. Shoemaker, incidentally, was the first to seriously propose that the large craters on the moon, along with many here on earth, were formed by impacts, and not volcanoes as previously believed.

In the last 600 million years, there have been about twenty-eight major world extinctions. These have been so vast and so widespread that they have become the yardstick for geological time scales. They form the boundaries between geological periods. Each geological period has its own unique collection of flora and fauna, which evolved during the period and was, in turn almost totally wiped out at the end of the period.

Geological periods are not determined from geological events. They are determined by biological events. The relative age of rock formations all across the world is assessed by simply observing the fossil remains embedded in the nearest sediments. The Mesozoic era was the age of the dinosaurs; it included the Cretaceous, Jurassic and Triassic periods. The Mesozoic era ended at the Paleocene boundary some 65 million years ago when the dinosaurs all but disappeared from the fossil record. That boundary was the start of the era of mammals—the Cenozoic era.

It is now generally accepted that at least one giant meteorite hit the Yucatan Peninsula in Mexico 65 million years ago and that impact ended the reign of the dinosaurs. The Yucatan hit was possibly accompanied by a few minor ones spread over the Caribbean and northern Pacific. The Yucatan meteorite probably weighed in at more than a trillion tons. That huge rock, travelling at the enormous velocities characteristic of meteors, created an impact with explosive energy that has been estimated at 10,000 times the world's total nuclear arsenal, and all going off at once—see page 53.

At the height of the Cold War, the term *nuclear winter* was coined to describe the potential effect of exploding thousands of nuclear weapons on the earth's surface. A nuclear winter however, would pale to insignificance compared to the winter following a Yucatan-size impact.

There were probably a few million significant species inhabiting planet Earth on the day of that impact. A reasonable guess is that at least three-quarters of all of them became extinct in the subsequent years of perpetual winter.

Mass extinctions leave giant ecological vacancies and niches. The extinctions at the end of this Mesozoic era left gaps that were rapidly filled by an explosion of species that all derived from some, generally, tiny insignificant creatures that survived the terror. The creatures were a primitive type of mammal, although some, it now seems, were big enough to hunt small dinosaurs.

The mass extinctions at the end of the Mesozoic era could (to coin a phrase) surely be described as a "severe crisis in biodiversity". Of course that particular wipeout did give mammals their chance. And that new evolutionary track led finally to us.

It is not the impact that wipes most life off the planet. It is the cancerous climate change caused by the debris moving around the world from the impact site. The materials alter the sensitive and vulnerable optical characteristics of the atmosphere. Indications suggest that some of these resulting climate changes would linger for a million years or more. Mostly the impacted species were never able to reestablish themselves.

Impacts answer a lot of questions on major extinctions, but things are not always that simple. The biggest-ever extinction, some 250 million years ago, marked the end of the Paleozoic era (the age of the invertebrates) and initiated the start of the reign of the dinosaurs. That particular extinction appears to have been triggered by massive volcanic activity in Siberia, occurring over a considerable period.

However, others still argue that even this event was impact-related. A small group argue that all impact-related extinctions depended on the impact initiating long-term seismic activity. An even smaller group argues that the impact evidence shows explosive seismic events and is not extraterrestrially related at all.

The jury may be still out on the causes of those old climate changes but all agree: massive species extinction and biodiversity loss is caused by the accompanying climate change and nothing else. It is certainly not caused by building hydroelectric dams, which actually minimize climate change. And is certainly not caused by building holiday resorts on tropical coastlines, as is argued by a vociferous few here in Queensland, Australia.

Patrick Brenchley and his associates at the University of Liverpool in the United Kingdom studied the cold Hirnantian Glaciation that occurred around 439 million years ago. Their research showed three separate and dramatic waves of species extinction. All the extinctions occurred in the very short period between 439.5 million years ago and 439 million years ago. That's a period of just half a million years. They too concluded from their studies that the only significant phenomenon that caused large-scale species extinction at any time through our Earth's long history has been rapid climatic change.

Let me state unequivocally: except for either a massive nuclear war or an impact from a very large asteroid, the only real threat to life on this planet and the diversity of life on this planet is the rapid global climate change being caused by our continued extraction and use of fossil carbon materials. By comparison all other factors combined approach almost total insignificance.

Despite this, it is becoming glaringly apparent that the whole issue of global warming and rapid climate destabilization has been reduced to lip service by the vast majority of biodiversity advocates. Carefully directed and narrowly focused enthusiasm is now dominating world environmental debates.

The much-publicized, highly promoted threat to world biodiversity needs examination. Are they making mountains out of molehills to suit their massive PR exercise? What really is the reality?

Even today the number and variety of all species currently living on the planet is still at best a collection of uncoordinated guesstimations. There is simply no definitive central register of species types. So we don't accurately know how many have already been discovered and named. Estimates for totals range from just under 2 million to way over 30 million.

If we include all species the numbers zoom. There are probably at least 2 million species of fungi. In a fungi study in South America, on just two different types of trees, 350 different fungi species were found. And bacteria—a few years ago Vidgis Torsvik, a Norwegian researcher, conducted a test on a single gram of soil and estimated it contained some 10,000 bacterial types.

In the grand total of all species types, a few billion unique species seems not a particularly high estimate for all life currently on earth. That's possibly a single species for every man, woman and child on the planet.

Some self-proclaimed biodiversity saviours are proclaiming we should include bacteria on lists of possibly threatened species. When just one insect can have a hundred different bacteria living on it and in it. This is foolish. Totally new species of bacteria can evolve in weeks, possibly even days. That's why antibiotics lose their effectiveness so rapidly.

When considering the long history of life on earth, estimates for the total number of species that have ever existed obviously vary widely. Estimates for just the number of plants and animals range from 5 billion to 50 billion.

A general consensus among biologists suggests that 99.9% of all species that ever existed through Earth's long history are now extinct. Obviously humans can't be blamed for those 99.9% of losses. If life on earth was shortened down to one day, then we humans have been around for a few seconds.

But some we can be blamed for and sometimes it just can't be helped. In the coastal waters of Tasmania for example, there is a small fish that moves by crawling along the sea floor. It's called a spotted handfish (*Brachionichthys hirsutus*). They grow to around one hand width long.

Unfortunately for the spotted handfish, the Northern Pacific starfish (*Asterias amurensis*) turned up in the southern Tasmanian waters sometime in the 1980s. It probably arrived in seawater being used as ships' ballast. In a bizarre twist of fate the Northern Pacific starfish developed a taste for, and started devouring, the eggs of the Southern Ocean spotted handfish.

Thus the spotted handfish may become the first ever known and recorded loss of an individual marine species, ever. The loss is not yet absolutely confirmed so the spotted handfish has not yet increased the 1,033 documented species known to be lost in the last five hundred years to 1,034.

Of course the biodiversity industry demand funding for the construction of breeding tanks to breed the handfish and funding to employ research personnel to find some fish to put in the tanks. And more funding to study and monitor "all aspects" of the fish's life cycle. Total funding, to be derived from Australian taxation, is expected to be well over US$1,000,000. Biodiversity is certainly the ultimate money sponge.

Many of the species living on the planet only continue to exist by accident. They just happen to live in some form of protective isolation well away from the harsh centres of competitive evolution. Marsupials in Australia are typical. Immigration of the more successful mammals, specifically the big cat species, never occurred. However feral house cats are rapidly evolving into bigger animals, so it's only a matter of time.

Apart from global warming, modern day humans simply don't wipe out species wholesale and never have wiped out species wholesale. We have wiped out a few species on almost every continent, but wholesale wipeouts, never. For wholesale wipeouts we must go back a few thousand years to our early ancestors. Those supposedly noble savages that, we are constantly told, lived in blissful and beautiful harmony with nature.

Humans started moving around the world about 50,000 years ago and where ever they went they systematically killed off all the big game, all the megafauna they could find. It only stopped a few hundred years ago. Those noble savages killed off 97% of all the large mammals and marsupials living on the planet 50,000 years ago, in one long continuous bloodbath.

In the last few hundred years things have changed and humans have become civilized. Today, for man to eliminate just 10% of the major and significant species on the planet at even five times the rate we have been for the last 400 years would take us 100,000 years, not 97% in 50,000 years. It would probably take longer because currently we like to preserve species. The bloodbath practices of our flintstone ancestors are now totally out of fashion.

Statistically, in that same 100,000-year period there is an estimated 10% chance of being hit by at least one extraterrestrial object with a diameter of one kilometre, say half a mile. It will be either part of a stray comet, or an asteroid dislodged from its stable orbit in the asteroid belt. When it hits it will have an explosive energy equivalent of more than a million Hiroshima bombs all going off at once. Such an impact would wipe out 10% of all species.

In a million years we stand a 1% chance of being hit by a 10 km object. That's an impact big enough to wipe out 80% of all species. In 100 million years, the odds are, such an impact is a certainty.

The extinction and creation of new species is a constant and rapid process in the evolution of life on earth. Wherever and whenever a small unique environment is formed, new species immediately begin to evolve to best suit that tiny unique environment. A new niche in some local environment can occur, and a new species can evolve and develop, and it now seems in an amazingly short period of time.

Individual species are like individual animals; they are born, they live for a period, they give birth to other species, and they die. Some live for a long time, some die young. Some live for as little as a few hundred years, others live for million of years.

In the United Kingdom, several species of moths became darker in color during the 19th century. The best-studied example is the peppered moth, *Biston betularia*, which gets its name from scattered dark markings on its otherwise white wings and body. The moth is active at night and rests by day on tree trunks. In areas far from coal mines and other industrial activity, the trunks of trees are covered with lichen. The mottled white moths were well camouflaged among the mottled white lichen.

In some areas, a severe combination of air pollution and coal soot killed the lichens and blackened the tree trunks. Against such a background, a predominately white moth stood out. The white moths were easy prey for insect-eating birds. A darker-coloured moth would have a much better chance.

In 1849, a completely black variety, a totally new species, or at least a subspecies of *Biston betularia*, was discovered near Manchester. Then within the next eighty to ninety years this black form had increased to 90% of the population in the region. The variety has been given the very appropriate name *Biston betularia carbonaria*.

An English geneticist, Kettlewell, released moths of both types and observed that birds, understandably, ate a much higher fraction of the light moths than the dark moths. That new, all-black species of moth evolved in the short period from the mid 1700s, before the widespread use of coal, to 1849. Given the right circumstances it is thus obvious that a new species can evolve in a period as short as a hundred years.

Since pollution abatement programs were put in place after World War II, the light form has been making a comeback in the Liverpool and Manchester areas. What would the disciples of biodiversity suggest we do about the black winged moth? Should we protect it? It is, after all most definitely a unique species. Do they suggest that areas of England should be set aside permanently for coal mining and coal dumps so that this new species, this black moth, has a permanent place to suit its camouflage? Some argue it didn't happen like that at all and no new species evolved. No matter what, the biodiversity industries are sure to demand huge grants to further the study of the threatened black *Biston betularia carbonaria*.

Another example is found in a giant crack, or series of cracks in the African continent. The cracks run roughly north south up through the eastern side of Africa. It's called the Great Rift Valley. Over the next several million years Africa will slowly split apart at these crack lines and East Africa will become an island. The cracks are often full of water and thus form a line of huge lakes. Lake Victoria for instance, is in a sort of associated subcrack. Near the end of the last ice age, the lake was completely empty. There was a climate change, it filled with fresh water and so became a lake 200 miles wide.

A little fish called a cichlid somehow got into these lakes in the Great Rift Valley. The main ones being Lake Malawi, Lake Tanganyika and Lake Victoria. The cichlid fish in some ways seems to be a fish version of the placental mammal, in that they too have an efficient and adaptable design. Cichlid fish also have an unusual internal mouth form that can adapt, or evolve rapidly so as to be able to munch on whatever food is available. Within the relatively short period of 12,500 years, those original fish evolved into 500 totally distinct and unique species. Some became mouth brooders, where the young swim into the safety of the mother's mouth when danger threatens. There are species of cichlid whose jaws can crush snail shells, and they live on snails. Some evolved to live on zooplankton. Others are insectivores. Some live on prawns. There are big fish and little fish. About a third of all the bigger species of cichlids live on smaller species of cichlids. Some eat the scales of other fish. Cichlids also come in an incredible range of shapes and sizes and colours.

Over the 12,500-year period, the average rate of evolution to produce that many totally different and independent species is therefore one new species every twenty-five years. And that all happened in mainly just one lake. Whether they like it on not, the simple reality is that biodiversity is totally impossible to prevent.

The fossil carbon industries use hypothetical biodiversity loss scenarios with consummate skill. Whenever a hydroelectric project is proposed on any river, there now has to be a long drawn-out "impact study". In such studies, global warming considerations are only ever conspicuous by their utter and complete absence.

Very carefully and deliberately, environmental impact studies always discover "unique" species. The studies are made sufficiently open-ended to ensure that some unique something will always be found. No matter where you are, or where you go on this planet of ours, nothing is absolutely the same and if something is not the same as everything else, then by definition it's "unique"!

Constructing a dam creates a lake with its own unique environment, which will, given time, just as assuredly create its own unique range of species. Just like the cichlid fish, new life will take up residency, adapt, develop, and evolve.

A lake is a nice place to live, and a new lake is just waiting for new settlers. The new settlers can evolve into new species, which breed rapidly until they are limited by food supply. Eventually predators evolve, or move in on this new abundant source of life, and they too change. Eventually a new ecological system becomes established.

Some well-organized groups of proclaimed environmentalists argue that our dams should be drained in an endeavour to restore "the old ecological balance". This argument, you might note, never seems to occur with new dams that aren't used for power generation. Naturally formed lakes used for power generation—these environmentalists must find very frustrating.

From a biological point of view, small lake ecologies are like the ecologies of small islands. Islands are patches of land isolated in an ocean of water. Lakes are patches of water isolated in an ocean of land.

A book, *Island Biogeography*, by the previously mentioned E. O. Wilson of Harvard University and Robert MacArthur of Princeton University, shows how species extinction and ecological changes are incredibly common in small island ecologies. Research done on the mangrove islands in Florida clearly indicates that extinction and creation of highly localized species are actually completely normal and natural events.

Of course, it is now possible with genetic engineering to actually create new species. In the near future we will be able to create almost any life form we wish to dream up. It will be done in the laboratory and at any time we like. Genetic engineering can now produce pest-resistant crops—crops that have no use whatever for pesticides. Being cynical one might wonder, is this the real reason why genetic engineering is currently receiving such a high volume of bad press?

Other companies engineer plants to be resistant to high applications of specific herbicide or pesticide chemicals. They then take out patents on the seed. The companies sell to farmers the resistant seeds, and to that same farmer, they can sell huge quantities of the chemicals the plants have been engineered to tolerate. This type of genetic engineering most certainly does deserve bad press.

Apart from genetic engineering creating new species, it is gratifying to know that older plant species are being preserved. Private, independent organizations are becoming established that collect rare and endangered seed stock to ensure worthwhile diversity is not lost. They grow and harvest the threatened species and then distribute the seed to responsible growers throughout the world. It's working extremely well. The concept, it seems, does not present a threat to the agrochemical industry so the "rent-a-crowd greenies" aren't in the least bit interested.

It is of course wise to establish large national parks. It is wise to preserve examples of strange ecological systems and the unusual flora and fauna they contain. But to enclose nation-sized chunks of land to protect biodiversity is self-defeating for it necessitates massively increased use of fossil carbon-based materials elsewhere. Such philosophical concepts are idiotic when global warming is altering ecosystems wholesale, but this is blindly ignored.

Remember how the Australian state of Tasmania, with an area about the same size as South Korea, has already had more than 50% of its total area locked up as delineated wilderness. The areas lost to humanity contain extremely practical hydroelectric sites. Good hydroelectric sites are incredibly rare in the almost universally flat and featureless landscape of mainland Australia.

In the early 1980s, a proposed hydroelectric scheme in southwest Tasmania was abandoned because of environmental protests. Instead the proposal put forward was to lay an undersea cable across Bass Straight to the mainland to access the mainland electricity grid. In other words, Tasmania was looking not to export green energy to the mainland but to import electricity, generated by the burning of brown coal, onto the island.

If the power cable had been built, quite possibly Tasmania might have been able, at some future date, to export hydroelectricity, across the straits and back into the mainland grid. What was the outcome? The electricity line didn't go ahead. Instead a gas line was laid across the 200 km wide Bass

Strait. That pipe ensures two things: the state has ample supplies of fossil fuel and Tasmanian hydroelectricity will never reach the mainland.

In stunning contrast, oil drilling has recently located small but commercial oil deposits in the state. That oil will be mined. The Australian and the Tasmanian green movements have been loud in their silence on these issues.

The initiatives that effectively turned Tasmania into a fossil-fuel dependent state was the first "success story" of what became the Tasmanian Green Party. The Green Party stopped hydroelectric power generation in Tasmania and "hooked" the state on fossil fuels. The people who so successfully stopped their state's hydroelectric power was the Tasmanian Wilderness Society, from which the Green Party sprang.

This action to prevent the expansion of hydroelectric power and to consequently further destabilize world weather systems seem to be of no consequence to any self-proclaimed green movement anywhere. In 1984 the Tasmanian Wilderness Society became simply the Wilderness Society and seems to have continued an ecological crusade to, in effect, market fossil fuels in other Australian states.

In 2003 the Australian Green Party was the only political party—left or right of centre—to protest against an expanded use of ethanol as an automotive fuel. Their argument was that sugar cane farming in tropical Queensland would need to expand. This was somehow inferred to be ecologically unsatisfactory. Their next obvious ploy to stop ethanol is to argue some hypothetical damage to the Great Barrier Reef. It will probably be a generalized argument and will, I'm sure, avoid references to the agrochemicals that actually do the damage.

This game plan seems to be a general characteristics of all green politics. In the 1960s, at the height of Soviet power it was described as the "red-green" political movement.

In 1995, a book was published in New York by the Free Press. Shortly afterward it was published in London by Weidenfeld and Nicolson. I had read a review in *New Scientist* in their October 1995 issue. I just had to get a copy. The book is called *Nature's Keepers*; subtitled *The New Science Of Nature Management*. It was written by Stephen Budiansky.

Quotations from *Nature's Keepers* are used with the much-appreciated permission of the author. (Copyright Stephen Budiansky 1995.)

Stephen Budiansky could be described as a mathematical environmentalist and a science writer. He holds a Harvard University degree in applied mathematics. Budiansky was, for a period, the Washington editor of the prestigious science journal *Nature* and a senior writer for *U.S. News And World Report*. He is the author of *Covenant Of The Wild* Subtitled *Why Animals Chose Domestication*. The book was a runner-up for the 1995 Rhone-Poulenc prize for science books.

Nature's Keepers is a book that will always receive criticism from the

biodiversity-environmental industry, for in it Budiansky points out much
of the innate stupidity of the pseudo-religious side of the environmental
movement. It is a brilliant work where so much of the cancer of environmental bigotry and incredible naïveté is exposed and removed with surgical
precision.

Budiansky considers the reality, or otherwise, of the existence of anything anywhere that could genuinely be called a wilderness area. Budiansky
states that (apart from Antarctica) there is not a continent on the planet that
has not been totally modified by the hands of man for at least 10,000 years.
He points out that on any continent where the vegetation could burn, it was
burnt; it was regularly and systematically torched for man's convenience.

Budiansky argues, and I think we have to accept his argument, that the
first tool used in farming and land management was not the plow, nor the
rake, nor the hoe, but fire. With the exception of Antarctica, man has been
massively modifying his environment with fire on every continent on earth,
at least since the end of the last ice age. I doubt academic theories on
ecological management ever crossed the mind of early man, not even for
one second.

In Australia, for instance, there is substantial evidence that the predominant tree species before the arrival of man were conifers, and not the
eucalyptus that now almost totally predominate. In Australia, man arrived
with his control of fire some 50,000 years ago and vegetation (and almost
certainly weather) in consequence was radically changed.

The unhampered, untouched wilderness that unthinking environmentalists imagine as their objective, has never ever actually existed. Nobody
knows what it was like before the last ice age and before the time man
started to burn landscapes for convenience. In Australia, the human-free
environment ended 50,000 years ago. That's exactly in the middle of the
last ice age. (Although in Australia it never got particularly cold.) That was
the last time "untouched wilderness" existed in my country. One can't help
asking, which "particular wilderness" do wilderness societies consider as
the "true wilderness"? And who defines it?

Budiansky establishes beyond any doubt that this planet's surface has
been so modified by man with his control of fire that it had become a
changed and tamed world well before the advent of recorded history.

He points out that the hunter-gatherers of sub-Saharan Africa have
been using fire for at least the last 60,000 years. He reports on controlled
experiments in Malawi and Zimbabwe, where it has been clearly established
that regular burning has become essential for the well-being of such grazing
animals as zebra and antelope. Living in a man-made, man-modified
environment suits them. That is the only "wilderness" the wild animals
know.

He points out that ancient man used fire for his own benefit in his
migration across the length and breadth of the planet. In doing so his

constant burning "manufactured" grasslands and in consequence made hunting easier.

Budiansky ridicules the popularized myth that North America, prior to the arrival of Western man, was covered with "primeval forests" "dark and untamed", where a squirrel might, in the days before the white man arrived, "have travelled from Maine to Louisiana never once setting foot on the ground". The pseudo-environmental movement loves to portray the high canopy as being extremely dense.

It seems to me that reality is quite different. It seems that the distant and absent portrayers, with wild poetic license, are the entities that are extremely dense.

Budiansky insists that to find the reality, we need to listen to the explorers that actually trod the land in those times. And so, in *Nature's Keepers* he quotes, "A stagecoach, said one [explorer], might be driven from the east coast to St. Louis without clearing a road." That alone obviously makes the squirrel story nonsense.

Budiansky tells us of Peter Kalm, a Swedish botanist sent by Linnaeus to collect specimens of New World plants made a similar observation. He described the forests of New Jersey in 1750 as so free from underbrush that one could drive a horse and carriage straight through them. Captain John Smith of the Jamestown, Virginia, settlement concurred, saying, "A man may gallop a horse amongst these woods any waie, but where creekes or Rivers shall hinder". (It should be remembered by us other English-speaking people that early Americans spoke Shakespearean English.)

Budiansky informs us that if there is one point on which the early European travellers and settlers who set down their observations of the New World agreed, it was that the forests of eastern North America reminded them of nothing so much as the carefully tended parks of the great estates of their homelands. An explorer in 1607 observed the trees around present-day Portland, Maine, "growing a great space asunder one from the other as our parks in England and no thicket growing under them." In the early days of the Plymouth colony, the Pilgrims found the woods "thin of Timber in many places, like our Parkes in England." In New Jersey in the mid-seventeenth century, the woods were described as "but thin in most places, and very little underwood". Another explorer noted an abundance of high grass and trees that "stand far apart, as if they were planted." And, "In such open, parklike wood, deer and turkey could be seen a mile away, cattle three miles."

Others told of vast, open grasslands with hardly a tree in sight. Passing through western Virginia in 1722, William Byrd noted, "There is scarce a shrub in view to intercept your prospect, but grass as high as a man on horseback." A seventeenth-century settler of Salem, Massachusetts, told of a place nearby where "one could stand upon a little hill and see divers thousands of acres of ground as good as need be, and not a tree in the same."

The writer Parkman romantically portrayed the sixteenth-century Italian navigator Verrazano lying off the coast of New England, espying one of his mighty literary forests as full of "shadows and gloom." Yet Verrazano himself told of marching inland fifteen miles from Narragansett Bay (in what would become Rhode Island), finding "open plains twenty-five or thirty leagues in extent, entirely free from trees or other hindrances." Where the explorer did encounter forests, they grew so open and unencumbered by underbrush that they "might all be traversed by an army ever so numerous".

The Europeans were uniformly impressed, if not surprised, by these open woods and meadows, but they did not have to search far for an explanation.

Budiansky relates the explanation, given in 1632, by Thomas Morton, an English fur trader and adventurer who travelled extensively through the backwoods of Massachusetts. (Sometimes it seems his wanderings were only just a little ahead of the law.) Morton was however a keen observer, writing:

> The Salvages are accustomed to set fire of the country in all places where they come; and to burn it, twize a yeare, vixe, at the Spring, and at the fall of the leafe. The reason that moves them to do so, is because it would be otherwise so overgrown with underweedes that it would be all a copice wood, and the people could not be able in any wise to passe through the country out of a beaten path ... The burning of the grasse destroyes the underwoods, and so scorcheth the elder trees, that it shrinks them, and hinders their growth very much: So that hee that will look to finde large trees, and good tymber, must not depend upon the help of a woodden prospect to find them on the upland ground; but must seeke for them ... in the lower grounds where the grounds are wett when the country is fired ... For when the fire is once kindled, it dilates and spreads itself as with the winde; burning continually night and day, until a shower of raine falls to quench it. And this custome of firing the country is the means to make it passable, and by that meanes the trees growe here and there as in our parks: and makes the country very beautifull, and commodious.

Budiansky also goes on to remind us that

> The extent to which the landscape of America prior to 1492 was the artificial creation of its native residents is almost impossible for us to grasp, so encumbered are we with the nineteenth-century myth of the forest primeval and the more recent myth of the Indian as an ecological hero who trod softly through the forest on moccasined feet without snapping a twig.

But at a minimum the Indian was the dominant source of fire, and "fire is the dominant fact of forest history" in North America.

The idea has not been easy for historians, ecologists, or even anthropologists to accept. Despite the overwhelming documentary evidence of Indian fire practices, the suggestion that Indian-set fires had any significant part to play in shaping the North American landscape was almost scornfully rejected by early twentieth-century foresters. Climatic determinists of the Clements school were especially resistant to the notion that fire (and thus man) rather than climate (and thus God and nature) was the force that shaped the grasslands.

It should be noted that when burning stopped, mesquite, juniper, sagebrush, and scrub oak began overrunning the grasslands of the U.S. Midwest and Southwest. By 1960 they covered some 75 million acres in Texas and surrounding states. The grasslands were no longer grasslands.

When modern ecologists and range managers saw a tangle of mesquite, sagebrush and juniper jungles invading drier grasslands from the west, they immediately blamed it on overgrazing by domestic livestock that, they proclaimed, had weakened the native grasses. Yet even in areas fenced off from stock, the tangled shrubs appeared and rapidly took over. It gradually became clear that, to a substantial extent, the native North American grasslands had climate and soil perfectly suitable for deciduous forests to grow. But fire created grasslands and then kept them as grasslands.

Nature's Keepers consistently recognizes and reminds us of these considerations.

Regarding fire, Budiansky notes that "The same pattern was repeated not just across America but throughout the world." Carl Sauer, author of *Man's Role In Changing The Face Of The Earth* (University of Chicago Press) observed "Wherever primitive man has had the opportunity to turn fire loose on a land, he seems to have done so, from time immemorial; it is only civilized societies that have undertaken to stop fires". Fire has been introduced by man onto every continent on the earth. Hunting peoples in Argentina, South Africa, New Zealand, Ceylon, the South Pacific, and Southeast Asia all set fire to the brush to improve grassland for game. (As one researcher observed of the Australian aborigines, "Perhaps never in the history of mankind was there a people who could answer with such unanimity the question, Have you got a light, mate?")

Others researchers note that even the tropics, long hailed as the last true untouched wilderness, appear to have been heavily shaped by man. Charcoal has been found buried in the soil virtually everywhere in the tropics. Radiocarbon dating of charcoal samples from a seemingly unspoiled tropical wilderness in Costa Rica and Panama shows that the supposedly unsustainable slash-and-burn agricultural practices that began as long as 6,000 years ago have been sustainable throughout all the intervening years.

We have to accept that in many tropical grasslands man may indeed have been the only significant source of fire, and so man himself created much of the grazing lands. The tropical savannas and grasslands of the world are not so much a wilderness as a garden. Ancient man evolved into a grassland animal himself and ancient man simply burned down the forests to expand his habitat.

The more one delves into this completely new gambit of ecological imperatives, the more one becomes aware of a common thread, a consistency of purpose unrelated to environmental values. It becomes glaringly obvious that the apparent significance of an ecological issue, the media attention it receives and the number and fervour of its supporters, is exactly proportional to the benefits that accrue to fossil carbon industries by furthering that particular ecological cause. The slightest suggestion of a risk to biodiversity is manna from heaven to the fossil carbon lobby. They will ensure it is highly publicized, and possible threats magnified out of all proportion to suit the motives of the marketers of their products.

Their guiding principles are at least consistent. They like to have areas of farmland and potential farmland locked away to encourage intensive agriculture. They want any river with hydroelectric potential to be declared sacrosanct, along with anything else that threaten the sales of fossil carbon materials. To achieve these aims any biodiversity-environmental cause will suffice. The petrochemical industries are heavily dependent on locking up the constantly regrowing timber resources of the world's forests. Biodiversity causes are perfect to help achieve these aims. Biodiversity becomes their triple-edged sword (if such a thing existed). With one fell swoop they can achieve all their objectives.

It is no wonder that biodiversity has become the new age environmental issue, and so extremely worthy of support from all "responsible" oil, coal and natural gas producers.

But there are other ways of preserving a special species. If the numbers of some really unusual animal or plant are down to the point of possible extinction, we can now quite easily preserve their DNA. Some day soon even *Jurassic Park* may well become a true story. If the DNA of dinosaurs had been preserved by the low-temperature storage techniques we now have, there would be no problem in recreating them.

Our enormous use of defoliants and pesticides in eradication programs was the most serious threat to biodiversity. Now global warming and cancerous climate change is leaping ahead of even those dangers.

In regard to defoliants and pesticides, perhaps the biggest culprit is the cotton industry, firstly in the United States and now Australia and other countries. The cotton plant is a perennial, growing and flowering continuously from year to year throughout its life. Long established practice however has been to treat cotton as an annual crop to be planted in early spring and harvested in late autumn. The timing of the harvest is important because the cotton fibre must be clean and not contaminated with leaves, as such contamination will greatly reduce its value.

Harvesting in the past took place after the early frosts of winter had killed off the foliage, allowing the leaves to drop. Today, with faster-maturing varieties and preplanned mechanical harvester schedules, growers do not wait for nature's natural defoliation by frost. Chemicals are used instead to kill off the cotton plant at a time that suits the grower. Every year, millions of acres of cotton are sprayed with chemical defoliants.

Being a huge monocrop operation, with little emphasis on plant health, cotton production suffers badly from insect pest problems. So now and for several decades past, cotton growers have been dosing their fields with enormous quantities of potent and powerful insecticides. Approximately 40,000 tons per year of insecticides are sprayed on cotton crops in the United States alone. At the same time around a million tons a year of chemical fertilizers are used to get the plant ready for harvest.

The Environmental Protection Agency considers seven of the top fifteen pesticides used on cotton in the United States as "possible," "likely," "probable," or "known" human carcinogens. Those chemicals are acephate, dichloropropene, diuron, fluometuron, pendimethalin, tribufos, and trifluralin. There are probably many others.

Cotton growers in the United States have undertaken huge programs to totally eradicate pests such as the boll weevil. Even the cotton growers admit that beneficial and useful insect species are wiped out by the insecticides. Over 14 million acres of cotton was "grown" in the United States in 2000. It's probably fair to say the total biodiversity over all this area amounts to just one species, and that's cotton—two if you count humans.

In contrast to cotton with all its problems we have industrial hemp (discussed in Strategy 41) which actually needs no chemical to produce a useful and economical crop, although small quantities are often used. Hemp is obviously not a favourite of the agrochemical industry.

Insect life and grasses aren't the only ones at risk of species annihilation through chemical overuse. Researchers in the United Kingdom are now discovering that although agricultural use of single pesticides or insecticides, at the listed safe recommended doses, do not appear to harm bird life, combinations of these chemicals can be lethal to them.

Chemically stimulated agriculture on soil with depleted organic matter produces sickly crops. Healthy crops, like healthy people, are extremely disease resistant. Sick crops more suit the palate and digestive system of insects. Birds then eat the insects. Birds, once upon a time, were the main biological control mechanism limiting insect populations.

Some pesticide sales people might well delight in these poisonous cocktail formulations. The pesticides can be sold to the farmer to kill his insect pests, but then at the same time their use will kill off the insect-eating birds. So even more pesticides will be needed.

Your local ecological enthusiasts and green protesters can never prevent the annihilation of species by waving banners while happily ignoring factors such as global warming and agrochemical poisoning. Yet they protest about any and every perceived environmental change with the glaring exception that no serious action is allocated to global warming. Why is this so? Global-warming-induced climate change, along with coating all the world's agricultural lands with stimulants and poisons, are the overriding factors that threaten biodiversity on this planet. It is pathetic that the very concept, the very essence of protecting biodiversity has been manipulated to suit the marketing of the products most likely to force a massive loss.

If there is one all-pervading mass of monumental nonsense that is totally distorting environmental logic and common sense, it is the sublime belief in the utter permanence and invariance of ecological systems. We are often asked, or more often it is demanded of us, that we cease to influence systems that mankind have been drastically influencing for as many as 60,000 years. We are expected to fence off vast tracts of land, at incredible cost, to encourage the formation of "natural" areas that in reality have never previously existed. We are ruthlessly and vigorously prevented from burning off scrublands that in reality we have controlled with fire for untold millennia. We are told we are an interloper on a planet that gave us birth, and we are constantly told it was a better place before we got here.

And while this is happening we are also being conditioned to accept that the only serious environmental structure that we can neglect with reckless and irresponsible abandon is the very air that envelops and protects our planet.

Budiansky himself emphasizes in *Nature's Keepers* the reality of the innate randomness of natural systems. He reminds us that there is no right system nor is there any wrong system in nature, nor is any system in any way innately permanent. This is quite a profound concept and for many of us it will take time to really appreciate its broad significance. He says succinctly

> One thing is clear: To leave nature to her own devices is no guarantee that what is here today will be here tomorrow. Nature has no eternal plan, no timeless purpose. It is ever-changing, a creature of the endless geological upheavals that are as old as the planet itself.

If it were not so we humans would never have evolved. Budiansky also states:

> The idea of a risky nature is one that is hard for many people to swallow. Environmentalists recoil at the notion precisely because it seems to give man license to transform nature at will. If what is here could just as well have been something completely different, then what is wrong with turning forests to deserts or prairies to cattle ranches or wetlands to sugar cane fields? The honest and uncomfortable answer is that from a scientific point

of view, there is nothing at all wrong with these things. The specter of ecosystems collapsing like a house of cards to the destruction of all life on the planet, ourselves included, if but one piece is tampered with, is one of the more successful myths of the modern environmental movement, but it is a distortion of ecological reality. An ecosystem is not a living organism that dies of infection if it gets a scratch or even bleeds to death if it loses a limb. Ecosystems are ever changing, dissolving, transforming, recombining in a kaleidoscope of new forms.

One thing that *Nature's Keepers* certainly does is force us to think.

The equilibrium and balance of nature believers, advocate and indeed demand what they themselves consider ecological systems "ought to be". Balance of nature believers do not like to recognize what the real world actually "is". They don't want to know that the earth, and all its ecological systems, are slowly and constantly changing. They don't want to know that it has always been like that and it always will be like that. That's Darwinism, and Darwinism doesn't suit their vision of enviro-political control.

The successful life forms on this planet today are the ones that do change and do constantly evolve. Even evolutionary rates have evolved to allow timely change. It seems that under extremely stressful environmental conditions, biological mutational changes are somehow enhanced and evolution actually speeds up. So when evolutionary changes need to happen in a hurry, they can. So the successful ones evolved much better than the ones that aren't here now. But that still takes more time than we are giving with global warming.

In *Nature's Keepers*, Stephen Budiansky reminds us that, "for at least a hundred thousand years it has been largely man who has chosen nature's path for her." That is reality. It is the reality that has existed on virtually every island, and on every continent, on the face of this planet of ours. It is wrong to expect us to feel guilt or shame. It's an invigorating realization that both the planet and mankind are evolving in conjunction. And we always will.

There are people in our affluent societies who do not produce any goods, who do not supply any services, who grow no food, who mine no minerals and who effectively contribute nothing to society, yet crave power. They want influence, and they even want respect, and they want it without earning it and they want it without deserving it. By hitching themselves to the new biodiversity cause they create and acquire their own momentum, their own juggernaut, with powers out of all proportion to its worth to any human society.

Genuine and responsible thinkers, people who appreciate life's realities, and are prepared to do something constructive to improve those realities, are constantly having their efforts trampled under by these endless orchestrated biodiversity stampedes.

Biodiversity is proclaimed to be "under threat" if the numbers of individual plants, animals, birds or reptiles, or now even insects, of any species whatever exist in less than plague proportions. Biodiversity can be claimed to be under threat if the population of anything appears to be just declining in any way whatsoever and in any place. The immediate conclusion then reached is that the "habitat" (that all-embracing term) for the nominated species must therefore itself be under threat. A "cause" has been created. A "cause" has been manufactured to suit some perceived marketing imperative.

This process is the fundamental all-embracing manoeuvre to justify never-ending claims for power, influence and interference in almost all human affairs. And the strings that juggle that power are very slippery and generally lubricated with oil.

It is no coincidence that implicit within these biodiversity arguments are always solutions that result in the expanded use of petroleum-based plastics and highly energy-dependent materials and fossil fuels.

Look at history. All idiotic causes, no matter where, no matter when and no matter how poisonous, are always held together with carefully twisted fine threads of truth. The biodiversity industry is the same. There are definitely a few species of animals, of birds and of reptiles that actually are under genuine threat of annihilation and we should do what we can and what is practical to save them. However all too often the genuine become irrelevant and are all too often lost in the sidelines of manufactured "causes."

Like all the best marketing strategies, biodiversity has now taken on a life of its own. It is now a massive "industry" in itself. Taxpayers are forking out millions to fund endless studies and create endless regulations that feed and foster this bloated science fiction. It is all to keep our minds off the very real problem of an overheating planet. Biodiversity is yet another excellent example of the principle of the "big lie".

> The great masses of the people ... will more easily fall victims to
> a big lie than to a small one. (Adolf Hitler, *Mein Kampf*, 1925)

It is frightening but we now have to recognize the deliberate creation of a mindless juggernaut, marching under the banner of biodiversity and marching to the manipulated beat of fossil fuel drums.

Could there be any other motivation for the creation of this juggernaut of fiction? Is it just happenstance? It seems unlikely. One wonders what Sherlock Holmes would conclude. Or do we remind ourselves of Ian Fleming's words in *Goldfinger:* "Once is happenstance. Twice is coincidence. Three times is enemy action."

The geology and the climate of the earth are constantly changing, and life on our planet is constantly evolving to accommodate those changes. Slow change allows life to adapt. But life and evolution simply cannot adapt to rapid changes from either meteoric impacts or human induced global warming. Both biodiversity and human society will be severely damaged by global warming. But global warming can be stopped, and it must be stopped.

Apart from global warming *Homo sapiens* have most definitely been slowly modifying the planet for at least 100,000 years, and we will continue to do so. And I see nothing wrong in that.

If I were a visitor from another world, I am sure I would find this planet a much more interesting place to visit now than it was 100,000 years ago, before the age of man.

Well I am not a visitor. I live here, and while I concede that we make a few mistakes as we learn, I for one, am proud of the achievements and accomplishments of my fellow man.

10

The sabotaging of nuclear energy

A SUPPLY of energy that is unlimited, nonpolluting, cheap and totally reliable is the nightmare of the fossil-fuel nations and industries. If motor vehicles ran on electricity generated primarily at coal-fired power stations there would be negligible decrease in the rate of atmospheric pollution and global warming. Since the electricity generated would produce the same amount of carbon dioxide and other atmospheric pollutants, there would be no significant logical justification for switching en masse to electric motor vehicles. As long as we continue using coal to generate electricity we will continue to use petrol- and diesel-fuelled motor vehicles.

However as soon as generating cheap electricity ceases to contribute to global warming then motor transport will cease to be a justifiable market for oil. Alternatives such as electrically produced hydrogen, or agriculturally produced ethanol, will become the norm. The oil states and the oil companies are well aware that the widespread adoption of nuclear energy will augur the end of their wealth, their international power and their influence.

To the oil companies and their coal lobby allies it is therefore absolutely essential to generate in the public mind intense fear, mistrust and confusion relating to all forms of nuclear energy and nuclear radiation. It's logical marketing. They must imply that the natural background radiation that has bathed the planet since before life began, hardly exists. They must claim that all forms of radiation, in even the tiniest of doses will kill, and therefore all radiation must be avoided at all costs. They must generate the belief that the disposal of nuclear waste is an unsolvable problem, and they must invent arguments against every proposed waste disposal system imagined.

Also for them, it wise to always associate nuclear-generated electricity with nuclear weapons. They must keep totally obscure the fact that military explosives and chemical weapons are all made from oil, and oil alone.

I think we all must agree that the oil-coal public relations people and their marketing gurus have been brilliantly successful. Most of us are now convinced by the antinuclear propaganda deluge; and sadly, we rarely question its validity.

Nuclear history and war

How did it all happen? What were the circumstances? How did they get their propaganda to succeed so effectively?

Central Europe, May 1945. The Nazis had been stopped. Germany—a nation of people that had become seconded to a self-centred dream, fooled by their own weaknesses, their own ambitions and their own fears—lay in the ruins of the war it had created. A whole generation of Germans paid the price of their own naïveté.

Fortunately for the world, German scientists and German industry had not been able to build an atom bomb in time to enable the Nazis to conquer and control the world.

The Nazis' ally in the Pacific, Japan, also quested for more territory. The Japanese nation wanted self-sufficiency in oil. To Japan, the suffering and deaths caused along the way were totally irrelevant. Around the time of the fall of the Nazis, the string of Japanese conquests had been halted with dreadful suffering and huge loss of life. The fall of Japan had become inevitable.

The Japanese soldier and most of the Japanese people had been trained, conditioned and indoctrinated to believe that to die fighting was somehow honourable. To die for their military junta, to die for the Emperor—the latest in that ancient mafia-like family of warlords that had ruled the nation for centuries, or to die for some satisfying after-death religious pay-off, that was the only "right thing to do". Kamikaze attacks were not just random cases of pilots with damaged planes with no hope of returning to base and deciding to take some enemies with them. No! Kamikaze pilots were never supposed to return.

The Japanese military used suicide attacks as part of their normal operational doctrine. Examples include the Yokosuka Ohka or Baka—a one-ton manned glide bomb with a rocket motor used to accelerate it into its target, the Shinyo—a motorboat loaded with two tons of explosive and one man, the Fukuryu—a swimmer with a mine attached, the Nikaku were human anti-tank mines—soldiers with explosives strapped to their bodies who crawled between the tracks of tanks; the Kaiten was a manned torpedo. The Japanese used all these. Other bizarre methods of suicide attack were planned, but fortunately for all, not used before the war ended.

Dictatorial regimes and religious jihads work the same confidence trick even to this day, relying on the uneducated and the unthinking, the gullible and the unsuspecting. But most notably relying on the power of indoctrination on young innocent children and young headstrong adults, for such influence can be immense.

The Japanese island of Okinawa lies about 400 miles (640 km) south of mainland Japan. It is about 60 miles (100 km) long and rarely more than 10 miles (16 km) wide. Okinawa was needed by the U.S. Forces as an air base and staging area for the anticipated invasion of Japan. The Americans committed over 180,000 troops to the invasion of Okinawa—code named Operation Iceberg—and they lost 12,000 killed or missing in action and 38,000 injured. The loss of life on the Japanese side was staggering; about 100,000 Japanese soldiers died. Estimates of civilian casualties varied, but somewhere around 100,000—something like a third of the island's population—were killed. The way in which these causalities occurred appalled the Allies. Virtually every Japanese soldier either fought to the death or committed suicide. Groups of Japanese civilians took it upon themselves to attack bare handedly, and die in "the Name of the Emperor".

Very reluctantly, U.S. President Harry S. Truman had already approved operation Olympic, the invasion of the island of Kyushu with a force of 800,000 troops for 1 November 1945. Kyushu is one of the four main islands of Japan. Nagasaki incidentally is on Kyushu. He had also approved operation Coronet, an invasion near Tokyo, with 1,120,000 troops. Coronet was scheduled to take place five months later.

It was expected that even more Japanese fanaticism would be encountered in these Japanese mainland invasions than was experienced at Okinawa. Estimates on the number of Americans that would die in those dreadful battles were frightening. An estimation of a quarter of a million was considered conservative. President Truman speculated up to one million. General MacArthur had predicted that if the Japanese switched from standard military deployment to a defence system based on guerrilla warfare, then the invasion of Japan could take up to ten years. MacArthur stated that if that occurred he could not put a ceiling on possible American losses. The Americans and the Allied troops who would have died were teenagers and young adults. Sadly it is always the young in the front line of battle.

Additionally, what was not known at the time was that Field Marshall Shunroku Hata had been appointed commander of the Japanese Second General Army and made responsible for the final defence of Japan. He had his pride, and made it known that Japan would not suffer an ignominious defeat under his command. Japan could not surrender!

Shunroku Hata had previously commanded the 500,000-strong Japanese army that controlled China in 1941. He was later accused of permitting his troops to commit regular and widespread atrocities against the Chinese civilian population and on American airmen forced down in China.

Field Marshall Shunroku Hata established his headquarters for the defence of Japan in, coincidentally, Hiroshima, but this was not known by the Allies at this time. His plan was to turn the expected invasion into a dreadful never-ending war of attrition. It would continue until the Americans finally lost heart and a peace treaty could be signed. Not an unconditional surrender, but a peace treaty, wherein the Japanese military would be permitted to remain in power.

On Kyushu there were 5,000 Kamikaze aircraft assembled and ready to be deployed. Hundreds of Shinyo suicide boats were ready to ram enemy ships. Children were being taught how to make petrol bombs and fuel was set aside and stored to make three million of them. The elderly and the women were taught how to make and throw bamboo spears.

Hata knew that Japan could never win, but he had no intention of letting America win either. Japanese deaths would have been at least several millions, by most estimates. Today that figure of several million is actually considered conservative. Such philosophical fatalism was exactly what General MacArthur most feared.

In July 1945, the Japanese military by all accounts, decided to murder all Allied prisoners of war. It was thought simpler and less expensive than feeding and guarding them. Several of the ruling Japanese military elite seriously argued for the death of the entire Japanese people—simply to create a "glorious defeat". The lives of Allied prisoners of war were not even a minor consideration.

In the spring of 1945 dozens of Japanese cities had already been bombed using incendiaries. The resulting firestorms had been devastating. In Tokyo, 100,000 people died in the first raid on 9 March when 325 B-29 bombers dropped more than 2,000 tons of incendiary bombs on the city. Additionally, casualties were estimated at half a million. Two hundred and fifty thousand buildings were destroyed in an area of some 225 square miles (580 square kilometres).

Undaunted, the Japanese military was determined to continue fighting.

But it didn't continue: the prisoners weren't murdered, the quarter of a million Americans and Allied servicemen that were expected to die bringing the war to an end, didn't die either, nor did those "several million Japanese".

It didn't happen because, at 8:16 AM local time on 6 August 1945, an atom bomb fuelled with uranium-235 was dropped on the Japanese city of Hiroshima, population 255,000. The immediate loss of life was approximately 64,000 people.

Four Japanese cities had been deliberately spared from conventional bombing. They had been kept as possible targets for atom bombs. The cities were Kokura, Hiroshima, Niigata and the ancient cultural city of Kyoto. President Truman vetoed Kyoto because of its great religious and cultural significance to the Japanese people. Nagasaki was subsequently added to the list.

Three days later, on 9 August, another atom bomb containing a central core of plutonium-239 was dropped from a Boeing B-29 bomber on Nagasaki, population 422,000. The death toll that day in Nagasaki was 39,000.

The Japanese already knew what atom bombs were. They started Project A, the code name for one of their own atomic bomb programs, almost at exactly the same time as the Americans. Although money and raw materials were a continuing problem, work on building nuclear weapons in Japan never ceased until the war's end.

A month earlier, on 26 July 1945, the Allies, including Russia, had issued the Potsdam Declaration threatening Japan with "complete and utter destruction" if they did not surrender.

On 9 August, the day they dropped the second atomic bomb, Russia formally declared war against Japan to strengthen its claims for some of Japan's real estate.

Conventional bombing continued; on the night of the Hiroshima raid, 635 bombers attacked various targets and dropped approximately 4,000 tons of conventional weapons. The last bombing raid against Japan was flown by the 315th Bomb Wing out of Guam on 14 August 1945.

The Americans had no atom bombs left; they'd had only enough raw materials to make three bombs, and one had already been exploded in a test run three weeks earlier, on July 16 at Alamogordo, New Mexico. Future production of bomb material would be slow. But the Japanese didn't know this. Dropping the second atom bomb was part of a ploy by the Americans, following up on the Potsdam Declaration, to make the Japanese believe that many more bombs lay in the American armory, ready and waiting.

Arguments still rage over whether the atom bombs "ended the war" and whether or not conventional means would have succeeded. However a report by the U.S. Strategic Bombing Survey sent to President Truman on June 1946 gives ample evidence that the bombs played a major role in allowing a faction of the Japanese command favouring surrender to gain ascendancy. In the high circles of Japanese government, the atom bomb was known as "the true Kamikaze" since it saved Japan from "loss of face" in surrender. The stark reality is that those two atom bombs dropped on Hiroshima and Nagasaki saved the lives of more Japanese people than any other single event in World War II. That simple and obvious reality is not taught in Japanese schools.

VJ Day is remembered each year on 15 August, six days after the bombing of Nagasaki. Actually the decision to surrender was taken earlier by the Japanese government on 10 August.

During the bomb development at Los Alamos, the code name Thin Man had been used to refer to work being carried out on a "gun" system designed for detonating both the uranium and plutonium bombs. The code name was chosen in the hope that if messages were intercepted it might be taken to refer to President Roosevelt. (President Truman took office on 12 April 1945 after the unexpected death of President Roosevelt. Truman had been sworn in as Vice President only 82 days earlier.)

However, as work progressed on the plutonium bomb it was realized that a different system of detonation would be needed. Rather than being long and thin, this system was large and round. It was code-named Fat Man in the hope that this might be taken to refer to Prime Minister Churchill. After Fat Man was initiated, the length of Thin Man was shortened and it became known as Little Boy. The dropping of Fat Man and Little Boy had stopped a vicious, ruthless and fanatical enemy, and brought peace to the world with the minimum loss of life.

Before their timely defeat both Germany and Japan had nuclear weapons programs. The Allies were well aware that the USSR, under Joseph Stalin, would ultimately have such weapons. Stalin had already said so.

After the termination of hostilities, the United States decided to continue research and development on nuclear weapons. Their most famous tests were at Bikini Atoll in 1946. These tests were immortalized in the name of a very skimpy lady's swimsuit.

By 1949, the Russians had exploded their first atom bomb. The nuclear arms race was in full swing. The United States tested a hydrogen bomb in 1952. A Russian-developed hydrogen bomb was just months behind the United States. A Russian hydrogen bomb was actually exploded within the year.

In the years immediately following the end of the war, things actually looked extremely promising for nuclear energy to become the universal fuel for all mankind. The oil producers, and they were not fools, were obviously acutely aware how such a possibility would influence the survival of their industry and their power.

The possibilities for producing power from nuclear reactors had been clearly recognized much earlier. In July 1941, well before the commencement of the Manhattan Project (the code name for the U.S. nuclear weapons program) a group of British scientists known as the MAUD committee produced two summary reports for their government. The first report was on the "Use of Uranium for a Bomb" and the second was on the "Use of Uranium as a Source of Power". The concept was known then as a "nuclear boiler". Ten years later, in 1951, the first nuclear reactor to produce usable electricity began operating. It was a small experimental reactor in Idaho.

In late 1953, after only a year in office, President Eisenhower attempted to put the brakes on the mad arms race by proposing an Atoms for Peace program to the United Nations. This ultimately led to the development of civilian nuclear energy production in the United States. Eisenhower rekindled the vision of nuclear power delivering unlimited and cheap energy to create a utopian future.

People talked again of automobiles running on tiny nuclear engines that never needed refuelling. The soot, sulphur and stench of coal-fired power stations would vanish. Dust-choked coal mines would close forever. Smog-drenched cities would sparkle with health and clean air. It all seemed possible. Nuclear energy did indeed hold a promise of a utopian future. But not for all—those most definitely excluded from such a future were the world's oil companies, the oil-producing countries and the big oil cartels.

There has never been a more catastrophic threat to the companies and countries that mine and market fossilized carbon. It was glaringly obvious. If nuclear energy ever got going, nobody would ever burn fossil carbon again.

If your income came from oil or coal, if they represented your major assets and wealth, then you would have to be stupid not to recognize the immense threat posed by cheap, nuclear energy.

What was even worse was the media were enthusiastic in their praise for a nuclear-powered utopian future and Eisenhower's vision. Everybody who sold any form of fossilized carbon fuels must have dreaded this clean "nuclear future".

The oil companies had two things going for them in the antinuclear propaganda campaign they needed to establish. Firstly they had plenty of time: the technological problems that had to be solved before nuclear energy came online would be considerable. And secondly: the frightening thought of a nuclear weapons attack and of living in a city that could be a nuclear weapons target, could be exploited.

Throughout the Cold War, from the 1950s right through to the final fission of the Russian communist state into a collection of small, sometimes quasi, but nevertheless democratic states, U.S. nuclear weapons policy had to rely on what critics called a MAD policy. It was a policy of Mutually Assured Destruction. The premise was you never start a war, because if one started, neither side could ever win.

With MAD there could be no winners had the buttons ever been pushed. The thousands of nuclear weapons that would have been detonated in such a war would have resulted in an instant change in the world's atmosphere and climate. Humans would probably have become a rarity on the planet and thousands upon thousands of other species would have been eliminated as the inevitable nuclear winter spread over the surface of the planet. In a hundred years or so, the earth would have undoubtedly recovered. But it would never have been this Earth as we know it today.

Mutually Assured Destruction did actually keep the world generally at peace. Albeit a peace between the major players that seemed constantly to hover on the brink of total war.

Nevertheless there has been no World War III and World War II was over half a century ago.

With such a threat hanging over the Free World, the public relations people of the oil producers had the perfect marketing solution. Take the horrific image of nuclear weapons and tie that image to nuclear power stations. Make the two synonymous. Instill in everybody the belief that the two are one and the same. There could be no other way. Of course, except for the two atom bombs dropped on Japan in 1945, all the guns, all the bombs, all the weapons, all the explosives used in World War II were made from oil and coal. That "irrelevant truth" should not be mentioned in any antinuclear energy debate. And it never has.

Incidentally, today Japan has 54 nuclear reactors supplying 34% of their electricity needs, but that fact receives a lot less publicity than the devastating images of Hiroshima and Nagasaki sixty years after the event. Today the rebuilt city of Nagasaki relies on a nuclear power station.

At the end of World War II the chemical factories making oil-based explosives made a slight change in their chemical production line and made chemically similar products, in many cases almost identical to the original explosives. They are called nitrogen fertilizers and are, in many ways, even more devastating. These same fertilizers are now a preferred bomb material for terrorists. The chemical warfare production facilities also made a slight change, and they produced insecticides, fungicides and herbicides. With only minor changes the chemicals designed to kill people were adjusted to kill insects, fungi and plants. In the public relations campaigns of the petrochemical industries, these facts had to be, and were carefully buried. The image builders know such discussion and planning should also never see the light of day.

The oil industries decided that "swords into plowshares" must not be allowed to happen with nuclear weapons. The oil companies' advertising and public relations people had to prevent it. Any other policy would have been foolish. And fools they were not. The use of "fear of the unknown" has surely been a successful marketing approach.

Big oil, the Kremlin and the antinuclear movement

Did the oil industries, a powerful forum of multinational corporations, a product of our free enterprise system and the principles of supply and demand capitalism, have a bed-mate? A bed-mate that was the extreme dictatorial left to all Western political ideologies? Well it seems so, and it certainly explains the establishment of some otherwise totally illogical sociological manifestations that we now see all around us.

Sir Frederick Hoyle (1915–2001) was the founding Director of The Institute of Theoretical Astronomy in the United Kingdom and was Honorary Professor at Cardiff University of Wales. He was a world-famous and extremely well-respected physicist, astronomer and philosopher.

One of his most notable achievements was in 1957 when he, along with his associates Herman Bondi and William Fowler, were the first to establish the concept that all the heavy elements, carbon, oxygen, iron, etc., were formed from primordial hydrogen, the gas formed during the Big Bang and the gas which pervades all the vastness of interstellar space. The heavy elements are those from which we ourselves are composed, and the elements that make up planets, like our Earth. Sir Fred Hoyle and his team established that these elements had to be the products of the complex nuclear reactions that occur deep inside the billions of stars throughout the

To Allan J. Yeomans

O.K.   to quote the term power from
Energy or Extinction .   But please emphasise
date of publication .   Okuwin some remarks
Would seem odd   as they do not relate
to the proscursdr .

F. Hoyle

universe. Before this was established the origin of the heavy elements was a total mystery.

The proportion of the individual elements existing anywhere in the universe depends on the number and sequence of fusion processes required to produce each element. It is all a matter of chance, but the laws of statistics apply universally. So any Earth look-alike planet, formed anywhere in the whole universe, is likely to be composed of the same basic elements pretty much in the same proportion as here on earth. Gold will be just as rare, iron, oxygen, silicon, and carbon will be just as plentiful. And of course, localized concentrations will be as variable anywhere as they are here on the planets in our solar system. This all follows from Hoyle's original concepts.

A remarkable book written by Sir Fred Hoyle was published in 1977.

It was called *Energy or Extinction?* The book discussed the probable necessity for the utilization of nuclear energy for power generation. It also considered, in depth, the safety aspects and the environmental aspects of nuclear energy. It discussed the distorted fallacies used by the antinuclear propagandists. It's a fascinating and enlightening book. When I was three quarters of the way through compiling information, researching facts, and writing the book you are now reading, I read *Energy or Extinction?*

Although *Energy or Extinction?* was written more than twenty-five years ago, and the world has changed much in that period, the wisdom and insight displayed in that book has, I believe been totally validated by events in these last few decades.

In all my readings, and all my studies of environmental concepts, I could never understand why it was that the people of the moderate to extreme left of the political spectrum appeared to be the only ones deeply concerned about environmental issues. Are the people on the political right, the people who believe in smaller government, the people who believe in free enterprise, self-help, self-determination and who are against regimented bureaucratic socialism, are they really totally indifferent to the environmental issues facing our communities and our world? I don't think so. It just doesn't make sense.

The simple self-interested motives of the oil and petrochemical industries are understandable. But something was missing from the environmental propaganda picture. Something didn't add up. That something stayed missing until I read Hoyle's book.

I could not describe his concepts anywhere near as well as in Sir Frederick Hoyle's own words. So I contacted him through the Royal Society in London. I asked his permission to quote the following text in full and explained why I thought it was necessary to do so. He kindly gave me his permission. Sir Fred Hoyle okayed reproducing the first chapter from *Energy or Extinction?* in *Priority One* but asked that people be reminded that it was written in 1974, in the middle of the Cold War.

The control of Middle East oil that so easily guarantees power and influence over the Western nations may no longer be a grand plan of the Soviets. But it must be presumed that others have considered the significance of Hoyle's ideas in their own manoeuverings.

Here it is. It's the complete first chapter in *Energy or Extinction? The Case for Nuclear Energy.* The chapter is titled "The Anti-nuclear Environmentalist". This is how Sir Frederick Hoyle explains it:

1
The Anti-nuclear Environmentalists

In a number of writings I have myself welcomed the concern now felt by many people for saving birds, trees, natural beauty, the whale, and the Atlantic salmon. It is unfortunately the case however that there are always individuals waiting around to seize on any worthwhile popular movement, political animals who manipulate such movements for their own ends. The invention of word-labels and slogans is important to these people, as George Orwell showed so bitingly in *Animal Farm*. Words like 'concerned person', 'friend of the Earth', are just the kind of word-label which political manipulators use to make us forget precisely what explicit issues are troubling us. For only by persuading us to forget explicit issues can a popular movement be perverted to serve the ends which the political animals really have in mind. In this short first chapter I shall explain what I believe the real motive of such environmentalists to be.

I believe the motive to be connected with the Soviet Union, and with a world struggle for energy. The economic system of the Soviet Union has many disadvantages. It is not technically very innovative. It does not produce consumer goods efficiently. But the Soviet system is not entirely besotted, as the Western democracies are, with the illusory importance of paper money. The crucial principle, that energy is more important than money, would be more easily seen in the Soviet Union, perhaps very easily seen,

1

Energy or Extinction?

than it is here in the West. So I would expect the geographical distribution of world energy reserves (of the kind that dominate our present day energy use) to be of great interest to a Russian.

The geographical distribution of coal is shown in Figure 1.1. The dominance of Soviet reserves is manifest.

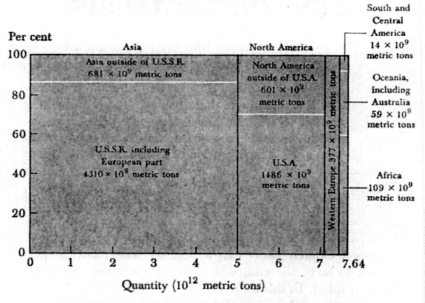

Figure 1.1   The geographical distribution of coal

The distribution of the world's major oil fields is shown in detail in Figure 1.2. If you were Russian, you would surely take careful note of that great crescent containing nearly 70 per cent of world oil reserves which starts in the U.S.S.R. and sweeps through the Middle East into North Africa. You would see the strategic importance of Israel nestling there between the horns of the crescent, Israel the one firm base from which your western enemies could

2

The Anti-nuclear Environmentalists

operate to prevent you from exercising direct physical control over the Middle East. You would also notice the great bulk of Africa around which tankers from Europe and North America must go to reach the oil fields of the Middle East, and you would realize that control of the western coastline of Africa would permit you to cut those tenuous shipping

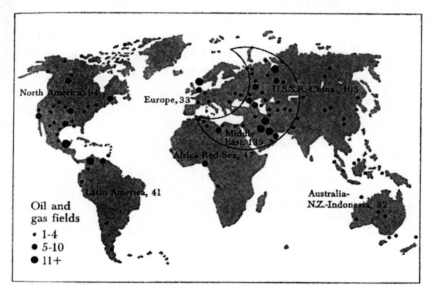

Figure 1.2   The distribution of major oil fields (from Arthur A. Meyerhoff,
     American Scientist, September 1976, reprinted by permission)

lanes. So you would set your many vociferous friends throughout the world howling and baying for the blood of Israel and South Africa. And to develop your muscle you would expand your navy, especially its submarine complement. You would also set yourself to exploit the many political troubles to which the continent of Africa is endemic. Believing in the all-importance of energy, you would scent victory in the world struggle. Marxists never stop talking about the world struggle — they believe in that too.

3

Energy or Extinction?

The fly in this otherwise smooth ointment, which in your Russian guise you have prepared, is nuclear energy. Your western enemies have a powerful nuclear technology, to a degree where it would not be outstandingly difficult for them to obtain access to all the energy they need. Evidently then, you start your vociferous friends in the West baying against nuclear energy. You instruct your friends to operate through a mild, pleasant, 'save-the whales' movement which you observe to be growing popular throughout the western democracies. And all this they do, right to the last letter of your Kremlin-inspired instructions.

4

I read that chapter of Sir Frederick Hoyle's book and it was like a revelation.

Suddenly a strange and incredible relationship, a diabolical relationship that would otherwise defy all common sense became logical and understandable. An apparent union of the worst of socialism with the unfettered extremes of capitalism; they were travelling the same road together. Suddenly the two most manipulative organizations of the modern world, the petrochemical industries and the sly manipulative power brokers of the Kremlin, were pulling in the same direction. These two powerful structures both wanted the Western nations hopelessly dependent on oil, and they wanted that dependency to be ever increasing. The two may never have connected one to another, we don't know, but they were both pushing in the same direction.

Suddenly the extreme left-wing bias and the peculiar highly selective nature of the whole environmental movement made sense. The contrived objections to hydroelectric power were explained. The objections to wind energy and solar energy were explained. Above all, the incredible voluminous mishmash of lies, exaggerations and distortions of truth and reality that is the "antinuclear energy debate" were explained. The strange lack of any positive suggestions for practical alternative energy systems also suddenly made sense.

That chapter of Sir Frederick Hoyle's book made it obvious how it was necessary for the powers involved and how it must have happened. Russian rubles were funnelled through the myriad of communist "cells" in the Western democracies on to cleverly orchestrated environmental movements. A quarter of a century later and after the collapse of the USSR, the Campaign for Nuclear Disarmament organization in the UK, the CND, finally admitted to its Soviet funding. In addition, a contact of mine, a colonel in the old KGB, also confirmed to me that the KGB funnelled money and support through to Western antinuclear movements. He said it was part of their overall planning.

Oil and the whole petrochemical industry, plus the huge complex of coal mines and coal-fired power stations, would unobtrusively be supported by the Kremlin. And the Marxist-Leninist regime would thus ultimately triumph. They would have achieved a result such that every demand they made to the West would have to be met, for the Russians would have their hands around the throats of Western energy supplies.

Save the rivers, save the forests, protect biodiversity, create giant wilderness areas, become friends of the trees, lock up the rainforests; it all made sense.

The left-wing media were on a bandwagon; they had a cause, "the great environmental cause," and they had the socialist left and the ruble-funded green movement to encourage them.

The right-wing media were, in their turn, manipulated by the economics and power of the advertising petro-dollar to effectively take up this very same "great environmental cause" and promote the same brand of distorted responsibility and morality. The oil industries, to this day, use left-wing activists to promote their own antinuclear promotions and anti-alternative energy propaganda.

The oil industries are still with us and the twisted truths live on, even though the USSR is no longer the heart of a world Marxist-Leninist movement. The heart of communism is dead. The Russian people in their incredible second revolution of the 20th century, again changed their own history and world history almost overnight. They abandoned the brutality and the hopeless frustrations of their one-party system, and the inefficiency and wasteful naïveté of the socialist state.

Many of the millions of tentacles that wove and twisted within the socialist system, although cut off from their blood supply of rubles and ideological doctrines, are still alive. Their activists still believing in causes that were for so long the propaganda creations of the Kremlin and their KGB.

Is Hoyle's Kremlin hypothesis farfetched? Well just think for a moment. If you were on the Supreme Soviet Politburo, ruthless, cold and calculating, and if you had sworn an oath to convert all nations to Marxism-Leninism, what would you do? Remember you are never answerable to any voters. There were no voters in the USSR. You are only answerable to the other members of your Supreme Soviet who measure only in results. The stakes were high, the cause was resolute. You knew that the USSR never wanted to go to war. For the Supreme Soviet a Cold War was vastly preferable. It seemed easier and not so prohibitively expensive to win a Cold War. It also seemed like you were starting to win.

For the Soviet Union the whole scenario was diabolically sensible. It was logical and extremely cost effective, and you didn't get to be a member of the Politburo by being other than ruthless, intelligent and manipulative.

Russia made an incredible effort to annex Afghanistan starting in 1979. This annexation attempt, in the concept of world domination (and according to Hoyle) was brutally logical. Controlling Afghanistan would close a noose on Middle East oil. Otherwise why ever would the Russians bother about such a poor, backward and bothersome country?

The Kremlin wanted a communist world under their personal control. That was the grand plan, the grand belief. Extreme left-wing unions invariably control the electric power grid, the wharves, shipping and transport facilities of so many Western nations. Is it an accident? Is it a quirk of fate in Western societies that the teachers and academics that educate our children, were, and often still are invariably represented by unions dominated by the extreme left? The proclaimed idealism and the promise of unearned power are great incentives.

If you were on the Soviet Politburo and communist domination of the world was your sworn cause, wouldn't you want to have your hands around the throat of Western civilization? Wouldn't you connive to control the education of the children of the Western world?

Ultimately it was U.S. President Reagan that initiated the collapse of the USSR's reign of lies and terror. It was President Reagan who devalued the U.S. dollar by 25%—a currency on which most Soviet export contracts were written. He also, through negotiations with Saudi Arabia, was able to lower the world price of oil on which the USSR depended for foreign exchange. President Reagan also kick-started the hugely expensive Strategic Defense Initiative, "Star Wars" as it became known, and of course the USSR had to keep up. But they couldn't. Even Mikhail Gorbachev conceded that the SDI significantly accelerated the internal collapse of the Soviet communist system and ended their aim for a Russian communist world.

Today there are other countries in the world whose power and monetary base depends almost entirely on Western nations remaining dependent on massive and continuous oil imports. The big oil industries are still there; so who is big oil in league with now? Has a new "holy alliance" come into being and with whom? That we have to think about.

The undermining of nuclear power generation in the United States

Nuclear power has been attacked on every front, especially in the United States—the country that uses the most oil. Consider a typical 1,000-megawatt power station: such a unit would power a city of one million people. In 1971, the cost of building a 1,000-megawatt nuclear power station in the United States was roughly US$150 million. Just five years later, in 1976, that cost had risen to $700 million. An increase equivalent to escalating the price 25% per year. That's more than double the high rates of inflation that then existed. Prior to then, the nuclear industry in the United States had been expanding, but by the mid-seventies it was struggling. Planned nuclear power plants were put on hold. Others were cancelled completely. What happened?

The early seventies was the time of the Arab oil embargoes. The cost of oil soared and queues for petrol were common. Detroit even started reducing the engine capacity of its cars because of a new consumer demand for energy efficiency. The cost of electricity also soared and in consequence, the demand for electricity dropped. People turned off their lights and their air conditioners. This created a glut in generating capacity and the bottom dropped out of the electricity market. Existing power stations, both coal-fired and nuclear, were in financial trouble. Proposed new nuclear power stations were systematically and deliberately cut the hardest. While their fuel costs are very low their capital costs are relatively high. By legislative manipulation, building a nuclear power station had systematically been turned into a very slow, time- and money-consuming process. Nuclear

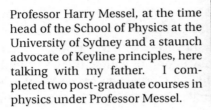

Professor Harry Messel, at the time head of the School of Physics at the University of Sydney and a staunch advocate of Keyline principles, here talking with my father. I completed two post-graduate courses in physics under Professor Messel.

power became a bureaucratic nightmare.

The price of oil stayed high which satisfied the oil producers. But this created a risk. It took a while but finally the Arab oil producers realized that an artificially high oil price might just be the catalyst to create a massive and frighteningly competitive system of fossil-fuel alternatives. They acted. Before any such alternative energy systems could become a threat, world oil prices dropped. Did the oil cartels really make such a calculated decision? Maybe, maybe not. It did however immediately put the brakes on the development of alternative energy systems and alternative motor fuels.

A quarter of a century ago the Saudi Arabian oil minister Sheik Yamani warned his fellow OPEC ministers, "if we force Western countries to invest heavily in finding alternative sources of energy, they will. This will take them no more than seven to ten years" (*The Physicist*, Volume 39, Number 3, May/June 2003.) It appears world oil prices are never allowed to significantly exceed US$55/€50 a barrel and certainly not on a permanent basis. Because that is where biofuels, especially ethanol from sugar cane, become competitive with gasoline and diesel.

The antinuclear lobby with their powerful influence on the media was able to deliver a final coup de grace to the nuclear power industry in the United States in 1979. There was, for them, a very convenient accident on Three Mile Island, a long narrow island in the Susquehanna River near Harrisburg, Pennsylvania. The Three Mile Island nuclear power plant accident gave them their field day. That accident incidentally, resulted in nobody dying, nobody getting hurt, nobody even getting a headache, except maybe from media generated fear and stress. (Details of the Three Mile Island accident are discussed later in this chapter.)

What did result from the Three Mile Island accident was an incredible, almost unbelievable tightening of safety requirements established by the U.S. Nuclear Regulatory Commission for nuclear power facilities. Almost certainly as a result of the creation of these incredibly expensive safety requirements, the construction of nuclear power stations in the United

States stopped. The construction of a further 100 nuclear power stations was cancelled. And the fossil fuel interests won an incredible battle.

It is not even that the safety standards are impossible to meet—most nuclear power stations today easily exceed the requirements—it is the time taken to issue licenses and to comply with the endless paperwork involved in constructing a nuclear power station. And then when it is finished, to go through similar time-consuming procedures to turn it on and start it up and operate it.

Regulations are such that it can easily take over ten years to plan, build and finally commission a new nuclear plant. To borrow a billion dollars to build a power station and expect to not see any return for more than ten years does not make a lot of economic sense for any investor. Fossil fuel power stations get a dream run. They can be planned and built and be selling electricity in a year.

There are signs that nuclear power is clawing its way back. The imposition of stringent safety standards has backfired on those who would see them as the death knell of a nuclear powered world. The nuclear industry has met and exceeded the safety standards and is now using the weight of common sense and scientific evidence to push for changes in some of the more ridiculous and idiotic regulations. We, the public, must not allow emotional and illogical arguments to stand in the way of this necessary development and its potential to halt global warming. It is our responsibility to get the facts, and then judge accordingly.

Sir Frederick Hoyle did point out to me that he wrote *Energy or Extinction? The Case for Nuclear Energy* more than twenty-five years ago. Nevertheless, I must very sincerely say that I don't think he was wrong.

Even if you are unconvinced by Hoyle's arguments and what his scenario may have evolved into, I ask you to withhold judgment until we look at the differences between the generally accepted picture of nuclear energy, its dangers and risks, and the true factual reality. There is an immense gap.

How do we recognize deliberate antinuclear propaganda and how do we combat it? To rediscover reality we need to understand some of the basic physics behind nuclear bombs and nuclear reactors. To the fossil carbon lobby our ignorance is their bliss. We can no longer afford to be totally ignorant.

Fortunately, neither complex mathematical theory, nor any mathematics at all is required to understand the basic concepts sufficient to become "street-wise" in basic nuclear physics. The concepts are surprisingly simple and some are quite fascinating.

Normally nuclear physics is a subject in which true proficiency is gained only after a great deal of study and several years of university training. Very few people study advanced nuclear physics. The rest of us have forgotten even the simple physics we learned at school. Therefore, with so little understanding of the subject within the community, half-truths, blatant lies and distorted facts can be manipulated by propagandists and twisted with complete abandon. That has to stop.

The formation of elements, according to Hoyle

In the very early universe, just after the Big Bang that formed the universe, temperatures were in the tens of millions of degrees allowing fusion to produce the very light elements, helium, lithium, beryllium and boron, but no heavy elements. They had to await the birth of stars.

Stars generally begin their lives containing about 74% hydrogen, 25% helium and 1% of everything else. A mix of materials floating around in space slowly coalesces by gravitational attraction and stars get born. The heavier elements in that 1% come from previous generations of stars that no longer exist.

In the very core of our own star we call the Sun or Sol, hydrogen nuclei are fusing together in a sequence of steps forming helium and releasing energy. In some rare cases of very massive stars there is a different process converting hydrogen into helium and releasing energy. This is sometimes called the carbon-nitrogen-oxygen cycle. In this process, protons (hydrogen nuclei) fuse with carbon, carbon-12 in a series of steps involving heavier isotopes of nitrogen and oxygen that undergo radioactive decay.

This series of steps involves converting four hydrogen nuclei and one carbon nucleus into a helium nucleus, a carbon nucleus and a lot of energy. The energy is mostly in the form of gamma rays. The carbon is not created, nor is it consumed in the process. The carbon acts as a nuclear catalyst to allow more efficient fusing of hydrogen. Regardless of how the hydrogen fuses inside stars, the product is always helium and energy is always released.

Helium is heavier than hydrogen so it sinks and accumulates at the centre of the star. Eventually, in very old stars the hydrogen left in the core becomes scarce and the helium becomes more common. Then the fusion of hydrogen begins to slow down, the production of energy and heat slows down. The star's core begins to collapse as it cools.

If you heat up gas in a cylinder then the pressure rises; if you cool it down, the pressure drops. When the core of a star begins to cool, its pressure drops too. But a star is not a metal cylinder, it's more like a balloon. When the pressure in a balloon drops, the balloon shrinks. When the pressure in a star's core drops, the outer layers begin to fall in. So the core begins to collapse under the action of its own gravity.

As a star's core collapses, the gases get jostled about and the temperature again rises. You may have noticed how a bicycle pump gets hot when you use it to compress air to force it into the tyre; imagine the effect of compressing a star's core with millions of times as much pressure. The increase in temperature in and around the core will start hydrogen fusing again. Strangely enough, the star can now access more of its hydrogen fuel as it packs together. The increased fusion of hydrogen around the core produces enough heat and pressure to push the very outer layers of the star out to great distances; when this process is rapid the extra brightness is seen as a nova.

Paradoxically, the outer surface of the star then becomes cooler as the greater outer surface area can radiate the heat away into space faster. A star that has undergone this change to burning hydrogen around a helium core is called a red giant. Red because it's cooler outer surface looks red, and giant because it expands to hundreds of time its original size.

Our sun is destined to become a red giant. In maybe another five billion years it will expand and consume all the inner planets, including the earth, while it too fuses its hydrogen around a helium core. It is estimated that the core of our sun is down to about 29% hydrogen, 70% helium and the 1% of heavier elements that it had when it was born some five or six billion years ago.

If the star is massive enough the helium core of the red giant can collapse and reach temperatures of around 100 million degrees, high enough for helium to begin fusing. This produces even heavier elements. Mostly carbon and oxygen are the end products but elements as heavy as neon or even magnesium, with 10 or 12 protons in the nucleus, can be produced this way.

Very massive stars, those more than 25 times the mass of our sun, probably reach core temperatures in the billions of degrees and create elements as heavy as iron or nickel.

At various stages in a star's evolution, during and after the red giant phase, catastrophic changes occur, these produce shock waves and "solar winds" that can blow material out to space. In this way the heavier elements can be distributed to interstellar clouds where they ultimately combine with more primordial hydrogen to become new stars again.

So far we've only considered producing elements no heavier than iron and nickel. These elements have stable nuclei at their centre. How then do the heavier elements like uranium form? The answer lies in the process called neutron capture. Neutrons can approach nuclei without any problems of electrostatic repulsion, as neutrons have no electric charge. Normally however, free-floating neutrons rapidly decay into protons and electrons so normally there's little chance for neutron capture to occur. However, in the core of massive stars things are not normal and electrons and protons can actually be forced back together to form neutrons. Neutron capture can now occur.

In stars that have reached the stage of having an iron core, neutron capture can produce elements as heavy as bismuth with an atomic weight of 209. Producing these elements absorbs energy, which cools the star's interior, hastening its further collapse. At this point a star is powered by the heat produced by its gravitational collapse, not by fusion energy release.

It's interesting to note that as a star progresses to fusing heavier and heavier nuclei, the reaction speeds up. A star with 25 times the sun's mass might take a few tens of millions of years before it begins fusing helium. But it will only take 600 years to fuse all its carbon, one year to finish off neon, six months on oxygen and just one day to convert silicon into iron.

At the end of that last day there is no more fuel left. There is no more fusion heat to generate internal pressure to support the outer layers of the star, and the structure collapses. The outer layers fall inward at a tremendous rush and "bounce" off the central core at close to the speed of light. And that's what they call a supernova. For a few days, as the star explodes in this giant bounce, it will outshine the entire galaxy. One is observed every few hundred years or so and they are of sufficient significance to be noted in historical records. In the core of a supernova things happen fast and there are plenty of neutrons around. That's when the really heavy elements like uranium are produced.

Finally the exploding core sends these elements off into space where they eventually coalesce with interstellar hydrogen clouds to form new stars and sometimes planets. So all the elements inside our bodies were once at the centre of a supernova.

The tiny nuclear scientists of ancient Gabon

That all happens on a massive scale, but fascinating phenomena in nuclear physics can happen on much smaller scales. Surprising as it might seem, humans did not develop the first nuclear reactors on our planet.

Once upon a time, long long ago, in a far off land, there lived a strange kingdom of tiny microorganisms. We think now they might have been bacteria, and these bacteria had very strange eating habits. They seemed somehow to have developed a taste for uranium.

They had the strange ability to drink and absorb uranium chemicals dissolved in the groundwater where they lived. Over a period of thousands, or maybe millions of years, these bacteria created quite large and rich deposits of uranium oxide. Just like tiny ancient sea creatures with their tiny bones created the white cliffs of Dover.

It all happened a very long time ago, way back further than the age of the mammals, way way back, further even than the age of the dinosaurs. It was at a time that geologists today call the Protozoic period, the second last period of the very ancient Precambrian epoch. It was a time somewhere between 1,200 million and 1,900 million years ago.

The Protozoic period is defined as the time of "simple life" and this story teaches us a little of the strange environmental history of our planet and its not-so-simple ancient life.

Prior to the Protozoic period there was no oxygen in the earth's atmosphere. Compounds of uranium salts do not dissolve readily in water unless oxygen is present. During the Protozoic period, simple algae evolved. Like plants, algae can photosynthesize, that is consuming carbon dioxide and releasing oxygen. Once these simple plant forms developed, oxygen became available in the earth's atmosphere and uranium salts were able to dissolve. The dissolved salts then drifted into the streams and watercourses of this ancient land.

And that is about the time these ancient bacteria must have developed their taste for uranium salt with dinner.

Uranium-235 decays with a half-life of nearly 700 million years. The middle of the Protozoic era was about two half-lives of uranium-235 ago. There must have been nearly four times as much uranium-235 on the planet then as there is now. Today, uranium-235 makes up only 0.7% of all uranium. Back then it would have been almost 3% (the rest is uranium-238).

Now these ancient microorganisms did not know the significance of this 3% number, but we do. We know that nice clean uranium oxide, enriched to about 3%, makes an ideal fuel for nuclear reactors. Reactors that, incidentally, can be "moderated" by water.

That ancient kingdom of primitive bacteria began busily eating uranium and concentrating it in their waste products. They were in actuality building nuclear reactors! Because that uranium contained 3% uranium-235 they had no need to search for a "moderator", there was one there already—water. When the concentration of uranium built up enough, the reactors "switched on" all by themselves.

What about control rods? Without them, might not these reactors get hotter and hotter and head for the inevitable meltdown that some people pretend threatens even the most modern nuclear reactors? No. That couldn't happen. As soon as one of these home-made nuclear reactors started to overheat the water would boil away, and with nothing to slow the neutrons down to their ideal reactor speed, the chain reaction would be starved of neutrons. The nuclear reaction would slow right down and almost cease to function. The nuclear reaction was controlled! Slowly over many years the uranium would become slightly depleted as its uranium-235 material was consumed.

There were several of these ancient kingdoms of uranium-eating bacteria, and they built many reactors. Those bacteria were the first nuclear physicists, and to this day we don't know just how many reactors they built. However, we do know that some of the reactors operated for millions of years or more.

It's a true story. The descendants of those ancient bacteria are alive today, and they still have this strange culinary habit of flavouring their meal with uranium salts. The reactors were located at a place called Oklo in what is now the small Republic of Gabon, in the Gulf of Guinea. Gabon is a few degrees north of the equator on the central West African coast.

Simple bacteria, 1.8 billion years ago, created enriched uranium reactors that were totally safe, totally self-regulating, produced thousands of kilowatts of power and appeared to operate for periods as long as a million years.

How was this ancient secret discovered? Well that too is interesting. The tiny Republic of Gabon, population 1.25 million, was once a French possession. The French have uranium mines in Gabon. Uranium accounts for 6% of Gabon's main export income. It was soon discovered that the uranium ore, mined in Gabon and shipped to France, contained less than 0.7% uranium-235.

Now the figure of 0.7% is something that comes about because of the radioactive half-lives of uranium-238 and uranium-235 and the age of the earth. It is a constant no matter where you are on the planet or on any planet in our solar system. How could this ore have a different fraction of uranium-235 to ores mined elsewhere? Had someone stolen it? If so, then how? After all, uranium-235 is extremely difficult to separate from uranium-238.

Could waste uranium, depleted of its uranium-235 content, be turned back into uranium oxide ore? Could it be substituted for the ore from the mines site? What other explanations might there be to account for the missing uranium-235? The answer possibly involved terrorist activities, and French national security. It all had James Bond-like implications.

Finally it was realized that the thieves were those ancient bacteria. They had used up most of the valuable uranium-235 running their very own nuclear power reactors almost two billion years before.

James Lovelock, in his excellent book *The Ages of Gaia*, talks about these ancient nuclear reactors:

> Bacteria could not have debated the costs and benefits of nuclear power. The fact that the reactors ran so long and that there was more than one of them suggests that replenishment must have occurred and that the radiation and nuclear waste from the reactor was not a deterrent to that ancient bacterial ecosystem. (The distribution of stable fission products around the reactor site is also valuable evidence to suggest that the problems of nuclear waste disposal now are nowhere near so difficult or dangerous as the feverish pronouncements of the antinuclear movement would suggest.)

James Lovelock is President of the Marine Biological Association. He is a fellow of the Royal Society and a visiting Professor in the Department of Cybernetics at Reading University. His invention of the electron capture detector revolutionized environmental analysis. Professor Lovelock, when he wrote *The Ages of Gaia*, established a new concept in our understanding of the nature of our planetary environment. James Lovelock is an internationally respected scientist.

At this time, six of these "natural reactor" sites have been discovered in Gabon. In *Radiation and Radioactivity* by Ivan G. Draganic, Zorica D. Draganic and Jean-Pierre Adloff, published in 1990, it is estimated that 100 million natural reactors were formed throughout the history of our planet. And this estimate is confined to reactors forming in the material in just the top 3,000 feet (one kilometre) of the earth's crust. It has finally been decided that the formation of natural reactors is the only possible explanation for the variations found in isotope ratios in uranium ore bodies on our planet.

Earth's uranium ore bodies have depleted themselves over the years since those ancient bacteria collected their fuel. So nowadays we have to enrich our natural uranium before we can use it as fuel.

Become street-smart in nuclear physics

As is mentioned in "Extra: very basic chemistry" (page 139), it's reasonably accurate to say chemistry is the study of how atoms locate themselves alongside each other to share their electrons and form chemical bonds. Whereas nuclear physics relates to what goes on inside the very central nucleus of those atoms. The study of protons and neutrons, and the strange little forces that glue them together, is nuclear physics, and the energy needed to squeeze them together in the first place, and the energy often released when they break apart, is nuclear energy. Let's now look at that central nucleus and what it is, and how it behaves.

The smallest fundamental unit of any element is an atom. An atom consists of a central nucleus surrounded by a cloud of electrons. The nucleus of an atom contains subatomic particles called protons. They are like little marbles. Each proton has a tiny discrete positive electrical charge. The number of protons in the nucleus determines what the atom is called. If it has 1 proton it's called hydrogen, if it has 2 protons it's called helium, and if it has 3 protons it's called lithium. If there are 6 protons in the nucleus, it's called carbon, 8 it's oxygen, 26 it's iron, 79 it's gold and if there are 92, it's called uranium. So we have $_{92}U^{235}$.

Mixed in with these bundles of proton marbles is a slightly different marble called a neutron. It's about the same weight and size as a proton but it does not carry any electrical charge. As a general rule for the lighter elements, there's usually about the same number of neutrons in the nucleus as there are protons. There are progressively more neutrons than protons in the heavier elements. For example, nitrogen has 7 protons and 7 neutrons. Iron has 26 protons and 30 neutrons, uranium-235 has 92 protons and 143 neutrons totalling 235.

Having all those positively charged protons in the nucleus presents a bit of a problem. Opposite charges attract and like charges repel. The positive charge of the protons attracts the negative electrons and holds them buzzing about the nucleus. The electrons, being all negative, don't like to get too close to each other, so they don't fall into the central nucleus.

But what keeps the protons from fiercely repelling each other and tearing the nucleus apart? The answer lies in something called the strong nuclear force. This is a force that acts between particles in the nucleus. It is a very short-range force compared to the electron's and the proton's electrostatic force, but it is very many times stronger if you get within its grasp. So long as the protons are close enough together, the strong nuclear force overwhelms the electrostatic force and prevents the nucleus from flying apart.

However, the forces holding a nucleus together are a little more complicated than that might suggest. There are no stable nuclei that consist of only protons (excepting only hydrogen which has a single proton). The problem seems to be that even the strong nuclear force cannot quite hold only protons together. Enter the neutron; the strong nuclear force acts between all the particles in the nucleus, protons and neutrons. However, the neutron doesn't have an electrical charge, so they help hold the nucleus together by contributing to the strong nuclear force without increasing the electrostatic repulsion that exists only between the protons.

The bigger the nucleus the bigger the proportion of neutrons required to stop it blowing apart. It seems that the more protons you pack together, the greater the percentage of neutrons you need to keep them happy.

If you have the right number of neutrons in the nucleus, the nucleus is quite stable. If there are too few, or even too many neutrons in the nucleus, then the nucleus can blow apart or "decay". Radioactive decay can be generated another way. If an otherwise stable nucleus is hit by some stray loose particle at just the right speed, the nucleus will often absorb it. If the new slightly heavier configuration is unstable it will decay.

The neutron, although it has no charge, can be considered as a positively charged proton and one tiny negatively charged electron all squashed together in one happy stable little ball. However, the ball is only stable if it resides inside a nucleus. A neutron all by itself is not at all stable and a quick divorce soon sends the two bits off in different directions and with reconciliation almost a physical impossibility.

(Actually there's a third bit involved in the marriage; when a neutron breaks down, or "decays" into a proton and electron, it also emits a third, unbelievably tiny and difficult-to-detect thing called an anti-neutrino. The existence of neutrinos was first proposed by the great physicist Enrico Fermi to solve the problem that conservation of energy did not seem to apply to neutron decay. He also proposed a new force to go with the particle, called the weak nuclear force.)

When a nucleus decays a particle is emitted and energy is released. The particle will always be either a beta particle or an alpha particle. A beta particle is an electron and an alpha particle is a little package consisting of two protons and two neutrons. An alpha particle is thus the nucleus of the helium-4 atom, the most common form of helium. The energy is released usually in the form of a very high frequency burst of light called a gamma ray. A gamma ray is like an x-ray.

How an atom behaves chemically is determined by the number of protons in the nucleus. This should be no surprise since the number of electrons matches the number of protons and it is the electrons that are involved in bonding atoms together to make chemical compounds. The number of protons therefore makes the atom oxygen, or gold, or whatever. On the other hand, with a few more, or a few less neutrons in the nucleus the atom stays the same element and, chemically at least, behaves the same way.

Atoms that have the same number of protons but different numbers of neutrons are called isotopes. Of all the oxygen atoms on planet Earth, 99.8% have eight protons and eight neutrons in their nucleus—those atoms are referred to as 8Oxygen-16 or $_8O^{16}$. The "8" is the number of protons and the "16" is the number of protons added to the number of neutrons. An isotope of oxygen with two extra neutrons, $_8O^{18}$, makes up almost all of the rest of the 0.2%. O^{18} feels, tastes and smells just like O^{16}. It reacts the same chemically; it's just a bit heavier.

O^{16} and O^{18} are different isotopes of oxygen. Isotope is a Greek word meaning "same place". Isotopes occupy the same place in the periodic table of the elements. The periodic table is a sort of catalogue of the elements. While isotopes are the same chemically, they have very different nuclear characteristics.

A lot of isotopes are stable; that means they can happily exist for millions or even billions of years, some until the end of the universe. O^{16} and O^{18} are both stable. However, just one more neutron to make O^{19} (8 protons and 11 neutrons), and this nucleus will very quickly readjust itself. Within a few seconds, one of the neutrons will spit out an electron, which rapidly leaves the scene. What remains is a nucleus with 9 protons and 10 neutrons. Having 9 protons, the atom is no longer oxygen. It is now a fluorine-19 ($_9F^{19}$) atom and the process of the nucleus readjusting itself is our radioactive decay. The departing electron is our beta particle. Beta decay is the only significant form of decay found in naturally occurring light isotopes.

In heavy atoms the decay process can be either by emitting a beta particle or by emitting an alpha particle.

Uranium has 92 protons in its nucleus. The most common isotope of uranium has, in addition, 146 neutrons. So 92 and 146 add up to 238 and that isotope of uranium is called uranium-238. Being specific it can be written as $_{92}U^{238}$, but if it's already recognized as uranium then you know it has 92 protons in the nucleus so it's abbreviated to U^{238}.

This isotope of uranium is almost, but not quite stable—sometimes a uranium-238 nucleus will decide to spit out an alpha particle (two neutrons and two protons).

Alpha decay is a common way for the heavier nuclei to adjust themselves

The Uranium Series

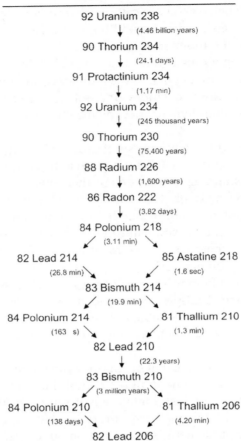

92 Uranium 238
↓ (4.46 billion years)
90 Thorium 234
↓ (24.1 days)
91 Protactinium 234
↓ (1.17 min)
92 Uranium 234
↓ (245 thousand years)
90 Thorium 230
↓ (75,400 years)
88 Radium 226
↓ (1,600 years)
86 Radon 222
↓ (3.82 days)
84 Polonium 218
(3.11 min)
82 Lead 214   85 Astatine 218
(26.8 min)   (1.6 sec)
83 Bismuth 214
(19.9 min)
84 Polonium 214   81 Thallium 210
(163 s)   (1.3 min)
82 Lead 210
↓ (22.3 years)
83 Bismuth 210
(3 million years)
84 Polonium 210   81 Thallium 206
(138 days)   (4.20 min)
82 Lead 206

but for uranium-238 the chances of this happening are very small indeed, you'd have to wait 4.5 billion years for a single uranium-238 nucleus to have an even chance of decaying. However, when it happens, the nucleus becomes an isotope of thorium, $_{90}Th^{234}$; "90" because it has two fewer protons than uranium's 92 and "234" because 238 less two protons and two neutrons leaves 234 particles in the nucleus.

This is just the first in a whole series of decays producing different "daughter" nuclei. The decay series is most easily summarized in charts like those shown here. Sometimes the daughter element has a long half-life, measured in millions of years. We come to half-lives later.

The final product in the first decay series is lead, $_{82}Pb^{206}$, which is stable. The isotope 82Lead-206 makes up about a quarter of the lead on our planet.

The Actinium Series

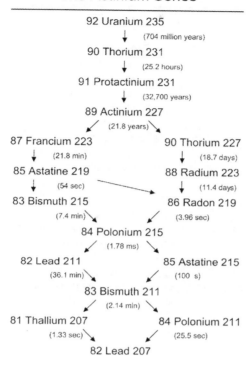

92 Uranium 235
↓ (704 million years)
90 Thorium 231
↓ (25.2 hours)
91 Protactinium 231
↓ (32,700 years)
89 Actinium 227
↙ (21.8 years) ↘

87 Francium 223   90 Thorium 227
↓ (21.8 min)   ↓ (18.7 days)
85 Astatine 219   88 Radium 223
↓ (54 sec)   ↓ (11.4 days)
83 Bismuth 215   86 Radon 219
(7.4 min) ↘   ↙ (3.96 sec)
84 Polonium 215
↙ (1.78 ms) ↘
82 Lead 211   85 Astatine 215
(36.1 min) ↘   ↙ (100 s)
83 Bismuth 211
↙ (2.14 min) ↘
81 Thallium 207   84 Polonium 211
(1.33 sec) ↘   ↙ (25.5 sec)
82 Lead 207

In all these series it can be seen that the nuclei decay by either an alpha or a beta emission. For example 83Bismuth-214 ($_{83}Bi^{214}$) can "choose" between alpha or beta decay but it can't go both ways at once. When $_{83}Bi^{214}$ decays, a certain fixed fraction of them will go one way and the rest will go the other. That may affect the path taken through the decay series but the end result for the Uranium Series is always $_{82}Pb^{206}$.

Radioactive decay only ever occurs by either emitting a beta particle which changes a neutron into a proton, keeping the weight the same but increasing the atomic number one position up—or alternatively by an alpha decay, which decreases the weight by four, which forms an atom two down in atomic number and four down in atomic weight. There are therefore four unique series of decay charts, each starting with the heaviest atom in the series existing on our planet. (There can't be a fifth or sixth, for a sixth series, for example, would simply be a replay of the second series, as six minus four is two.)

The Thorium Series

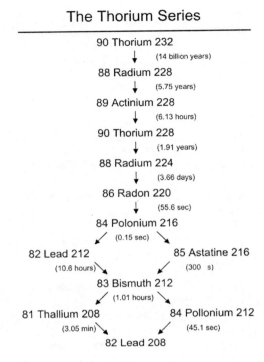

In nuclear physics, there needs to be a way of describing how fast particular isotopes decay. It is not possible to ever know when any single individual nucleus will "decide" to decay; that's totally random. However, as with most random processes, there is something we can say about the statistics. Let's go back to the time-honoured example of tossing a coin.

If you toss a perfectly balanced coin, then there is no way of knowing whether the result will be heads or tails. Also, if you keep tossing the coin then there is no way of knowing how many tosses it will take until you do get "heads". Another way of saying that is, if you toss the coin once per second, then there is no telling how much time will pass before you toss "heads". But we all know that if you toss the coin enough times or for long enough, then half of the time you will get heads and half tails. If you don't then the coin is not perfectly balanced. We say there is a 50% chance of heads on any given toss. There is a way of applying the same concept to radioactive nuclei.

Take a single nucleus of some isotope, for example, oxygen-19 that was mentioned earlier. Watch a single $_8O^{19}$ atom for 26.9 seconds and there is a 50% chance that you will see its nucleus decay (if we could see something that small). Single atoms are difficult to keep track of so a more practical

The Neptunium Series

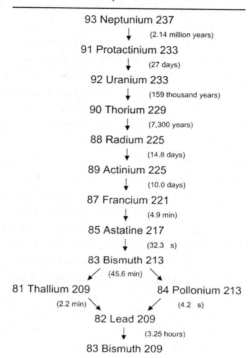

93 Neptunium 237
   ↓   (2.14 million years)
91 Protactinium 233
   ↓   (27 days)
92 Uranium 233
   ↓   (159 thousand years)
90 Thorium 229
   ↓   (7,300 years)
88 Radium 225
   ↓   (14.8 days)
89 Actinium 225
   ↓   (10.0 days)
87 Francium 221
   ↓   (4.9 min)
85 Astatine 217
   ↓   (32.3 s)
83 Bismuth 213
   ↙ (45.6 min) ↘
81 Thallium 209   84 Pollonium 213
(2.2 min)↘   ↙ (4.2 s)
82 Lead 209
   ↓   (3.25 hours)
83 Bismuth 209

approach is to watch a lot of O^{19} atoms. Now regardless of how many you watch, in 26.9 seconds half of them will decay. This time interval is a characteristic of the isotope, and is called the half-life. The longer the half-life of an isotope then obviously the more stable it is. We've already mentioned uranium-238 with its half-life of 4.5 billion years. Start with one ton of uranium-238, wait 4.5 billion years and you will have half a ton left, the other half will have turned into lead via the sequence described before. Of course, some isotopes are so stable that they never decay. Lead has three of these, $_{82}Pb^{206}$, $_{82}Pb^{207}$ and $_{82}Pb^{208}$.

How can we possibly measure half-lives like that of uranium-238 at 4.5 billion years?

There are always some uranium nuclei decaying in any sample. In a microgram of uranium-238, a tiny speck barely a couple of thousandths of an inch across (0.04 mm), there are 2.5 million billion atoms. In 4.5 billion years you expect half of these to decay, that's an average of about 300,000 a year, or one every two minutes. Actually the decay rate is a bit higher than this at the start, about one every 80 seconds because there is more there to decay. Even us short-lived humans can keep track of the decays when they occur this frequently. So by measuring the rate of decay in a known amount of uranium, we can work backwards to determine its half-life.

All the elements heavier than uranium have half-lives that are short compared to the age of our solar system, so even if they did exist at the time of the earth's formation they have long since decayed away. Only uranium still exists because of the exceptionally long half-lives of its two major isotopes. Plutonium-239, the longest-lived isotope of that much-maligned element, has a half-life of only 24,000 years; there can't be any plutonium left from the early days of the solar system, but it does exist naturally in minute quantities, as we will see.

There are no completely stable elements heavier than bismuth-209 ($_{83}Bi^{209}$). Thorium-232 is heavier and with a half-life of 14 billion years comes about as close as you can get to being stable without quite making it. Rhenium-187 is lighter than bismuth but is still slightly unstable, it has a half-life of 45 billion years. At the opposite end of the half-life spectrum is polonium-212, which has a half-life of only 0.0000003 seconds!

Surprisingly, there are also two lighter elements, technetium and promethium, which do not occur naturally. The longest-lived isotopes of these two elements have half-lives of 2.6 million years and 17.7 years respectively. These elements have never been found in any minerals on earth. There is one report that the characteristic spectral signature of promethium may have been detected in one star in the Andromeda nebula—and that must be about as rare as you can get.

The radiations in radioactive decay

When a radioactive element decays, something gets "spat out". That's how we detect the fact that a nucleus has decayed, by looking for the things that are emitted. You can also look for the changes in chemistry that occur when one element changes into another. But that's a lot more difficult.

Shortly after radioactivity was first discovered it was realized that three different types of "particles" or "rays" were being emitted. These were broadly classified according to their ability to penetrate matter and were named after the first three letters in the Greek alphabet—alpha, beta and gamma. Alpha particles could be stopped by a piece of paper. Beta particles could penetrate a few millimetres of aluminium. Finally, there were gamma rays, which could pass through several centimetres of lead. It was only later that it was discovered that alpha particles were two protons and two neutrons stuck together, effectively a helium nucleus. Beta particles were just electrons, and gamma rays were not particles but were simply a more energetic form of x-rays (both being electromagnetic radiation, just like light).

In alpha and beta decay, the nucleus changes dramatically and a lot of energy is released. Often this energy comes out in the "kinetic" energy of the alpha or beta particle—that's the energy of motion. Faster particles carry more kinetic energy. However, both alpha and beta emissions are commonly accompanied by the emission of a gamma ray. The particle comes out with a little less energy and the gamma ray takes the rest. Most of the decays shown in the uranium-238 decay sequence earlier in this chapter are accompanied by gamma ray emissions.

When an alpha particle is emitted the number of protons left in the nucleus decreases and the nucleus changes to one of a different element.

As mentioned, it is convenient to think of a neutron as a proton and an electron stuck together. The neutron has no charge as the negative electron and the positive proton cancel out each other's charge. In beta particle decay, a beta particle (which is an electron) is emitted from the nucleus. One of the neutrons has given up its close-knit electron leaving the proton bit left. The neutron has thus become a proton. Now the nucleus, with one extra proton and one less neutron, is that of an element one step up on the table of elements. It still has the same atom weight, as protons and neutrons weigh almost the same. Lead has 82 protons in its nucleus. Bismuth has 83. Now 82Lead-214 has 82 protons and 132 neutrons so when lead-214 decays by emitting a beta particle it ends up with 83 protons and 131 neutrons and so becomes 83Bismuth-214.

Beta decay only occurs in elements with more neutrons than protons. However sometimes nuclei with fewer neutrons than protons are created. These also decay by beta emission, but this time the beta particle is actually a positron, the antimatter counterpart to an electron. Positrons are like electrons but they carry positive charge. When a positron is emitted, one of the protons changes into a neutron. The element moves one step down the table of elements but retains the same overall weight.

Positrons can't survive long; very quickly, they will encounter an electron. When this happens the positron and electron "annihilate" each another and two very energetic gamma rays are given off in opposite directions. Positron emissions are used in a medical diagnostic procedure called Positron Emission Tomography (PET). A cyclotron (small particle accelerator) is used to smash protons into targets to produce short-lived isotopes, usually of oxygen, nitrogen or carbon, with an excess of protons in their nuclei. These isotopes are then chemically combined into tracer drugs or chemicals that are injected into the patient. The tracers are designed to accumulate in the area where some biochemical process takes place. As the positrons are emitted, they annihilate electrons; the two gamma rays travelling in opposite directions are then detected outside the patient's body. The information is processed in much the same way as a CAT scan that fires a beam of x-rays from a revolving x-ray generator through the patient. But PET scans measure biochemical activity rather than physical structure.

A decay mode that competes with positron emission is called K-capture. One of the inner electrons that normally buzzes about close to the nucleus in the K-shell falls into the nucleus and combines with a proton to become a neutron. In the weird equations of nuclear physics, absorbing an electron is essentially the same as emitting a positron. In this case, when the electron and proton marry to form a neutron, a tiny neutrino is emitted—the reverse of neutron decay which emits an anti-neutrino. The neutrino released during K-capture is virtually impossible to detect. But we can detect K-capture because the remaining orbital electrons "fall down" to occupy the space left vacant in the K-shell and in the process emit x-rays (low-energy gamma rays) with precisely predictable energies.

Gamma rays don't carry away any of the particles in the nucleus. Gamma rays carry away energy. This usually happens when a nucleus is left jiggling about either as the result of a violent collision with another particle or because it was left that way as the result of a previous radioactive decay. One way to visualize it is to image the nucleus as a drop of water. After some disturbance, the drop of water may be spinning like a top or it may be wobbling like a lump of jelly. When it is doing either of these things it's slightly more energetic, and it may relieve itself of this extra energy by emitting a tiny pulse of electromagnetic radiation. The nucleus is still the same nucleus, it's just settled itself down.

For example, 5Boron-12 can decay to 6Carbon-12, by emitting a beta particle with a specific amount of energy. But a small fraction of the time, $_5B^{12}$ emits a less energetic beta particle resulting in a $_6C^{12}$ nucleus that is left "excited" with excess energy. The excited $_6C^{12}$ nucleus will then emit a gamma ray to get rid of this energy.

There are other modes of radioactive decay, for example delayed emission of a neutron following a beta decay, but these are far less common so we can ignore them here. However, two other nuclear processes that are vitally important and can't be ignored here are the fission and fusion of nuclei.

The difference between fission and fusion

All radioactive decay is driven by nuclei trying to reach a more stable configuration. In the process, energy is released either as a gamma ray or as the kinetic energy of the escaping alpha or beta particles. The way that nuclear physicists measure the stability of a nucleus is in terms of something called "binding energy per nucleon". A nucleon is a generic term for protons and neutrons. Binding energy per nucleon sounds complicated, but it's not really.

If you happen to have an old school physics or chemistry book you can look up the atomic mass of the hydrogen and helium atoms in the periodic table. To keep life simple when dealing with the weights of such tiny things as atoms, physicists have defined something called an "atomic mass unit" or "u" for short. You'll find hydrogen listed as having a mass of 1.00794 u and helium as having a mass of 4.00206 u. If you look a bit further you will also find the mass of a neutron as being 1.00867 u.

A helium atom consists of two protons, two neutrons and two electrons, the equivalent of two hydrogen atoms plus two neutrons. If we add the mass of two neutrons to two hydrogen atoms, we get 4.03322 u. But the mass of helium is only 4.00206 u. Where did that little bit of mass difference of 0.03116 u go to? It went into "binding energy". Einstein's famous $E = mc^2$ equation tells us that mass and energy are interchangeable and in this case some of the mass has indeed become energy.

The easiest way to think of it is to imagine converting the helium atom back into two separate hydrogen atoms and two neutrons. You'd need to get some extra mass from somewhere. Einstein tells us that this is equivalent to feeding in some energy—in other words you'd have to work hard and expend energy to pull the helium atom apart. The energy you put into pulling the helium apart actually creates that little bit of extra mass.

For now, what is important is to understand that binding energy is the glue that holds a nucleus together; the more binding energy per nucleon, the better the nucleus is stuck together. If you did a similar calculation for all the elements in the periodic table, you'd find that the very light and very heavy elements have less binding energy per nucleon than those in the middle, like iron.

All nuclear reactions tend towards an increase in binding energy. It's a bit like a road built across a valley. On one side of the valley live the light nuclei—they'd like to roll down the road on their hillside to reach the bottom. On the other side of the valley are the heavy nuclei—they'd like to do the same thing. In the bottom of the valley live "iron" and his mates, who are happy enough where they are. Fortunately for us there are a lot of potholes in the road and most of the nuclei are stuck in them, not going anywhere—these are the nuclei of stable elements. There are also some shallow potholes barely capable of holding a nucleus back—these are where the radioactive elements live.

If you try hard enough, you can knock a nucleus out of its pothole and it will roll a little way down the hill before getting stuck again. On the "light" side of the valley, the hillside is steep and the potholes are generally deep. On the "heavy" side of the valley, the slope is gentler but the potholes are shallower.

Very heavy nuclei, like those of uranium, normally decay by alpha emission, which would be like a jump from one pothole to the next downhill. Sometimes they decide to take a different approach and they gallop down the hill. They then, in effect, trip and split apart to form smaller bits. These new bits are now totally different elements and generally more stable.

Uranium has quite a number of known isotopes but only two are of interest to us here. Uranium-238, which we've already talked about, makes up 99.3% of all uranium on our planet. The other 0.7% is practically all uranium-235. Both uranium-238 and uranium-235 are normally alpha emitters. Uranium-235 has a half-life of 704 million years—short compared to its more common brother. Sometimes, these uranium nuclei undergo something called spontaneous fission—the nucleus breaks into two pieces of roughly equal size. This is the one that tripped and split from falling down the hill. Over time, about one in every 18,000 U-238 nuclei will decay by spontaneous fission instead of by alpha decay. For uranium-235 the figure is about one in 140 million. Several of the plutonium isotopes also undergo this spontaneous fission.

What's more important is that uranium-235 and plutonium-239 nuclei can be forced to fission by bombarding them with neutrons and so release their pent-up energy. The process is called induced fission. Neutrons are ideal for the job. They carry no electric charge so if you fire them at a nucleus there is no electrostatic force to push them away. If a uranium-235 nucleus is struck by a neutron then it can absorb the neutron and become U^{236}. But that doesn't last long; in the process of absorbing the neutron the U^{236} nucleus becomes highly excited, so much so that within about a pico-second (1 trillionth of a second) it breaks up into two pieces. An enormous amount of energy is released in the process. Free neutrons are also released. Some of these neutrons come out immediately, but some, 0.6% for uranium-235, come out a little later (delayed neutrons) as the two new nuclei decay to more stable configurations. The extra free neutrons make nuclear bombs and nuclear reactors possible. The delayed neutrons however are particularly important in reactor design.

On the other side of the valley, getting a light nucleus out of its relatively deep pothole and down the hill towards the mid-weight elements can be a bit more complicated. A stable light nucleus can only become a heavier nucleus by addition, by adding a neutron, a proton or another nucleus. That won't happen spontaneously, but it will occur under the right circumstances. This is called fusion because the bits are forced to fuse together.

One way of turning light elements into heavier elements is to bombard stationary targets with either protons or neutrons. That has been done for many years using particle accelerators to create special radioactive isotopes for scientific and medical uses. This method generally requires a target made from one of the lighter metals and is an expensive way to make small quantities of special isotopes.

What we are really interested in here is when two light nuclei combine to form a heavier nucleus. You can do this by accelerating the nuclei towards each other, but it's difficult to get two nuclei to collide head on. There are two problems. Firstly, you have to have them heading directly at each other and secondly, you've got to give them enough speed so that they can get close enough together to fuse. Remember, both nuclei carry a positive charge so there is an ever-increasing repulsive force between them. This dominates until they get close enough for the "strong nuclear force" to become effective and pull then all the way in.

It is possible to fuse light nuclei together by colliding beams of atoms that have been accelerated to very high speeds. The trouble with this approach is that direct fusing impacts are very unlikely. Mostly what happens is the atoms collide at glancing angles and bounce apart. The energy needed to generate the colliding beams is often billions of times the amount of energy released by any fusion reactions that do occur.

Another way to get lots of nuclei going fast enough to create fusion reactions is to make them very hot. As a gas heats up, the average speed at which its atoms (or molecules) move about increases. Heating up a gas is an easy way to make a lot of atoms move very fast. The trouble is that you have to rely on luck for two atoms in a hot gas to collide head on. But it does happen if you can keep the gas confined in a small enough volume. Temperatures in the tens of millions of degrees are required before hydrogen atoms will fuse together, and even then it's only a small percentage that will be going fast enough. At these temperatures molecules break apart and electrons buzz about independently of their atom's nucleus—we have what is called a plasma rather than a gas.

Reaching those temperatures is actually not too difficult; the main problem is really keeping the nuclei close together—the confinement problem. One place where nature has solved the confinement problem is the centre of stars like our sun. Here the enormous pressures and temperatures force light nuclei, mostly hydrogen, close enough that some of them will fuse. When they do fuse, an enormous amount of energy is released, both as kinetic energy of the fusion products and in the form of gamma rays. That energy is the source of solar energy. The outside of a star glows because of the heat produced in the core; the hydrogen in the outer layers is not fusing.

Fusion is easier to achieve with small light nuclei because they have less positive charge and smaller repulsive forces. It's even easier if you can get light nuclei with an excess of neutrons because the neutrons make the nuclei bigger targets and they don't have to get as close before the strong nuclear force takes over.

The easiest fusion reaction to achieve is the fusion of two tritium nuclei. Tritium is an extremely heavy form of hydrogen. It's hydrogen with two neutrons, $_1H^3$ and it's half again as heavy as deuterium, $_1H^2$ or heavy hydrogen. Unfortunately tritium is very rare. Minute quantities are formed in the atmosphere by cosmic ray bombardment of the hydrogen nuclei in water vapour, but it rapidly decays into 2Helium-3 with a half-life of just 12.32 years.

The next best fusion reaction is the combination of deuterium, $_1H^2$, with tritium, $_1H^3$. The third best is the fusion of two deuterium nuclei. There are very few water molecules made from deuterium atoms in ordinary water but there certainly is a lot of water to work with.

Any fusion reaction involving a nucleus with more protons than hydrogen—and that's all the other elements—becomes more and more difficult the heavier the element is.

Even this simple introduction to fission and fusion probably seems a bit complex. But all you really need to remember is that fission is the breaking apart of heavy elements and fusion is the combining together of light elements. Both processes produce energy in the form of heat and gamma rays. Fission is relatively easy to achieve and control; all you need is some uranium, preferably uranium-235, and some free neutrons. Fusion, on the other hand, is generally difficult; you need lots of light nuclei at temperatures in the tens of millions of degrees and you need to somehow keep them contained at these temperatures.

How nuclear bombs work

Nuclear bombs using uranium and plutonium rely on the induced fission of nuclei to liberate vast amounts of energy very quickly.

Fission in uranium occurs most easily in the isotope uranium-235 that makes up a small portion of natural uranium, just 0.71%; the rest is uranium-238, with trace quantities of plutonium and other uranium isotopes. Natural uranium refined into metallic form is a very dense lackluster metal. A golf-ball-sized piece would weigh a couple of pounds (about a kilogram). It is quite safe, safe enough to use as a paperweight on your desk.

The physics and engineering involved in making a uranium bomb are not at all difficult. Getting enough high-quality weapons-grade uranium— about 90% pure uranium-235—however is extremely difficult. Because uranium-235 and uranium-238 are isotopes of the same metal, their chemical behavior is identical. The only factor that can be used to separate them is their different weights. Uranium-235 is about 1% lighter than uranium-238. That is why whenever you hear about nuclear arms control, it is always plutonium that's mentioned. Separating out plutonium from a mixture of nuclear fuels is vastly simpler than separating uranium-235 from a mass of uranium-238.

When the United States set out to make the first uranium bomb they had first to develop a practical technology to separate out the uranium-235. One proposed method involved firing ionized uranium atoms through a magnetic field; the lighter atoms follow a slightly different path than the heavier atoms, so you could catch them separately. The magnetic separation plant, built during the war, used 6,000 tons of silver (borrowed from the U.S. Treasury and later returned) for the windings on the electromagnets. It was housed in buildings that were, for that time, the largest ever constructed. However this system proved impractical and was abandoned.

The method that was finally used involved reacting the uranium with fluorine to produce uranium fluoride gas. The slightly lighter portion of this gas containing uranium-235 atoms would diffuse through barriers just a tiny bit faster than the heavier portion. After diffusing the gas through a succession of barriers, the percentage of uranium-235 gradually rises. The same technology is still used to "enrich" uranium up to the point where it contains about 3% uranium-235 which is sufficient for use in commercial power reactors.

A nuclear bomb relies on something called a critical mass of uranium-235 (or $_{94}Pu^{239}$). It works like this. When a uranium-235 nucleus fissions, a few free neutrons are produced as we have noted. If one of those free neutrons collides with another uranium-235 nucleus then it can cause induced fission in the second nucleus and more neutrons will be produced. Those neutrons go on to induce more fissions and more neutrons. A so-called chain reaction occurs.

In a small piece of uranium-235, almost all of the neutrons produced by fission will escape out of the metal before they can produce another fission event. But if the piece of uranium-235 is large enough almost all the neutrons will collide with another uranium-235 nucleus and have a chance to induce a fission before they reach the surface of the metal and escape. If the rate at which neutrons can be produced by fission exactly equals the rate at which neutrons escape from the metal we have just enough metal to form a critical mass. With more than the critical mass, the production of neutrons will escalate out of control producing a rapid release of energy that physically breaks up the mass. If a considerably oversized mass is assembled, almost instantaneously and with great precision, it explodes violently.

The determination of how much uranium would constitute a critical mass was a key point in the development of the first uranium bomb. Werner Heisenberg, who did early work on developing a nuclear bomb program for the Germans, calculated that several tons of pure uranium-235 would be required. On learning of the detonation of the Hiroshima bomb, he could not understand how the Americans had produced enough uranium-235. Heisenberg had miscalculated; the critical mass for a sphere of uranium-235 is only about 100 pounds or 50 kilograms.

Now, suppose you can get your hands on this much uranium-235. Make a spherical target from most of the uranium then bore a cylindrical hole in one side of the sphere. From the rest of the uranium, make a slug that will fit neatly into that hole. Put the slug in a gun barrel. Block the other end of the gun barrel with the spherical target. Stand well clear and fire the gun. When the slug of uranium fills the hole in the sphere, a "super-critical mass" is instantaneously formed and an atomic explosion results.

It has become generally believed that you only need a critical mass for a nuclear explosion to occur, but this is not so. A critical mass can only sustain a chain reaction; you need a super-critical mass to ensure that the reaction builds up fast enough to cause an explosion rather than a mild "fizzle".

The gun design was used to make the first atomic bomb. The long thin shape of the gun barrel used for achieving super-critical assembly was what inspired the Thin Man code name used at Los Alamos during the bomb development.

That's about all there is to it, although there are a lot of refinements one needs to make to get a bomb reliable and "efficient". One thing always necessary is to be sure there are some free neutrons around to kick-start the reaction. Although uranium-235 and uranium-238 generate neutrons from spontaneous fission, it happens too infrequently for a reliable start. Even a 50 kg piece of 90% uranium-235 will only produce about 100 neutrons a second by spontaneous fission. But you can increase the number of neutrons by mixing in some lighter nuclei. For example, a little boron can be added to the uranium. The alpha particles emitted by natural decay of the uranium will collide with the boron nuclei to produce nitrogen nuclei and free neutrons—enough to ensure the chain reaction really gets going.

It is also critical to get the size of the explosive charge that drives the uranium down the gun barrel just right. The two pieces of uranium metal have to come together fast enough to avoid a problem called pre-ignition. In pre-ignition, a chain reaction starts but it only produces enough heat to blow the assembling mass of uranium apart, not enough to fission a significant part of the mass and produce a real explosion.

At Los Alamos, an experiment to determine the required critical mass of uranium was undertaken. It was dubbed "tickling the dragon's tail". A small slug of uranium-235 hydride was dropped through the open centre of an almost critical mass of the same material. As the slug passed through, the pile would become critical and generate tens of megawatts of heat, but only for a fraction of a second. Workers in nearby labs were known to take long hikes away from the area when they knew these tests were being undertaken. And there were accidents tickling the dragon's tail. On one occasion, in February 1945, enough heat was generated to melt some of the uranium and two experimenters received fatal doses of radiation from a tiny flash of pre-ignition.

You can also arrange to put some uranium-238 around the critical mass to help reflect some of the neutrons back into the uranium-235 to get a higher "yield". Usually only a tiny part of the uranium-235 will fission in such a bomb; despite your best efforts, the super-critical mass will be blown apart by the chain reaction before all the uranium-235 nuclei can fission. Only about 1% of the uranium in the Hiroshima bomb actually fissioned.

In contrast to a uranium bomb, making a plutonium bomb presents almost the opposite set of problems. Plutonium can be made from uranium-238 in a so-called breeder reactor—more about this later. The uranium-238 is bombarded with neutrons to produce $_{92}U^{239}$. U^{239} quickly decays by emitting a beta particle to form neptunium-239. Neptunium has 93 protons in its nucleus so this isotope would be written as $_{93}Np^{239}$. It then in turn emits another beta particle to become 94Plutonium-239.

However, to build a bomb out of plutonium is vastly more complicated.

You can't simply shoot two blocks together. The problem is that the chain reaction in plutonium builds up so fast that it will blow the assembling masses apart before they can become super-critical. No gun can fire the plutonium pieces together fast enough. Originally, J. Robert Oppenheimer at Los Alamos believed that the gun assembly would work for both plutonium and uranium. When it was finally realized that a gun could only be used for uranium, the barrel was shortened and took on the name Little Boy.

The problem with plutonium is that one of its isotopes, Pu^{240}, likes to spontaneously fission, releasing free neutrons in the process. Although you need some free neutrons to initiate the chain reaction in the bomb, but too many too early can cause excessive heating before the super-critical mass is properly assembled. The chances of pre-ignition when using plutonium are far greater than with uranium. Chemists at Los Alamos went to a great deal of care to ensure that there were no light nuclei, like boron, in the plutonium so that there would not be too many free neutrons about.

The longer the plutonium stays inside the reactor where it is made, the greater the proportion of plutonium-240 that will build up. Weapons-grade plutonium is generally taken to mean plutonium with less than 7% plutonium-240. Plutonium for use in power reactors can have much higher levels of plutonium-240. While you can chemically remove light nuclei that might cause an excess of neutrons, the separation of the only slightly heavier $_{94}Pu^{240}$ from $_{94}Pu^{239}$ is an even more monumentally difficult task than separating the heavier uranium-238 from uranium-235. The plutonium-240 is one neutron heaver than plutonium-239. Whereas uranium-238 is three neutrons heaver than uranium-235.

About 35 pounds (16 kg) of plutonium was used in the original plutonium bomb design. The metal was carefully machined into subcritical pieces that could be fitted together very precisely to form a hollow sphere. The whole thing was then surrounded with conventional explosives. The explosives were specially shaped and fitted together to form a sphere around the plutonium. The assembly looks like a huge soccer ball. When detonated simultaneously, the explosives generated a perfectly uniform, spherical shock wave travelling in creating an "implosion". Of course, there was also a shock wave travelling outwards, an "explosion", but that has no bearing on the functioning of the bomb. The pressure inside such a spherical shock wave is enormous and proved enough to compress the plutonium metal into a super-critical mass.

But even this construction needed some additional sophisticated refinements. Having gone to a great deal of trouble to remove all the contaminant light nuclei you'd find that, even with the presence of plutonium-240, the reaction would still not start fast enough to cause more than a relatively small explosion, the equivalent of maybe a thousand tons of TNT. So a trigger was needed.

A tiny quantity of beryllium and polonium at the centre of the plutonium sphere did the trick. The polonium produces alpha particles, which are absorbed by the beryllium to form a radioactive isotope of carbon. The carbon isotope immediately decays and so produces the necessary neutrons. At detonation the whole thing must fuse perfectly, and it's all got to happen in about one ten millionth of a second. Only then did the plutonium atomic bomb work effectively.

The round shape of the final huge assembly that comprised the plutonium bomb gave rise to the code name Fat Man.

Thanks to the extensive nuclear test programs carried out in the past, plutonium bombs can now be made using far less material. The manufacturing process however, is still extremely complex.

How hydrogen bombs work

Hydrogen bombs or fusion bombs don't use the "splitting " or fission action to operate. They use the "joining together" action or the fusion action to produce energy. Hydrogen bombs are therefore quite complicated to make. The first hydrogen bomb, detonated in the Marshall Islands by the United States in 1952, stood three stories high and weighed 70 tons—but it worked. Development proceeded quickly during the 1950s. The first fission bombs produced explosions equivalent to about 15,000 tons of TNT. The first hydrogen bomb produced an explosion equivalent to 50 million tons, or 50 megatonnes, of TNT, that's 3,000 times bigger.

Edward Teller is usually credited as the father of the hydrogen bomb. He actually started work on the design at Los Alamos before work on the first fission bombs had even been completed. For more on Teller see "Super safe nuclear reactors" in this chapter.

A small sphere shape of very exotic conditions has to be created to produce a fusion reaction and explosion. Such conditions normally only occur at the centre of stars. To build this into a warhead that has to travel on a missile travelling through the atmosphere at many thousands of miles per hour, is not an easy job. Nevertheless, several countries have now successfully detonated hydrogen bombs and built missiles to deliver them.

To build a fusion bomb, a conventional fission bomb is first constructed. Then a few modifications are added. When a fission bomb explodes, temperatures at the very centre of the explosion can reach nearly 100 million degrees centigrade.

That's the first explosion. The temperatures and pressures generated near the centre are enough to fuse hydrogen. So the fusion bomb is surrounded with a layer rich in hydrogen atoms. However, to make it more workable deuterium (heavy hydrogen) is used. Deuterium fuses much easier than normal hydrogen. Fusing deuterium nuclei also releases lots of neutrons. The deuterium is also chemically combined with 3Lithium-7 to form solid lithium deuteride. In this way as many deuterium nuclei are packed in as close as possible.

When the fusion bomb ignites, it will not only produce the temperatures and pressures needed, it also produces large numbers of high-energy neutrons. These neutrons will actually cause the Li^7 to fission into helium-4 and hydrogen-3 (tritium). As noted, tritium in combination with deuterium is an even better fusion fuel than deuterium alone.

When the deuterium and tritium nuclei are subjected to the enormous temperatures and pressures of the first fission explosion, they begin to fuse. This forms an instantaneous second explosion. This is the fusion reaction. And that is the hydrogen bomb.

But why stop there? The whole construction can then be enclosed in a metal casing made of normally inert, common, garden variety, straight-out-of-the-ground uranium-238. The dense uranium-238 forms a good "tamper" to help confine the pressure of the fusion bomb and make a better fusion environment.

But that's not all. Now the high-energy neutrons from the fusion explosion come into play. You can't make an atomic bomb from uranium-238. That isotope is normally not regarded a fissionable material. But it will fission quite happily if it is hit by very high-energy neutrons. The second explosion is the fusion explosion or the hydrogen bomb explosion and it releases a burst of neutrons so intense that the normally inert outer uranium-238 casing will itself "ignite".

This produces an instantaneous and enormous third nuclear explosion—another fission explosion.

Most of the energy released in hydrogen bombs comes from the second and third nuclear "events".

There is another bomb concept called a neutron bomb. In this bomb the outer tamper is made of a metal such as lead, which does not itself explode but instead produces an even more massive quantity of high energy, very lethal neutrons. This weapon is not used to destroy the target. It is described as a "clean" bomb. It is used to kill the inhabitants but still leave the area ready for immediate reoccupation. That, of course, is the type of result that the best military weapons are designed to accomplish. After all that's what territorial wars are all about.

Another variation which was proposed, but hopefully will never be built, is the cobalt bomb. It is the complete opposite as it is the ultimate "dirty bomb". It would produce long lasting lethal levels of radiation where it exploded and so create a permanent wasteland. But it gets worse. The tamper would be made from cobalt-59. When Co^{59} is bombarded with neutrons it forms Co^{60}. Co^{60} produces high-energy, highly penetrating gamma rays as it decays. Co^{60} with a half-life of about five years is extremely deadly. With this bomb, radioactive cobalt-60 would spread around the world before it decayed to any reasonably safe level. The dust cloud would coat things indiscriminately, everywhere.

Theoretically people could hide in shelters for a short while and survive the worst effects of a conventional nuclear war. But with a cobalt bomb they would have to shelter for decades. Leo Szilard, co-author with Albert Einstein of the letter to President Roosevelt, which prompted the Americans to begin work on nuclear weapons, coined the term "doomsday device" for such a bomb.

Individuals cannot build cobalt bombs. But cobalt bombs could easily be built by some fanatical military dictator and hold the world to ransom. That must not ever be allowed to happen, ever, under any circumstances.

There is also the possibility of terrorists constructing a baby "dirty" bomb. This generally refers to a device containing conventional explosives packed with highly radioactive materials. It would be planned to disperse large amounts of radioactive material into the surrounding neighbourhood. The reality is that such a bomb is more of a psychological weapon than a weapon of really massive death or destruction. There are a lot of chemicals that can be used that would be far more lethal and permanent than radioactive materials in such a bomb.

Depleted uranium: huff and puff

Depleted uranium has been developed into a antinuclear public relations gimmick. Depleted uranium has been made to appear as somehow something worse than natural uranium. That is the power of the antinuclear lobbyist. It is more logical to describe the material as cleaned uranium or safe uranium because that's what it is. Naturally occurring uranium is mined. Then as much of the radioactive uranium-235 as is possible is extracted from the parent metal. It is now depleted of the very important radioactive isotope. It's safer than naturally occurring uranium.

Uranium is about 70% heavier than lead, so it's an ideal metal from which to machine armour-piercing bullets. The International Atomic Energy Agency's laboratory in Siebersdorf, Austria, under pressure from the antinuclear advocates, tested sites in Kosovo where the bullets were used. They also assessed the possibility of health risks. Risks were determined to be ludicrously low. Then it was argued that the bullets contained plutonium and therefore could be some kind of threat. Tests could not find any evidence that even vaguely suggested this as a threat. They couldn't even detect the existence of plutonium. The UK Royal Society and the European Union also looked at the "depleted uranium issue" and came to the same conclusion as the International Atomic Energy Agency. The whole concept of depleted uranium as a human health problem is part of an antinuclear public relations fairy story. Nothing more.

The natural background radiation we live in

The solar system is between four and six billion years old. The supernova explosion which produced the heavy elements in our planet might have occurred a few billion years at most before that. Elements such as uranium, formed in that supernova blast, have been undergoing radioactive decay ever since.

Uranium-238 has a half-life of 4.5 billion years and, 4.5 billion years after the supernova blast, half of the uranium-238 that was produced would have decayed to form lead-206. If the supernova blast occurred 9 billion years ago, then today there would only be a half of that half left or a quarter ($\frac{1}{2} \times \frac{1}{2} = \frac{1}{4}$) of the original uranium-238 still around.

The other "common" isotope of uranium is uranium-235 which has a half-life of "only" 700 million years. Nine billion years is about 13 times the half-life of uranium-235. The quantity of uranium-235 has therefore "halved" 13 times and $\frac{1}{2} \times \frac{1}{2} \times \frac{1}{2} \times \frac{1}{2} \times \frac{1}{2} \times \frac{1}{2} \times \frac{1}{2} \times \frac{1}{2} \times \frac{1}{2} \times \frac{1}{2} \times \frac{1}{2} \times \frac{1}{2} \times \frac{1}{2} = 0.000122$. So there would be a little more than one ten-thousandth of the original uranium-235 left. But even that small fraction, 0.0122%, still represents an enormous quantity in the earth's crust and oceans.

Any element with a half-life much less than uranium-235 will have decayed away completely; or at least to completely undetectable levels. The quantity of plutonium-239, with a half-life of only 24,000 years, would have halved so many times in 9 billion years that the fraction remaining is too small to be expressed in a meaningful way. Even if the entire solar system had been made of plutonium it would all have long since decayed into its more stable daughter elements. They are called "daughter elements" as sometimes they can in turn decay to create daughters of their own.

But there are still plenty of radioactive substances in our Earth's crust with much shorter half-lives. These isotopes exist because they are produced naturally, and continuously, from the gradual decomposition of some of the longer-lived isotopes. Have a look back at the decay series for uranium-238 shown earlier. As long as uranium-238 exists, there will be a source of supply for elements like radium and radon. Other long-lived isotopes that serve as a major source for many other radioactive elements are uranium-235, thorium-232, and potassium-40.

The decay of long-lived isotopes is not the only source of short-lived isotopes on our planet. Cosmic rays also play a role. Our planet is constantly bombarded by radiation coming from outer space. Some of this radiation is in the form of rays like gamma rays and x-rays but mostly it's in the form of very high-speed particles travelling close to the speed of light (186,000 miles per second or 300,000 km per second). About 2.5% of cosmic ray particles are large atomic nuclei, up to the size of the nucleus of an atom of iron. About 20% are super high-energy alpha particles and the rest are single protons. Some of the particles striking the earth come from our sun, but most come from ancient novas and supernovas. They are part of the remnants of those catastrophic explosions that distribute the heavy elements throughout the universe.

Our best high-energy atomic particle accelerators can only produce particles with energies that are peanuts in comparison to cosmic-ray energies. The cosmic rays constantly bombarding us from outer space include particles tens of millions of times more powerful and more deadly than those produced in our best accelerators. They were first called cosmic rays in 1925, because it was found that they did not originate on earth and nobody knew what they were or from whence they came. Now we know they are really cosmic particles.

Fortunately, our atmosphere acts as a shield, stopping most of these cosmic rays. When a cosmic ray particle hits the nucleus of an atom in the atmosphere new elements can be formed. Alpha, beta and gamma rays are given off and single neutrons are produced in the process. That's how cosmic rays get stopped. What we get at ground level is a constant shower of radioactivity produced from this high-altitude bombardment. Cosmic radiation is the only significant source of the traces of the lighter radioactive elements, like tritium and carbon-14 found in the earth's crust. They are formed from cosmic-ray particles hitting atmospheric gases.

The end result of all these processes is that we live in a sea of radioactivity. We always have and we always will. This radioactivity is referred to as background radiation. Also we are constantly receiving beta radiation from the decay of potassium-40 and carbon-14 that naturally occur in your own body. We are constantly breathing in radon gas that seeps up from the ground everywhere. You'll find radon-222 in the decay series of uranium-238 shown earlier. Radon-222 is an alpha emitter, and two of its immediate daughter nuclei decay rapidly to produce more alpha particles. Breathing alpha emitters into your lungs is considered to be about the most dangerous process of radiation exposure that you can get, yet we are all doing it all of the time. Gamma rays, because they are highly penetrating, can and do come from the decay of trace elements all around you.

In spite of this constant radiation dose we can all expect to live normal, happy and long lives provided other things don't bother us. Our lives are put at risk from such things as poor diet and lack of exercise; not from nuclear radiation at even hundreds of times current average background levels. Some radiation is good for you.

Radiation dosage and what it all means

For most of us, trying to understand levels of radiation exposure has become a "can of worms"—probably, deliberately so. We are bombarded with esoteric scientific jargon to the point where common sense gets totally buried in the verbiage. So let's cut to the chase.

When nuclear radiation hits our bodies in whatever form, some will pass straight through us missing everything. Some of the radiation will hit flesh or bone and be absorbed. The number of hits and the related effect is generally described as a dose.

To understand what it all means, imagine the radiation hits to be like tiny painless bee stings with one bee sting being made of thousands of particles. You can never feel them. The bee-sting analogy has its drawbacks as these bee stings are all through our body, not just on our skin as a real bee sting would be. Anything up to 250 "bee stings" is good for you. Above three or four thousand is usually fatal. The number of these "bee stings" is measured in units called sieverts (Sv). For small numbers, quantities are measured in millisieverts. A millisievert (mSv) is one-thousandth of a sievert. In our analogy we might say that one "bee sting" comprising thousands of nuclear particles and thousands of flashes of electromagnetic radiation, is one millisievert.

Some types of nuclear radiation have slightly more effect on human tissue. Some have less. But that's really all OK as the sievert unit was established to measure radiation effects on human beings. If it doesn't "sting" you somewhere in your body, it doesn't count. It therefore takes into account variations in specific radiation types. So, although the type of nuclear radiation may be quite different, a sievert of x-rays is much the same as a sievert of beta particles, and both are the same as, say, a sievert of high-speed neutrons. Therefore to understand and appreciate the level, or the amount of nuclear exposure being discussed, you don't really have to know any nuclear physics.

It is also pertinent that, like a number of bee stings, if a moderately high radiation dose is spread over a year or more, no permanent damage results as the human body constantly heals itself. A radiation dose spread over time, usually more than a few months is called a chronic dose.

If all the bee stings happen at once, or within a period too short for the healing process to have an effect, it is called an acute dose. For the same total dose an acute dose could be fatal whereas a chronic dose, being spread over time, would not be.

The size of a radiation dose in the media is described using a variety of units, which gets totally confusing. So for comparing radiation doses and understanding their meaning, it is easier to always think in sieverts (Sv) and millisieverts (mSv), being one-thousandth of a sievert. You'll find that if you stick with millisieverts (mSv) for everything and convert any other units to mSv, it will make understanding nuclear danger jargon very much simpler. More accurate definitions of units are given later along with the limits for health benefits through to lethal doses and all in sieverts or millisieverts.

These are the other units you may come across but for all practical purposes stick with mSv. When you read or hear about radiation, change all the units into mSv. Then radiation readings can be realistically appreciated and compared and you won't be fooled.

sievert (Sv) and millisievert (mSv) are now the most accepted general measure for radiation doses.

gray (Gy) and milligray (mGy) roughly mean the same as Sv and mSv and are the same size.

One hundred times smaller but also sometimes used in measuring radiation doses are the:

R the abbreviation for "roentgen"

RAD an abbreviation for "radiation"

REP the abbreviation for "roentgen equivalent physical"

REM the abbreviation for "roentgen equivalent man"

MREM (the millirem) is often used. Divide the dose by 100 to get mSv.

Measuring and knowing the radioactivity of a radiation source as opposed to a dose is usually totally irrelevant unless you work with radioactive substances. The media use the names of the units while generally not knowing what they are comparing. I think they use them just to bedazzle readers. For our purposes, the important gauge is not how much radiation potential they contain but how they affect us.

Measuring a radiation source

When a substance is radioactive, atoms in the substance are constantly breaking down. When this was first discovered a unit was suddenly needed to compare the radioactivity of various samples. The unit was called the curie.

The curie was named after Marie Curie who, with her husband Pierre Curie, discovered and isolated radium in 1898. They also isolated the element polonium. They showed that thorium was also slightly radioactive and determined how strong that radioactivity was.

The curie was originally defined as the number of disintegrations per second that occurred in one gram of radium. A teaspoon would hold about 75 grams of radium. The curie measures its "activity". Actually it is disintegrations in radium-226, but natural occurring radium is mainly radium-226 so there is little difference. The number was about 37 billion atomic disintegrations per second. The curie has now been redefined as exactly 37 billion disintegrations per second.

You might come across the term picocurie written as pCi. One picocurie is one trillionth of a curie. A picocurie is therefore as radioactive as a tiny one trillionth of a gram of radium. It is therefore 0.037 disintegrations per second. The actual number of breakdowns that occur, even in a small quantity of any radioactive substance, is always enormous. From a health point of view, counting them singly is meaningless. If picocuries were pepper you could sprinkle them on every meal you eat for the rest of your life in absolute and total safety.

Another unit was then created, the becquerel. The becquerel is one single disintegration per second. So it's 37 billion times smaller than the curie.

Extra: radiation measurements in more detail

The following more detailed explanation of radiation units will show that for all practical purposes:

The roentgen, REP, REM and RAD are all equal and all effectively mean the same thing.

The gray (Gy) and the sievert (Sv) are equal and both these units are 100 times bigger than the first four units mentioned.

All the units measure the same thing—the radiation you receive.

roentgen. One roentgen of radiation will produce about 2,000 million ions. The technical definition is, "one roentgen is the quantity of x-rays or gamma rays that will produce a number of ions, equivalent to one electrostatic unit of charge, in a cubic centimetre of air, at zero degrees C, and at one atmosphere pressure." The roentgen unit is no longer in common use.

REP or "roentgen equivalent physical". Alpha particles, beta particles, and neutrons also ionize tissue. The REP is the same size as the roentgen but has a slightly expanded definition that includes the ionizing effects of these particles. The REP is also rarely used now.

REM. Tissue varies between living things, so the REM, or "Roentgen Equivalent Man", was adopted and is defined as producing the same effect on human tissue as that of absorbing one roentgen of either x-rays or gamma rays. The REM takes into consideration such facts as an alpha particle having ten to twenty times the ionizing effect as a beta particle. Quite often you see the term "mrem" and of course this means millirem. The "mrem" (sometimes written as mR) is 100 times smaller than a "mSv". To illustrate: 250 mrem is equal to 2.5 mSv.

RAD The definition of the roentgen, the REP and the REM is based on ion production. However the ionization of different individual molecules in human tissue produce variation in the biological effect. A unit, the RAD, an abbreviation of "radiation", was introduced to get over this problem. When the RAD was adopted, the concept of defining it by ionizing effects was abandoned and the RAD is defined as a quantity of absorbed energy, not of actual ionization produced. A RAD is "any form of absorbed radiation that will liberate 100 ergs of energy per gram". The RAD has this particular energy definition for convenience to become virtually identical to the REM.

If you are reading about nuclear radiation, all these terms are equal and virtually all mean the same.

In 1960, scientists had an international Conference of Weights and Measures and decided on yet another "international metric system" of "international units", the "SI" system.

This system abandoned ergs and calories for energy, and adopted the joule, which is actually an electrical unit. The gram was dropped as the basic unit of weight, and the kilogram was adopted. Metres stayed as metres and seconds stayed as seconds. In addition, a number naming system was adopted. This numbering system rose in multiples of one thousand above the basic unit, and decreased in steps of one thousand below the basic unit.

The radiation units decreed are:

gray (Gy). The gray is the unit created for measuring "absorbed dose". One gray equals one joule of energy absorbed per kilogram. One gray therefore equals 100 rads. The milligray is denoted as mGy.

sievert. The sievert is the unit now adopted for measuring "the absorbed dose equivalent". This unit is becoming well accepted. One sievert also equals one joule of energy absorbed per kilogram. One sievert therefore equals 100 REM. The millisievert is denoted as mSv.

The becquerel (Bq) and the curie (Ci) measure how radioactive a rock or a sample of any material might be. It is not a measure of dose.

becquerel. When a substance is radioactive, atoms in the substance are constantly breaking down. One atom breaking down per second means the substance has an "activity" of one becquerel or one Bq.

curie. The original "unit of activity" is now defined as exactly 37 billion atomic disintegrations per second. That is 37 billion becquerels. (The radioactivity of air samples are often measured in pico-curies per litre. To make things confusing it is also often measured in becquerels per cubic metre. So to compare these two units the arithmetic will show that: 1 pico-curie per litre equals 37 bec-querels per cubic metre. For example 4 pC/l air means there are 4 times 37 which equals 148 disintegrations per second occurring in a one-cubic-metre-sample of that air. It can be written as 148 Bq per cubic metre.) For example if you see something being rated as having a radioactivity of 37 Bq then it is one billion times less radioactive than one single gram of radium. To put things in perspective, an average human being has an activity of around 10,000 Bq; that works out at about 100,000 Bq per cubic metre of flesh.

The linear no-threshold model and the zero-dose thesis

Despite the abundance of naturally occurring radioactivity around us and in us, the antinuclear movement constantly tries to convince us that any radiation, no matter how little, is dangerous. They claim that no matter how small the radiation levels are, they will always ultimately and inevitably cause frightening numbers of cancers and deaths. This dogmatism is based on the zero-dose thesis. It is also described as the linear no-threshold or LNT risk model. The antinuclear movement also likes to add in "terrible childhood mutations and deformities". Both these propaganda ploys are absolute fiction. The reality is that for the best of health we should receive a constant dose of nuclear radiation. Most of us don't get anywhere near enough.

The concept of the LNT model presumes that all nuclear radiation, or more accurately ionizing radiation, is harmful to human life and that the lower the radiation levels, the fewer people will die. And no matter how low the radiation level might become, what still remains will inevitably kill some small percentage of the human population.

There is a history to these idiotic concepts. The first tests on radiation effects were on genetic mutational changes and were done in 1911 by Her-man Muller, a graduate student at Columbia University. He experimented by irradiating fruit flies at various doses. The more radiation he subjected them to, the bigger the genetic effects. It was approximately a straight-line relationship. Therefore extrapolating backwards (but not testing) suggested that mutations would only cease at a zero dose rate. The U.S. Atomic Energy Commission, after World War II, irradiated thousands of mice by giving them short bursts of high-intensity radiation. They found that the more intense the radiation the greater was the following incidence of genetic mutation. Again the numbers were extrapolated back to zero radiation, producing zero radiation mutational changes. In other words a straightedge and a pencil was used to extend the line back to zero dose. Of course it came out at zero effect.

Apart from that nonsense flies are short-lived creatures and it's not unreasonable to argue that they would never have needed to develop repair mechanisms to cater for long-term exposure as bigger creatures would.

For testing general radiation damaging effects in other laboratories, animals were exposed to high and increasing radiation doses, until finally levels were reached where all the test animals died. It always seems logical and reasonable to argue that at a zero-dose level, death from ionizing radiation must be zero. So once again a line was drawn to connect the extreme dosages of the experiment to zero. From such tests the relative risks of soldiers exposed to high levels of nuclear fallout, or nuclear workers involved in accidents could be easily assessed. At high doses results were well studied. From such concepts came the zero-dose thesis and the linear no-threshold or LNT risk model.

In simple terms, the LNT argument says that if some dangerous dosage is reduced by 50%, then only 50% of the people will die from radiation poisoning or radiation-induced cancer. If the dosage level is reduced to 1%, then only one person in one hundred will die. If the dose rate is reduced to 0.1% of the lethal dose, then the LNT model says that the death rate reduces to one person in one thousand. The death rate is assumed to increase and decrease "linearly" with dose, with no safe minimum; hence the name linear no-threshold.

The origin of the linear no-threshold concept was explained in a paper "Radiobiology of Plutonium" in 1972. The paper explains that it was "adopted specifically on a basis of mathematical simplicity, not from radio-biological data, during the period between 1950 and 1964 as the only practicable mathematical approach to estimates of the maximum effects of worldwide fallout" from nuclear weapons.

The key error in the LNT model is that no threshold dose, no dose below which there are no ill affects, is ever considered and is consequentially never allowed for. It might seem hard to refute an argument that says if you are not exposed to a dose of something dangerous, you cannot die from it. But it can have totally illogical interpretations. The lack of small quantities of something can sometimes be as deadly as excessive quantities of the same thing. Whether something in human health is a benefit or a danger is invariably determined by the quantity involved. An excess quantity of anything ultimately becomes a poison.

When considering human health there will always be some dose level that everyone will tolerate with absolutely no ill effects. The concept of a zero dose never ever applies anywhere in the real world. It is almost universally accepted that there is no poisonous gas, no poisonous chemical, no degree of electric shock, no hazardous substance, no hazardous kick or hazardous punch, no hazardous anything else, for which the linear no-threshold concept is valid. A dose of even the worst poison or pathogen can be low enough to have no effect.

Consider the example of common table salt. We all eat salt, and provided we eat only small amounts in our diet over prolonged periods, we should not suffer a higher than normal risk of heart disease. But salt is deadly; the "lowest observed lethal dose" for sodium chloride in humans is 1,000 mg/kg, that is 0.1%. Meaning if you weigh 70 kg and you eat 70 grams of salt then you could die. You probably have several lethal doses of salt sitting in your pantry right now. Fifty percent of rats, fed three grams of salt per kilogram of body weight, die. What if we eat no salt and remove all traces of it from all the foods we eat (as the LNT concept demands)? Again we die. Salt is an essential part of our diet. We are "salty" creatures. When doctors need to give us fluids intravenously, they will use a saline solution to match our body's salt content. If they inject us with straight distilled water, we die, and die painfully.

A total lack of salt will kill. Excessive salt will kill. And there is a wide range between these extremes, which cover the whole spectrum of harmless or beneficial, through to dangerous.

Even oxygen, that most precious component of our atmosphere, can be toxic. Ask any scuba diver, they learn about it in their training. Deep-sea divers breathe gas mixtures containing very small percentages of oxygen; otherwise oxygen toxicity at high pressures would kill them. Once again when something necessary or just beneficial is force-fed to extremes, it can be fatal. Just as too little can be fatal.

Here is another scenario of the illogical "logic" of the linear no-threshold model. If you drink a full bottle of whisky in ten minutes you will probably die from alcohol poisoning. If the bottle of whisky is served up into a hundred small glasses, and a hundred people each drink their own small glass within a ten-minute period, everybody will be fine. But the LNT thesis categorically claims that one person in that group of one hundred will certainly die of alcohol poisoning then and there. That sounds just plain ridiculous. And of course it is.

At the height of the Cold War, it was quite irrelevant whether a linear-dose model was actually applicable to low levels of radiation or not. The only consideration then was the destructive and killing power of nuclear weapons delivering doses at extreme levels.

The linear no-threshold model and the zero-dose thesis came from applying this data direct to low-dose civilian, day-to-day situations, without recognizing nor collecting the wealth of data on beneficial effects available even then.

Nevertheless, today the model and the thesis is used with religious fervour by the antinuclear movement. The antinuclear movement loves the concepts. Some of their members even claim they actually believe them.

The problem with assessing risks associated with radiation doses is that it is impossible to tell the difference between a cancer caused by radiation exposure and one caused by something else. So we are forced to look for slight changes in the incidence rates of cancer in those exposed to "above-normal" radiation.

Extra: statistically significant, what does that mean?

Many of us have little understanding of statistics and this makes us vulnerable to manipulative claims. So let's consider some simple basic statistics so we are not so easily fooled.

The United States is used here to illustrate as it has a large population and U.S. numbers and statistics are reliable and easily available.

Suppose that on average the risk of developing some particular type of rare cancer in the general population is one in a million per year. There are about 280 million people in the United States so you'd expect to see 280 new occurrences of the cancer each year. That's a logic, and a statistic we are familiar with.

But what if there are 281 occurrences, or 282 or 283? Does that mean that those one, two or three extra cases are somehow unusual and must be therefore caused by some new phenomenon such as nuclear radiation? No. It is completely normal to see variation around "average" numbers and statistical analysis tells us exactly the range of variations we can expect. It is actually quite easy to work it out and to see how such numbers can fluctuate from year to year and also over many years. In the above example, the count would be expected to vary around a standard deviation of 17 more cases per year, or 17 less. That's 280 plus or minus 17.

Then the count can fall outside this range a statistically calculable number of times in any given long period. If we kept statistics for 100 years then the number of cases would fall outside the 17 standard deviation range in 32 of those 100 years. In calculations in common practice, the standard deviation is often doubled. This is done to cover fluctuations caused by unknown or unavoidable errors. A standard deviation is derived from the previously observed data to show how wide that data can be scattered around the average and mean nothing.

The concept we rely on to get useful meaning is variations that are "statistically significant". It is usually considered statistically significant if something does occur frequently that would only be expected to occur once in 20 times if the original measurements were correct. In biology they like to narrow the field further and say it's statistically significant if that something occurs once in 100 times, in our example once in 100 years. Using the common doubled figure for standard deviation and the 100-year period, we would need to see more than 280 plus 34, or less than 280 minus 34 cases to claim a statistically significant change had taken place in any year. And additionally even that calculation itself would be wrong once every twenty times. In other words the number of cases, and they average one in 280, can go up or down by 34 in any one year and it's not genuinely statistically significant. In a once-off case, less or more than 34 probably means nothing too.

You can see that these variations are relatively large. In a year where there were 314 cases of the cancer an unscrupulous lobbyist might say that there had been a huge rise in the cancer rate in the local population and 12% of the population can now expect to get the cancer. And that wouldn't be true at all. We can only decide there has been a jump in the occurrence of the cancer if we continued to see a higher number of cancers each year for several years. Looking at only one single year the reality is that an unusual number is much more likely to be a "statistical blip".

The use of confusing radiation dose units, allied with the reporting of radiation levels that are usually of utterly insignificant quantities and risk, and the deliberate misinterpretation of statistical information is, and has always been, a major tactic of the antinuclear movement.

The quip "there are liars and there are statisticians" is rather incorrect. Whereas "there are liars and there are liars that like to misquote statistics" is totally correct. The strange thing is that truthful, accurate and honest statistics are showing that increased background radiation levels (as much as several times normal) show decreases in cancer rates. The decreases are small but they are most definitely statistically significant. The doubling or tripling of normal background radiation levels is a definite health benefit. It prolongs average health and life spans. And that now seems uncontestable. We also must appreciate that about half of all cancer cases in most Western countries are treated by hitting the cancer with high radiation doses to kill the cancer. It is a very effective treatment. Generally speaking radiation cures cancer; it doesn't cause it.

The effects of very high radiation doses have been studied and documented meticulously. Hiroshima and Nagasaki victim's figures, along with figures for people inadvertently exposed to very high radiation levels in medical or other occupational situations, have now accurately established exact numbers for long- and short-term radiation-induced cancer and other human risk factors. The statistical significance of high radiation levels is well studied and tabulated (see further on).

What about risks from low doses—meaning what happens when we don't get enough radiation in our daily living? It is very difficult to measure the effects of low doses of radiation on cancer rates because of the normal statistical variations mentioned above. To get meaningful answers it is necessary to follow the medical history of several large groups of people—groups that are exposed to various "above-normal" radiation doses and groups that were never exposed. Known influences, from other cancer effects, both good and bad, have also to be taken out of the figures. The process is complicated and by necessity has taken years of observation and recording. Although the information is now available, it has never been disseminated through the media and public press in a manner that would alleviate the currently advertised and now perceived dangers. Undoubtedly this is because the information totally refutes the zero-dose thesis and the linear no-threshold model.

Such facts cannot and will not suit the fossil fuel interests and their allied antinuclear movements. As a result, forecasts of radiation dangers and deaths universally reported in today's public media are still based on the imaginary results obtained by relying on the fiction that is the zero-dose thesis and the linear no-threshold model.

It is probably reasonable to assume that the oil interests would be unstinting in their funding for research supporting an LNT concept. In recent years there has actually been redeveloped enthusiastic effort by lobbyists to try and justify the use of the LNT model, or to at least minimize its non-use.

The internationally respected United Nations Scientific Committee on the Effects of Atomic Radiation or UNSCEAR originally supported the LNT concept, but always with the proviso of "pending further information". The scientific work on which UNSCEAR's support was based relied in part on using DNA technology to measure the damage to DNA in cell cultures exposed to various levels of radiation. It is well documented that very high radiation levels can damage and sometimes modify DNA. We know that further damage and alteration to already modified cell DNA can cause cancer. We know that eventually damage to this DNA can sometimes turn a cancer malignant. A conclusion is thus reached; the observed damage to cell DNA naturally suggests that only zero radiation can be considered safe.

But single cell cultures are not necessarily an indication of what happens in the human body. Our bodies have well-developed mechanisms to cope with damage to cells. There is a whole group of enzymes designed to do nothing else except constantly repair DNA. Not only do cells have the ability to repair themselves and their own DNA, but our bodies have an immune system which detects and destroys badly damaged cells. That, of course simply cannot happen to a damaged cell or modified cell cultured in an isolated and sterile laboratory dish.

In 1994 UNSCEAR confirmed from their own studies the existence of adaptive and beneficial effects in humans of increases in nuclear radiation above normal background levels. It was found that cancer mortality rates were *lower* after exposure to low dose radiation.

In 2000, UNSCEAR updated their reports on the Chernobyl nuclear reactor accident. They noted that, apart from the thirty radiation deaths of firemen and power plant workers, and a very slight increase in almost entirely curable childhood thyroid cancer, there has been no increase in overall cancer incidence nor mortality, nor any increase in hereditary disorders in the supposed "thousands of future victims" of the Chernobyl accident.

Since its 1994 report on indicated benefits of exposure to radiation, UNSCEAR funding has been systematically and consistently reduced. It has been one of the world's most respected nuclear radiation assessment organizations and despite its critical importance in determining the safety of the whole nuclear energy debate, it may be closed down. In the meantime the funding of UNSCEAR was taken over by the United Nations Environment Programme in Nairobi! Work that one out?

The fossil fuel industries and the antinuclear movements are unrelenting in efforts to manipulate and create public abhorrence to anything nuclear. The media go along for their own self-interest. Very few of their writers ever bother to determine the real truth that would allow them to make and then print informed judgments. They just believe in the LNT model because it's convenient. The linear no-threshold concept is blithely accepted as an acknowledged truism. But it's not. Silencing UNSCEAR would be of benefit only to the fossil fuel lobby. That's why it happened.

The truth about low-level radiation exposure in humans is amazingly different than the stories we are told. Since as far back as 1980, over 1,200 references have been cited in papers confirming the benefits of human exposure to low-level radiation. The papers confirm that low-level radiation, that is radiation considerably higher than natural background levels, does prolong human life. It doesn't shorten it as is constantly inferred.

The U.S. National Council for Radiation Protection states, in their report No. 136 "Evaluation of the Linear No-Threshold Dose-Response Model for Ionizing Radiation", that "It is important to notice that the incidence of cancers in most of the exposed populations to low-dose radiation has not been found to be increased, and that in most of the cases this incidence seems to have been reduced."

The actual biological process involved is now termed hormesis, derived from the Greek word *hormen* which means "to excite". It's a sensible, and actually very apt name. We now know cell metabolism and even some photosynthesis is stimulated by low-dose radiation. It stimulates DNA, RNA, and also stimulates cell membrane repair. Not only that but low-level nuclear radiation also strengthens the immune system. This increased immunity has a beneficial side effect for it significantly decreases human mortality rates from other infections in addition to cancer.

In Japan alone, at this time of writing, there are fourteen universities studying the beneficial effects of low-dose radiation on, for example, hypertension, on the enhancement of the immune system, on its ability to suppress cancer. They also find increased radiation levels seem to simulate general DNA repair. They too are finding that enhanced radiation levels also appear to stimulate cell rejuvenation.

As radiation levels rise they eventually reach a point where health-enhancing dose levels are exceeded, as happens with sunshine. A threshold is reached above which radiation exposure should not generally be exceeded. This threshold is referred to as the zero-equivalent point or ZEP. A ZEP will apply in both long-term exposure and short-term exposure although they do differ.

Of course the zero-equivalent point concept is the fundamental opposite to the zero-dose thesis and the linear no-threshold idea. The zero-dose thesis is a theory, or more of a pronouncement, that says any radiation at all, no matter how tiny, no matter how minute, is life threatening. The zero-equivalent point (ZEP) however, refers to a radiation dose rate below which radiation is actually beneficial. The names refer to two totally conflicting concepts. It's just confusing that both terms start with "zero".

When radiation levels sit at the zero-equivalent point, there is no statistical difference in the health and mortality of people exposed to "normal" background radiation. Between the low normal level and the higher ZEP, health is improved and people live longer. To check Web sites, search "zero-equivalent point and nuclear radiation".

While the naturally occurring background level radiation does vary considerably over our planet, the ZEP levels generally exceed all natural radiation background levels on the planet by a big margin. In other words there are very few places on this planet where human beings are exposed to enough nuclear radiation to ensure optimum health. That's because world background levels are in constant decline as the earth's natural radioactivity burns out.

Many substances are naturally radioactive. Potassium-40, K^{40}, makes up about 0.012% of natural potassium. Your body contains about 0.2% potassium by weight. A 60 kg person would therefore contain about 15 milligrams of K^{40} and which produce about 4,000 potassium-40 decays per second. That's means that at least we all rate as a source of radiation at 4,000 becquerels just on potassium.

Carbon-14 is another radioactive element that occurs naturally in the human body and this will add another 3,000 carbon-14 decays, bringing the total to around 7,000 becquerels per second. Put your hand near a sensitive Geiger counter and it goes mad with clicks from this in-house or in-body nuclear radiation. For good health, there is normally just not enough clicks.

Radiation has always been a factor of our environment and an influence on evolution; life has learnt to use it for its own benefit as it often does.

Expected effects of acute and chronic radiation exposure

Acute exposure is exposure over short time spans but at high intensity. That's a short, sharp, high-dose type exposure. Acute exposure would typically occur near a nuclear blast or well inside the safety lines around a nuclear reactor or high-level storage facility. An acute exposure is currently defined as a dose of more than 100 millisieverts received over no more than a few days. It is actually a very a tiny dose. Effects of high acute exposure vary from person to person, often by 20% or more, so of course figures quoted can vary accordingly. Again it's exactly the same with bee stings.

Acute exposure effects are known as "deterministic". The severity and onset of a particular effect is determined by the dose received. Below the particular threshold dose level indicated no harmful effect can be expected to occur.

To appreciate the relative doses, here are a couple of examples. A chest or dental x-ray would deliver 1 mSv. A spinal x-ray would give an exposure of 4 mSv. A series of x-rays over a few days delivers anything from 10 to 30 mSv, sometimes even more. The Three Mile Island accident gave the people in the broader surrounding area a dose of 0.012 mSv. The highest known individual dose was 0.8 mSv; that's less then one visit to the dentist with one tooth x-ray.

Table of acute radiation exposure effects

(Acute meaning over a short time period)

0 to 100 mSv. Health improves with increasing doses, then as doses rise further health-benefiting effects gradually return to normal as levels exceed 100 mSv. Below 100 mSv is considered as low-level radiation. 100 mSv is thus the zero-equivalent point.

100 to 250 mSv. While health benefits are no longer apparent, there appears to be absolutely no detrimental effects.

250 to 500 mSv. In general there are no apparent detrimental symptoms except for a limited few who experience some nausea at doses around 500 mSv. Sometimes slight changes in blood chemistry have been detected at these same levels. These short-term blood chemistry changes appear to have no significant consequences.

500 to 1,000 mSv. The same as for 250 to 500 mSv doses but in addition temporary sterility can occur. At these doses there now is a 2% increase in the total lifetime chance of developing radiation-induced cancer. Such cancers are as dangerous and as curable as cancer from any other cause. Cancer rates then begin to climb.

1,000 to 2,000 mSv. Acute doses of radiation at these levels cause a series of clearly identifiable symptoms or syndromes. Damage occurs to cells that reproduce rapidly such as bone marrow, spleen and lymphatic cells. Skin reddening occurs for doses approaching 2,000 mSv. Recovery is fairly certain and all symptoms disappear within a few weeks. Genetic mutation in humans is rare. Its incidence would however double after an exposure of 2,000 mSv. To put things into perspective, delaying parenting by ten years or more has exactly the same effect. Increase in the total lifetime chance of developing radiation-induced cancer increases to around 2.5% and stays there, even if there is a complete recovery from all other radiation symptoms. From these levels on, leukaemia rates rise dramatically to five or six times normal, and general cancer rates rise to around 20%.

2,000 to 7,500 mSv. Above 2,000 mSv, bone-marrow syndrome can develop and lead to increased chance of death. Survival within this dose range is very dependent on individual health, sex and age. It is even more dependent on the availability of specialized medical treatment. Symptoms include internal bleeding, fatigue, bacterial infections, and hair loss within a few weeks. Fatalities would approximate 50% from exposure of 4,500 mSv.

7,500 mSv. Chances of death occurring within months increase to almost 100%. Slightly higher doses, up to 10,000 mSv, are generally fatal within about two months.

10,000 mSv. Gastrointestinal tract syndrome becomes apparent for doses above 10,000 mSv. At these levels, cells that reproduce more slowly are damaged, e.g. the lining of the intestine. Symptoms include vomiting and diarrhea in addition to all the lower-dose-level symptoms. Death follows within one or two weeks.

20,000 mSv. At these doses, cells that do not reproduce are also damaged, such as nerve cells. Death follows within several days.

50,000 mSv. Central-nervous syndrome manifests. Symptoms include loss of coordination, convulsions and shock, in addition to all previous mentioned effects. Unconsciousness occurs within minutes of exposure and death within days.

Effects of chronic radiation exposure

Radiation exposure spread over several years to lifetime periods is described or defined as chronic exposure, and results in a chronic dose.

The word *chronic* itself implies definite ill health, yet if exposure is not excessive, chronic radiation exposure is a health benefit. The name is either unfortunate or has been chosen to be deliberately misleading and frightening.

Unlike the acute cases discussed above, the time over which chronic exposures occur is important. In some literature the concept of lifetime exposure is used. As healing is an ongoing process and aging is too big a factor in considering radiation effects, annual exposure becomes more relevant than lifetime exposure. The term "accumulated dose" is sometimes used, but in many ways it too is somewhat meaningless. It's like totalling the hours spent in the sun over a person's lifetime.

The annual dose rate is based on the total dose accumulated over the year. If we imagine we have all these bees buzzing around us, then we are talking about how many stings we might get in any one year. We must also consider if they are good for us, or there are too many and they are bad.

To start with, nowhere in the world are background radiation dose rates much below one millisievert per year. For generations, people have lived, with no ill effects, in areas where the chronic doses received are as high as 200 mSv. The world average is around 2.7 mSv. This average slowly declines as the earth's radioactive materials decay.

Accidents don't happen that expose humans to high radiation levels for months or years on end. Therefore few figures are available to determine the consequences of high-level chronic doses. Some information comes from previous dictatorships where safety was often of little consideration. Unfortunately in these cases the records are so incomplete that they too are of little value. One source of reliable information can be derived from evidence from localities on earth with very high natural radiation background levels. The only other information comes from long-term exposure to people that occurred prior to the recognition of radiation levels and dangers.

Radiation risks also depend on the nature of the exposure, and to what part of the body, if it is not full-body exposure. Exposure could also be from material that is inhaled, or injected, or eaten. It can also vary somewhat by the specific type of radiation although this is compensated for by our radiation units that now allow for such variations.

The highest naturally occurring source of radiation in populated areas comes from the beach sands at the Brazilian tourist resort of Guarapari, population 70,000. Sunbathing on Guarapari beach gives an annual exposure of 800 mSv—that's 300 times the world average. Multistorey hotel and apartments line the beachfront. Lying on the beach has been promoted as a local Guarapari health benefit for decades, apparently justifiably. So soaking up the nuclear radiation is actually good for you.

Natural background levels up to 200 mSv occur in populated regions of China, Brazil and India. No harmful effects have ever been noted in the local populations. In contrast, beneficial effects are known. The inhabitants of the town of Ramsar in Iran receive a dose of 70 mSv per year.

There are a few well known, quite unintentional but well documented examples of hugely excess chronic radiation exposure that have occurred over the past several decades. From these occurrences dose rate effects can be tabulated with reasonable accuracy. Some typical examples follow.

In the UK between 1935 and 1954, before radiation exposure was fully understood, 14,000 people with spinal arthritis (ankylosing spondylitis) were treated with x-ray exposure as a cure. Accumulated doses averaged 3,000 mSv over just a few years.

In Germany they treated the same disease with radium injections. Often 9,000 mSv were administered to the bone.

In Germany, Denmark and Portugal, between 1928 and 1955, radioactive thorium was injected into patients to aid x-ray diagnosis. In some cases the liver could receive up to 50,000 mSv.

In New Jersey in the United States, between 1915 and 1935, female factory workers licked the tip of fine paintbrushes to paint radium-laced paint onto watch hands and dials to produce luminous watches. Doses averaged 17,000 mSv. In the above cases most of the people, but not all, were apparently unaffected.

Between 1920 and 1968, thousands of underground miners in the United States received doses that averaged 60,000 mSv. The mineshafts were poorly ventilated and high concentrations of radon gas were able to accumulate, which resulted in these high exposure rates.

In the above examples of extreme dose rates, fatalities or at least severe or serious medical consequences occurred in 5% to 10% of those exposed. The majority of the cases involved some form of cancer. For the rest of those exposed, when there were effects, they were apparently of no real significance.

Table of long-term radiation exposure effects or chronic exposure

Generally considered as exposure for ten years or more. Units are mSv absorbed per year.

Up to 1 mSv. As dose rates rise, a statistically significant decrease in the incidence of cancer occurs. General health improves considerably and no evidence has ever shown health or longevity decline.

1 to 100 mSv. Health continues to improve with increased dose but the health-giving effects seems to peak out at between 100 mSv and 150 mSv or possibly up to 200 mSv. Exact level are yet to be determined. (In the UK legal limits are set for radiation workers at 20 mSv. Living and working in areas with background levels so dangerously low is itself a health hazard.)

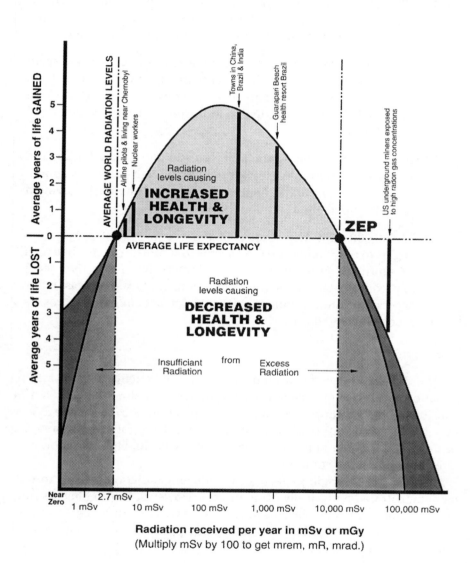

Health and longevity effects from long-term exposure to nuclear radiation.

100 to 250 mSv. Natural background levels up to 200 mSv occur in some populated areas. No harmful effects have ever been noted in the local populations. In contrast, beneficial effects are known.

250 to 2,500 mSv. Possible increase in some forms of cancer, although rates of occurrences are almost certainly below 2%. Apart from cancer, no other significant medical consequences result from quite high long-term radiation exposure. Health benefits still exceed risks.

2,500 to 10,000 mSv. This upper limit is considered by T. D. Luckey and others to be a reasonable assessment of the zero-equivalent point. (Professor Emeritus T. D. Luckey, University of Missouri-Columbia School of Medicine.)

10,000 to 60,000 mSv. The chance of the occurrence of cancer first begins to rise rapidly and then seems to stabilize, roughly between 6% and 10%. At the high radiation levels other health risks seem to predominate. Almost no information, or at least no reasonably accessible information, is available for accumulated exposure much above 60,000 mSv.

The ZEP (zero-equivalent point) is where the benefits from increasing radiation levels are outweighed by the dangers. Below the ZEP can be considered as "low-dose" radiation. The position shown for the ZEP is mainly suggested by Professor Luckey's studies. Determining a more exact position will happen only when space flight, with its high radiation dose rates, becomes more common.

To date the damaging effects of insufficient radiation levels can only be demonstrated empirically using insects. However, health benefits from living in areas with high background levels are well documented.

Average years of life lost or gained are approximations based on the limited statistics available.

Sunshine and skin cancer

Sunlight is good for you. Sunlight allows the skin to produce vitamin D. It also stimulates the brain in various ways. High sunlight radiation levels, such as from a magnifying glass, will produce blisters in seconds. UV-C in sunlight is an ionizing-type radiation. It's just not as penetrating as x-rays.

Everything good for you is bad for you in huge doses. And it is consistently shown that almost everything bad for you is actually good for you in tiny doses. Apparently it stimulates and rejuvenates the immune systems. It seems possible that the immune system needs a little mild exercise to keep it up to speed.

In space, the levels of UV radiation in sunshine are dangerous. UV-C is the really dangerous one. Luckily for us ozone in the stratosphere filters out almost all of these shorter, more damaging wavelengths, but not completely. Ozone reduces the UV-C levels by a factor of about 100,000. However, some always gets through. But that's generally OK.

The thickness of the skin on the back of your hand is less than one millimetre. If your hand is exposed to the sun for just one hour a day for a year, then that layer of skin will receive a long-term, or "chronic" dose, of something like 70,000 mSv. The radiation is in the UV-C wavelength. White skin suddenly exposed to tropical sunshine can therefore receive a short-term, or acute radiation dose of 1,000 mSv in a few hours. As was noted in the effects of acute radiation doses, "Skin reddening occurs for doses around 2,000 mSv", so that's why a white-skinned person, suddenly exposed to tropical sunshine, can expect to get the radiation burn we call sunburn.

For those communities which have done some long-term evolving in tropical latitudes, the darker skin developed can easily handle these doses.

It's different for fair-skinned people who evolved over millennia to live in the higher latitudes and whose skin became modified to absorb all the limited sunlight available for vitamin D production. Admittedly when these fair-skinned people move to tropical and subtropical latitudes their skin colour will, in a few weeks, modify and change as they develop a suntan. A suntan however, is only a partially satisfactory screen for fair-skinned people.

Nuclear radiation also comes from our own bodies. It comes from space in the form of cosmic rays and it comes from the ground. It's everywhere and all of us have evolved to live with it. Not only to live with it, but it now also seems that, like sunshine, we evolved to benefit from its presence.

Biological concentration of radioactivity

There is another aspect of ionizing radiation damage that has to be considered. That is the accumulation and concentration of radioactive elements within the human body following a nuclear accident.

The human body uses certain elements in specific ways and so tends to concentrate these particular elements in quite specific locations within the body. While iron and potassium are distributed throughout the body, iodine is collected and stored in the thyroid gland. Calcium is accumulated in teeth and bones.

In the Chernobyl power reactor accident (and any accident that might conceivably occur in a similarly unenclosed reactor) iodine-131 and strontium-90 were the only dangerous isotopes that at low doses could pose an accumulation risk. It should be noted that all Western power reactors are totally enclosed so these chemicals can't escape to the atmosphere as they did at Chernobyl.

The thyroid gland requires iodine. If iodine is ingested it can therefore collect in the thyroid gland, but only if the thyroid gland concurrently has any iodine deficiency. If such a nuclear accident occurs then iodine tablets, or a few drops of household Lugol's iodine, both available from the local pharmacist, should be taken to insure the thyroid is "topped up". The excess iodine then prevents any possible accumulation of radioactive iodine in the body that could come from food or dust particles. Ingested iodine then simply passes straight through the body's system.

If ignored, the accumulation of iodine-131 in the thyroid can ultimately cause localized damage that could exceed the body's repair capabilities. A tumour might form. Thyroid cancer however is rarely fatal.

In Russia, iodine was not distributed immediately following the Chernobyl accident, as it should have been. It was eventually distributed but well after the time when real benefits would have resulted. Despite this irresponsibility and incompetence of the Russian authorities there were still only three deaths from thyroid cancer due to the so-called Chernobyl nuclear "disaster". Iodine was distributed quickly and efficiently in nearby Poland. In Poland thyroid damage was thus nonexistent.

The element strontium is chemically very similar to calcium. In a Chernobyl-like nuclear accident small quantities of strontium-90 can be released into the environment, and if ingested can accumulate in bone material. The quantity of strontium that can be absorbed is very tiny and therefore couldn't be considered chemically as a poison. An extremely tiny amount of radioactive strontium in the body is possibly beneficial for its ionizing effects. However, if too much strontium-90 accumulates in bone material it will persist and be damaging for years.

Iodine-131 and strontium-90 represent the extreme examples of radioactive biological concentration within the human body that could result from a Chernobyl-type reactor accident. There is no evidence of strontium-90 being a factor in the total Chernobyl death toll of less than fifty people.

Radioactive elements can accumulate in animals as they can in humans. If we eat those animals then it is possible that we can be exposed to a more concentrated dose than might be expected from the radiation levels in the environment. This can happen with iodine-131. Dairy animals eating radioactive fodder can concentrate iodine in their milk. Children, with their generally higher dairy intakes, are therefore more susceptible to iodine-131 contamination. However, the likelihood of such scenarios is extremely remote. Statistically, being struck by lightning is a far greater risk.

Harmful and beneficial effects of radioactive radon

The element radon occurs naturally as a radioactive gas. It is continuously being produced in the earth's crust by the radioactive decay of radium. Radium occurs in trace quantities in most soils and rocks and so radon accumulates naturally in caves and mine shafts, often to high concentrations.

Radon gas also builds up under the floorboards and in the basements of houses all over the world. The daily warming and cooling of a house creates a vacuum-cleaner effect that sucks the radon gas from the surrounding soil into the area under the house.

Radon is an alpha emitter. Alpha emitters are only dangerous when inside the body as they have difficulty penetrating even the outer layer of human skin. However, radon, being a gas, can be inhaled into our lungs and the "skin" in the lung is very thin.

When this was realized it was immediately presumed that the alpha particles would damage the surface tissue in the lungs and ultimately cause lung cancer. Based on the linear no-threshold model, ridiculously high mortality rates from radon-induced lung cancers were immediately predicted.

The whole concept was simply not true. In areas where the radon concentration in houses is higher than average, the average incidence of lung cancer is more often lower than average.

Although naturally occurring accumulations of radon gas are now generally believed to have no effect on the incidence of lung cancer, there is a downside. Inhaled radon tends to concentrate in bone marrow and this appears to possibly influence the incidence of leukaemia. It is arguable that a slight reduction in lung cancer from beneficial radiation effects would outweigh the suggested slight increase in leukaemia. However the numbers involved on both sides are minuscule.

There are tens of thousands of houses in the United States with radon concentrations that produce 1,000 becquerels of radioactivity per cubic metre (37 picocuries per litre). The U.S. Environmental Protection Agency, using the zero-dose concept, informs its citizens that any level above 4 pCi per litre is dangerous to health. In stark contrast, the human body is normally taken as being somewhere around 75,000 becquerels. To worry about there being 1,000 Bq in a cubic metre of air seems ludicrous. That is unless imagined dangers are being promoted by public relations organizations.

A study in Finland showed the incidence of lung cancer was actually lower in areas where radon concentrations in homes were higher, at 8 pCi per litre. Large areas in the United States have radon concentrations in homes at similar levels. None of these areas show a higher incidence of lung cancer.

Researchers, led by Denis Henshaw at the University of Bristol in the UK, did discover a link between the inhalation of radon gas and the extremely rare disease myeloid leukaemia. Susceptibility to myeloid leukaemia is a genetic trait. Areas in the United Kingdom were compared with geologically similar areas in Canada. The comparison confirmed the UK findings. Henshaw now believes that 12% of myeloid leukaemia cases in the UK are caused by radon gas and possibly 25% of all cases worldwide.

The correlation between naturally occurring radon concentrations and the incidence of myeloid leukaemia was eventually investigated in fifteen separate countries and was reported as being very consistent.

If you are one of those few with a genetically high risk of developing myeloid leukaemia, don't live in an area with high naturally occurring radon. For the rest of us, above-normal radon levels could, paradoxically, possibly save our lives. Again, it's the complete opposite of what the publicity machines tell us. If you look at the actual numbers, if you look at the actual recorded statistics, you will discover that if you inhale naturally occurring radioactive radon gas at naturally occurring levels, the good effects outweigh by far any bad effects.

It must be remembered that radon gas is a naturally occurring radioactive substance. Radon is like thorium or radium or uranium, it's there, it's always been there, all around us, and it's been there long before nuclear power stations ever existed. So it is conceivable that the process of evolution has produced within us systems that not only tolerate but actually use the radioactivity from radon for our benefit.

More examples of low-dose radiation health benefits

One investigation studied the mortality rates over a 21-year-period of some 70,000 white male nuclear workers. The workers were employed in 8 U.S. shipyards. The study started in 1960.

Personnel in nuclear facilities all wear a personal dosimeter, a kind of clip-on badge that is sensitive to ionizing radiation. The original badge design used a piece of photographic film. If the film was exposed to radiation then it would show "fogging" when developed and so indicate the total dose. Now radiation doses are recorded using a thermoluminescent device, or TLD. Radiation causes small changes in the crystal structure of the device. When it is later heated these changes produce tiny flashes of light that indicate the amount of radiation received. Thermoluminescent devices can be reused and are more convenient than photographic film.

A total of 32,510 U.S. shipyard workers that received no more than normal background radiation were compared to 38,230 workers constantly exposed to radiation during the course of their work. Over the 21-year-period of the study the actual main causes of death for both groups were the same, and were the same for the general population. People died in the main from cancer, cardiovascular diseases and respiratory diseases. However, the workers exposed to nuclear radiation and who had accumulated an exposure more than a standard "lifetime dose" in the period of their employment were significantly healthier and had by far the lowest total death rates. They lived longer. The results showed that if you were an "unexposed to radiation" worker, you had a 30% greater chance of dying than the group accumulating the higher radiation dosage. Life expectancy therefore increased very significantly as radiation levels increased.

A mass of similar data and information has been produced by Radiation Science and Health and by the Massachusetts Governor's Advisory Council on Radiation Protection. Others sources for information on the health benefits of prolonged exposure to elevated levels of background nuclear radiation can be found by searching the Web for "hormesis health benefits nuclear radiation".

In a Canadian study the cancer mortality rate of 21,000 male workers employed in coal- and gas-fired power stations was compared to the cancer mortality rate of 4,000 male nuclear energy workers. This study covered a twenty-year period. Both groups were employed by the same energy corporation and thus extraneous errors were at a minimum.

The total cancer deaths in the coal and gas workers were actually 0.5% less than the average for Ontario males in general. Again, in this study it was found that the nuclear workers had a higher life expectancy than both their non-exposed co-workers in the coal and gas power plants and also the population in general. The 21,000 non-nuclear energy workers had a 72% higher likelihood of contracting and dying from cancer than their fellow nuclear workers.

In a study involving three separate nuclear weapons plants in the United States cancer mortality rates showed a dramatic decrease in proportion to the increased radiation exposure. There was almost a 75% drop in cancer mortality rates as exposure rose to maximum plant permissible levels.

The Los Alamos National Laboratories, located about 70 miles (120 km) north of Albuquerque, New Mexico contains a nuclear weapons plant. Here a small study of the mortality rate of 303 white males exposed to nuclear radiation was compared to the mortality rate of 15,420 white males that were not exposed to nuclear radiation.

The radiation doses varied in this case between 10 mSv and 50 mSv. Exposed workers received the following benefits. Their incidence of total cancer deaths dropped by 23%, deaths from leukaemia dropped by 65%, and deaths from lung cancer dropped 49%. Although in this study only 303 people were exposed to radiation, the results were consistent with the larger studies.

Other, quite independent groups have studied mortality rates for workers in U.S. nuclear weapons plants. In all cases and in all studies, mortality rates were reduced as exposure to nuclear radiation increased.

Across the Atlantic, leukaemia mortality was compared in British nuclear plants. In a report 70,600 nuclear workers exposed to radiation were compared to 24,500 workers in the same plants that were not exposed to nuclear radiation.

In this quite long study the leukaemia mortality rate for unexposed workers was just under one death per thousand. The leukaemia mortality rate in the 70,600 exposed nuclear workers declined as the individual's exposure rate rose. When the lifetime dose had risen to about 700 mSv, in the exposed nuclear workers, which is at least ten times the average background dose, death from leukaemia had dropped to near zero.

As exposure increased to approaching four times this dose, standard "safety" procedures came into play and workers were apparently then restricted from further exposure. Even at these higher levels, workers unexposed to nuclear radiation were twenty times more likely to die from leukaemia than their supposedly radiation-suffering co-workers.

A 25-year-long study was conducted to investigate the incidence of cancer and particularly the increase in leukaemia among children living near nuclear power plants in Scotland. There was no increase in leukaemia, as was and still is constantly implied. It was found that leukaemia rates were lower than average in the areas around both nuclear power stations. On further investigation it was also found that around one of the plants, the incidence of leukaemia in the local population fell to zero soon after the nuclear reactor became operational.

In 1974 the prestigious medical journal *The Lancet* published an in-depth analysis of cancer mortality in nuclear workers. This analysis looked at just under 100,000 workers from the United Kingdom, the United States and Canada. With an unsubstantiated but just vaguely possible exception of leukaemia and multiple melanomas, the analysis showed absolutely no significant relationship between increased mortality rates from any form of cancer by radiation received by workers at all these nuclear facilities.

The Lancet, in their usual meticulous manner, also noted that low-level radiation did seem to be beneficial. They reported that the incidence of cancer actually declined among those exposed.

Probably the biggest single correlation between population health and background radiation was assembled by Professor Emeritus T. D. Luckey, University of Missouri-Columbia School of Medicine, a pioneer in hormesis research. He considered the United States' entire population, some 273 million people. Luckey combined the information collated by H. T. Sauer, Washington, DC Department of Health and Human Services, in a 1980 paper entitled "Geographic Patterns in the Risk of Dying and Associated Factors, Ages 35–74 Years".

Luckey divided the United States into three zones. The first was the southeast zone which contained the highest general U.S. incidence of cardiovascular disease causing death and also the highest incidence of respiratory and cancer-related deaths. This same southeast zone also proved to be the area of the United States with the lowest naturally occurring ionizing radiation levels.

By contrast, the study then showed that the lowest level of cardiovascular, respiratory, and cancer death rates occurred in the second zone, a region
comprising the entire west and central west area of the country. This area
has the highest levels of natural background radiation, being in general two
to three times that of the southeast area.

The third area, sitting between the first two, had average U.S. death rates
and also average U.S. background radiation levels.

In this study, the researchers went to great lengths to ensure that socioeconomic factors and similar considerations did not influence the results.

Christopher Wills, an evolutionary geneticist at the University of California, looked at the reports of the Atomic Bomb Casualty Commission (ABCC).
The Commission spent years searching for signs of genetic damage or mutations in the survivors in Nagasaki and Hiroshima. There was virtually none.
James Crow, a member of the ABCC advisory committee, had no doubt
that genetic changes and mutations "must have occurred", but commented,
"They were below the threshold of detection". From this it would appear
that working in the nuclear industry, and in and around nuclear reactors,
is generally less dangerous than a regular visit to the dentist. That's if our
infrequent dental x-rays are ever proved to have a detrimental effect.

The normal background radiation dose completely outside the bomb-
affected areas around Nagasaki and Hiroshima is considerably below 10
mSv. As you move closer to the bomb areas, dose levels rise in the inhabitants, but death rates from leukaemia decrease. Deaths rates rise back
to normal as exposure rises to approximately 200 mSv. Above 200 mSv
leukaemia mortality rates rise gradually to normal and then continue to rise
slightly.

With considerably higher exposure levels, leukaemia cancer death rates
can rise to as high as six times normal population levels. Generally all other
cancer death rates rose by about 20% above normal at the very high dose
rates.

The French Academy of Science feels that low-dose risks are at least
wildly exaggerated. A report from the Academy stated that there was
absolutely no epidemiological evidence to suggest that cancer was caused
by any sustained radiation dose less that 200 mSv.

The French Academy of Science clearly rejects as totally inappropriate
the method of estimating low-dose radiation risk by simply extrapolating
down from known high-dose instances, usually quoting those from Hiroshima and Nagasaki victims. These reports show that the French Academy
of Science also considers the zero-dose thesis and the linear no-threshold
model wrong and misleading.

Radiation doses in summary

After all the misinformation we have been fed over the years the reality seems quite incredible. The reality is that as radiation levels rise above the general background level, the health of people improves significantly. All the evidence is in complete contrast to what the orchestrated antinuclear movement scream from the rooftops. Mortality rates from cardiovascular disease, respiratory diseases, lung cancer, leukaemia, all drop dramatically as ionizing radiation rises.

Mortality rates don't rise at all, they drop! They drop as exposure to radiation increases.

Eventually, of course, these surprisingly beneficial effects of radiation exposure peak out and start to reduce back towards the average health levels of people that receive normal background radiation. As the zero-equivalent point is reached statistically beneficial results decline to zero. Health effects are then the same as those at normal levels. As levels rise above the zero-equivalent point, the ZEP, only then do statistical mortality rates begin to increase in proportion to the increased radiation dose. The evidence that confirms these statements is as surprisingly overwhelming, as it is deliberately obscured.

Nuclear power stations and how they work

Today, nuclear power stations come in a wide variety of designs, shapes and sizes. They all use the fission reaction. Nuclear power reactors require a self-maintaining chain reaction as do atomic bombs. The bomb reaction is too fast and so is useless for power generation. For power generation, a slow sustainable and easily regulated reaction is required.

The chain reaction inside a power reactor, to be self-sustaining, has to produce enough neutrons to keep itself going, therefore a non-explodable "critical mass" of a suitable fissionable material is required.

Unfortunately or possibly deliberately, in the popular media the concept of a critical mass is widely linked to nuclear weapons. The reality is that the critical mass in a reactor and the critical mass in a bomb are not the same thing. A bomb depends on the perfect and instantaneous assembly of what is actually a super-critical mass. It is not even possible to make a bomb using critical-mass concepts applying in a nuclear power reactor.

Plutonium is an excellent reactor fuel but very little naturally occurring plutonium exists on this planet. To obtain commercial or even any mean-ingful quantities, plutonium has to be manufactured or created in another nuclear reactor. You can't use it as a fuel until after you've already built an operational uranium reactor.

So let's look at how the uranium reactor process works. Natural uranium contains about 0.7% of the readily fissionable uranium-235. Atoms of uranium-235 are constantly being broken down, emitting neutrons. The uranium-235 atoms fission easily when they capture a stray neutron and become unstable.

The problem is that the neutrons emitted by the fissioning of uranium-235 are too fast. Typically they move at about one-tenth the speed of light. They are moving at about 18,600 miles per second or 30,000 km per second. Fast neutrons are not very good at inducing fission in another uranium-235 nucleus. They are too difficult to "capture" as they go by. If you can slow the neutrons down to about a millionth of their initial speed, then they are much easier to capture and will be hundreds of times better at initiating fission reactions. Only in a nuclear bomb with highly concentrated uranium-235 do the fast neutrons stand enough chance of initiating fission to produce an explosive reaction.

The trick in a reactor is to make the fissioning self-sustaining so the reactor can supply useful power and to do this the neutrons have to be slowed down.

Slowing neutrons down is not too difficult, you just need to give then a lot of things to run into and use up their excess energy. When a neutron bounces off a nucleus of an atom the neutron loses energy. The neutron slows down and the atom speeds up—just like different-sized billiard balls hitting each other. Also the nucleus you are using to slow things down shouldn't be too big. Not just any lightweight nuclei will do the job. You don't want the light nuclei itself absorbing the neutrons as some do. You can't use hydrogen. (Unless the uranium-235 content in the uranium is higher as was the case with the bug-built nuclear reactors in ancient Gabon.) Hydrogen is just too good at absorbing neutrons. You can't use deuterium, because it's already got an extra neutron and would break down if hit by another neutron. Helium and oxygen are OK but they are gases and it's hard to pack enough of them around the uranium fuel. Carbon is the next best. Carbon is still relatively light and it doesn't absorb too many neutrons. Carbon thus becomes the "moderator"—the "something" that slows the neutrons down so that the chances of them producing more fissions are sufficiently increased.

Sometimes it's helpful to add some element to the process that will more readily produce neutrons. For this neutron source boron can be used. It can simply be mixed into the uranium.

Uranium and the source are surrounded with carbon. Graphite is the carbon form usually used. The alpha particles, from the natural uranium decay, will collide with the boron nuclei and produce plenty of neutrons. When a slow (speeding bullet type speeds) neutron from the source hits, and is captured by a uranium-235 nucleus, the nuclei will fission. The fast neutrons from that fission will whiz off out of the uranium mix, bounce around in the carbon for a while and so slow down. If one of these slow neutrons finds its way to another atom of uranium-235 and gets captured in its nucleus, it will induce another fission "event". With enough uranium pieces in the system a chain reaction can be maintained. Useful quantities of heat can be produced. Water can then be pumped through the system to produce steam. The steam in turn powers turbines that drive a power generator. Electricity is produced.

As in any furnace the generation of heat has to be controlled and regulated. If the chain reaction gets too slow it might stop. That's safe enough but it could be annoying. If it's too fast then the heat might build up in the reactor faster than it is being removed by the steam. It's then the same as any other steam boiler that runs out of water. It's not dangerous but it could easily ruin the entire reactor by melting pipes and other structural components. In that sense only is it dangerous, but it just cannot become a nuclear bomb. A nuclear reactor that overheats has the same result as a car engine that overheats. They cook themselves and produce a heap of junk.

For practical considerations the chain reaction has to be speeded up and slowed down at will. So an easy means of controlling the reaction is needed. One way this can be achieved is by first leaving some access holes in the assembly. Cadmium metal rods are then fitted into these holes. Cadmium is an excellent neutron absorber. The cadmium rods soak up the neutrons and thus put a damper on the nuclear reaction. For more power, the rods are pulled out a little, for less power they are pushed in. It can also be arranged for cadmium rods to automatically drop into the reactor and shut the whole thing down completely as a safety system.

The first nuclear reactor was called a pile. It was dubbed a pile as it was in essence a big pile of graphite and uranium. The name stuck for reactors in general. This first pile was built in 1942 under the stands of the University of Chicago's sport stadium as part of the Manhattan Project. It used the shut-off safety system just described. However it wasn't automatic. A man armed with an axe stood by ready to cut a rope that held reserve cadmium rods in readiness to drop into the reactor. In an emergency, the plan was for this Safety Control Reserve Axe Man (SCRAM) to cut the rope to let the rods drop and so stop the reaction. Today, the acronym SCRAM is still used to refer to the emergency shutdown of a nuclear reactor.

That first reactor had a second safety system consisting of men armed with buckets containing a solution rich in boron. They actually stood on top of the pile and as a last resort they could pour the boron solution into the pile. Fortunately this was never needed. These guys were unkindly referred to as the suicide squad, a name not so honoured in the ongoing history.

Remember those "delayed neutrons" mentioned when considering the difference between fission and fusion? They are the ones released a little bit after an actual fission event. Delayed neutrons are important in nuclear re-actors. If all the neutrons from a fission event were released instantaneously then it would be very difficult to regulate a nuclear chain reaction. If there were no delayed neutrons, then pushing the control rods in just a little bit too far would shut the reaction down instantly. If the rods were pulled back out a bit, the reactor would start up again, but also instantly. There could be no "fine control".

Delayed neutrons keep the reaction going slightly after the rods are pushed in. They also mean that the reaction is maintained a little bit after the rods are removed to a new position. In both cases they give the controlling systems time to react and adjust. It almost seems as if nature designed fission reactions so that nuclear reactors could work.

The danger in a nuclear reactor accident is not and never will be the possibility of a reactor turning into a nuclear bomb. The danger in a nuclear reactor accident results from a heat-generated explosion. Such an explosion might splatter the surrounding countryside with radioactive materials. That's what happened at Chernobyl. Chernobyl was the equivalent of a terrorist's "dirty bomb"; and about as bad as it's possible to get, even in theory.

We will see further on in this chapter that Chernobyl was nowhere near the tragedy it was purported to be. The horrific image most people now have of the Chernobyl nuclear accident is simply an oil-fuel-industry marketing creation.

An operating uranium reactor produces plutonium. It happens automatically as the placid uranium-238 in the natural uranium absorbs neutrons.

When a neutron with enough energy strikes the nucleus of the common uranium-238 it can be absorbed to become U-239. The odd neutron however is not stable in its new environment and splits with its mated electron. The electron shoots off as a beta particle and the neutron becomes a proton. Our nucleus now has 93 protons and is therefore a new element. It has become 93Neptunium-239.

This nucleus is also unstable, and again, one of the neutrons in the neptunium then changes by emitting a beta particle, and the neutron turns itself into a proton. This produces 94Plutonium-239. These reactions forming plutonium all happens in seconds.

In nature, this process is rare and so the plutonium content in naturally occurring uranium is very small. To try and extract it from the uranium ore would be totally impractical, but it is there. Plutonium is not some mysterious, new, dangerous and poisonous element never seen before on this planet, as is always stated in media reports.

In a nuclear reactor a lot of neutrons are produced, and if plenty of the relatively inert uranium-238 is present, plutonium will be produced in usable quantities. Some reactors are designed to produce an excess of fast neutrons specifically for the purpose of "breeding" plutonium from uranium-238—so called fast breeder reactors. Fast breeder reactors can produce almost as much fuel as they consume.

In a normal power reactor the aim is to slow the neutrons down so that the chain reaction can proceed with either natural or slightly enriched uranium. Recent fast breeder reactor designs use more highly enriched uranium without a moderator. They do not use water as the coolant since it would slow the neutrons too much, and instead these reactors are cooled using a liquid metal, usually sodium. Now, most power reactors in the West do not use graphite moderators. Graphite-moderated reactors are cumbersome and mainly existed in the early days to produce plutonium from natural uranium.

The U.S. Navy wanted nuclear reactors to power its submarines. U.S. Admiral Hyman Rickover directed a program to develop a much lighter, more efficient reactor for naval use. The result was the "pressurized water reactor", PWR for short. Pressurized water reactors are now the most common in the West.

In a pressurized water reactor normal water is used as the moderator and coolant for the reactor core. The hydrogen nuclei in the water doesn't just slow the neutrons down; they also absorb some as well. If too many neutrons are absorbed the reaction will slow down below a usable level. Such reactors need uranium fuel that is richer in uranium-235 to compensate for losing some neutrons in the water moderator. Uranium in which the percentage of uranium-235 has been artificially increased to around 3% is suitable.

The U.S. military of course had the enrichment facilities left over from developing the bomb, so enriching uranium for their reactors was no real problem. The Russians however continued to use modified graphite-moderated reactor designs for both plutonium production and power generation. This is probably because they could not financially sustain an operational enrichment facility. They probably also made more use of "heavy" water as a moderator in submarine reactors since it allows the use of uranium containing less uranium-235.

Plutonium and MOX as fuel in nuclear reactors

Nuclear reactors can also use plutonium as fuel. In normal reactor operations, uranium-238 will capture neutrons and turn into $_{94}Pu^{239}$. This plutonium then happily joins in the fission reactions with $_{92}U^{235}$ typically contributing half the total power generated by the reactor.

There's a lot of talk about plutonium and weapons proliferation, about plutonium in radioactive waste, about the toxicity of plutonium and the long-term hazard it represents. But the reality is that coal and its waste products are a much bigger hazard to our world.

The best thing to do with plutonium is to burn it for energy in nuclear reactors where it would be converted to shorter-lived fission products while providing electricity with no carbon dioxide emissions.

Can today's reactors use plutonium as a fuel or do we need a whole new technology? Yes and no. Almost all of today's reactors can use something called MOX (short for mixed-oxide) fuel with little or no modification. The uranium used in reactor fuel is not in metallic form; it is uranium oxide, a ceramic material, stable at high temperatures. In mixed-oxide fuel, plutonium oxide is mixed with depleted uranium being uranium-238. MOX fuel with around 7% plutonium is equivalent to uranium enriched to around 5% uranium-235. It is so very much easier to add a little plutonium-239 to natural uranium and turn it into useful reactor fuel, than it is to laboriously enrich the uranium-235 content. Most reactors can use MOX for between 30% and 50% of their fuel load. Some design changes are required for reactors to operate on more than 50% MOX.

The concept of accelerator-driven reactors

At the heart of all nuclear reactors are neutrons. The chain reaction inside a reactor sustains itself by being able to produce all the neutrons it needs to initiate new fission reactions.

A thorium-fuelled reactor works by having thorium capture a neutron to become U^{233} which then fissions to produce energy and more neutrons. It can easily be arranged so that not enough neutrons are produced to both sustain the chain reaction and to turn thorium into U^{233} faster than it is consumed. Such a thorium reactor design would therefore always rely on a source of fresh neutrons. Conventional designs for thorium reactors are discussed in more detail further on but the above problem with thorium is relevant to the accelerator driven reactor.

In 1993 Carlo Rubbia was the Italian Director-General of CERN, the European Centre for Particle Research. A few years earlier, in 1985, Rubbia won the Nobel Prize for the first detection of a rare and elusive nuclear particle using the CERN particle accelerator. Rubbia proposed the concept that the neutrons required to keep a thorium reactor going could be supplied from a high-energy particle accelerator. A powerful particle accelerator would fire high-speed protons into a heavy-metal target to produce neutrons in a process call spallation.

Surround the target with thorium fuel and the neutrons will begin to breed U^{233} which will then fission to power the reactor. The reactor produces more power than is needed to run the accelerator so, once started, the system produces useful output. One of the nice things about Rubbia's design is that if you turn off the accelerator, the reaction cannot sustain itself so the reactor shuts down.

Another interesting application of Rubbia's idea is that it can also use some of the long-lived waste products, normally found in spent nuclear fuel rods, as fuel. Isotopes like neptunium, americium and curium, which are formed in nuclear fuel rods, are long-lived and currently complicate otherwise acceptable disposal concepts for high-level nuclear waste. In an accelerator-driven reactor, these isotopes could be made to fission to produce useful energy. At the same .time, the fission products from the reactions have much shorter half-lives and so they only need to be stored for short times to allow their radioactivity to reduce to safe levels. Some of the long-lived fission products like technetium-99 and iodine-129 could also be broken down into shorter-lived isotopes in an accelerator reactor system.

The accelerator reactor thus becomes an energy-producing nuclear waste incinerator.

In spite of the promise shown by this concept, so far not even an experimental accelerator driven reactor has been made. It's possible that currently the availability and low cost of uranium is such that newer technologies are not being sufficiently considered. Another possibility is that the antinuclear propagandist would not relish the development of a super-efficient nuclear waste incinerator.

Other reactor designs

Accelerator driven reactors are not the only new concept in nuclear power.

Several countries are developing so-called fourth-generation reactors. The objective is to simplify the reactor designs, not only to make them cheaper, but also more inherently safe. Many of these designs eliminate the active safety systems and replace them with passive systems.

As an example, in most power reactors an unwanted increase in power level is detected by the control system computers which then adjust how far the control rods are pushed into the reactor. This is an active system because it relies on electronics and mechanisms to function properly. Newer reactor designs use the physical properties of the material to achieve the same result—just as those ancient reactors in Gabon regulated themselves when the power level rose too high simply by boiling off some of their moderator, so too will lithium. Lithium is a very light metal with good neutron-absorption properties that can be used as a passive control system. When the reactor heats up the lithium expands and occupies more volume in the reactor core thus absorbing more neutrons and slowing the reaction down.

Because of the success of the anti-plutonium campaign, another design goal in new reactors is to increase the "proliferation resistance", that is to reduce the amount of Pu-239 bred in the reactor by more selective control of neutron behavior.

Thorium and thorium-fuelled nuclear reactors

Thorium metal is only slightly radioactive. It is found in usable ore bodies and as a trace element in most rocks and soils. It is estimated that worldwide, current economically extractable thorium reserves amount to 1,200,000 tons of refined thorium metal. Thorium has several isotopes, but apart from $_{90}\text{Th}^{232}$, these are short-lived, existing only briefly in one of the uranium decay series. Natural thorium is therefore virtually 100% thorium-232.

Thorium does not fission. So how can it be used as a nuclear fuel? The answer lies in its ability to absorb slow neutrons to become thorium-233. It then beta decays (an electron splits off from a neutron thus producing a proton) with a half-life of 22.3 minutes into 91Protactinium-233. The $_{91}Pa^{233}$ in turn beta decays with a half-life of 27 days into $_{92}U^{233}$. And uranium-233 can comfortably power a nuclear reactor. Just as plutonium-239 fuel can be made from otherwise useless uranium-238, so uranium-233 fuel can be made from abundant thorium-232. Given a kick-start with some other fissionable fuel like uranium-235 or plutonium-239, it is easy to start breeding uranium-233 nuclear fuel from thorium.

It is conceivable that a bomb could be made from uranium-233 bred from thorium, but it has never been done and it seems unlikely that anyone would bother while other processes are easier and other types of weapons more frightening.

Reactor designs and thorium-based fuel cycles have been studied for about 30 years but nowhere near on the same scale as uranium and plutonium. In the United States, a light water breeder reactor that uses fuel where thorium surrounds a uranium-235 seed has been demonstrated. In the Netherlands an aqueous homogeneous suspension reactor has been operated for several years—in this interesting design a highly enriched uranium-thorium fuel mixture is continuously circulated in solution so removal of the waste fission products and "topping up" of the fuel can occur continuously. India is particularly interested in thorium as a fuel. India's thorium reserves are considerable and are six times larger than even their uranium reserves.

Thorium is now being considered as a more practical and foolproof nuclear fuel than is either uranium or plutonium. With thorium fuel, the reactor is next to useless for producing nuclear weapons. Fly ash from a coal-fired power station might be a better source of nuclear materials for bomb making than waste from a thorium reactor. Probably for this reason no money is ever earmarked by oil-backed governments for developing thorium power reactors. Could it be because nuclear energy might suddenly appear too safe?

Super safe nuclear reactors

An imminently practical concept for an ultra-safe nuclear power reactor was proposed by the Hungarian-American physicist, the late Dr Edward Teller. It is described in his *Memoirs*, first published in the United States by Perseus Press.

Edward Teller is often referred to as the "father of the hydrogen bomb". This is both an oversimplification and an exaggeration, although he was instrumental in the design and construction of both atomic bombs and hydrogen bombs in the United States.

Teller was born in Hungary and experienced communist rule firsthand. As a result he believed, and kept insisting to all, that it was necessary that the United States should never ever fall behind Russian weaponry development. Partly because of Teller, development of the U.S. hydrogen bomb was not halted, as many demanded.

A hydrogen fusion bomb is extremely difficult and time consuming to design and build. Much more so than a uranium or plutonium fission bomb. The Russians' atomic bomb, a fission bomb, was copied off U.S. designs. Spies stole those designs. However, the Russians designed and built their hydrogen bomb themselves from scratch. They exploded their bomb on 12 August 1953. The first U.S. hydrogen bomb was tested less than a year earlier in October 1952. Stalin did not get his hydrogen bomb before the Americans, as he had hoped. If U.S. research had not continued Stalin would have had a hydrogen bomb exclusively, and the world would have been a very different place. We can thank Teller that it didn't happen.

Teller's ideas on a simple idealized nuclear power reactor design have to be listened to as his concepts do work. Nuclear reactors are now often built with "negative temperature coefficients". That means if the reactor warms up above the operating design temperatures the nuclear reaction slows down. Even a very quick over-heat will instantly and totally stop the nuclear reactor. It's the nature of the nuclear reaction itself.

Edward Teller was both a theoretical and practical nuclear physicist. He once proposed the concept of a small safe nuclear reactor using these concepts for universities. A reactor that would also be suitable for installation in hospitals for medical isotope production. It was built and it worked. It was named the Triga reactor and produced by General Atomic. Triga is an acronym for Training, Research, Isotope, General Atomic. Over eighty Triga reactors were built and supplied to hospitals and research centres around the world. Not one has ever malfunctioned, even when operated by students. The Triga is a negative temperature coefficient reactor.

In slightly simplified terms Teller's concept for a nuclear power station is to dig a lift well hole, several hundred feet deep and install a lift. Then excavate a room at the bottom of the well and install a self-limiting power reactor designed with a negative temperature coefficient. The reactor would then be connected to the surface with both a feed water pipe and a steam delivery pipe. The hot steam from the reactor would then be delivered to turbo-electric generators on the surface.

If the reactor warmed up much above the temperature of any steam being piped to the surface, the nuclear reaction would slow down. Only by pumping cold water down the long feed pipe, could the reactor react. If no water is being fed in, the nuclear reaction stops and the entire nuclear power plant goes into hibernation. There need be no moving parts. The operation could be totally automatic.

The reactor could even use a uranium breeder system to start a sequence of thorium breeder cycles. The number of secondary thorium reactors would determine how long the installation could operate to produce turbine steam.

After construction was completed and the plant commenced operation, if it was desired the lift well itself could then be filled with concrete. Then we could all just forget about reactor risks. There wouldn't be any.

For all practical purposes it would be inaccessible by any body, or any thing, at any time. After say fifty years, or even a hundred years, when the reactor finally ran out of its nuclear fuel it would simply be left there, safe and sound for ever.

Nuclear power using the fusion reaction—a pipe dream

If the temperatures and pressures produced inside the core of the hydrogen bomb could somehow be produced on a tiny and harmless scale in a laboratory, safe free energy would be available to man forever—a worthy dream. If hydrogen could somehow be made to fuse in a continuous, controlled manner, or even in a continuous series of very tiny controlled reactions, then just maybe fusion reactors could power the world. That might be the vision but might well be an illusion. So what has happened? Incredible sums of money have been consumed in research in an effort to produce electricity from the fusion reaction, and it's still a far off-pipe dream.

Green movements are happy with the fusion concept. The image is fostered that the fusion reaction would produce utterly negligible quantities of nuclear waste. It is presumed that no heavy nuclei would be needed or produced in a fusion energy process. Therefore material for fission bombs could not be extracted from the reactor. Green movements and the oil companies want humanity to wait for this false and impossible dream. In doing so they are having considerable success. It is now a commonly accepted concept that atomic power should be phased out while we await some golden age of hydrogen fusion power.

This never-ending delaying tactic by the fossil fuel advocates and the antinuclear movement will then be absolutely ongoing as any future pos-sible utilization of fusion power will, in its turn, be totally frustrated. That this would happen is inevitable. A new crop of green movement arguments would portray fusion itself as being too dangerous to be acceptable for power generation.

The reality is that there are a lot of neutrons released in the hydrogen fusion reaction, and wherever there are high-energy neutrons you'll have radioactive materials being produced. Expose some common uranium to the neutrons generated by some future hypothetical fusion reactor and plutonium will be produced in any quantity required.

Even now in endeavoring to create fusion reactions, the experimental Tokamak Fusion Reactor produces large quantities of radioactive waste. (Tokamak is a Russian word meaning a torus-shaped magnetic bottle.) This seems to indicate the high probability that a fusion reactor would produce as much waste, and possibly more, than a conventional fission reactor. The new and suddenly generated anti-hydrogen-fusion environmentalist will have their own brand of well-orchestrated field days, and the arguments and the delays and the confusions will continue.

Researchers pursuing the nuclear fusion concept generally consider heavy hydrogen or deuterium as the fuel. Fusing deuterium or tritium nuclei is much easier than fusing plain garden-variety hydrogen. There are about 3 kilograms of deuterium in every ton of seawater. Almost the only tritium on our planet is made using the neutrons from fission reactors.

It is a big problem to generate the incredible pressures needed to hold hydrogen nuclei extremely close together against their repelling forces and at the same time, somehow heating them to 100 million degrees or so to make them fuse. Normally such conditions only exist in the centre of a star, and in the centre of a hydrogen bomb.

The construction of a fusion reactor to generate commercial electricity is a long long way off. It is more likely to never ever happen, at least for the next thousand years or so. And it is also not needed. There is just no point in hopefully waiting for somebody to magically develop a usable, practical and vaguely safe fusion reactor. Fission reactors, on the other hand, work extremely well and are very economical. They are also considerably safer than most other human creations, fusion concepts included.

Nuclear fission power plants are safe and practical, and unless they were specially designed to do so before they were built, nuclear fission power plants do not produce useful and accessible bomb material. The reality is that power reactors are difficult and sometimes even impossible to convert to make them usable as a feasible source for nuclear weapon materials. In total contrast, it is far easier to make nerve gas and biological agents under the guise of a "harmless" petrochemical or biochemical industry than it is to make plutonium using conventional power reactors. It is far easier to obtain and fly a few hundred tons of aviation fuel into a skyscraper than it is to obtain even non-weapons-grade plutonium.

Offbeat nuclear power ideas that might work

One concept that received a lot of publicity was cold fusion. Cold fusion is the concept of being able to fuse hydrogen, deuterium or tritium at near normal room temperature. There is no doubt that if this could be achieved then it would provide a truly remarkable source of utterly limitless power. The theoretical basis for this is disputed by most physicists and possibly rightly so.

Pons and Fleishmann are two names most associated with cold fusion. In March 1989 Stanley B. Pons and Martin Fleishmann claimed to have discovered that deuterium fusion could be "catalyzed" at room temperatures using palladium. Palladium is a moderately rare metal that has an unusual property of being able to soak up hydrogen. The theory was put forward that deuterium atoms could cram themselves together inside the palladium metallic structure close enough to spontaneously fuse and release energy. The phenomenon was reported to have occurred on a laboratory bench, in a common glass laboratory beaker.

What followed was a flurry of experiments in laboratories around the world, all trying to reproduce Pons and Fleishmann's strange results. The phenomenon simply had to be confirmed, or otherwise. Some of these experiments in other laboratories seemed to support Pons and Fleishmann, most did not. The ramifications of cold fusion were so great and the evidence so contradictory that, as early as late 1989, the U.S. Department of Energy commissioned and received a comprehensive review from an expert panel of 23 scientists from a range of institutions. This panel delivered, in somewhat subdued scientific language, a fairly scathing report on the "evidence" for cold fusion. They noted that in many laboratories the basic procedures used to eliminate error in data analysis had not even been followed. The panel however agreed that the potential benefits of cold fusion were such that moderate funding be continued.

Since the original announcement, Pons and Fleishmann received funding from hopeful benefactors and so were able to continue their research. Other labs around the world also continue to work on cold fusion. Unfortunately to date nothing has been reported anywhere that definitely confirms that cold fusion even exists. As a result there are now vastly more skeptics of cold fusion theory than there are believers.

Another cold fusion concept being investigated is "sonofusion" or bubble fusion. When a liquid is blasted with powerful sound waves bubbles are formed within the liquid. These minute bubbles immediately collapse creating a miniature implosion. That microscopic implosion sometimes generates enough concentrated energy to create a burst of light. The phenomenon is known as sonoluminescence. To create the observed light requires a tiny instantaneous localized burst of temperature of several thousand degrees.

By using cunning techniques, temperatures high enough to produce nuclear fusion have now apparently been produced. Rusi Taleyarkhan and a group of colleagues at the Oak Ridge National Laboratory in Tennessee seeded the bubble-formation process with bursts of neutrons and claimed they produced fusion reactions.

Like the work of Pons and Fleishmann, the whole bubble-fusion concept was ridiculed with vicious ferocity. One researcher in the team is Dick

Lahey, an engineer with the Rensselaer Polytechnic Institute in New York. He believed the criticism was politically motivated and thought the motive could have been that hot fusion advocates were defending their grant money supply. I doubt that. Oil interests have a greater motivation.

One thing must be recognized. If cold fusion or bubble fusion was a reality and was developed, it would be the worst scenario possible for the fossil fuel companies and their suppliers. That, for them is reason enough to always ensure that cold fusion is never given serious funding, and efforts should also be made to totally deny its possible reality. For it just might work!

There is a theoretical basis for yet another form of cold fusion. It's described as "muon-catalyzed" fusion. It involves hydrogen atoms that have had their electrons replaced by particles called muons. Muons share a lot in common with electrons except they are many times more massive. With muons in place of electrons in the hydrogen atom it is theoretically possible to get the nuclei of hydrogen to come close enough to fuse at room temperature. Unfortunately to create muons consumes more energy than that released by any subsequent fusion reaction. Muon-catalyzed fusion might, in the near future, also be used, like hot fusion, as a bottomless alternative energy money sink.

Another hot fusion reaction which has received some unwarranted favourable press is the fusion of helium-3. Helium-3 is a rare isotope of normal helium. It has two protons and only one neutron in its nucleus. Theoretically, fusing 2Helium-3 nuclei looks promising—it releases no neutrons so it is not a source of radioactive waste.

Unfortunately there are only impossibly tiny quantities of helium-3 here on earth. This is no problem to the proponents of helium-3 fusion. It turns out that helium-3 is produced in the core of our sun and carried out into the solar system by the solar wind. It has thus been accumulating in the stable surface dust of the moon for a few billion years. Proponents of helium-3 fusion suggest flying space shuttles to the moon, setting up mining operations and shipping the helium-3 back to earth. They argue that maybe a dozen shuttle loads a year would be enough to power the world. Currently space shuttles cannot reach the moon. Apart from these problems, it is also unfortunate that fusing helium-3 appears more difficult than fusing heavy hydrogen.

Such hypothetical energy production concepts often generate a flurry of excitement in the media but do little more than generate confusion and uncertainty, and delay what should be the urgent adoption of well-proven systems. For the simple fact is, we already have perfectly reliable, safe and economical nuclear power stations and we already have the capability of generating virtually unlimited energy by building dozens more of them. Admittedly, research into novel concepts has to be fostered but we must not and cannot pin our hopes on some futuristic designs to halt or even mitigate global warming.

Are nuclear power systems more dangerous or less dangerous than other systems?

There are now about three dozen countries that have nuclear reactors. Theoretically every one of those reactors could produce materials from which nuclear weapons could be produced. But we know that rogue nations, by allocating vast sums of their national resources to the development and production of weapons, still always have immense difficulties in doing so. Nuclear weapons are just not easy to make. Estimates that such countries could eventually make one or two bombs a year illustrates the impracticability of terrorist organizations attempting such a task. But the antinuclear lobby always feed us a different story.

Invariably when nuclear power stations are discussed, the arguments usually centre on dangers that might be encountered. The relative degree of risk is not considered relevant. It is argued that because some risk exists then that remote possibility is sufficient to oppose their use. Being safer than a coal- or oil-fired power station is deemed irrelevant. Risks, and generally vague hypothetical risks, are the ongoing criticism levelled by the antinuclear movement. Even hypothetically: if the worst happened it might kill a few hundred people, not thousands and neither would the surrounding real estate be "contaminated for generations"—a few months at the most, and then the land could be promoted as a health resort. Sounds ridiculous but that's what they do with the beach at Guarapari, Brazil and its radioactive sand.

It is important to differentiate between relative risks and dangers. It is blind bigotry not to. Twenty gallons of gasoline is dangerous, it could start a fire, which could raze your house in minutes, but the risks we happily tolerate. We all drive around the country and through our cities at 60 miles per hour, or 100 kilometres per hour, with twice that much petrol slopping around in a relatively flimsy thin sheet metal fuel tank, mounted under the car and next to a hot exhaust pipe. But cars are built to reasonably safe standards and we accept that. Everything in life involves some dangers and some risks. The arguments about nuclear energy must be related to relative risks so that logical, sensible and realistic decisions can be made concerning them.

The risks associated with nuclear power stations must be compared to the risks and dangers of non-nuclear energy such as coal, natural gas and oil. When we do such comparisons we find that nuclear power generation is actually ludicrously safe.

The most significant risk mankind now faces will happen if we don't switch to nuclear power.

If we only considered potential danger and ignored relative risks, humanity would be very different, if it existed. The development of knowledge would cease. It could never have started. As an example, medicine as it exists today, couldn't exist. Testing new medications involves risk and dangers. There would not be one single solitary medication on the shelves at the local pharmacy, and there could never be. We all know that pharmacological preparations can be dangerous and involve risks, but more importantly, what is the risk if we don't avail ourselves of our medications. Not accepting any risk would mean there could be no iodine, no Band-aids, no aspirin. Nor, of course would there be such a thing as a pharmacy. Penicillin would never have been discovered, or at least never developed. If zero risk was insisted upon the use of penicillin would never have been permitted. Also streptomycin, amoxycillin, erythromycin, and roxithromycin and the entire range of antibiotics, could never have come into being. Without taking a risk, without looking danger in the face, we would not have learnt to ride a horse. We never would have learnt to use fire. Without taking some risk there would be no inventions. There would be no development. Mankind would have been a miserable failure. Mankind would have long since faded away and been replaced by some totally different species. A species that had the guts to try. They, and not us, would have been the species that landed on the moon.

Likewise we have to accept some risks in adopting nuclear energy as the world's major energy source for power generation. But that risk is tiny and accidents are comparatively insignificant. Risks using nuclear energy are as nothing compared to the risks and deaths and dangers we constantly experience in fuelling our civilization on fossil fuels. Burning fossil fuels, and planning to burn more fossil fuels as we currently are, is a threat, a risk and a danger a thousand times worse than that posed by utilizing nuclear energy.

In the oil-inspired, media-managed, so-called nuclear debate, the arguments we are fed always manage somehow to convey a sense of imminent and colossal danger even thinking of nuclear energy. We are force-fed images that we would be creating a world that would soon become uninhabitable, or at best, barely habitable. The frightful conditions created would then supposedly exist for thousands of generations to come. That's if those generations ever came. It is always and not too subtly implied that evil owners and evil operators tell us lies about the safety of their nuclear plants. It is constantly inferred that evil scientists design these mysterious power stations with no thought of our future, and therefore no thought for their own future and for the future of their children. Such propaganda is illogical rubbish.

These messages, these supposed warnings are no more than blatant pro-oil, antinuclear drivel. The frightening dangers and disasters of our current fossil fuel reliance, they never ever mention.

Deaths from nuclear reactor accidents

Three large-scale nuclear reactor accidents have occurred:

Sellafield-Windscale. United Kingdom, 1957, no deaths.

Three Mile Island. United States, 1979, no deaths.

Chernobyl. Former USSR, 1986, 48 deaths.

This is the reality of those three reactor accidents.

Sellafield-Windscale

At the end of World War II the army of the USSR had grown to become an enormous military establishment. At that time the Soviet Union was in effect controlled by one man, Joseph Stalin. Stalin was callous, cruel, vicious and greedy to a level almost beyond comprehension. In the years following the defeat of Germany there was nothing to stop the USSR from annexing what was still left unannexed of the pre-war European states. It would be done by creating a series of situations to "justify" their army moving in to "preserve order and stability". What would stop them? No individual situation would ever be made sufficiently significant to warrant the intervention of the distant United States.

The United Kingdom was well aware that the Soviets were working on nuclear weapons development, and would soon have them. The United Kingdom, without nuclear weapons, would be unacceptably vulnerable to Joseph Stalin and his Russia.

Although the initial development work for the U.S. atomic bomb was actually commenced in England, access to U.S. nuclear weapons was not available to the United Kingdom after the war. The United States passed an act in 1946 forbidding nuclear weapons information and technology being passed on to another country, any country.

In the United Kingdom it had already been decided a year earlier that, for their own security, the United Kingdom needed nuclear weapons. The weapons material of choice would be plutonium. Of course nobody knew much about building nuclear reactors in the late 1940s. It was mainly all complex theory. But what was grim reality was Stalin's ultimate desire for a communist world, dominated by his own USSR.

A rushed program was immediately commenced at the Windscale Royal Ordinance factory on the Cumbrian coast facing the Irish Sea. The name of the location was later changed to Sellafield. Sellafield is roughly halfway between Glasgow and Liverpool, and faces west to the Isle of Man.

Money and effort was unlimited. Atomic Pile No. 1 began operation in October 1950. Pile No. 2 became operational eight months later. By March 1952 enough plutonium had become available to produce the UK's first weapon. That first bomb test, code named Hurricane, was exploded off the West Australia coast in October 1952.

The powers within the Kremlin suddenly had to appreciate that the United Kingdom was no longer a comfortably defenceless target, despite the orchestrated protestations of the ultra-left "ban the bomb" puppets.

Those first Windscale reactors were crude affairs with possibly inherent dangers, but they worked. They were put together in a tremendous rush. They were air-cooled graphite reactors fuelled with naturally occurring uranium—not enriched in any way. Ultimately an accident happened and by the standards of "possible nuclear accidents" it was a bad one. Yet compared to other industrial accidents it too could almost be described as a total non-event. Always nuclear reactors of any shape, size or type receive well-stimulated publicity if anything whatever goes wrong and the Sellafield-Windscale accident is still cited to illustrate the potential "horrors and dangers" of nuclear energy.

Those reactors were built over half a century ago. They were built to produce plutonium to produce nuclear weapons to defend the United Kingdom. They were built to establish in the minds of the Soviet regime the feeling that a war with the United Kingdom would not be a sensible and economical exercise. And no war happened.

The death toll from the Sellafield-Windscale nuclear accident was, and still is, zero. Like Three Mile Island, nobody died and nobody got sick. From surveys following the accident it was found that the highest level of radioactivity occurring anywhere in the surrounding countryside peaked out at 0.04 mSv per hour. Sounds bad? Well remember that sitting on the beach, at the Brazilian tourist and health resort of Guarapari the nuclear radiation dose rate from the beach sand you're sitting on would be more than twice that. And you have to pay to sit on the beach and soak up the healthful radiation.

The British Medical Research Council Committee investigating the health results from the Sellafield-Windscale nuclear reactor accident concluded "that it is in the highest degree unlikely that any harm has been done to the health of anybody whether a worker in the Windscale plant or a member of the general public".

In the UK, one month earlier in November 1957, 17 miners were killed in a coal mine accident in Ayeshire, 11 more were injured. Nobody outside Ayeshire remembers the coal mine disaster. People all over the world are constantly reminded of the "disastrous nuclear accident" at Windscale in 1957.

Three Mile Island

New York City, the date March 16, 1979. The release of a new film called *The China Syndrome*. It was a box office hit. The film was about a nuclear reactor that went into overdrive and was heading for a disastrous meltdown with horrendous repercussions.

The name China Syndrome comes from a hypothetical, that if a nuclear reactor ever overheated and had a meltdown, the heat would be so tremendous that the whole thing would melt its way down through the planet and all the way through to China. In the film the threat was that a meltdown would sink deep into the earth, hit a water table then explode, and in so doing render uninhabitable an area "the size of Pennsylvania". The whole thing is based on a total, theoretical impossibility. In the film, the good guys just managed to avert this seemingly inevitable scenario and we were given a happy ending, and a safe reprieve.

Now back to reality, and a true story that is in some way remarkably similar to the more accurate parts of the film.

The Susquehanna River drains most of the American state of Pennsylvania. It drains into Chesapeake Bay just north of Baltimore. On a small low-lying island in the Susquehanna River, the Metropolitan Edison Company built a nuclear power station.

Twelve days after the release of *The China Syndrome* in New York, a serious accident occurred at this nuclear reactor plant. It was then the most serious, most well publicized nuclear accident ever. There was however, negligible danger. But this was not given any media attention whatsoever.

The strip of land on which the reactor was built was called Three Mile Island. The island is no more than 15 miles long, about 24 kilometres. It's downriver from Harrisburg, the capital of the state of Pennsylvania.

There were two nuclear reactors at Three Mile Island, both were pressurized water reactors. The first reactor, TMI-1, had been operating since 1974. The system produced 800 megawatts of electricity. That's about enough power for a city of 800,000 people. The TMI-1 is still operating, although it was shut down for an extended period after the accident involving TMI-2.

All nuclear power plants operate on the same basic principle. The nuclear reactions in the core generate heat, which is used to produce steam, which in turn drives turbines attached to generators that produce electricity.

The accident at Three Mile Island involved the cooling water and steam flow. If you drive past a power station, whether it is nuclear or coal-fired, you'll see enormous clouds of steam coming out of huge tapered cooling towers. The clouds are not really steam, they are clouds of tiny water droplets produced from the water vapour in the warm air rising out of the cooling tower condensers.

The media love to show these clouds on television whenever there is talk of greenhouse gas emissions, but these clouds of water droplets are as harmless as the naturally occurring clouds of water droplets in our skies. In a coal-fired power station the really dangerous stuff, carbon dioxide, is invisible and comes out of the smaller exhaust stack and doesn't make for such sensational television. But it is easy to see how big clouds of highly visible steam can be easily linked with any mention of water or steam in a nuclear power plant accident and also how this can be manipulated to cause panic in a poorly informed, or deliberately misinformed general public. That's what they did with Three Mile Island.

There are three entirely separate systems using circulating water in a nuclear power station like that at Three Mile Island. The first system is the core cooling system—sometimes called the primary cooling system. This cooling water is circulated by pumps and moves heat from the core to the steam generators. Under normal operation in a pressurized water reactor this water is never allowed to boil into steam as it is held under very high pressure. The high pressure increases the boiling point temperature to a maximum of 380°C. Above that it boils no matter how high the pressure. This water stays in the "containment building". A "containment building" is a massive, reinforced concrete structure, built to contain the core and associated equipment and prevent any escape of radioactive material in the event of some hypothetical worst possible accident.

The "secondary cooling system" involves steam generation. The name "secondary" can lead to the impression that it is some form of back-up system to take over when the primary system fails, but this is not the case. In the secondary cooling system, water is pumped into the steam generators where the very hot primary coolant water supplies heat to turn the secondary coolant water into usable steam. The primary and secondary coolant waters are not in contact. The generated steam then turns the turbines to produce electricity. After the steam leaves the turbines it needs to be condensed back into a liquid so it can be pumped around the system again. Distilled water is always used to stop scale buildup so this is saved in all power plants, no matter what the heat source.

To turn the steam back into liquid water, a third coolant system comes into play, the condenser system. In this system, water from a nearby river or lake, or even the sea, is pumped over heat exchangers to cool the secondary water. This happens at the bottom of those big concrete cooling towers. An updraft in the cooling towers draws air over the heat exchangers and evaporates the water pumped from the river. The resulting warm moist air rises up the cooling tower creating the updraft. At the top the moisture condenses into those highly visible clouds that the media like to film.

Why not just boil the water in the reactor core, let it pass through the steam turbines and have it condense back in the cooling tower?

There are two main reasons. The primary coolant water flows though the core and is therefore exposed to high-energy neutrons. Some of the hydrogen in the water absorbs the neutrons and becomes deuterium or tritium. Both are very valuable and so are periodically recovered. Secondly, the primary coolant water can pick up traces of radioactive material from the metal surfaces through which it flows within the core. The primary coolant water can therefore be radioactive and so must be housed in the containment building. The primary coolant water is the only water that can ever become radioactive.

During the Three Mile Island accident it was suggested that there had been a steam leak releasing radioactivity into the environment. This was not the case at all. However, the mention of radioactive steam and the sight of clouds of vapour coming out of a cooling tower was enough to generate panic.

In the accident at Three Mile Island, pumps in the secondary coolant system, that's the steam system, of TMI-2 "tripped" or stopped operating. A later investigation revealed that a faulty valve in a maintenance system probably caused the pumps to trip. The power company apparently had known of the valve fault but had failed to rectify it. Once the pumps stopped, insufficient water was being pumped into the steam generator to supply steam to the turbines. Safety systems automatically shut down the turbines and power generation ceased. The reactor core continued to produce heat and the primary coolant system continued to move this heat to the steam generators, which of course no longer required heat.

Without heat demand, the temperature in the primary coolant system, the radioactive water, began to rise. As the temperature rose, the water expanded and increased the pressure in the core from the normal 2,155 psi to 2,255 psi. This activated a pressure-relief valve. The relief valve of course, cannot vent primary coolant water or steam to the atmosphere. It simply allows excess water to flow into a low-pressure holding tank. This is a normal operation. However, at the time of the incident the reactor was operating at 97% of its rated capacity and the sudden drop to zero meant the pressure relief valve was not able to release pressure quickly enough, and temperatures and pressures rose still further. Other independent systems cut in that automatically dropped control rods into the reactor core, sucking up all the neutrons and so shutting down the nuclear reaction.

All of this took just eight seconds following the initial pump trip, and normal functioning of safety systems prevailed. Once the control rods dropped into the core, the chain reaction in the core stopped. There is however, always some natural radioactive decay in the core and this generates heat. It is a small fraction of the heat being generated when the reactor is operating at full capacity. However this heat energy still needed to be removed.

The pressure returned to normal thirteen seconds after the accident, but the pressure relief valve did not automatically re-close. Control systems showed that the electric power that opened the relief valve had been turned off, but the valve was stuck open, and there was no direct indication of the valve position in the control room. This valve stayed open for more than two hours, letting over one third of the primary coolant water drain into the holding tank. The holding tank eventually overflowed into the sump of the containment building and some of this water was pumped into the auxiliary building before the sump pumps were turned off. Even so, emergency backup systems that should have maintained safe conditions did come into operation, but operators, overwhelmed by the number of alarms, misunderstood the situation and actually shut these down.

A cascading series of mistakes and missed warnings, probably the result of poor training, led to the water level in the core dropping. The core began to overheat from residual radioactive decay and high-pressure steam formed inside the core. As the water level dropped in the core, the high-temperature steam came in contact with the zirconium alloy cladding on the fuel rods. Zirconium is a fairly corrosion-resistant metal used in alloys for the manufacture of surgical implants such as screws, pins and skull plates. It is used to clad reactor rods, as it has what is called a low neutron-absorption cross section. Zirconium does however react with high-temperature, high-pressure steam, and this reaction produces hydrogen gas.

Hydrogen burns and when mixed with air or oxygen can explode. Hydrogen was formed in the reactor core. Some of this gas actually escaped through the open relief valve into the giant reinforced containment building and did cause a small explosion. At the time, staff in the control room recalled an audible "thud" which coincided with a pressure spike on one of the automatic pressure recorders in the containment building. Which would be expected. The explosion may have increased the amount of damage done to the equipment inside the containment building, but it had no effect on external radiation release.

Later analysis showed that two thirds of the core had lost coolant cover and some parts reached temperatures as high as 2,000° C or 3,500° F. At these temperatures some of the fuel rods ruptured, releasing radioactive gases into the core and eventually into the containment building via the open relief valve. More mistakes by the plant operators meant that the containment building was not then properly isolated and so a small quantity of radioactive materials was released into the auxiliary building and from there some eventually got into the atmosphere.

As far as human health is concerned and despite this almost unbelievable series of mistakes and failures, the Three Mile Island nuclear accident was a complete non-event nor could it have been anything else. Nobody got hurt, nobody broke a leg, nobody got cancer, no radiation burns, nothing. The Pennsylvania Health Department maintained a register of 30,000 people who lived within 5 miles (8 kilometres) of Three Mile Island for 18 years after the accident. It was discontinued in 1997 without any evidence whatever of unusual health trends in the area. The only ever detectable effect was "psychological stress" during and shortly after the accident because people believed the media hype.

The average radiation doses received by residents within 10 miles (16 kilometres) was 0.08 mSv, about the same as the dose received from a chest x-ray. The maximum dose to any individual amounted to about 1.2 mSv; an amount equivalent to the difference between the annual background dose of Colorado and Florida. Three Mile Island was the worst peacetime release of nuclear radiation in the United States and there was not one single casualty. In 1988 an explosion on the Piper Alpha oil platform in the North Sea killed 167 people. In the Australian state of New South Wales, where coal mining is considered to be the safest in the world, 112 miners have been killed since 1979. In China 5,670 coal miners died in 2001 alone, maintaining their average.

The reactor accident at Three Mile Island in 1979 was expensive. The TMI-2 reactor was not repaired. It was cleaned up and de-fuelled—a process that took 12 years and cost nearly one billion dollars. About 1% of the fuel and debris still remain in the reactor vessel so they still monitor the site.

Economically the accident was a disaster, especially because of the damage done to the image of nuclear power.

The antinuclear movement had a field day with Three Mile Island. And they still do. At the time they were probably hoping for some really dramatic explosion but in a Western designed nuclear power reactor that is difficult to even orchestrate. The small amounts of radioactive material that did escape, and even infinitesimal amounts of radioactivity is enough to send Geiger counters clicking like mad, had to be enough. That clicking sound really excites the media and they seem to go into a feeding frenzy. Their coverage at the time said it all. One Boston newspaper had a front-page headline that simply said "RADIATION".

Chernobyl

Undoubtedly the initial design and maintenance planning for the Chernobyl nuclear reactor was as narrow-minded and as irresponsible as could ever possibly be under any circumstances. It was one-eyed bureaucratic inefficiency on a mammoth and deadly scale. The continuing lack of basic and sensible safety considerations ensured that an accident was very possible.

But then, when a state is controlled by an unsackable, cruel and murderous mafia-like dictatorship, a citizen's life becomes very cheap. We must not forget that 30 million citizens of the old USSR were murdered just to maintain that dictatorship's vicious and awe-inspiring control. Stalin murdered far more people than the Nazis and it was Stalin's system that built Chernobyl and monitored its safety.

The town of Chernobyl is in the northern Ukraine. It is north of the Black Sea, about the same latitude as London, Warsaw and Amsterdam. From Chernobyl, if you head south, you hit the Mediterranean Sea between Greece and Israel. Chernobyl is also just over 50 miles or just under 100 kilometres north of the city of Kiev, with a population of 2.5 million. Kiev is the third largest city in the old Soviet Union after Moscow and St. Petersburg. It is now the capital of Ukraine.

There were four reactors at the Chernobyl nuclear plant. Reactor Number 4 was a 1,000-megawatt RBMK-1000 model. A 1,000-megawatt power station will power a city with a population of about one million people.

The RBMK-1000 was designed to produce both plutonium and electrical power. The design was later modified to produce power alone.

Reactors are normally encased in a "containment" structure as an ultimate safeguard in case of accident. In the West, these containment structures are incredibly strong vessels. In the RBMK design, the containment structure was simply a concrete-lined pit with a 200-ton steel lid held in place by its own weight. It was designed so that the lid could be removed to give access to the core, thus allowing refuelling even while the core was operational! Such a design could never hope to contain any but the most minor of explosions. Under the old Soviet regime, safety in reactors was not a major concern, only secrecy, minimum cost, and their ability to produce weapons-grade materials.

On the afternoon of 25 April 1986, prior to a routine shutdown, the operators were preparing for a test to determine how long the turbines and generators would be able to supply power after steam flow was cut off. Part of the preparations involved disabling the automatic emergency core cooling system because it would or might interfere with the test.

The old military-designed RBMK-1000 had a built-in design fault, which made the reactor unstable at low power settings. As mentioned earlier in this chapter, chain reactions in a reactor often rely on the presence of a moderator. The moderator slows down the fast neutrons produced by a fissioning uranium-235 nucleus so they can be absorbed to trigger fission reactions in other nuclei. In many power reactors, pressurized water acts both as a coolant and as a moderator. The water also absorbs a small fraction of the neutrons, but this effect is offset by using a more enriched uranium.

If a reactor produces too much power for the amount of coolant, then some of the water will boil to steam. Steam is a much less effective coolant than liquid water but fortunately it is also a much less efficient neutron moderator. The presence of steam in the core means less moderation and fewer slow neutrons to support the chain reaction. The result is that, in a properly designed reactor, the power will drop. Such reactors are in effect almost self-regulating. Too much power means more steam, which means fewer slow neutrons, which slows or stops the reaction. Conversely, too little power means less steam, more slow neutrons and an increasing reaction. This self-regulation works right at the point it is needed. If part of the core produces too much power then the steam forms in that part and the reaction slows or stops. It's the same system that those ancient Gabon reactors used.

The RBMK-1000 was not like this. Firstly, it used both graphite as a moderator and pressurized water as a coolant. Unlike the Three Mile Island reactor, in the RBMK-1000 the primary coolant water was boiled to form the steam that drove the turbines. It was therefore a normal part of operation to have steam being generated in the core in the Chernobyl reactors. Also, uniquely and unwisely, the actual absorption of neutrons by the cooling water played a vital role in limiting the reaction rate.

In the RBMK-1000 the sequence was this. Too much power meant excess steam; more steam meant less absorption of neutrons and also less efficient cooling. The graphite moderator was always present so that meant that all the excess fast neutrons would still be slowed down by this ever-present graphite and so produce more neutrons capable of increasing the reactor output. It's not hard to see that this is a fundamentally unstable concept, and could lead to runaway situations. Inherent stability features were not incorporated in the design.

Such a reactor can only be kept stable by some external control. In the case of the RBMK-1000 the control rods, which act as neutron absorbers, were designed to move in and out to control and stabilize the power level. These rods had an automatic control system.

In the minutes leading up to the planned test, the operator attempted to stabilize the reduced power level in the reactor by manually controlling coolant feed rates and by extracting manual control rods. Although he thought the core was stable, it was not. The coolant feed rates were too low and too many control rods had been withdrawn to their non-functioning position. The core was thus unstable. Ignorant of this, the operator went ahead with his test. The valves controlling the steam flow to the turbines were closed. Bizarrely enough, the next step in the test involved withdrawing the automatic control rods for 10 seconds. With cooling water being pumped into the core and no steam exiting, a rise in core pressure was expected. A rise in pressure would mean a rise in the boiling temperature and so for a short time the amount of steam in the core was expected to drop. Less steam should have meant less neutrons and less power, which is why the control rods were withdrawn. But there was not enough coolant water entering the core to give the expected rise in pressure. The operator recognized that an uncontrolled situation had developed and pushed an emergency button that lowered the control rods into the core.

But the reactor control rods all fed in from the top of the core.

Down at the bottom of the big core there was therefore no restraint on reaction buildup. The power levels in the bottom of the core had enough time to climb to 100 times the maximum design levels. The steam pressure buildup must have been incredible. The resulting explosion blew the 200-ton cover clean off the top of the containment structure. This was followed by a second explosion. This is thought to have resulted from chemical reactions associated with the ruptured fuel pellets. With the top off and the reactor split open, air entered and the super hot graphite started burning.

Some radioactive material was ejected in the first explosion, but most was released during the next nine days as the graphite moderator continued to burn. Of the 140 tonnes of nuclear fuel rods in the core, 8 tonnes were ejected to be scattered around within the Chernobyl complex. Radioactive iodine-131 and cesium vapour spread into the air.

A total of 237 workers and rescue workers at the reactor received acute radiation doses from 2,000 mSv to 16,000 mSv in the first few hours after the accident. They were all hospitalized and checked for acute radiation sickness. Of the 237 that were hospitalized, 134 cases were confirmed. Within three months, 28 of these patients had died. Two others died from injuries received at the time of the explosion, and one died from coronary thrombosis. Fourteen more died over the next ten years most likely, but not certainly, from injuries or radiation effects received at Chernobyl. Three children in the surrounding area died from thyroid cancer caused by the accumulation of radioactive iodine in their thyroid glands.

Deaths from injuries and radiation as a known or most probable direct result of the explosions at Chernobyl and the release of radioactivity, ten years after the accident, totals a maximum of 48.

The standard and logical procedure when exposed to an environment containing radioactive iodine is to immediately take iodine tablets. The thyroid is then saturated with excess iodine and rejects any radioactive iodine as an oversupply. If iodine had been given to the children those three lives would undoubtedly have been saved.

What about the long-term results from Chernobyl—are the headlines true? "Terrifying Outlook for Chernobyl's Babies"—"Chernobyl's Floods put Millions at Risk"—"100,000 to Die"—"Chernobyl, Widespread Cancer Risk",—etc., etc., etc., etc., etc.

In the Bryansk region of Russia, in the Belarus republic and in the northern Ukraine, the states or regions surrounding Chernobyl—in none of these areas were iodine tablets correctly distributed. There was not even a recommendation to switch to iodized salt. Iodized salt is quite common on supermarket shelves in many parts of the world. New Zealand is generally deficient in iodine and when you buy salt in New Zealand it is always iodized. In the regions around Chernobyl there was a total from all causes of 682 diagnosed cases of thyroid cancer in the decade following the Chernobyl disaster. The attending doctors report that most of the cases have been successfully treated. Only those three children have died.

The incidence of thyroid cancer in the Ukraine resulting from the Chernobyl nuclear reactor accident showed as a detectable rise above normal levels after four years. In Hiroshima and Nagasaki very slight increases in thyroid cancer appeared some ten years after the detonations. This markedly lower incidence of thyroid cancer in the Japanese experience compared to Chernobyl is most likely due to the plentiful iodine supplies in the Japanese high-seafood diet.

Leukaemia is a form of cancer that is constantly claimed to be "easily induced" by nuclear radiation. A barely measurable increase in the incidence of leukaemia is claimed to have occurred within five years at Hiroshima and

Nagasaki. Chernobyl had less. In the "fallout" areas to the west of Chernobyl and in nearby Belarus, the Ukraine and Russia itself, there has been simply no statistically significant increases in leukaemia or malignancies (other than thyroid cancer) in the ten years following the Chernobyl accident. A United Nations–sponsored report on Chernobyl, held in Vienna in 1996, concluded there was "no constant, attributable increase ... either in the rate of leukaemia or in the incidence of any malignancies other than thyroid carcinomas".

Some researchers in Greece, a country claimed by the media to be "heavily contaminated with fallout", suggested a higher incidence of leukaemia in those Greek babies exposed to Chernobyl fallout radiation while still in the womb. Any radioactive materials that got to Greece had to travel 875 miles (1,400 km) to get there. In doing so most of it would had to have travelled over the city of Kiev just 50 miles, or less than 100 km, from Chernobyl itself. Greece has a total population just four times more than the city of Kiev. Kiev itself noted no change in leukaemia numbers.

The incidence of leukaemia in these Greek children was stated to be more than twice that of unexposed children. The incidence of leukaemia in either case is always extremely low. The numbers are so low that the statistics themselves are possibly bordering on meaninglessness. Increase those risks ten thousand fold and you wouldn't even approach the deaths and dangers to Greek children from breathing air forever laced with huge quantities of pollutants spewing from the exhausts of petrol and diesel engines and coal-fired power stations in their neighbourhood. Visitors to Athens comment on the murky smog haze covering the city and corroding the ancient monuments. But the media earn their pay and highlight Chernobyl.

The European Union and Canada funded a scientific review of the RBMK type reactor as used at Chernobyl. One hundred and seventy scientists from eleven countries investigated and reviewed the operation and safety of these types of reactors. As of 1996 there were still 15 RBMKs operating in Lithuania, Ukraine and Russia.

Michael Hayns is a physicist, formerly at the UK nuclear research plant at Harwell. He became co-chairman of the investigating group. Now that the technology of the RBMKs is well understood, Hayns conceded that "they are much more benign beasts than we thought they were". A whole lot of additional safety features that are typical of reactors in Western countries have been fitted. Hayns comments that the improved understanding of the reactor design and a whole host of additional safety and shutdown features, now make "the prospect of another Chernobyl, very unlikely". This despite the fact that these reactors are absolutely nowhere near as safe and inherently stable as reactors built in the West.

The investigation group has advised Lithuania, Ukraine and Russia that they can now keep their RBMK nuclear reactors operating for as long as they want.

By 1995, the Chernobyl nuclear disaster cost Belarus alone US$55 billion. The vast majority of this $55 billion of taxpayers' money was squandered on unnecessary rents, pensions and a host of compensations "for millions of people who will receive doses of radiation lower than the natural levels present in many parts of the world". It was a Russian government public relations exercise where, in effect, over one billion dollars was spent per head for each death resulting from the Chernobyl fiasco.

Chernobyl was the ultimate "meltdown" but it was no holocaust. There was no massive death toll. There were no mass mutations. Insidious cancer and radiation did not poison the millions claimed. Millions is plain ridiculous, even hundreds is wild exaggeration.

It was the inspired media that created the most significant havoc. It was the media that created the panic and put the fear of hell into 200,000 young Russian women hundreds of kilometres away, and convinced them they had to abort their babies. Those 200,000 women really believed their children would be born ugly and deformed. It was a publicity lie, not a nuclear accident that created the greatest human suffering and the greatest loss of life following the Chernobyl nuclear reactor accident.

Science is the worldwide respected journal of the American Association for the Advancement of Science. In the 27 July 2001 issue they updated the report on the total death toll to date from radiation resulting from the Chernobyl accident. The numbers came from the United Nations Scientific Committee on the Effects of Atomic Radiation (UNSCEAR). The fate of the 106 remaining from the original 136 that received massive radiation exposure had been monitored for fifteen years. Of the 1,106, eleven had died. Only three had died from conceivably radiation-related effects. The report also considered the fate of the 381,000 people in the most contaminated area near Chernobyl. These people received on average a dose of 100 mSv. The death toll for this carefully monitored group never rose above the unexposed national average.

There is an interesting paradox. If the health benefits of low-dose nuclear radiation are taken into consideration, it is statistically probable that the overall health benefits of Chernobyl outweigh the known health losses. That's never mentioned anywhere.

The last reactor at Chernobyl closed down on 15 December 2000, about the time that Russia began to emerge as a major world player in the oil production game.

Bhopal: by comparison, a non-nuclear chemical accident

Let's examine an accident in a non-nuclear complex producing chemicals from oil for the agrochemical industry. Chernobyl we all remember. Bhopal, we are almost forced to forget, except at anniversaries.

Methyl isocyanate (CH_3NCO) is an industrial chemical in relatively common use, particularly in the manufacture of pesticides and herbicides. Phosgene (COC_{l2}) is another relatively common chemical used in the manufacture of dyes, pesticides and pharmaceuticals. Phosgene was also used as a chemical warfare agent in both World War I and World War II. It's about twice as lethal as chlorine gas. The effects of methyl isocyanate and phosgene on humans are quite similar. They both produce severe respiratory problems. In toxicology tests on mice, methyl isocyanate has been shown to be about 60 times more lethal than phosgene.

The United States National Institute of Occupational Safety and Health specifies a maximum exposure of 0.05 milligrams per cubic metre (mg/m^3) for workers exposed to methyl isocyanate over an eight-hour day. A level of 7 milligrams per cubic metre is nominated as "immediately dangerous to life or health". That's one tenth of an ounce evenly distributed throughout a reasonably sized suburban house.

Forty tons of methyl isocyanate is enough to contaminate the air over more than 100 square kilometres so as to be "immediately dangerous to life or health". To reduce the concentration levels of that 40 tons down to even maximum recommended exposure limit, evenly spread, would require an area of 20,000,000 acres or 80,000 square kilometers.

In December 1984, at the Union Carbide pesticide plant near the city of Bhopal in central India, water leaked into a huge storage tank containing liquid methyl isocyanate. Methyl isocyanate reacts with water to produce monomethylamine and carbon dioxide. The reaction also produces a considerable amount of heat. Monomethylamine is a gas at room temperature. It is also extremely toxic, producing a range of symptoms similar to methyl isocyanate. The production of gases and the release of heat increased the pressure in the storage tank, which then ruptured.

Somewhere between 30 and 40 tons of methyl isocyanate spewed from the tank. Methyl isocyanate boils at around 40°C so a lot would have been instantly vapourized into a gas by the heat of the chemical reaction. Any remaining liquid would have quickly evaporated into the warm surrounding air. Methyl isocyanate in vapour form is heavier than air, so it stayed at ground level.

The choking, burning fumes woke the sleeping people in the city of Bhopal and exposed 672,000 people to the toxic gases. Many did not stay awake for long. They died in their beds and they died on the streets. As the gas spread through the day people died in forests and towns miles from the plant.

The original official body count was 2,500, but the sale of cremation wood and shrouds for the dead indicated a death toll more like 7,000. The "immediately after accident" death toll is now accepted to be 6,954 men, women and children.

And that, horrific at it was, wasn't the end of it for the people living near that agrochemical production plant.

In a study involving 80,000 inhabitants conducted over nine years, indicators showed that at least 50,000 people still suffered from the effects. One sample study, involving 865 women pregnant at the time of the accident, showed 43% miscarried. Of the babies born 14% survived for less than one month. Other studies showed a 39% incidence of respiratory impairment. Over 90% of exposed children experienced irregular coughing five years after the accident. 51% of all women within a 10 km (6 mile) radius of the plant had abnormal uterine bleeding.

Even the legal morass of that Bhopal accident is never-ending. There were still 600,000 claims for injury, and 16,000 claims involving death filed at the time of writing. Union Carbide refused to pay initial claims for compensation. After five years the Indian government accepted an out-of-court settlement of US$470 million to be distributed to the victims.

That accident killed 6,954 within days. In 1993, almost ten years after the accident it was estimated that 5 people per week were still dying from the effects of methyl isocyanate poisoning from the accident. A later estimate in 1995 put the continuing death toll at one every two days. Most likely, at the very minimum, about 20,000 people have died because of the Bhopal accident. Three Mile Island happened five years before Bhopal and no one was killed or injured or even got a headache. Chernobyl happened two years after Bhopal and 48 people died. The Sellafield-Windscale nuclear accident happened in 1957 and nobody died.

Which accidents are we encouraged to remember? Three Mile Island, Chernobyl and Sellafield-Windscale, all were nuclear accidents, Bhopal was a petrochemical accident. The Bhopal accident was as deadly as 500 Chernobyls. The oil and the petrochemical lobby obviously have a big influence on the media.

In 1999 there was a nuclear chemical accident in Japan. It occurred at an industrial chemical plant, not a reactor site. The nature of the accident is ludicrously unbelievable. Enriched uranium compounds were being chemically separated. Inexperienced workers, not even experienced in handling toxic chemicals of any kind, somehow managed to be pouring ordinary buckets, filled with radioactive liquid, into a container that was simply too big. Instead of 2.4 kilograms going in, they manually poured in 16.4 kg. The 16.4 kg actually exceeded the critical nuclear mass! Radiation levels skyrocketed way above danger levels. Three workers subsequently died from radiation exposure.

Even though critical mass was exceeded, a nuclear explosion didn't happen and couldn't happen. If similar carelessness or incompetence had occurred involving any number of the common more toxic non-nuclear chemicals used in industry, the accident could have been really devastating, killing possibly thousands of people.

Coal, natural gas, oil, or nuclear energy—what's more dangerous?

The antinuclear lobbies and their spawned antinuclear movements have, as their only real weapon, their store of blatant lies. The technique they depend on is their never-ending manipulations, and their never-ending distortions of truth and fact. They are weapons which stop the safe, life-saving adoption of nuclear energy from powering a clean healthy future for humanity. Their public relations exercises cause the deaths of thousands of human beings and will ultimately be responsible for many times more deaths than from the nuclear bombing of Hiroshima and Nagasaki.

There are risks in everything human beings do. If we are informed, we can judge fairly. If we are knowledgeable, then we will generally adopt the least risky of our available alternatives. Therefore, we need to know the safety reality of nuclear-generated electricity compared to its fossil-based rivals. Then we use common sense.

A sobering piece of information comes from *Science* Vol. 298. It noted that the World Health Organization (WHO) estimated the deaths from worldwide air pollution, mainly resulting from our use of fossil fuels, at 600,000 people per year. That is a statistic always worth remembering when you hear the antinuclear crusaders selling their cause.

Coal

Nuclear power stations haven't been built in the United States for decades, and as is in many countries, even the mention of any possible construction is greeted with storms of protest. At the same time, new coal-fired power stations are being built every day in countries all over the world, all with barely a whisper of dissent. Which is really the most lethal? Is it the nuclear-fired power station or is it the coal-fired power station? When you check the facts properly, there is no doubt. It's coal that's the big killer, and by far.

Of the electric power generated in the United States, over 55% is produced by burning coal. Of all the fossil fuel reserves in the United States, 85% is coal. It has been the deliberate policy of successive U.S. administrations to support and encourage the utilization of these reserves. The first Bush administration's "National Energy Strategy" was structured around the increasing exploitation of all local fossil fuel reserves—particularly coal. That policy is now almost ingrained in U.S. administrations. Similar policies are similarly ingrained in the administration of most Western nations.

About 20 million tons of concentrated sulphuric acid is formed in the atmosphere every year from power stations burning fossil fuels. Coal burning is responsible for 70% of that total. Fossil fuel burning produces about 15 million tons of nitrogen-based acids such as nitric acid. These corrosive acids combine with atmospheric humidity to produce acid rain.

The removal of the sulphur dioxide from the exhaust gases of coal-fired power stations by "scrubbers" is being made mandatory in most developed nations. The coal-fired power stations are then publicized as "clean". The public relations people push the image of "clean coal". Clean coal doesn't make using coal safe any more than clean needles makes using heroin safe.

Unfortunately, the scrubbers themselves that clean the exhaust gases require enormous power to operate, and so in turn increase coal consumption. In consequence carbon dioxide production is increased by about 4%.

The waste product from the scrubbers is also, unfortunately, enormous and becomes a giant waste problem. One large U.S. power plant is slowly building a waste dump of mainly calcium sulphate from the sulphur dioxide collectors. Waste from its scrubbers will soon cover 80 acres and will be as high as an eight-storey apartment block. That same power station uses 200 coal-filled rail cars every day to fuel it. In burning its coal it pumps 60,000 tons of carbon dioxide into the atmosphere every day.

In addition, coal-fired power stations on average actually produce about the same quantity of low-level radioactive waste as an equivalent capacity nuclear power station. Some coal-fired power stations produce considerably more low-level nuclear waste materials than is produced from a comparable nuclear plant.

How is this so? There are several reasons. One reason is that one of the most common radioactive substances on the earth's surface is potassium-40. Potassium-40 occurs as a fixed percentage, 0.012%, of naturally occurring potassium.

Potassium is essential to all life. As plants grow they absorb potassium from the soil. Unless the soil is overabundant in potassium the concentration of potassium in healthy plant cells is much higher than in the soil. Because of this, plants are in general more radioactive than the environment in which they grow. Other nutritional elements containing radioactive isotopes are also absorbed and concentrated in the same way.

In the past, in hot tropical swamplands and over millions of years, vast deposits of dead and rotting vegetation accumulated to form peat bogs. Over more millions of years, sediments accumulated over the peat bogs. Over even more millions of years, the weight of the accumulating sediments compressed the peat until it ultimately formed coal. The radioactive potassium and the other radioactive elements, already concentrated by plants, are in the coal. They have been concentrated yet again by the compression forces that created the coal.

Most of the material that constitutes coal is carbon. At the beginning of the development of life on our planet, this carbon existed as carbon dioxide in the atmosphere. There was no oxygen. Today carbon dioxide makes up a mere few hundredths of 1% of our present-day atmosphere. The carbon in the carbon dioxide became coal. The oxygen in the carbon dioxide became the oxygen we breathe today.

As we mine and burn the coal, we reverse the process. The huge bulk of the coal material becomes atmospheric carbon dioxide once again. But not so with many of the other elements that produced those ancient plants. They, and their radioactive constituents, end up as fly ash. In this way another concentration process has occurred as the carbon from the original plant is separated out by burning.

Not only that, but coal can accumulate radioactive elements and a whole range of strange compounds in a totally different way. Old wartime gas masks used carbon to filter out poisonous gases. Carbon filters are used in all kinds of household and industrial applications. Coal in the ground appears solid and looks like it should be impervious to water, but it's not. It has millions of little fractures all through it. Water can percolate through these tiny fractures with relative ease. Because of these properties, a coal seam can be considered as a giant underground collection filter pad, covering hundreds, or even thousands of square miles.

Many of the elements in sediments with long-lived radioactive isotopes form chemical compounds that are slightly soluble in water. These compounds will be slowly leached out of surface rocks by normally slightly acidic rainwater. When rainwater percolates down through a coal seam, the compounds get trapped in this giant carbon-coal filter.

And there they remain until the coal seam is dug up and burnt.

When coal is burnt these radioactive elements don't generally go out the exhaust stack. They collect at the bottom of the furnaces or are collected by filters inside the exhaust stack. The solids are ash. The material caught in the filters is fly ash. The two are lumped and dumped together as fly ash. In addition some waste will accumulate, and later be removed from the boiler as "slag".

The majority of fly ash takes the form of microscopic ceramic particles. It is separated from the exhaust gases in "precipitators". This is so we do not see huge black clouds issuing from coal-fired power station stacks anymore.

Disposal of fly ash and boiler slag is always a problem. The fly ash is a fine dust-like material, easily blown about if not kept wet and muddy, or else completely covered. It is therefore usually dumped as a wet slurry in permanent, specially built tailing dams. Huge shallow flat tailings dams of fly ash surround all coal-fired power stations.

That fly ash contains all the radioactive material originally contained in the coal. It also contains all the radioactive elements filtered out of the water constantly percolating through the coal seams over eons.

Fly ash is a very fine powder. When the surface of these tailings dams dry out and the wind blows, clouds of fly ash cover the surrounding country. When we breathe it in, the particles deposit in our lungs.

Worldwide about 52,000 tons of uranium and thorium is extracted from the ground every year by one means or another. Approximately 40,000 tons is used in the nuclear energy and nuclear radiation industries. The remaining 12,000 tons of nuclear materials comes out of the ground as a component of coal. Coal often contains uranium and thorium. That 12,000 tons ends up being discharged into the air from the power station's exhaust stacks. Or it is mechanically collected in scrubbers and becomes a component of the station's fly ash. Then it is simply dumped as landfill.

If the scrubbers and exhaust gas cleaners are particularly efficient, the coal-fired power station is boasted about as being very "clean".

In most Western countries fly ash is regularly used as a component in concrete. The proportion of cement in the mix can be reduced thus lowering the cost but the strength of the concrete is maintained. It is used in construction and for the manufacture of building blocks. The blocks are used to build factories, houses and schools. The mix is also used as a road surfacing material.

There is nothing particularly dangerous and there are no significant health hazards in using fly ash this way. It's probably a very sensible and practical method of using it and disposing of it. Nevertheless, it is often as radioactive as conventional low-level nuclear waste. But the different safety disposal standards for the two waste materials is certainly an extremely well orchestrated double standard.

Brown coal is mined in big quantities and burnt as power station fuel in, among other places, the Latrobe Valley in the Australian state of Victoria. That brown coal is moderately high in nuclear materials. Every year, from that brown coal in the Latrobe Valley in Victoria, 100 tons of uranium and 200 tons of thorium in the fly ash is collected in tailing ponds.

If low-level nuclear waste was hazardous, the sums show that it would be about one hundred times safer to live near a nuclear power station than to live near almost any coal-fired power station.

It seems incongruous, but there is regularly more energy in the nuclear waste material from an average coal-fired power station than there is energy produced from the burning of the coal in the first place.

Why are these things never mentioned? Are the complaints and the complainers, at nuclear energy sites and about nuclear energy generation generally, being carefully orchestrated? For there is never logic and there is never balance in their arguments.

Now let's consider the relative risks of an energy supply coming from mining and burning coal and an energy supply coming from mining and burning uranium. For simplicity we'll just consider the United States.

During the last 100 years, 100,000 American coal miners have died in mine accidents. The death toll was averaging 1,400 per year. With increased safety standards, U.S. coal mining accidental deaths have now come down to a mere 250 per year—that's worse than five Chernobyls a year.

In one U.S. study, "disability days per million man hours" were 8,441 days for coal mining and 8,702 for uranium mining. So, per million working hours the risks are almost identical. Uranium mines are therefore as hazardous and as safe as any other mining operation. The difference is that uranium ores contain at least 100 times more energy per ton than coal. That's one mine instead of 100 mines. Coal mining therefore kills 100 times as many miners as uranium mining.

If the United States switched totally to nuclear energy, those 250 coal miners would not die each year but two or three uranium miners would. The lives of 247 people per year could be saved.

That's just mining. In transporting the coal to the power stations U.S. studies indicate an additional toll of approximately 100 deaths per year. So by switching totally to nuclear energy an additional 99 people per year would be saved. Remember the death toll from the Chernobyl accident, even after twenty years of scare tactics, remains at just 48.

Miners extracting uranium ore absorb radiation generally at a higher level than the surrounding population. They also breathe in more radon gas, which is constantly and naturally being formed in the ore body. Workers at uranium mines usually wear radiation dosimeters. If their readings approach the maximum levels set by the regulatory authorities, they must cease working at the mine face.

These safety levels are actually set well below those radiation levels where peak health benefits occur as indicated by the previously discussed radiation health benefit statistics.

Regardless of dose limits, uranium miners can't help but breathe more radon gas than normal. A highly pessimistic study by Professor Richard Wilson of Harvard University, in which any health benefits of higher-than-background radiation doses were ignored, estimated that mining enough uranium to supply the electricity needs of the United States would result in the deaths of 46 miners per year from radon-induced lung cancer. This figure could easily be disputed and should be, as they are based on the LNT model. LNT or not, any coal miners' radon deaths would always be far worse than mining the same energy as uranium.

Coal miners have other health problems. Coal miners inhale coal dust and this affects their lungs. They get a disease called pneumoconiosis. It is known to coal miners as black lung disease. Professor Wilson also calculated the existing death toll in the United States from black lung disease due to mining coal at 2,300 deaths per year.

Black lung disease already kills 50 times as many miners as even the most pessimistic estimates of radon-induced lung cancer. A lot more coal miners, in the United States alone, have died from black lung disease than all the Japanese people killed by radiation in Hiroshima and Nagasaki combined.

What about the effects of other pollutants in the exhausts of coal-fired power stations? Exposure to the low-level radiation from the fly ash will not be included in the following. Power station exhaust gases go into the air just like car exhausts. The major pollutants in coal-fired power station exhaust, apart from the overwhelming problem of carbon dioxide, are nitrous oxides, sulphur dioxide, fine sooty particles referred to as "particulate matter", and trace quantities of heavy metals such as mercury and lead. Of these, nitrous oxides, sulphur dioxide and particulate matter smaller than 10 microns (called PM10s) represent the greatest health hazards. A PM10 is about half a thousandth of an inch across.

One detailed study estimates the deaths due to atmospheric pollutants from a 1,000-megawatt coal-fired power station at between 40 and 120 people per year. In a totally separate study the numbers were between 20 and 100 deaths per year. These estimations are surprisingly close and so tend to support each other.

Almost 60% of the electricity generated in the United States comes from coal-fired power stations. That is the equivalent of about 175 of our "standard" 1,000-megawatt or 1,000,000-people power stations. Let's be conservative and take the minimum of 20 deaths per year from atmospheric pollutants from each plant. That's a total of 3,500 deaths from the pollutants from all the power stations in the United States. If only half of the coal mined in the United States is used in electricity generation then we can add to the total half of the 2,650 deaths from black lung disease and accidents in mining and transporting coal. That's a total of over 4,800 deaths per year due to coal-fired power stations. If you take the worst-case figure of 120 deaths from atmospheric pollutants for each power station then that rises to more than 22,000 deaths per year. That would be the equivalent death rate of more than a Chernobyl nuclear accident every day.

If the United States changed completely to nuclear power generation and one Chernobyl accident somehow happened every year, the United States would save 21,952 lives out of the 22,000 lives it takes to run the nation's coal-fired power stations.

Power generation using oil

With oil again we must ask, which is really the most lethal? Is it the nuclear-fired power station or is it the oil-fired power station? When you check the facts properly, there is no doubt; it's oil that's the big killer and by far, just like coal.

A 1,000-megawatt power station, again sufficient for a city of one million people, burns a minimum of about 6,000 tons of oil per day. Oil-fired power stations need to hold about six weeks' supply of oil. That's 250,000 tons of oil. That amount of oil contains fifty times more energy than was released at Hiroshima and Nagasaki combined. Oil contains four times as much raw energy as does TNT, but there is no requirement to store oil with anything like the same safety standards as is required for nuclear materials.

Oil is used to generate 3% of the electricity consumed in the United States. At the very least, to run these power stations, there must be scattered around the United States and mostly in or near cities over 2,000,000 tons of very flammable oil. But that's only a six weeks' supply. The U.S. government requires that a strategic reserve of oil has to be kept in store in sufficient quantities to keep the country operating for months or even years.

Oil is a highly flammable substance and accidents in oil storage and transport systems happen regularly. When oil burns in an uncontrolled fire, it produces clouds of toxic smoke and soot.

Perhaps the most horrific images are those of the burning oil wells in Kuwait in 1991. In total 730 oil wells were destroyed by explosives and 656 of these ignited. The combined plume of smoke was clearly visible in satellite photographs stretching for hundreds of miles across that part of the world. Visibility on the ground was reduced to 10 feet (3 m) in places. A rain of unburnt oil droplets and soot fell and coated everything in a sticky tarry mess. For a while there were concerns in the media about the toxic plume in the upper air causing a worldwide haze cover but the heroic efforts of oil-fire fighters extinguished the fires much sooner than was initially thought possible.

Some military reports suggested that the health effects on soldiers exposed to the toxic smoke and fumes were not serious. Compared to being shot at, this may well be true. However we do know that exposure to oil-fire fumes is known to cause a range of medical problems, including cancer, asthma and skin rashes. Many Gulf War veterans reported exactly these symptoms.

Many media articles have quite falsely suggested that this "Gulf War syndrome" was related to the use of antitank shells and bullets made from depleted uranium. Not so. Given the range of toxic, oil-derived airborne chemicals that were floating around, depleted uranium as a health hazard makes no sense at all. Depleted uranium only becomes relevant as part of the never-ending pro-oil, antinuclear public relations campaign.

Depleted uranium is largely U-238, but it still contains about 0.2% to 0.3% U-235. Uranium is a very hard dense metal and that makes it ideal for armour-piercing shells. About 320 tons of depleted uranium was used in the Gulf War, and at least the same in the Iraq War. Some uranium would have burned as the shells hit the tanks and the uranium oxide may have been spread about as an aerosol. As an aerosol it would be poisonous, but being extremely heavy it immediately falls to the ground and becomes relatively harmless.

In the media, the Gulf War syndrome is repeatedly blamed on exposure to depleted uranium. But the exposure to oil-fire smoke is rarely mentioned. If you search for information on the oil fires you'll find very few mentions of their unpleasant health effects, but you'll find a plethora of articles damning depleted uranium.

It is now well established that residual depleted uranium in the quantities and manner of its occurrence presents either no risk, or absolutely negligible risk to human life or health. When the bullets stop moving, the health risk drops effectively to near zero.

Oil is much more frightening—even when it's stationary. Storage facilities can catch fire and they can explode. Accidents only ever receive tiny media coverage, but major fires and dangerous explosions occur at oil terminals regularly all round the world and a lot of people die because of them. In 1994 an oil fire in Seoul in South Korea killed 500 people. In 1998, a fire resulting from a leak in an oil pipeline in Warri, Nigeria, killed more than 500 people. You see it all the time but always only briefly, before the media quickly move on.

And New York City has some really frightening examples of what can happen. An oil storage accident happened in Bayonne, New Jersey on 6 January 1973. The Bayonne terminal has a huge capacity but, very fortunately the quantity of oil stored in the complex at the time was relatively low. There was a collision between two ships manoeuvering in a small docking area. The collision ignited oil storage tanks in the adjacent oil terminal complex.

The giant clouds of black smoke and soot that belched from the fires at Bayonne were infinitely more dense that the infamous smog peak levels that occurred in London in December 1952. That London incident resulted in an excess death tally of almost 4,000 people.

The dangers from the dense smoke and fumes from an oil explosion is similar in many ways to the dangers from a radioactive cloud following a nuclear blast. In both cases the deadliness of the event is determined by the weather conditions prevailing at the time.

The port facility of Bayonne is in the centre of an extremely populated area. It is centrally located between Jersey City, Newark, Manhattan, Staten Island and Brooklyn. But New York City was lucky that day. Strong turbulent winds broke up and dissipated the dense smoke and fumes. Also, and very fortunately, the winds were mainly from the west. The cloud of soot and half-burnt oil blew harmlessly out into the Atlantic. The city was saved. There is however no question that if the weather had been different, many thousands of people in New York City would have died from that oil storage accident.

Three years later, and almost to the day after the oil terminal fire in Bayonne, it happened again, and again very fortunate weather conditions saved New York City. It happened on 3 January 1976 on the Brooklyn waterfront not far from Coney Island.

The storage facility there can hold 90,000 barrels of oil. That's over 12,000 tons, and there was nearly that quantity there at the time of the accident. That's about the same energy as four Hiroshima bombs. An oil tank caught fire and exploded. The resultant fire could not be put out. Nor could it be brought under control. It burnt all day and all through the night. The next day there was another horrendous explosion and a gigantic fireball erupted from the site. A second tank ignited and a third tank was ruptured. Out of control, the fires burnt for four days.

Again it was only the weather that saved New York from horrendous loss of life. The inversion layer that often sits over New York City and causes their stifling hot days was absent. The smoke cloud was therefore able to billow straight up and away from the city. It was blown out to sea by a very fortuitous and consistent offshore breeze.

The people that died were mainly firefighters trying to get the disaster under control. The majority of the deaths from the Chernobyl reactor accident were also firefighters trying to get their disaster under control.

The design of oil storage facilities and the principles involved in determining where they are located have not changed. The risks are "deemed to be acceptable". The safety standards for oil storage and transport are a joke compared to those required for nuclear fuels. Every single day of the year, oil, often in the form of highly refined and highly flammable petroleum product, is allowed to travel our roads and freeways at high speed. They are confined in thin-shelled metal tankers. The energy released in burning a single, fully loaded road tanker can be the equivalent of 50 tons of TNT.

Nevertheless the safety standards for oil storage and transport are generally fairly good. And we accept them. On the other hand it is the ridiculously and idiotically high standards set for the storage and handling of the relatively harmless low-level nuclear materials that is the real joke.

The risks to life is far greater using oil as a power station fuel than it could ever be using nuclear fuels. To quote Petr Beckmann, a nuclear safety researcher at the University of Colorado, oil is not only a greater risk "but it is greater by a factor of tens of thousands".

Petr Beckmann wrote *The Health Hazards of Not Going Nuclear*. It was published by Golem Press, Boulder, Colorado, ISBN 0-911762-17-5. This contains a most concise collection of facts on the relative dangers of energy systems and how nuclear energy compares as a health risk. It is an excellent source of factual information and is well documented. The book is undoubtedly extremely unpopular with the fossil carbon lobby.

Supertankers are coming on line that will carry 500,000 tons of oil. That's about the same energy content as 100 Hiroshima-size atomic bombs.

Natural gas

Now let's consider the gaseous fuels. "Natural gas" is a general term for gas that has accumulated in deep porous rock formations usually associated with coal or oil deposits. The source of the gas is the same as that for coal and oil. It is ancient plant and animal material. Natural gas is a fossil fuel. Natural gas is used to generate about 9% of the total U.S. electricity demand.

The composition of natural gas varies widely depending on the particular location. The flammable component of natural gas can contain gases such as carbon monoxide, hydrogen, methane, ethane, propane and butane. Generally, methane makes up 80% to over 90% of the flammable gas content. Mixed with the flammable gases are varying quantities of technically incorrectly labelled "inert" gases; generally nitrogen and carbon dioxide, predominantly the latter. These gases do not burn. They simply reduce the useful energy content and cash value of the gas. When these non-flammable gases are present in large percentages they must be removed to make the gas saleable. This process requires energy—energy that is supplied by burning more gas.

Natural gas from fields in Papua New Guinea and in Indonesia for example often consist of 50% carbon dioxide, so burning the gas from these fields is as bad as burning straight coal. And very much worse if methane gas leakage is factored in.

In the Australian state of Queensland, just south of Papua New Guinea, there are plans to pipe the New Guinean natural gas thousands of miles to provide power for the state. The government hails this as a great step towards a "greener" future and an unsuspecting public is duped into supporting the idea. Because of the high carbon dioxide levels in the gas, Queensland might just as well stop the pretence and just keep burning the local coal deposits.

Two of the natural gases that sometimes occur in gas fields are propane and butane. These can be turned into liquid form simply by compressing (pressurizing) the gas. Once liquefied, propane and butane can be easily separated from the remaining gases and piped around like petrol; providing only that the pressure is maintained. The pressure required depends on the mix of propane and butane but is less than 10 times normal atmospheric pressure (150 psi or 10 bar). Pressurized propane and butane mixtures are marketed as liquefied petroleum gas or LPG. The use of the word *petroleum* in the name stems from the fact that propane and butane are also byproducts of oil refineries.

Then there is liquefied natural gas or LNG. LNG is generally close to 100% straight methane. Methane normally boils at $-164°C$ so even at 250 psi (17 bar), methane must be kept below $-112°C$ to turn it into a liquid. Methane is thus considerable more difficult to liquefy than the other natural gases.

Liquefied natural gas must be stored or transported in double-walled tanks packed with extremely good thermal insulating material. Unfortunately even the best thermal insulation always lets some heat through, so to keep the temperature down some of the methane is allowed to boil off into the atmosphere.

Water boils at $212°F$, that's $100°C$. If you turn up the heat it just boils faster, it doesn't boil at a higher temperature. The steam carries away as much heat as you put in. It's the same when methane boils. The temperature doesn't rise as the methane boils off or evaporates. The constant boiling or evaporating process keeps the rest of the gas cold enough to stay as a transportable liquid. As has been previously mentioned, methane is more than 20 times more potent a greenhouse gas than carbon dioxide and LNG is kept cold by constantly releasing methane to the atmosphere.

It takes a lot of power to compress and cool methane into its liquid form in the first place. As much as 25% of the gas energy is wasted in the cooling and compressing process.

When the LNG reaches its final destination it is warmed up, often using seawater to provide the heat, and allowed to convert back into a gas at low pressure. Only then can it be piped to homes and factories. If the gas is supplied under high pressure, but not in liquid form, it is referred to as compressed natural gas or CNG.

In discussing risk factors we have to consider how dangerous gases are to use, to store and to transport. LPG, LNG, natural gas and CNG are all widely used and the accidents with these gases we seem to accept as tolerable. We accept the risks. But in comparison to nuclear energy the stuff is incredibly dangerous.

Liquefied natural gas from the North West Shelf off the coast of Western Australia is shipped to Japan in huge, spherical tanks mounted on specially designed ships. This is the most common way natural gas is shipped around the world.

When a gas leaks from anywhere and is ignited it will burn rapidly but it doesn't necessarily explode. To get a big explosion the gas first has to be mixed with air. Both liquefied petroleum gas and liquefied natural gas rapidly boil or evaporate in air and form explosive mixtures. If a storage container is suddenly ruptured, often from a minor fire, the contents then spill forth at a hugely accelerated rate. The mixture then explodes, totally shattering the container and sending shrapnel flying. It's called a Boiling Liquid Expanding Vapour Explosion, a BLEVE (rhymes with Chevy). Unfortunately the grim truth is that BLEVEs, resulting from fires near big LPG tanks, are not at all uncommon. BLEVEs have been occurring for a long time.

In 1944 an horrific liquefied natural gas accident occurred in Cleveland, Ohio. The storage facility had been in operation since 1941 and a new tank was needed to increase capacity. A general shortage of stainless steel alloys, during and at the end of the World War II, meant that the inner tank had to be constructed using a steel with a lower nickel content. This alloy became subject to brittle failure at the cold liquid methane temperatures. At 2:15 PM on 20 October 1944, not long after it was commissioned, the tank wall failed, releasing its liquid contents. There were inadequate embankments surrounding the tank to contain such a spill and the contents spewed into nearby streets and sewers. The gas cloud ignited and set off explosions in the underground sewer lines, a subterranean BLEVE. The tank fire burned for about 20 minutes until the heat weakened the supports of a second tank. This tank then collapsed and its contents also burst into flame.

That LNG accident, and the subsequent fires and explosions, killed 128 people. In addition there were 225 more injured, many with terrible burns. Proponents of LNG give explanations and reasons for the accident and suggest it won't happen again as improvements in safety standards have reduced risks considerably. They now claim "an excellent track record". But always an inherent danger remains. Such containers hold tons of extremely flammable and explosive substances. Another big one can happen any time, as the potential dangers of LNG are always enormous. Small minor accidents with only a few deaths, that result from something going wrong with LNG storage and handling, it now seems are no longer particularly newsworthy. Who says so?

One of the most powerful non-nuclear weapons conceived by military designers is the fuel-air bomb. Basically a large tank of flammable gas is allowed to spill and mix with air above the ground. It is then ignited. The resulting explosion resembles a nuclear explosion. If the gas in one of those giant pressurized LNG tanker ships ever escaped and got well mixed with air before ignition, the explosion and destruction would exceed that of a nuclear bomb.

Natural gas is often promoted as a "clean" and "green" fuel. But it's not. That image is a marketing and public relations fiction. Apart from its small natural hydrogen content, all the flammable constituents of natural gas are carbon compounds, just like petrol.

Any system using LPG, LNG or CNG as a fuel, produces almost as much carbon dioxide as does the burning of oil to do the same job. They have slightly more hydrogen in their structure than petrol, which makes them slightly better, but, being gaseous, more unburnt compounds get leaked to the atmosphere. Also most have carbon dioxide in them to begin with. These more than offset their slight chemical composition advantage. Energy for energy, these gases are just as bad as petrol or diesel in causing global warming. Their only valid environmental advantage is that they don't contain sulphur compounds and so do not add sulphuric acid to the atmosphere, as do oil derived fuels. Acid rain effects are reduced but global warming effects are not.

Proper safety measures reduce the risks of LNG and LPG accidents. The same is true for nuclear facilities, but the basic inherent dangers of nuclear accidents are minuscule in comparison to gas plants. With nuclear power any risk is minimized by layer upon layer of safety systems. Such safety systems are not required to anywhere near the same extent in the natural gas industry, yet natural gas accidents and explosions kill and maim more people, every month, than ever happened at Chernobyl.

We now willingly and happily accept the use of LNG, LPG and CNG but we have all been conditioned to be in mortal fear of anything nuclear.

In a conventional Western-style nuclear power station, to prevent even the possibility of a similar disaster to the above oil and gas accidents, fail-safe systems are built into the designs. There are fail-safe systems to cover any emergency and contingency. In addition there are fail-safe systems in case a fail-safe system should fail. There are fail-safe systems on top of these fail-safe systems and fail-safe systems on top of those again.

Five totally independent fail-safe systems are generally incorporated in reactor designs. But what if they all fail? In that case, and then only in a few nuclear reactors, you could have a meltdown. If a meltdown occurred it would be the excess heat buildup, following the almost impossible string of safety system failures that could cause an explosion. An actual nuclear explosion is impossible. You can't make nuclear bombs out of power station reactors. A nuclear power station explosion can only come from superheated steam, or chemicals, or more probably from oil stored inside the building for some unrelated reason.

Such an explosion would probably be comparable with those used in mining and earth-moving operations. But even then, the entire assembly is enclosed in the incredible "containment building" structure. The round walls of the containment building in one Westinghouse design are almost a metre thick, over three feet thick. They are solid reinforced concrete, with a greater mass of heavy steel reinforcing rods than there is concrete.

Containment buildings are designed to withstand aircraft crashing into them. They are designed to withstand trucks crashing into them. They are designed to withstand the effect of terrorist packing explosives around them and setting them off. No internal explosion could breach these structures. They will stay together in earthquakes.

The probable death toll from a Western-designed nuclear-reactor melt-down is very near zero to zero. It's virtually impossible to dream up any scenario for such a reactor to kill a thousand people as is always carefully suggested. You just can't do it. They aren't like gas storage facilities. You couldn't kill that many people with a nuclear reactor sabotaged by terrorists even if they all had doctorates in nuclear physics.

Nuclear waste disposal is not a problem as the quantities are so tiny

A nuclear plant produces a few cubic yards or metres of relatively high-level waste per year. That is enough to fill an average sized walk-in kitchen cupboard. Such a nuclear plant would supply the power to a city of a million people. If you divide the waste into a million pieces then each person in the city is responsible for considerably less than one teaspoonful of high-level nuclear waste per year. Over an entire lifetime, a person living in a nuclear-powered Western-style city would at most be responsible for no more than a couple of coffee cups full.

Petr Beckmann, in his thought-provoking book *The Health Hazards of Not Going Nuclear*, likes the explanation that in a totally nuclear-powered society the amount of high-level waste produced per person, per year is about the size of an aspirin tablet.

In complete contrast, if the power station for that city ran on coal, and even if that power station was one of the newly touted "clean coal" power stations, the figures are simply horrendous. Each person would be responsible for discharging into the atmosphere about a thousand tons of carbon dioxide from the 350 odd tons of coal needed to supply the same lifetime of power requirements. All this, plus fly ash, plus sulphuric acid, plus highly polluting nitrous oxides, and that's for a "clean" power station burning high quality coal. Three quarters of all coal-fired power stations worldwide burn "dirty coal", and always will. That's because there's more of it.

There is more low-level waste from a nuclear reactor than high-level waste. In the United Kingdom, in its fifty years of nuclear involvement, the country has accumulated 50,000 cubic metres of mostly low-level nuclear waste. To visualize this quantity, an average football field covered to a depth of 12 feet (4 m) would be covered with 50,000 cubic metres of material. But low-level waste is not very dangerous. If you covered the stuff in the football field with a few feet of soil (a metre or so) it would be safe enough to walk on and play on and probably build houses on. That's the extent of the nuclear waste problem for the United Kingdom after fifty years. On the other hand, a single coal-fired power station after fifty years would produce close to a billion tons of carbon dioxide and would produce around 10 million tons of solid waste, which is itself radioactive.

How were we ever convinced that nuclear waste disposal is some mysterious and insolvable problem? The advertising people know. After all, it was their job to convince us. And they did. But surely not for ever.

The "problem" of nuclear waste disposal does not exist. The "problem" of nuclear waste disposal is something that only exists in the minds of people fed a lifetime diet of lies and deliberate misinformation about nuclear energy.

In media references to nuclear waste and its disposal, the articles will sometimes differentiate between high-level and low-level waste, but more often than not the distinction will be glossed over. One argument says that the total weight of high-level waste ever produced is considerably less than the weight of newspaper used criticizing its disposal. That's probably true.

In real life there is actually a spread of concentrations from very low-level to very high- level waste. For convenience material is often considered as either high-, intermediate- or low-level. The level of waste is categorized on the basis of the total concentration of radioactive material in the waste. It is rarely related to whether the waste generates heat or doesn't. It is also rarely considered if it is actually hazardous, and if so, for how long will it remain at hazardous levels.

Low-level waste consists mainly of things like paper, rags, tools, disposable clothing and filters. It can contain small quantities of short-lived isotopes. Low-level waste is generally classed as being less radioactive than natural ground-level radiation near even a poor-quality uranium ore deposit—an ore body that's hardly worth mining. In many parts of the world farmland is more radioactive. This category of waste makes up over

90% of all the labelled radioactive waste in the world. It does not require special handling. It's less radioactive than most fly ash. Currently it has been decreed that it must be disposed of by burial.

Intermediate-level waste is sufficiently radioactive that some shielding is required. Shielding can be concrete or water, or lead, or simply dirt and rocks. Such materials will all stop even any excess high-penetration gamma rays that might be emitted. Generally, this waste is solidified in concrete and buried. If it is long-lived then it is disposed of in deeper burial sites. Large quantities of long-lived intermediate waste are usually only produced when reactors are decommissioned and dismantled.

High-level waste accounts for 95% of the total radioactivity in nuclear waste from any source, but generally of main concern is waste from power generation reactors. The total quantity is amazingly small. High-level waste contains a wide range of radioactive elements. Some of these elements are heavier than uranium and are described as transuranic elements. Transuranic elements have been produced from heavy elements capturing and holding neutrons in the reactor and becoming still heavier. Typical is americium-241, which has come into wide commercial and household use, as is noted later.

Nuclear reactor fuel is almost always radioactive. Nuclear reactor designs vary and each reactor is designed to use a particular fuel mix. Generally the fuel is placed in easily removable tubes commonly referred to as fuel rods. Eventually when the fuel rod can no longer supply useful heat for steam generation, the fuel rod is described as spent. (A surprisingly apt description!)

If uranium is the fuel of choice, it is the radioactive uranium-235 in the uranium that supplies the energy. Although in the life of a uranium fuel rod, some of the uranium-238 is converted into plutonium-239. The plutonium-239 is itself a useful and valuable reactor fuel.

Other short-lived but extremely reactive materials are formed as the fuel is burnt. The spent fuel rods therefore contain extreme levels of radioactive materials. These must be allowed to decay to safe levels before recovering the new fuels. This is simply a matter of waiting a few years.

Spent fuel might typically contain 95% uranium-238, 1% uranium-235 and 1% plutonium. The remaining 3% are fission products and radioactive transuranic elements.

Spent fuel rods comprise the majority of high-level waste. Spent fuel rods contain relatively dense material so they don't occupy much volume. A 1,000-megawatt nuclear power station will produce about 5 cubic metres of what is classified as high-level waste per year. It might thus just fill a walk-in kitchen pantry but would weigh about 25 tons.

Generally 6% of the heat generated in a reactor core comes from decay of short-lived fission products produced as the core operates. When the fuel rods are removed from the reactor core, they will thus still generate a fair quantity of heat from this residual radioactive decay.

Because the spent fuel rods contain valuable materials that should be recovered they are stored for long periods, up to forty years, to allow the radioactive levels to decrease to more easily handled levels. They are stored in recessed tanks under water. The level of radioactivity will drop a thousand-fold in the 40-year period.

The material is then finely mixed with a type of glass, a borosilicate glass and vitrified into small blocks. The radioactive material is thus trapped in solid chunks of glass, generally formed as a glass brick for convenience. Synroc, which we talk about further on, is a particularly good, long lasting and stable material for this type of radioactive entrapment.

At any time the glass bricks can be "reprocessed" and the remaining uranium-235 and the various plutonium isotopes can be separated out for reuse. The glass bricks, when transported to a reprocessing facility, are packed in corrosion-resistant containers.

Ultimately only the 3% is waste requiring long-term and safe storage. That 3% amounts to about a 44-gallon, a 200-litre drum of very dangerous waste per year for a power station that could supply a Western city of one million people.

At present, high-level category waste is accumulating at the rate of about 12,000 tons per year worldwide. It mainly consists of spent fuel rods that are still in storage waiting for reprocessing. If they were reprocessed the entire world's high-level nuclear waste disposal problem would amount to finding a safe place for less than 400 44-gallon drums.

High-level nuclear waste is only accumulated in these quantities because there are not enough reprocessing facilities available. Protests by green movements both prevent the construction of more facilities and the transport of waste to existing facilities. Most of the world's reprocessing is done in three plants in the United Kingdom and France. There are a few smaller plants in Russia, Japan and India.

The power of the oil and fossil fuel lobby is so awesome they have been able to ensure that there is not one usable reprocessing plant in all the United States. Not only there are no plants but also U.S. legislation actually prohibits the very reprocessing of spent fuel rods. Thus the fossil fuel lobby have guaranteed a totally false and fabricated, but ever growing public relations monster for the nuclear energy industry.

Currently the legislated procedure is that high-level waste has to be stored in some safe, stable, permanent and accessible but also inaccessible place. So no place on earth can ever satisfy the idiotic and deliberately impossible requirements of such antinuclear laws.

How long the waste must be stored depends on the half-life of the elements involved. Fission products generally have reasonably short half-lives. Storage times of 100 years is ample for their radioactivity to wear out and decay so the material becomes at worst low-level waste. In many parts of the world we build houses out of materials that are more radioactive and the people that live in them are probably healthier for it.

It is a valid argument that some of the transuranic elements from fuel rods require true long-term or permanent storage. The main reason being that they are chemically very poisonous. However they are not particularly deadly compared to bio-weapons and many industrial chemicals. The transuranic elements we don't want for industrial use now are of course in our once-a-year 44-gallon drum, and buried.

The transuranic elements are often convertible to usable nuclear fuels and of course, after use they can be disposed of in things like the accelerator-driven reactors, already mentioned.

Currently, intermediate-level nuclear waste is physically stabilized and then stored in containers until the radiation levels reduce to safe handling levels for more permanent storage. Alternatively they can be buried and allowed to decay to harmless low-level waste.

Low-level waste is not a safety issue; it is merely a public-relations issue. Low-level waste contains concentrations of radioactive material that are about a million times less than that in high-level waste. A lot of people in the world live their entire lives in areas where the ground they build their houses on, and the ground their children play on, is far more radioactive than much of the low-level radioactive waste from nuclear reactors. With the health benefits of regular mild doses of radioactivity the health and longevity of these people is certainly enhanced.

Low-level waste is less radioactive than many of the foods we eat. One report likened it to eating Brazil nuts. Many farm areas in Brazil are fortunate enough to have relatively high and health-benefiting natural background radiation levels, so Brazil nuts are often radioactive. Eat them and your health will benefit.

Today's society generates enormous quantities of dangerous and hazardous industrial, medical and agricultural chemical waste. Most of these toxins are developments of modern chemistry. Unlike radiation, they never existed on the planet before they were created by man. Our evolutionary history allowed adaptation to background radiation levels but it never evolved to tolerate toxic petrochemicals. Disposing of these wastes is far more hazardous than dealing with nuclear waste.

The reality is that low-level nuclear waste is not an issue at all. A nuclear power station produces less than 100 cubic metres of low-level radioactive waste per year. If you collected all this waste material over the normal 30-year life of a nuclear power station, ground it up and mixed it into concrete in the same proportion as used for fly ash, then you'd need to make 600 cubic metres of concrete, enough to build a couple of hundred metres of four-lane freeway. In contrast with fly ash from a coal-fired power station, the waste over a 30-year period could build a freeway that would span a continent.

Building roads is often what we do with fly ash, whatever its radioactivity might be. But can you imagine the protests from the antinuclear anything movements, if low-level nuclear power station waste was used to build roads, or houses or schools?

Intermediate and high-level waste requires it be treated properly, with the same care we exercise in handling and transporting other often more dangerous materials, such as dangerous gases, toxic chemicals and biological agents.

The United States Environmental Protection Agency, the EPA, have nominated a period of 10,000 years storage for high-level nuclear waste as being more than ample. This is based on the concept that by then it would be indistinguishable from the low radiation levels in surrounding farmlands. The EPA unyieldingly bases its determinations on the linear no-threshold hypothesis, which now appears to be no more than a convenient fiction fostered and promoted by fossil fuel supporters.

Fission products in high-level waste typically have half-lives of less than 50 years. After just 1,000 years, their activity will have halved twenty times over. It will have been reduced to a millionth of the initial activity. A million to one is also the difference between high-level waste and low-level waste. So 10,000 years is moronic. If poisonous materials are included in the waste materials then disposal should be at safety levels applying to other equally poisonous materials. Double standards are illogical.

In terms of radioactivity, about the worst stuff in high-level waste is americium-241. Americium-241 emits a highly energetic alpha particle along with moderately energetic gamma rays. It has a half-life of 432 years. Americium-241 is produced when plutonium-241 decays. It is the americium-241 in reactor plutonium that mandates special handling procedures for plutonium at reprocessing facilities. It's not the plutonium.

But even transuranic materials have their story and especially 95Americium-241. Most smoke detectors, those things we are constantly encouraged to install in every room in the house, contain 200 micrograms of americium-241 oxide. The alpha particles emitted by the americium-241 collide with air molecules inside a chamber to produce charged particles, or ions. A small electric voltage applied across the chamber is used to collect these ions causing a small steady electric current to flow between two electrodes. When smoke enters the space between the electrodes, the alpha radiation is absorbed by smoke particles and so they don't produce as much ionization in the air. The flow of electricity drops. The drop is detected and sets off the alarm. The gamma rays on the other hand escape the smoke detector. They radiate out into the room. If you sleep close to a smoke detector you will receive a radiation dose of about 0.2 mSv. That's about three times the dose received by the people living within the 10-mile radius of the Three Mile Island "nuclear disaster".

The radiation from your smoke detectors is perfectly safe. You should install more as a fire safety precaution. But if the linear no-threshold hypothesis is used as a basis for determining safety and antinuclear legislation, then we should take them all out. More antinuclear insanity.

The fossil fuel lobby and their antinuclear energy supporters argue and bluster for hundreds of thousands of years, or even millions of years of storage for nuclear waste materials. This, they proclaim is justified by quoting that plutonium-239 has a half-life of 24,000 years. They suggest humanity should wait 500,000 years so the plutonium radioactivity can reduce to a millionth of its initial level. This is propaganda rubbish, as it totally ignores the reality that plutonium makes up only 1% of the mass of un-reprocessed high-level waste, and makes up less than one ten-thousandth of the radioactivity, and this is a level that is already harmless. The EPA's own 10,000-year requirement is already over the top. Demanding more time is ludicrous.

Even if we cater for 10,000 years, then there are a host of locations, storage and confinement systems that more than easily suffice. It took archaeologists nearly 10,000 years to find the King's Tomb in one Egyptian pyramid. And for all that time people knew exactly where the tomb was, at least to within a few hundred yards for the tomb had to be somewhere within the pyramid, and the Egyptian pyramids themselves are not well hidden. If all the world's high-level nuclear waste was buried in one of these ancient structures, and there certainly is plenty of room for such burial, and then after placement, the entrance was filled with concrete, nobody would ever know. Nobody would ever find it. It would hurt nobody. Of course maybe some incredibly powerful earth-digging machine of the future might accidentally dig it up. But then the same machine would certainly be good enough rebury it.

Theoretically one of the easiest ways to get rid of high-level radioactive waste is to dilute it. Spread it as thinly as possible. Remember the material can never slowly accumulate above a certain radioactivity level, for eventually, as fast as material is added old material is decaying. It's like filling a bucket with too many holes. Once the level gets to a certain point the water runs out as fast as you're pouring it in.

Add the same quantity of nuclear waste to a dump for fifty years, and the radiation level will peak out. From that time on the old waste is decaying and becoming harmless as fast as new waste is being added.

The antinuclear pawns often avow the nebulous concept that radioactive waste material is "different". Well, in one way it certainly is different. In 50 or 100 years, the danger from a container of radioactive waste material will have approximately halved, and then keep halving. In absolute contrast: a waste container of say, concentrated mercury or cadmium compounds, or many of the very lethal petrochemical waste products we constantly produce, will stay toxic, stay dangerous, and stay hazardous, for as long as the earth exists.

The other key point to remember about radioactive material and radioactive waste is that it only becomes dangerous when it is concentrated. In Australia nobody demands that we cover over the areas where uranium ore occurs with some incredible concrete cap. Nobody suggests we try and prevent native tribes from living in these areas as they have for countless generations with absolutely no harm to themselves whatever. It's only when the uranium ore is mined and loaded into drums for shipping and use, does it somehow instantly becomes the target of the antinuclear protesters.

So nuclear waste, as unpalatable as it sounds, could simply be spread everywhere. So let's consider an exercise in straight surface dilution. The surface area of the earth is 560,000 billion square metres. If all the world's current stock of nuclear waste and all we could produce in the ongoing future, were spread evenly over the earth's surface, any rise in radiation levels would be utterly undetectable and would remain utterly undetectable for ever, for they can never actually rise.

But restricting disposal to only ocean dilution makes more sense. By far and away the best way to dispose of even the very highest of high-level nuclear waste, is to mix it with water and dump it in the ocean. On face value, that sounds like environmental vandalism. But it's the safest, most environmentally benign, most stable long-term, most sensible, most economical and the most utterly obvious place to put all levels, and any level, of nuclear waste material.

With mixing and diluting nuclear waste in seawater the numbers are much better than looking at land areas. The world's oceans cover 70% of the planet's surface. They have a total volume of some 2 billion cubic kilometres. If we ground up the waste and dissolved it in the oceans, it would add less than 0.2 micrograms per cubic metre. In that same cubic metre is already 3,000 micrograms of uranium—a microgram being a millionth of a gram. It would be totally insignificant, and again it would be insignificant for ever. But while that is just as totally impractical, it is also as totally unnecessary. It would be completely safe to add a few hundred micrograms, not just a fifth of a microgram, so we would only have to spread the waste over an area of just one-thousandth part of the world's oceans. That's a piece of ocean only 400 miles square and in which no damage would be done in any way, shape or form. No wonder there was so much objection to ocean dumping—it's simply too cheap and too sensible.

Disposal in ocean sediments

The spreading action is difficult and time consuming. It is much more practical and just as safe to simply drop containers into the ocean. The Kara Sea borders north central Russia. The Kara Sea is relatively shallow—about 1,500 feet deep. That's less than 500 metres. There are 17 Russian nuclear reactors at the bottom of the Kara Sea; maybe more. Seven of these reactors still contain their spent nuclear fuel. These reactors came out of old nuclear-powered submarines and nuclear-powered ships. They were not carefully buried in ocean silt. They were not encased in concrete and strategically placed on some remote inaccessible sea floor. They were just dumped.

From 1959 onwards the Russians dumped all sorts of radioactive waste into the Kara Sea. Four of their dumping sites were in small fjords at depths less than 150 feet (50 metres). That's about the depth for easy skin diving. The locations of the dump sites and of the dumped reactors are all known. The waters around the dumped reactors are regularly tested for signs of the radioactive material that, we are told by the antinuclear activists, must most certainly be leaking and spreading from the rusting reactors. None has been found. Some sediment samples taken from very close to the dumped reactors show slightly elevated levels of radioactivity. This indicates that radioactive material is definitely leaking. Then why don't seawater samples show signs of above-normal radiation levels? The reason lies in the nature of the silt on the floors of our oceans.

Silt materials form from biological activity in the upper ocean close to the surface where sunlight is still able to reach. The silt then slowly but constantly drifts down to the ocean floor. It happens in all seas and in all oceans. The ocean silts actually bonds to the waste materials in the water, trapping them and carrying them down to the seabed. This is why some radioactivity can be detected in the sediment around these dumped reactors but absolutely none in the seawater above.

Two U.S. nuclear submarines, *Thresher* and *Scorpion*, and five Russian nuclear submarines now lie at the bottom of the oceans of the world. The most recent addition was the highly publicized Russian submarine *Kursk*, which went to the bottom with its crew of 118 men. The *Kursk* had two nuclear reactors and an undisclosed number of possibly nuclear-armed cruise missiles aboard. The *Kursk* was recovered. There were no radiation problems.

The locations of nuclear-armed and nuclear-powered wrecks are no great secret. Not one of these vessels is spreading anything, and every one of them is constantly monitored for radiation leaks. Ocean sediments are obviously trapping anything and everything that leaks out.

Nothing much grows in the sediment covering ocean floors. Without sunlight there is negligible biological activity. It's not like a grass-covered prairie.

In 1968 a B-52 bomber from the U.S. Strategic Air Command crashed off Greenland. It was armed with plutonium-fuelled nuclear bombs. It didn't stay intact. It hit an iceberg and disintegrated. The plutonium sank into the shallow coastal waters.

The crash site has definitely not been ignored. A comprehensive study was even undertaken by the International Atomic Energy Agency. Their final report was published in 1994. The report detailed the many years of careful investigation and study that was devoted to the accident. The report was compiled by Scott W. Fowler and his colleagues at the agency. One of the conclusions was that "These studies demonstrated that plutonium ...was rapidly bound by the sediments, thus becoming effectively retained in the benthic ecosystem." The report also stated "no significant increases in plutonium concentrations were found in either the overlying waters, zooplankton, pelagic fish [fish that live in the open sea], sea birds, marine mammals, or the indigenous population."

The report must have been frustrating for the antinuclear movement. The report got utterly negligible editorial, no publicity whatever in the media—anywhere.

Deep ocean sediments are incredibly stable. Away from geologically active sites like undersea volcanoes, the sediments just keep accumulating for millions upon millions of years. Any radioactivity that somehow, in some inexplicable way escaped from this silt trap, would be so diluted to be totally harmless to any life forms.

Silt penetrator disposal

Probably one of the best, simplest and controlled ways to ensure high-level waste is positively trapped in ocean sediments is to use penetrators. Penetrators are torpedo-shaped objects, either made of cement mixed with nuclear waste, or simple torpedo-shaped containers filled with waste. When these are dropped from ships they sink rapidly and hit the bottom with enough speed to bury themselves deep in the thick silt. Such nuclear waste would never move, never in a hundred thousand years. Its nuclear waste would never move even if the containers were made of cardboard and fell apart in a week. Penetrator disposal is very sensible. It's so simple and would be so economical.

Dumping the gases from burning oil and coal into the air we breathe, and in so doing change the climatic patterns of the entire planet, is many millions of times more dangerous and more irrational than entrapping what in reality is minute quantities of radioactive waste in deep ocean sediments.

The Hunt For Red October: We can't find a nuclear submarine cruising at 3,000 feet (one klick) below the surface and powered with an operating nuclear reactor and loaded with a dozen or so nuclear weapons. If we can't do that then what influence will a few blocks of nuclear-waste concrete, buried in ocean silt at ten times the depth, have on any environment anywhere for at least the next million years?

Subduction zone disposal

Nuclear waste as concrete blocks or as penetrators can also be dropped with even more utter and complete safety into oceanic "subduction zones".

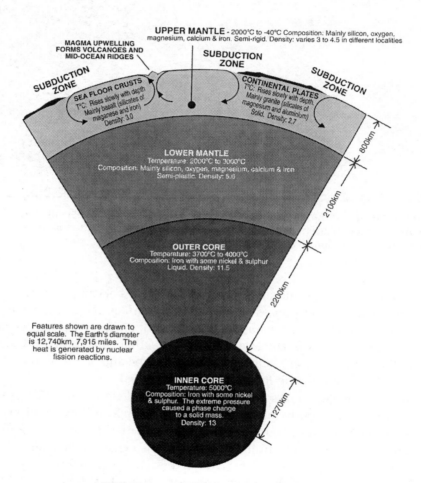

UPPER MANTLE - 2000°C to -40°C Composition: Mainly silicon, oxygen, magnesium, calcium & iron. Semi-rigid. Density: varies 3 to 4.5 in different localities

MAGMA UPWELLING FORMS VOLCANOES AND MID-OCEAN RIDGES

SUBDUCTION ZONE

SUBDUCTION ZONE

SUBDUCTION ZONE

SEA FLOOR CRUSTS
T°C: Rises slowly with depth. Mainly basalt (silicates of maganese and iron) Density: 3.0

CONTINENTAL PLATES
T°C: Rises slowly with depth. Mainly granite (silicates of magnesium and aluminium) Solid. Density: 2.7

LOWER MANTLE
Temperature: 2000°C to 3000°C
Composition: Mainly silicon, oxygen, magnesium, calcium & iron
Semi-plastic. Density: 5.6

OUTER CORE
Temperature: 3700°C to 4000°C
Composition: Iron with some nickel & sulphur
Liquid. Density: 11.5

800km

2100km

2200km

Features shown are drawn to equal scale. The Earth's diameter is 12,740km, 7,915 miles. The heat is generated by nuclear fission reactions.

INNER CORE
Temperature: 5000°C
Composition: Iron with some nickel & sulphur. The extreme pressure caused a phase change to a solid mass.
Density: 13

1270km

THE EARTH SHOWN IN SECTION

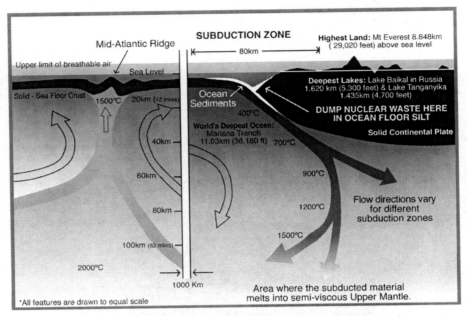

A composite illustration of a subduction zone. Most of the earth's oceanic crusts are in constant recirculation, generally from subduction zone to mid-ocean ridge and return. It's a 100-million-year round trip.

In a line along the middle of many of the world's ocean floors the deep molten earth constantly oozes up magma to the surface of the ocean floor by heat convection forces in the upper mantle. As it emerges it forms a chain of undersea volcanoes. The Mid-Atlantic Ridge that runs north and south down the Atlantic Ocean, halfway between Europe and Africa on one side, and North and South America on the other, is typical.

After the magma oozes out, it sets into a semi-rigid mass. It forms a wave of rock that slowly moves off sideways away from these mid-ocean ridges towards the far-off continents. It takes millions of years for this once volcanic material to move from the centre of the ocean to the edges of the continents. The top surface of this river of rock is the ocean floor.

The continents and the ocean floor form the lithosphere. The lithosphere is the cooler, rigid or semi-rigid surface layer of our planet. A continent floating on the earth's molten interior might typically be 25 miles (40 kilometres) thick and the moving semi-rigid ocean floor material 4 miles (6 kilometres) thick.

The continents themselves are like rafts floating on the molten magma. When the heavy semi-solid magma gets to the edge of the less dense continents it takes a dive and flows down and under them. It drags adjoining materials down with it like a sinking ship. At the edge of the continents the process forms deep trenches that slowly suck and trap everything nearby into them. These areas of geological drain holes are called subduction zones.

They may behave like a elongated kitchen sink but the sinking action is in unbelievably slow motion. So in terms of days or years nothing seems to move. The only action in these dark abysmal depths is the snow-like downdrift of waste matter falling from the sunlit life thousands of feet above.

The material slowly pouring into the subduction zone, as it goes deeper, eventually melts. It once again reforms itself and reunites itself back into the earth's deep hot magma at typically over 100 kilometres down. The mix continues down and because of convection effects finally turns and loops over backwards, reversing direction to flow back out to once more become part of a mid-ocean ridge. The round trip might take a hundred million years.

In its original journey, from the mid-ocean ridge to the edge of the continent, the material becomes covered with thick layers of carbon-rich, silty ocean sediment. The silty ocean sediments are then off on the long slow journey. In the silt at the bottom of the deep ocean trenches we have the perfect safe repository for even the worst possible poisons that humankind could ever dream up and manufacture. All materials would become as nothing as they vanish to form a component of the deep molten interior of the planet.

Material in subduction zones descends at speeds of a few inches per year. Battleships, multistoreyed buildings, or drums of nuclear waste, after sinking through the soft silt will then continue to sink into the earth's magma. The waste materials would be on a hundred-million-year journey as a milkshake of molten magma.

Yet even this would undoubtedly not satisfy the orchestrated rantings of the antinuclear and million-year storage advocates and their petro-dollar financiers.

Which trenches are the best can easily be decided by observing the characteristics of existing trench silt deposits. For example: in some types of trenches the silt tends not to descend with the cool magma but to accumulate in the trench. But even if these were selected, it would still guarantee at least a million years of isolation. More information on subduction and subduction zones can be sourced from "Subduction—Top to Bottom", an excellent series of papers published under the aegis of the American Geophysical Union.

In any subduction zone there is by definition constant movement, albeit very slow. Subduction zones are subducting and are therefore described as "geologically active". Of course they're active—the drains are draining. When most types of geological structures are considered for nuclear waste disposal, geological inactivity is invariably demanded. With a subduction zone, geological activity, not inactivity, is required, otherwise the drain won't be draining.

Two things occur as a result of subduction-zone geological activity (or occur concurrently with it). Firstly, the ground moves. This is felt as earthquakes or earth tremors. Oceanic subduction trenches are extremely deep and with relatively steep sidewalls. The deepest is the Challenger Deep at 10,900 metres, that's 35,760 feet to the bottom. Here the Caroline Plate on which sits the Caroline Islands is not only diving into the earth's mantle but part of it is tearing and being forced under the Mariana Plate on which sits vulnerable Guam. The earth tremors can sometimes make the trench's sidewall material collapse, totally burying anything lying at the bottom of the trench. Such a collapse can cause a tsunami and wreak havoc on neighbouring coastlines. That's the luck of these islands. Material at the bottom of a trench will however be buried in the process and effectively buried for ever. And there is just no human or geological way it could ever be exhumed.

Secondly, over thousands, or more likely millions of years, the deeply subducted material, typically a few hundred kilometres down, melts and lighter materials in the melt can form giant "bubbles" of magma. The bubbles work their way to the surface and become volcanoes. These volcanoes are often hundreds of miles inland.

More than 80% of known, on-land, volcanic eruptions are associated with subduction zones. Typical are Mount Pinatubo (Philippines 1991), Unzen (Japan 1991), Redoubt and Mount St. Helens (USA 1989 and 1980) and Tambora and Krakatau (Indonesia 1815 and 1882).

The geological structures above the subduction zones, from the coast to the volcanoes are described as being within a "suprasubduction" environment. In this geological environment, mineralization is often very pronounced and this produces some of the richest mineral deposits in the world.

Most carbon dioxide in volcanic eruptions was once the biological sediments on the floor of ancient oceans—the round trip for the carbon atoms taking many millions of years to complete. This ongoing phenomenon is an integral part of the earth's long-term carbon cycle.

The wisest is definitely deep ocean disposal

Ocean silts and ocean subduction zones are about the safest, most economical and most logical repository for high-level nuclear waste materials that exist.

That they are not used is a crime against the whole ecology of the planet. It is a crime against all humanity to prevent the dumping of nuclear waste into deep ocean silts. All it does is guarantee our continuous dependence on fossil fuels and in consequence the ongoing massive destabilization of world climate and world ecological systems. How did this stupidity happen? If we are going to lay the blame on any single organization for following and promoting the dictates of the fossil fuel industrial complex, then that organization would have to be Greenpeace and their backers.

In the early 1980s Greenpeace conducted an incredible "environmental campaign" to prevent not only deep ocean nuclear waste disposal, but also it seems to prevent even researching the possibility of such disposal. Greenpeace even perfected techniques for placing people in inflatable rafts at the side of ships where containers of nuclear waste would be dropped overboard. The United Kingdom power authorities had to design ships with multiple unloading points to avoid Greenpeace harassment. All the world's oceans and all the world's seas, three quarters of the total area of planet Earth, were placed out of bounds by the strokes of the pens of hopelessly ill-informed international politicians and bureaucrats.

The final result of course, was that the fossil fuel interests won. And a great win for them it was. All they had to do was throw a little money around in the right places, give a little help where it was asked and sit back and watch Greenpeace do all their work for them.

Land-based disposal

As long as the fossil fuel lobby can maintain the ban on ocean disposal, the alternative automatically switches to emotive, environmentally charged and politically sensitive, land-based systems. However despite the protestations, surprisingly there are plenty of viable systems available. Most protests and objections against land disposal hammer "contamination of groundwater". For the concept of somehow polluting groundwater is a wonderfully vague and nebulous threat.

It is obvious that nuclear waste, irrespective of how well it is packaged and contained, will never be buried in the middle of a freshwater artesian basin. That's pointless. Disposal in geological strata wherein groundwater is nonexistent or minimal and also classically slow-moving, can be totally safe. Slow-moving groundwater can take 100 years to move a hand's width. That's half a mile, or one kilometre in 10,000 years. That coincidentally is the time period the U.S. Environmental Protection Agency currently nominates as an absolute and completely safe period. That period itself is 5,000 years more than even extremely conservative common sense would dictate.

Back to those ancient natural reactors in Gabon: during the time since those reactors first operated, the area would have experienced every possible climatic variation imaginable. Today and for at least the last few million years, Gabon has been subjected to a wet tropical climate. Surely such an area would be the most unlikely choice for a long-term nuclear waste dump. Yet the tons of waste generated by these reactors are still there alongside ancient reactor locations all over the country. And it's all as safe as houses. It hasn't moved. It just wore itself out.

Are we really expected to take the antinuclear lobby seriously when they mouth their rehearsed platitudes about groundwater contamination?

Let's examine some sensible and practical places to deposit nuclear waste on land.

Salt mine disposal

Salt deposits around the world come from ancient dried seas. For the salt deposit to survive intact, it had to be protected from weathering by at least several layers of silt, shale, or sandstone. Those layers would have taken at least several hundred thousand years, or more likely several million years to accumulate and solidify. Commercial salt deposits are always found to be many millions of years old. If there had been even the remotest movement of groundwater, the salt deposit would have long since gone. The salt would have simply dissolved in the water and moved off. Old salt mines are therefore a perfectly safe and practical on-land repository for nuclear waste.

In the United States in the remote Chihuahuan Desert of southeastern New Mexico is the Waste Isolation Pilot Plant facility. It has been operating since March 1999 storing transuranic wastes from nuclear-weapons programmes. It took over 20 years of battling well-structured red tape for this facility to receive licensing to accept waste. It stores high-level waste in chambers 2,150 feet (650 metres) below the surface in a 200-million-year-old salt formation that is 2,000 feet (600 metres) thick.

One of the supposed advantages of salt mine disposal, compared to ocean floor disposal is that the waste is accessible and can therefore be monitored. It is thought that this would make it much harder for antinuclear propagandists to raise objections about possible unknown leaks into the environment. But contrary to proclaimed environmental lobbyists, ready access is not necessarily a good thing at all. If the nuclear waste is easily accessible then it has to be under constant guard.

Coal mine disposal

Perhaps coal and oil will come to the rescue and provide us with more totally ideal waste storage sites than we can ever use. As was mentioned before in this chapter, coal seams contain not only their own radioactivity but also radioactive material that, over millions of years, has leached down into the coal and become firmly entrapped. Coal seams can be several thousand feet below the surface. The coal seam can extend horizontally over hundreds of square miles. All we need to do is dig out cavities under the coal seams and dump the nuclear waste there. The coal seam itself is already a natural waste repository for ancient atmospheric carbon dioxide and has not moved or been exposed for a very long time. Most coal seams in the world were formed during the Carboniferous era. That's why the era gets it name and the Carboniferous era was a quarter of a billion years ago.

Burying the waste under coal seams has the added advantage of hindering at least some of the coal from being mined and becoming a contributor to global warming. That indeed would be poetic justice.

Oil dome disposal

Just as paradoxically, oil can also play its part. If an impermeable geological dome structure is stable enough to confine oil or even gas for millions of years, then surely it is stable enough to contain nuclear waste for a measly five or ten thousand years. Every abandoned oil well in the world can now become a totally safe repository for nuclear waste. That also happily ensures that it remains, an abandoned oil well.

Vitrified glass and ceramic blocks

Arguments against all forms of nuclear waste disposal always embrace fears of leaks occurring in the storage containers. In 1978, Professor Ringwood of the Australian National University invented a synthetic rock material called Synroc. Synroc refers to a range of ceramic materials based on titanium compounds that can incorporate all the radioactive elements found in high-level nuclear waste completely within their crystal structure. The nuclear waste actually becomes an integral part of the ceramic material. Synroc is superior to the borosilicate glass currently used for most waste stabilization, yet sales of Synroc technology were always frustrated.

Usually, when faced with no alternative, protestors will attack the methods of transportation used to move the waste from its initial storage at power station sites to waste repositories or to possible reprocessing facilities. Yet the daily transport of millions of tons of oil, natural gas and agricultural poisons around the world goes on unchallenged.

Let's look at some actual numbers and statistics on the transport of nuclear materials. There are about 20 million packages containing some level of radioactive material shipped worldwide annually. Since 1971, there have been more than 20,000 shipments of spent fuel and high-level waste. There has never, not once, been an accident in which highly radioactive material has leaked during transport. In contrast, how many major oil slicks resulting from tanker accidents do you see? They are so common and so regular, they're hardly newsworthy.

For years the U.S. military has been transporting tons of weapons-grade nuclear materials, both in weapons and loose, all over the country and all over the world. And so did the Russians. Nuclear waste is sufficiently safe enough to transport as any accidents that might occur are no worse than other industrial accidents. With nuclear waste trips are fewer and accidents less likely.

Australia should get in the nuclear waste disposal business

Australia is the site of some of the oldest, most stable geological formations on the planet. So in 1999, an organization called Pangea Resources put forward a proposal for Australia to accept waste shipments from other countries for reprocessing and final disposal in these lonely and remote formations. Synroc technology was to be used. Such a project would have generated billions of dollars of income for Australia. Predictably the proposal brought howls of protest from various green organizations.

In 2000 and 2001 Australia exported almost 10,000 tons of uranium, in the form of yellowcake, the energy equivalent of around 600,000,000 tons of coal. That uranium prevented maybe as much as 2 billion tons of carbon dioxide from entering the atmosphere. Australia has the technology, geology and political stability to provide a repository for vast amounts of nuclear waste; a repository that could totally wipe out any balance of payment problems almost overnight.

In the United States, nuclear power generating companies have paid US$18 billion to their federal government, by way of a tenth of a cent levy for every kilowatt of power generated. This levy was to fund, through the Department of Energy, the eventual disposal of spent fuel at new disposal sites. That money would be enough to fund the complete setup costs of the Pangea proposal three times over. But Australia's well-orchestrated green movements have so far prevented concepts like this from happening.

As early as 1987 a site at Yucca Mountain was chosen as the most suitable site for a U.S. repository. The money is there, the site is there, and only the over-loud protests of green movements are preventing the solution from happening rapidly. The irony is that if reprocessing was reestablished commercially, Yucca Mountain would not even be needed.

The reality is that there are no commercial or environmental problems

Amazingly as can be seen, the reality is that nuclear waste disposal is not, most definitely not, a genuine and significant problem for human society. It is not now and nor will it be at any time in any future.

There is no problem, there is only a well-constructed illusion of a problem. Most people have been artfully indoctrinated to the point where they are very frightened and often terrified of the supposed hazards of nuclear waste and nuclear waste disposal.

Nuclear waste exists and has to be disposed of in a safe sensible way, and preferably in a manner that is safer and more sensible than the currently haphazard disposal of many other hazardous or slightly hazardous materials. Accidents have happened in the nuclear industry as happens in any industry. But the effects of those accidents have been trivial compared to the loss of life in coal mines, oil fires and gas explosions. It is also trivial in comparison to the deaths caused by agricultural chemicals.

The nuclear industry has come a long way since the initial tremendous rush to build nuclear reactors to produce nuclear weapons materials to fight wars. Today, commercial reactor design and construction far exceeds even the stringent safety requirements imposed by government regulators and environmental protection agencies. Now nuclear reactors are all a whole lot safer than they ever need be.

It is now easy to build nuclear reactors that are as safe as, or safer than almost any other human endeavour. And history proves it.

Two thousand nuclear explosions have happened

Incredibly as it seems, we have to remember that around 2,000 nuclear weapons, including hydrogen bombs, have already been detonated on the planet. These were real explosions. They weren't barely possible, and unlikely to happen, dangerous hypothetical meltdowns. They happened. Bombs were detonated in the sea, under the ground, on remote islands, in the middle of continents, in the atmosphere and in space.

Man-made lakes have been produced using nuclear explosions. Those lakes are used for fishing and recreation. They are safe. They are even considered as health resorts. In spite of the horrific images we associate with nuclear explosions, the physical world hasn't changed in any way for the worse because of them. Not one iota. The total increase in background radiation over the planet is infinitesimal, yet those detonations were never "cleaned up". Waste materials were never stored in glass, or concrete, or steel drums, or buried in salt mines.

It must be recognized that Stalin did leave a real mess at several locations in the USSR, but Stalin was a disgusting person.

Fossil fuels are changing our planet. Nuclear fuels can't and won't. Fossil fuels are destroying the stability of all world weather systems. They are modifying the world in a manner that will kill off thousands of species, kill millions of people, cause untold suffering and decrease the health and wealth of all people, and all nations. Floods will rage and tinder-dry forests will burn. Yet nuclear power that can significantly prevent these things happening, that can never create a nuclear explosion and that is inherently safer than almost any other form of power generation, has imposed on it safety requirements that are higher than on any other human creation, or business, or enterprise on the planet.

If sensible, practical reality was allowed, the money wasted on demanding incredibly and excessively safe nuclear reactors could save the lives of hundreds of thousands of people. The very people who are today dying from the poisons and the pollution from other far more hazardous human energy systems and their wastes.

We have all been told about the "problem of nuclear waste disposal". We are never told how really tiny this supposed problem is. The truth is there are fewer problems with nuclear waste disposal than there are with disposing of worn out car tyres.

The nuclear industry produces their measure of toxic chemical waste, but the volume and the toxicity of this waste material is minuscule when compared to the long-term storage of toxic chemicals produced by paint companies, plastic manufacturers, agricultural fertilizer companies, drug companies and producers of herbicides, fungicides and pesticides.

Nuclear power is absolutely sustainable

Today, most nuclear power stations use enriched uranium as their fuel. Uranium is everywhere. Granite contains four parts per million (ppm) of uranium, about 4 grams per ton, that's about a tenth of an ounce. Sedimentary rocks contain about half as much, seawater contains 0.003 ppm. At today's prices, commercially extractable high-grade ores contain around 2% uranium. Current estimates put the total amount of recoverable and easily available, low-cost uranium in the world, at over three million tons. That's enough to fuel existing conventional reactors with enriched uranium for at least 50 years. But the waste is also fuel. Breeder reactors, those that turn uranium-238 into fissionable fuel will extend that period to 3,000 years.

Along the way, we could dismantle all those nuclear weapons still in store and use up that material. Remember nuclear bombs require either highly enriched uranium-235 or nearly pure $_{94}Pu^{239}$. Both these isotopes can be diluted to produce fuel for conventional reactors. It must also be understood that once diluted it is exceedingly difficult and expensive to un-dilute it.

So in more than 3,000 years time we are either going to have to find more reserves of uranium ores or switch to a different fuel system. International Atomic Energy Agency figures suggest that there are a further 16 million tons of ore that would be economically extractable at twice the current price. It is estimated that 4 billion tonnes of uranium could be extracted from seawater at a price ten to fifteen times the current price. That makes such extraction a reasonable possibility.

A bay or a harbour, ten, maybe twenty miles wide, could easily contain a couple of cubic miles of seawater (say 8 cubic kilometres).

Simple arithmetic then tells us that a bay of that size will contain a quarter of a ton of lead, a quarter of ton of mercury. It would contain almost one ton of cadmium. It would contain 100 kilograms of gold, 2.5 tons of silver, 25 tons of copper and 25 tons of arsenic. It would also contain 25 tons of uranium.

Natural occurring uranium contains about 0.71% of the bomb material

Elements in a typical cubic kilometre of seawater

A cubic mile contains 4.17 times as much. Proportions will vary slightly depending on location.

Oxygen	883,000,000 tons	Krypton	2 tons
Hydrogen	110,000,000 tons	Manganese	2 tons
(combined as water)		Vanadium	2 tons
Chlorine	19,400,000 tons	Titanium	1 ton
Sodium	10,800,000 tons	Cesium	500 kilograms
(forms the table salt content)		Antimony	340 kilograms
Magnesium	1,290,000 tons	Silver	300 kilograms
Sulphur	904,000 tons	Cobalt	280 kilograms
Calcium	410,000 tons	Neon	140 kilograms
Potassium	390,000 tons	Cadmium	110 kilograms
Bromine	67,000 tons	Yttrium	100 kilograms
Carbon	28,000 tons	Tungsten	100 kilograms
Strontium	8,200 tons	Selenium	90 kilograms
Boron	4,500 tons	Germanium	60 kilograms
Silicon	2,900 tons	Xenon	50 kilograms
Fluorine	1,300 tons	Chromium	50 kilograms
Argon	450 tons	Thorium	50 kilograms
Nitrogen	550 tons	Gallium	30 kilograms
Lithium	170 tons	Mercury	30 kilograms
Rubidium	125 tons	Lead	30 kilograms
Phosphorus	85 tons	Zirconium	20 kilograms
Iodine	64 tons	Bismuth	10 kilograms
Barium	25 tons	Lanthanum	10 kilograms
Indium	20 tons	Gold	10 kilograms
Aluminium	10 tons	Niobium	10 kilograms
Iron	10 tons	Thallium	10 kilograms
Molybdenum	10 tons	Hafnium	8 kilograms
Zinc	8 tons	Helium	5 kilograms
Nickel	6 tons	Tantalum	2.5 kilograms
Uranium	3.32 tons	Beryllium	500 grams
Arsenic	3 tons	Protactinium	2 grams
Copper	3 tons	Radium	0.06 grams
Tin	3 tons	Radon	0.0000006 grams

uranium-235. That means the bay contains about 177 kilograms of the fissionable material uranium-235. That is enough to make three atomic bombs the size of the one dropped on Hiroshima.

Every square mile of the world's oceans contains that same amount of uranium-235 and the oceans of the world occupy an area of 140 million square miles. There is enough uranium-235 in the oceans of the world to make 630,000,000 atom bombs. That is enough for an atomic bomb for every ten people on the planet.

Plutonium is made from irradiating uranium-238, so in the world's oceans there would be enough uranium-238 to make well over a trillion plutonium bombs. That is simple reality.

Then there is thorium as a nuclear reactor fuel. Thorium will almost certainly become a major reactor fuel in the near future.

Nuclear power can be sustained for thousands of years, without even considering the inevitable advances in technology that will undoubtedly prolong nuclear power for all human and future human needs.

World energy use will rise tenfold

We must recognize that currently no more than 20% of the world's population has an acceptable standard of living. The remaining 80% want to catch up. And that will happen. To have that standard of living they will need electrical power. That means power stations have to be built to cater for four and half billion people. That means the world needs 4,500 new power stations right now. Imagine those running on coal. Nuclear energy has to happen now.

The antinuclear movement and most of the green movements have got it wrong. Because of global-warming-induced disasters, these people by their objections are effectively guaranteeing the deaths of thousands—if not millions—of human beings. The green movement's sustained objection to all things that in any way compete with the fossil carbon industries makes them responsible for these deaths. Such philosophies must cease to be the main theme of green movements. Alternatively, such green movements must cease to exist.

The killing effects of global warming and the products that cause global warming have now easily out-paced tobacco as a health hazard in Western societies. With tobacco, your children have a choice, when they become adults. With global warming you have to make the wise choice for them, before they become adults, while they are still children trusting us to protect them.

Make the wise choice and we will all live longer, we will have a higher standard of living, our air will be free of its major pollutants. We will halt the creation of enormous coal waste dumps. We will end the destabilization of our world's climate and we will save untold millions of human lives. All these statements are true, if we power our world with nuclear energy.

So first we must recognize and cease being influenced by the incredible lies, the unbelievable distortions of truth, the never-ending implications of death and horrendous destruction, the visions of never-ending cancer and unnumbered deformed babies. We must learn and we must realize that all these fictions are the tools of trade of the antinuclear lobbies and their trained antinuclear pawns.

We have to recognize and accept right now that the generation of electricity in nuclear power stations is an absolute essential for humanity. Wind power, wave power, solar power, geothermal power, hydroelectric power, all these attractive and idealized alternative energy sources, can and must play their role. But their role in any foreseeable future can only ever supplement nuclear power in our somewhat overpopulated and overpopulating world.

11

Energy systems we use now and what we must use tomorrow

W<small>E</small> have to end our reliance on fossil fuels as our most significant source of energy and we have to do it now. Fossil fuels must become no more than a minor contributor to our energy needs.

To switch to non-fossil fuels, to make it actually happen, we need to know what our energy options are. We need to know what are the practical, the most logical and the most economical and cost-effective alternatives.

In this day and age we are constantly bombarded with a myriad of alternative energy systems. Many are so ludicrous that they often tend to give the whole alternative energy industry a somewhat impractical image. In this chapter I will endeavour to clarify the relative advantages and disadvantages of the options we have, and to consider their costs and practicalities. To halt global warming I will also suggest the systems I think we should immediately move to.

The following major energy concepts will be considered, categorized as A and B.

A. Industrial electric power generation

Energy and energy systems for the generation of electric power distributed through some form of electric power grid and the possible short-term storage of such power is discussed. The systems are

1. hydroelectric power
2. tidal power
3. ocean wave power generation
4. trapping ocean currents

5. wind power

6. geothermal power

7. hot rocks at great depths

8. ocean heat and hot air

9. biomass

10. solar thermal

11. nuclear energy

12. power storing systems

B. Power and fuels for transport and off-grid installations

Energy that is mobile and transportable and mainly used to power self-contained transport vehicles. The concepts and fuels are

13. ethanol

14. biodiesel

15. solar photovoltaics (PV)

16. fuel cells and the hydrogen economy concept

The average costs of conventional and renewable fuels assessed by the "Commission of the European Communities Green Paper Towards a European Strategy for the Security of Energy Supply", published in 2000, lists average cost per kilowatt hour (kWh) for various energy supply systems.

Electricity costs in U.S. cents per kWh

coal	3.6
nuclear	4.3
wind	7.6
gas turbine combined cycle	3.3
solar PV	70.0

The first requirement for the prevention of global warming is that we make a conscious decision now to recognize and accept that the age of large-scale fossil fuel use is over. As we have seen, coal, oil and natural gas can never again be taken as "safe".

It is now the time to bite the bullet and initiate changes to alternative energy systems. From now on fossilized carbon materials must stay in the ground.

Concurrently, mankind has to have access to virtually unlimited energy supplies. A good standard of living requires a constant supply of energy. For all of mankind to have a reasonable and comfortable standard of living, man's energy requirements are going to go through the roof. The atmosphere can't handle the carbon dioxide buildup as is. We have no choice. Our sources of energy have to change and that change will not cause the often-claimed economic devastation.

Omitting motor fuels, which we will talk about later, the raw cost of energy in the production of all the goods and services in a Western society is surprisingly small. It varies around 1% of GDP (Gross Domestic Product).

The industrial revolution started when the steam engine was invented. For a long time those engines were fuelled with wood. We only switched to coal in the first instance because we ran out of wood. Oil and gas came later. The industrial revolution and the eventual rise in the standard of living of the industrial countries did not start and did not happen because fossil fuels were cheap, as is so often proclaimed. The recent rapid creation of wealth and prosperity in oil-starved South Korea and Taiwan occurred when world oil prices had already risen fivefold following the formation of OPEC (Organization of Petroleum Exporting Countries).

With most oil- and energy-importing countries, a change to locally produced non-fossil fuels for power generation would almost certainly increase the countries' national wealth. Job creation and massively reduced import expenditure would assure that happens.

Currently, in the vast majority of power stations across the world some form of fossil carbon material is burnt to produce energy. There are very few exceptions. Canada is mainly powered by hydroelectricity, France is mainly powered by nuclear energy and Iceland is mainly powered by geothermal energy. But that's about it.

Let's look at each of the fossil fuels we have become so conditioned to depend on.

Coal

Coal is promoted and sold on the basis that it is cheap. Coal deposits occur in almost every major country around the world. Deposits can cover thousands of square miles and are often extremely cheap to mine. Coal is in essence straight carbon, but contains a variety of contaminants.

Weight for weight, coal has about half the energy content of oil. Coal is carbon and oil is a hydrocarbon. Burning one ton of coal (carbon) produces 3.7 tons of carbon dioxide, about 50% more than from burning oil. Coal also produces huge quantities of fly ash waste from its contaminants. This has to be disposed of. A great proportion of the acid in acid rain also comes from the contaminants in coal.

Coal is a dangerous fuel. Acid rain is a serious world problem. Airborne coal dust is a killer. The mining, handling and transport of coal is a deadly industry. (For details on coal deaths see chapter 10.)

Global warming is our real concern and carbon dioxide is therefore the most serious waste product coming from coal-fired power stations. But coal is cheap only as long as it is legal to use the atmosphere as a carbon dioxide waste dump.

Natural gas

Natural gas deposits, like coal, are also for all intents and purposes unlimited. Natural gas has about the same energy content by weight as oil.
Apart from conventional gas fields, there are virtually unlimited quantities
of natural gas buried safely in the silt at the bottom of the world's oceans.
It occurs as frozen methane hydrates on the ocean floor. Methane is about
twenty times more potent a greenhouse gas than carbon dioxide. Moves are
now afoot to mine the methane from the ocean floor. Methane spill risks
are greenhouse deadly. They make oil spill risks no more than just a talking
point.

Natural gas can be a very cheap energy source where transport and
laying pipelines is not a problem.

Burning natural gas in power stations produces no fly ash. It produces
only small quantities of acid rain chemicals. This is the basis for natural
gas's fictitious but extensively advertised and publicized claim of being
environmentally friendly.

Natural gas is mainly composed of hydrocarbons. Other gases are
present in trace quantities. Natural gas is our main source for helium. Often
it contains hydrogen. The disadvantage of natural gas is the carbon dioxide
produced when it's burnt. Just like oil, burning 1 ton of natural gas dumps
about 2 tons of carbon dioxide into the atmosphere. That CO_2 will remain
there excessively heating the planet for five human generations.

To store natural gas in bulk is difficult, expensive and particularly dangerous. Transporting natural gas is also extremely hazardous. Deaths are far
more common than is ever imagined.

Like coal, natural gas is only a cheap source of energy as long as it is legal
to use the atmosphere as a carbon dioxide waste dump.

Oil

Oil is somewhat less hazardous to transport and store than natural gas.
At the moment we are not running out of oil. Oil reserves however are
definitely not unlimited. Oil reserves are more limited and restricted by their
particular locations around the world and the people and the administrations in the oil-rich countries. The world wholesale price of oil is therefore
readily subject to manipulation. By our continued reliance on oil as a
transport fuel, we in the West therefore effectively fund some unpleasant
totalitarian regimes.

Its use in motor vehicles produces huge quantities of acid-rain-
generating chemicals. But CO_2 is the main villain. Like coal and natural
gas, oil is cheap only as long as its carbon dioxide can be dumped into the
air.

It must also be appreciated that oil is an incredible mix of hydrocarbon compounds and as such, in this day and age, it is an invaluable source of raw materials for the petrochemical industries. It's also a wonderful lubricant. To burn this valuable resource just for its energy content is inexcusable. To turn it into agrochemicals to drench the rural lands of the world and destroy their fertility is equally inexcusable.

It is essential we have abundant energy to generate our electricity and it is equally essential we have portable fuel to run our motor transport systems. That won't change. It is even more essential that we prevent this impending world climatic chaos from proceeding. We can remove carbon dioxide from the atmosphere and bring levels back to near normal by massively increasing soil fertility—but that can only be done once. So, concurrently we must stop using fossil fuels as the prime energy source for our civilization.

We don't have time to wait the development of some yet-to-be-invented magical engineering system to restore atmospheric carbon dioxide levels to normal. Nor do we have time to wait on some esoteric, magical energy breakthrough to solve the problem of energy supplies. Soil fertility buildup solves the first problem. For the second, we already have developed climatically and planetary benign energy sources. Those sources are nuclear energy along with the wide conglomeration of minor and location-specific and less reliable "sustainable energy" and "renewable energy" systems. As previously mentioned these terms are at best only ever vaguely defined despite their widespread use. The meanings of the terms "alternative energy" and "sustainable energy" vary depending on the rhetoric. Throughout this book I have considered them to mean the following.

Alternative energy is any energy produced by not burning fossil carbon materials, being oil, coal, natural gas, methane hydrates and peat. (Peat is burnt as fuel in several countries.)

Sustainable energy is when the raw materials for that energy are still available, even after huge quantities has been used or extracted, possibly over millennia. The energy source is still usable and to all intents and purposes is still there in virtually the same quantities.

Let us now consider these energy sources and their systems. Nuclear energy is one that the fossil fuel lobby and their green movements prefer not to include in the above definitions, but that is a marketing fiction. Nuclear fuels are definitely "alternatives" to burning fossil carbon materials. Nuclear energy produces no carbon dioxide, nor any other greenhouse gas whatever. Nuclear energy is also "sustainable" and will be forever (see chapter 10).

The understanding of power costs and how they are calculated can be very confusing. Let's dispense with the confusion. The cost of producing electric power is dependent on three things: the capital cost, the fuel supply cost, and the day-to-day operational costs. Here we will use costs per kilowatt-hour (kWh). (Some times costs are described as cost per 1,000 kWh so divide those costs by 1,000.)

The capital costs of a power station include the cost of money to finance the operation and the cost of depreciation over the lifetime of the plant. To put this in perspective we can use typical figures. For the cost of money, allow around 5%, and allow for depreciation over 30 years. Then for all practical purposes it works out that for every $1,000 spent building the plant, 1 cent per kWh must be added to the cost of the electricity generated.

Let's assume the capital cost of a power station is $3,000 for every kilowatt of production capacity. Let's assume the plant is operating continuously, thus the electricity cost, apart from fuel, has to include 3 cents per kilowatt-hour. If the station caters for 1,000,000 people it has to be a 1,000-megawatt power station and it will therefore cost $3 billion to build.

Secondly, fuel costs have then to be added. This is usually described as fuel costs per kWh generated. The following costs are typical, but of course vary somewhat from place to place. Hydroelectric and solar-power fuel costs are of course zero. Nuclear fuel, including disposal costs generally, is around 1 cent per kWh. If we assume that fossil fuel waste, that is fly ash and the mainly carbon dioxide exhaust gases are dumped at no charge, then the cost of coal, allowing around $40 per ton, gives us 2 cents per kWh. Oil costs are around 7 cents per kWh minimum with oil at a low $30 per barrel. Gas varies widely but 4 cents per kWh has been a common figure. It's about 4 cents if gas is at $4 dollars a unit. The metric unit and the imperial unit by which gas is sold are, close enough, the same.

Thirdly is the cost of day-to-day operation of the power station. On a per kWh basis this is very low, being generally only fractions of a cent.

So to illustrate using a natural gas power station: a typical capital cost would be around $800 per kWh of generating capacity. That gives us 0.8 cents. To this we add 4 cents for fuel costs. Then we add a little for operations to give us a total of 5 cents per kilowatt-hour.

When power costs are expressed in kilowatt-hours, not megawatt hours, multiply the cost by 1,000 to get kWh. Four cents per kWh becomes $40 per MWh.

Fuel and energy systems have here been divided below into two main categories, firstly industrial electric power generation and secondly, fuel systems for self-contained power applications and independently powered transport.

Extra: total power use and the electricity grid system

Before we talk about the electricity grid itself, we need to know how people talk about power and power supplies and what they are talking about.

When electricity is generated in power stations the quantity of power generated is described in several manners. This can be confusing. So this is how I like to think of it. In a city in any Western society you will find that the average power use per person, over 24 hours, works out at about one horsepower each. City to city, country to country, it's always around that figure. One horsepower equals 746 watts. For simplicity I use one kilowatt per person. That's 1,000 watts each. So every person in a city uses the equivalent of a single-bar, 1,000-watt, electric radiator running 24 hours a day. A city of a million people therefore requires enough power to run one million radiators. That's 1,000 megawatts. (Mega means a million.) One megawatt (MW) supplies 1,000 people. A city of one million people needs a 1,000-megawatt power station.

Most power stations around the world are designed to produce about 1,000 MW of electricity constantly. Cities with bigger populations simply have more, or multiple power stations. Smaller power stations are built either a quarter or a half that size. Of course this is not always the case as power stations can be built any size.

Sometimes the concept of total power use per year is used. This is simply the power station output multiplied by the hours in a year. The measure is gigawatt-hours per year. A giga (G) being a billion.

A "power grid", an "electricity grid", or simply a "grid", is created and operates in all advanced countries. After electric power is generated it is delivered to consumers generally through a national power grid.

In very simple terms this is how it works. Electricity is generated at a power station and the electricity is then pumped out along heavy copper or aluminium wires mounted on power poles.

The wires then branch, and branch, then branch again, until finally a much smaller wire ends up delivering power to your individual house. For technical convenience the voltage, or electrical "pressure" in the wires is modified to enhance the efficiency of the system.

Another power station might be built, maybe a hundred miles down the track, and it too pumps electricity into the same set of wires. It takes additional power to pump the electricity through the wires, so power stations are best built near areas of high demand. As the population expands and more power is required, more power stations are built and more transmission lines are added to the system.

Finally the whole state or the whole country is serviced with power stations, busily pumping electricity into the planned and logical, but apparent tangle of interconnected power lines that make up the electricity grid. Houses, factories, and businesses then pull their electricity out of the system as needed.

Every house, every power station, every factory is ultimately connected to each other through the grid. Just like a road network. If one power station stops working all the other power stations work a bit harder. All the generators in all the power stations are exactly synchronized. Overnight, when the electricity demand slows down, some power stations will be slowed down, while other stations are completely stopped and restarted the following morning as demand increases.

A. Industrial electric power generation

1. Hydroelectric power

An immediate program to massively boost hydroelectric power generation worldwide is an absolute necessity, and there is no realistic downside.

The energy of moving water can be converted to electricity. It is then hydroelectricity. The term is usually restricted to systems involving dams, lakes and rivers.

Flowing water is used to turn some form of fan or impeller, or even a paddle wheel. The rotary motion turns a generator and electric power is produced. The amount of electricity produced is determined by the volume of water flowing and the vertical distance, or fall, between the inlet pipe and the outlet pipe. The height between inlet and outlet is described as the head of water and is measured in feet or metres. The power is proportional to the head multiplied by the flow volume.

Therefore, for maximum efficiency water has to be collected and stored in dams with the highest elevation possible. High upstream dams usually cost more per unit of stored water so there is always a compromise between lower-level low-cost dams with reduced head, or higher costing dams with a greater head.

Because the water is free, the only meaningful cost involved in the production of hydroelectricity is the capital cost of the scheme. Anywhere on the planet, a well located hydroelectric power station is the cheapest most efficient power source conceivable. Systems are exceptionally versatile as power can be regulated from zero to maximum and virtually by turning a tap. Such dams are also energy storage systems so in effect, the dams act like batteries.

In most developed countries the best sites have already being utilized. However hundreds, or even thousands of excellent hydroelectric sites still exist all over the world. Many would produce electricity cheaper than from the cheapest fossil fuel power stations. Many thousands more hydroelectric sites would be viable with minor rises in electricity wholesale prices. Coal and nuclear are the only cost-competitive systems to a well-placed hydro-electric power station. (See also Strategy 25.)

2. Tidal power

Sometimes viable; tidal power should be used wherever possible, but is only practical in very limited locations.

In this system, a dam wall is built across a river mouth, or across a large estuary or bay. High-volume low-head turbines are installed in an opening in the constructed wall. The turbines are driven by the flow of the incoming and outgoing tide.

Unlike many power systems, tidal power is utterly reliable as it finally depends only on the moon continuing to revolve around the earth. The single worrying proviso being that there are no substantial sea level changes and especially no significant changes in the pattern of ocean current flows. These could seriously modify local tidal heights.

In the open ocean, the tides are only about 3 feet (900 mm) in amplitude. But near the coastline, particularly where the water is funnelled between landmasses, the tides can be much larger. Tide changes of over 40 feet (12 m) are not uncommon in some parts of the world.

Naturally the maximum head (i.e. pressure) can only ever be the difference between high tide and low tide and the usable head averages half that total difference. Large tidal changes are therefore almost essential. The volume of the water flow must also be large and this can only be achieved by building reservoirs with the greatest possible surface area. Any depth below low water level is irrelevant. Excessive depth is also more of a deterrent as it makes the retaining wall unnecessarily expensive. The floor of the reservoir need be only a little below the low tide level.

Continuous energy generation of course ceases when tidal flow is changing direction. If it is necessary to cater for continuous energy generation, separate storage ponds need to be constructed to allow for the tide reversals.

As with hydroelectricity, the only meaningful cost involved in the production of tidal power are capital costs. Unfortunately it is rare to find suitable sites that can produce tidal power at sensible costs and that are also close to electricity demand centres. (See also Strategy 26.)

Tidal power for large power generation is somewhat impractical. The numbers don't work. Our standard city of 1,000,000 people, if located near a coastline with 12-foot tides would require a tidal reservoir 75 miles across. That's a 4-metre tide and a 120 km round tidal pond. The real estate alone could cost a few billion dollars. Another illustration: if somehow a barrage wall was built across the Straits of Gibraltar, to lock up the entire Mediterranean, it might generate enough tidal power to run, say Spain and Italy.

3. Wave power

Where the waves are right this can produce power cheaply and efficiently. It should be promoted but also can never be significant.

Electricity generated using wave power requires grid connection for backup as wave action has inevitable variability. No matter where, wave action can at times drop to nothing.

With tidal power the tide might rise and fall 12 feet (4 m) twice a day, whereas with wave power, that 12-foot variation can occur maybe every twenty seconds. Locations where consistent and substantial wave action occurs are not at all uncommon. The western coastlines of the British Isles and Ireland receive a constant supply of near-perfect waves coming in from the vast, open, windswept North Atlantic.

The quite reasonable capital cost of small power facilities using wave energy makes the concept a practical and viable renewable energy option. Systems have been developed, installed and debugged and they are effective. There are installations operating along the west coast of the UK and they work reasonably well.

There are three distinct concepts for utilizing wave action. The first concept uses the motion of a bobbing float to operate a generator. The mechanisms to achieve this are generally complex and costly. No successful large-scale demonstration unit has been constructed as yet.

The second method traps water in an open ended vertical pipe that creates an artificial blowhole. As the water level rises and falls it first sucks air in and then blows it back out as the wave moves past. The rush of air drives a bi-directional turbine connected to a generator.

What seems the best and simplest method is to use or build a wave-focusing structure conventionally in the form of a funnel-shaped bay. As the wave moves up the constantly narrowing bay its height increases, until at the end of the bay the water spills over into an elevated reservoir. The water can then spin a turbine as it drains back to the sea. The best concept in this system is to have the water collected from several bays and feed a single reservoir with a single turbo-generator.

In Japan a catamaran-type wave-power-generating boat dubbed the Mighty Whale is being researched. The machine is designed to be anchored facing the oncoming waves. The waves enter the open front, the energy is extracted and the wave vanishes. A fence of these machines across a harbour could theoretically act as a breakwater. But costs will almost certainly prove the downfall of the Mighty Whale.

In the United States an interesting system for producing electricity from wave action is being developed by a company in Princeton, New Jersey. This design is called a hydropiezo electric generator. It uses the piezoelectric phenomenon. When some materials are forcibly deformed, they produce a voltage difference across their ends. When the two ends are connected, an electric current flows. If a spark gap is structured in the system a spark can be produced. The principle is used in gas cigarette lighters and igniters in gas appliances.

In the hydropiezo electric generator the material deformed is a piezoelectric polymer, a plastic. The polymer comes either as a sheet or a rope attached to a floating buoy, which bobs up and down as a wave passes. The constant extending and shrinking of the polymer attachment generates an electrical current. The current is then suitably modified into alternating current to suit the local power grid. Initial cost estimates indicated electricity could be generated at competitive prices, but currently the system has prohibitively high capital costs and low energy conversion efficiencies.

In Australia, research on a wave concentrating system has resulted in the development of a concept whereby the waves are concentrated, not in a funnel but by focusing them in a carefully formed parabolic-shaped harbour. The system also uses manipulated air flows to run generating turbines. The University of New South Wales is involved in the testing. The Australian company Oceanlinx Limited (formerly Energetech Australia) is developing a 500-kilowatt demonstration at Port Kembla on the New South Wales south coast.

However, no matter how the energy is harnessed and no matter how ideal are the wave heights and consistencies, the wave energy available is ultimately determined by the length of coastline available. Estimates vary but in ideal conditions a reasonable compromise for the length of coastline needed to power a city of 1,000,000 people would be 150 miles (250 km). Constructing such huge facilities could never be feasible.

For small-scale installations in ideal, ready-made locations the fundamental hindrance to progress and development is ultimately the unavailability of commercially acceptable long-term contracts for sale of the power generated.

If utility companies and state electricity supply authorities could be made to sign up on moderately long-term contracts, say ten or twenty years at least, and at reasonable electricity wholesale prices, then immediately hundreds of ocean wave-power generating stations could be built to harness consistent ocean swells around the world. Utilizing North Atlantic waves could produce quite respectable quantities of power for the UK and Western European grid systems. Apart from excessive capital requirements, which need to come down considerably, there is no real downside. (Also see Strategy 27.)

4. Trapping ocean currents

Definitely something for the reasonably near future but only at a few locations. It is sensible and feasible but requires encouragement.

In many parts of the world, locations exist near coastlines where underwater valleys and gorges trap and concentrate consistent and fast-moving ocean currents. These ocean current flows are huge and very consistent. The concept is to manufacture what amounts to underwater windmills to collect the power.

The problems are immense. In the time frame we have to reverse global warming it is unlikely that they will ever produce any substantial or commercially viable electric power. But, like wave power, at some locations they could become a contributor and the idea of harnessing ocean currents must not be dismissed. Fast consistent ocean currents occur in a number of places.   Generally a 6-knot (3 metres per second) current would be considered as very fast. Water being so much heavier than air such a current contains a lot of energy, but alas, energy that is not easy to collect.

Again, the numbers for ocean current costs rule them out for substantial power generation for any immediate future.   There are many factors involved but one calculation suggests to power a 1,000,000 people city would require a line 300 km long of underwater propeller blades facing the current.

5. Wind power

Where the winds are strong and consistent, power can be produced at prices that are very competitive with all coal or nuclear energy. Wind power requires grid connection for backup but has no downsides.

A modern wind turbine consists of a slender tower as much as 150 ft (50 m) high on which an electric generator is mounted at the top. Or more rarely, a gearbox is installed driving a vertical shaft down to a generator in the base. The top housing looks like a streamlined aircraft engine installation. Usually a three-blade propeller, much the same as an aircraft propeller, is mounted at the front of the housing. The propeller can usually swivel to face into wind although this is not always absolutely necessary, as at some locations only the prevailing wind is harnessed. A swiveling ability is usually a luxury. Wind machine blades look like extremely long thin propeller blades. They can be up to 150 feet (50 m) in diameter. Blades revolve at up to 30 revolutions per minute.

To function efficiently wind turbines operate best at wind speeds of about 25 knots (45 kph). The operational wind speed range is roughly between 5 knots and 30 knots (say 10 kph and 55 kph). Wind speeds and wind directions need to be reasonably consistent as wind turbines of the above configuration don't like wind gusts, nor do they like sudden wind shifts.

At low wind speeds power generation become negligible. Above maximum operating wind velocities, turbines have to be stopped to prevent structural damage. Their major fault has traditionally been high maintenance cost, and to a considerable extent, it still is.

Nevertheless, a modern wind turbine complex can be very competitive with fossil fuels. But to prevent global warming it shouldn't ever have to be.

For commercial wind turbine operations, location is the crucial factor. If the earth was a totally smooth ball, all oceans, or all flat land, global air circulation would be very consistent. Landmasses upset the consistency. The warm tropics and the cold polar regions automatically create strong consistent westerly winds in the mid-latitudes. Mariners knew these winds as the Roaring Forties, referring to their latitude. Slower easterly winds prevail near the equator. These are the northeast and southeast trade winds. Near the poles easterlies again prevail. The Roaring Forties are the preferred latitudes for wind farms but of course local effects have to be taken into account.

Even well away from these latitudes, localized climatic peculiarities and unusual land shapes can still create near-perfect wind-farm sites. At some of these idealized locations the number of turbines erected can run into the thousands.

While power can often be generated on a twenty-four hour basis, weather anywhere can be fickle. Therefore stand-alone wind-power systems are not possible. Wind-turbine systems require a totally different, totally independent, full capacity backup electricity supply system. For this reason it is more logical for large-scale wind generated electricity to be sold into a local grid system. An extensive grid can both average out the electricity supply from a multiplicity of generating systems and supply power when the wind stops.

Wind farms can substantially and economically reduce carbon dioxide emissions. They are a must where conditions allow. (See also Strategy 30.)

6. Geothermal power generation

At suitable sites, geothermal power can be extremely economical. Even plants at less than ideal sites should be encouraged and developed. Backup power is not usually necessary. But as ever, long-term contracts are.

Geothermal means simply geological heat. In some parts of the world the interior heat of the planet is close to the surface. Underground water is heated to extreme temperatures and escapes to the surface through natural vents. The discharge of this superheated steam can be spectacular.

Geothermal heat sources invariably occur near volcanoes or earthquake zones. In these unusual and fascinating areas we have this unique source of heat energy that is totally free and virtually unlimited. Drill a hole and pump in water. Drill another hole alongside (or alternatively put another pipe inside the first pipe) and up comes high-pressure steam. This drives steam turbines that drive generators that produce electricity. The vast majority of power stations the world over use this same principle. It is only the nature of the steam supply that varies. Electricity costs from geothermal installations are low.

The areas where geothermal activity occurs are geologically unstable. They are in a state of constant change, but in terms of human life spans they are an unlimited and permanent source of easily accessible concentrated heat energy. Geothermal concepts work because hot molten magma is very close to the surface.

Utilizing geothermal heat is an excellent system of power generation and is only limited by the rarity and accessibility of the necessary geological structures. (See also Strategy 28.)

7. Hot geological rock structures

Hot rock systems will not slow current global warming and have little chance of ever becoming a viable electricity-generating system.

No matter where you are on this planet, if you dig a hole deep enough you eventually hit geological structures hot enough to produce steam. The drilling depth varies considerably although usually depths measured in kilometres or even miles are expected. Drilling holes to these depths is very expensive. With conventional geothermal power generation the heat is already at surface level. The concept in hot rock technology is to drill two holes some distance apart. Pump water down the first hole, have it percolate through the hot rock to the second hole and finally come out as a never-ending flow of useful superheated steam. Unlimited clean green power is the promoted dream. But it's not that simple.

Just to force the water into the solid rock at the bottom of the inlet bore would undoubtedly take an immense amount of energy. If this proved too difficult explosives would need to be used at the bottom of the bore to crack the underground rock formations. Then, by Murphy's Law, the water would naturally select the easiest and fastest path to the outlet bore. This would soon cool the surrounding rock in the immediate vicinity of the pathway and defeat the whole concept. Rock is a good insulator so heat flow would also be a problem.

If the hot rock structures were naturally porous, channels would probably have more difficulty in forming and the system might work. Unfortunately, if the rock is indeed porous the input water might simply dissipate in all directions and return negligible quantities of usable steam to the delivery pipe.

Then again the outlet water or steam would of course dissolve any salts trapped within the rock structures and transport them to the surface. These salts would not only cause corrosion problems but the accumulated salts would have to be disposed of.

At this time it appears that it would take a lot of money and a lot of time for any form of hot rock technology to establish any genuine commercial practicality.

8. Ocean heat and hot air

Systems based on ocean heat or variations in atmospheric temperatures with height, are most unlikely to be of practical use and won't be useful for combating global warming.

Water at the bottom of deep oceans is always a few degrees colder than water near the surface. From time to time there are proposals to somehow utilize this temperature difference to generate electricity. Thermodynamics tells us that the greater the temperature difference between the heat input and exhaust, the easier it is to utilize any available energy. In systems with small temperature differences, energy conversion efficiencies are very low and so flow volumes have to be correspondingly huge.

The engineering problems involved in building monstrous pipes connecting the ocean floor to the surface and insulating them, and then having those pipes capable of withstanding damage from fickle ocean currents and unpredictable storms, are mind boggling. With global warming causing so much havoc now, spending any substantial research money on such projects is a waste of resources. Results of such research are unlikely to be more than academic curiosities.

Similar concepts have been proposed using atmospheric temperature variations. In the most promoted of these proposals air is confined under heat-absorbing canopies near the ground and warmed by solar radiation as in a greenhouse. Vertical hollow pipes are then constructed in which the hot air is allowed to rise up the pipe and drive a horizontal windmill. Any possible merit in such concepts is most unlikely. The concept relies on vertical pipes that need to be some 3,000 feet (one kilometre) high. Theoretical power delivery efficiency is tiny. Commercial power generation, if it ever happens, will be decades away.

9. Biomass as power station fuel

Utilizing existing biomass, and growing new material should definitely be encouraged wherever and whenever possible.

The term biomass fuel is generally accepted to mean recently grown plant material that can be conveniently burnt to produce useful heat or energy. The growing of biomass entraps as much atmospheric carbon dioxide into itself as it releases when it is burnt. From a global warming point of view utilizing biomass is an absolute neutral. No additional carbon is added to the biosphere's total, and useful energy is produced in the process. The energy released by burning is fundamentally the solar energy absorbed by the plant as it grew.

The practicality of biomass as an energy source for power generation finally depends on the rate and the efficiency at which solar energy can be converted into usable biomass. The best plant is almost certainly sugar cane. At peak growth sugar cane can convert sunlight energy into combustible fuel energy at around 3% efficiency. That is similar to the efficiency of cheap solar cells. But producing an acre of even the cheapest solar cells is a huge expenditure. The really nice thing about sugar cane is that firstly, the sugar is so easily fermented into ethanol. Secondly: the bagasse (the waste residue) can fuel boilers for steam and power production.

Growing wood for fuel is too slow. Fuelling modern centralized power stations on randomly collected wood or even plantation grown wood is neither easy, nor practical. To grow enough wood to feed such stations won't work. So to promote the concept that wood could be grown in sufficient quantities to sequester the carbon dioxide from fossil fuel use is utterly ludicrous.

Admittedly wood did power the industrial revolution in England until eventually they ran out. Then they switched to coal. Harvesting wood for fuel was not cheap. So cheap energy is not the prerequisite for rapid mechanization and increasing standards of living as we are always told.

Most biomass fuels contain moisture, and energy is wasted boiling off the moisture. All things considered, the useful energy content of a given mass of wood or bagasse is about half the energy content of a similar mass of fossil fuel. From a global warming point of view however, that really doesn't matter as biomass use does not contribute to the biosphere's total carbon content.

One serious problem with wood and bagasse, or any other flammable biomass waste, is the cost of transportation to their place of use. Being two or three times as bulky as fossil fuels, they cost two or three times as much to transport. Small localized power generation is a wiser choice and then the compact electricity is transported. Coal is similar. Transporting coal to coal-fired power stations often considerably exceeds the mining costs.

Wood is a delightful material for household heating, and is especially viable in smaller towns and cities. When warmth is the primary requirement, producing direct heat on site is extremely efficient and replaces fossil fuels most efficiently. Many environmental movements and green movements oppose wood fires. This attitude is counter-productive and the alternatives (which they avoid mentioning) add to global warming.

A whole range of viable options using biofuels for power generation may well manifest themselves when carbon dioxide waste from fossil fuel power stations is equitably assessed and subsequently allocated a sensible and realistic disposal charge.

Additionally or at least alternatively fossil fuels simply must incur a hefty and just carbon tax.

10. Solar thermal

Straight solar thermal power generation, especially when hybrid with biofuels (or natural gas in the interim) has large-scale commercial viability now. Solar thermal concepts must receive substantial encouragement.

Solar cells or photovoltaics, as opposed to solar thermal, will be too expensive for commercial power generation for too long to be of relevance in our endeavours to prevent global warming. Photovoltaics are discussed later in "Power for transport and off grid or isolated installations".

Solar thermal is the process whereby solar energy is first made to heat some heat-absorbing material, generally a liquid. Then that thermal energy is used to produce steam or simply hot water. Solar energy can also be used as a heat source in industrial processes. The collection of the solar energy

Three modules of the author's solar thermal project. Each module is composed of a hollow concrete pad on which glass mirror strips are set in the top surface. The mirrors concentrate the sunlight onto a set of secondary mirrors in the upper sheet metal structure. This boosts concentrations to 150 times. Steam is flash-formed in the receiving pipe at 950°F and 1,000 pounds per square inch (500°C and 70 bars). Units have operated for short times at 700°C.

A complete power unit would be 110 metres in diameter and contain 340 modules, all pinned together to form a large floating raft able to turn to follow the sun. The pond would be like a football field surrounded by a waist-high brick fence. For hail protection a high-volume, low-pressure irrigation pump flash floods the primary mirrors. Maximum power output, one megawatt, depending on latitude. Cost estimates are one dollar per peak watt.

can occur in various ways depending on the final uses and temperatures required. Usually the process is described as low-temperature solar thermal or high-temperature solar thermal.

Low-temperature solar is used for such things as household hot-water systems, steam cleaning, food processing and various sterilizing functions. Temperatures involved are generally below 100°C, the normal boiling temperature of water. From a global warming point of view the supply of hot water to buildings is by far the most significant application for low-temperature solar thermal. Excellent systems are now on the market in most countries and are competitively priced. They should receive government support to absolutely ensure the rapid phasing out of all forms of fossil-fuel-dependent hot-water systems.

Solar-powered hot-water systems work beautifully at the latitudes and in the climatic conditions where the majority of the world's populations live. They are invariably more expensive to buy than electric or gas hot-water systems but are a lot cheaper to run. They usually incorporate an electric or gas-heating element to top up water temperatures during bad weather. This is generally the only ongoing cost associated with their use. Systems today are exceptionally robust and reliable.

In total contrast, an electric hot-water system powered from a coal- or oil-fired power station is environmental vandalism. The figures speak for themselves. Suppose you had a coal-fired hot-water system in the basement—like a gas hot-water system but made to run on coal. Further suppose that you could supply all your hot-water needs for a year by burning 1 ton of coal in your furnace. These are not unreasonable numbers. Now as an exercise take that 1 ton of coal to a power station and burn it to produce electricity. Use that electricity in an electric hot-water system and you'll only get enough hot water for four months. The reason being that the conversion of heat energy to electrical energy in a coal-fired power station averages at best a 33% efficiency, although highly efficient plants can sometimes exceed 37%.

With the energy going through the power station you would now need to burn 3 tons of coal for your annual hot-water supply. A massive 10 tons of carbon dioxide would automatically be produced. Proponents of electric hot-water systems might argue that the latest technology for coal-fired power stations can achieve higher efficiencies than a coal furnace in the basement producing direct heat. It might therefore not be 10 tons. It might only produce 8 tons of CO_2. Of course the solar system produces zero tons of CO_2.

There are alternatives to electric hot-water systems. Direct gas hot-water systems are immeasurably better than electric hot-water systems that use any form of fossil fuel to produce the power. Direct gas heating produces less than 3 tons of carbon dioxide. That's not good but remember electric systems produce 9 tons. Solar hot-water systems produce zero and that's what we need.

Solar hot-water systems can substantially contribute to combating the constant modification of world climates by global warming.

High-temperature solar thermal is used mainly in the generation of commercial electrical power, and is not yet a significant power production system. But it will be.

With high-temperature solar thermal sunlight is firstly concentrated using focusing mirrors and then the concentrated sunlight is directed to produce superheated steam to power conventional steam turbines. Unconcentrated sunlight cannot produce steam at conventional turbine temperatures and pressures.

Generating usable steam from concentrated sunlight has generally been a two-stage operation. Firstly, a temperature-resistant fluid, such as heat-resistant oil or mixtures of molten salts, is heated in the optical solar concentrator. The hot fluid is then passed through a heat exchanger to turn water into steam. Gases can also be used as the heat transfer medium. Different gases have various advantages; both nitrogen and air can be used. Ultimately superheated steam is fed into conventional steam turbines and electrical power is generated.

Alternatively the steam can be produced in a single stage. The steam is its own heat-transfer medium. Direct steam production usually has design problems.

Serious interest in solar thermal systems started back in the 1970s, and around the world quite a few large research projects were funded. Most of this funding dried up. Now solar thermal power stations are again being seriously considered.

The efficiency of converting solar energy to electricity with older solar thermal systems was never much above 10%. Newer designs should approach 20%. Solar thermal systems and photovoltaics therefore now have similar overall efficiencies. The working face of a solar cell is an exotic photovoltaic miracle and it will always have a significant cost. The primary working face of a high-temperature solar thermal system is a mirror. It will be a very long time before photovoltaic surfaces can be made as cheap and as weather resistant as a common bathroom mirror.

A few big non-oil companies are funding research in solar thermal concepts. Countries without fossil carbon deposits or low in fossil carbon deposits are taking a big interest. But we can't ever rest assured. Solar power can only ever partially power a modern affluent society.

Whether a power station runs on solar energy, nuclear energy, geothermal energy, oil, natural gas or coal, or whatever, superheated steam is produced and used to drive steam turbines. The steam temperatures used don't exceed about 550°C (1,000°F). Above these temperatures normal, average good quality steels become unreliable, and the whole system has to be constructed from expensive heat-resistant materials. Also at these temperatures turbine blade construction becomes more difficult. The slight increase in overall efficiencies at temperatures above 550°C does not usually warrant the higher cost. Increasing operating pressures is generally more practical.

Solar thermal systems using high-temperature oil as a heat-transport medium are limited to maximum temperatures of around 350°C (650°F) as even the best heat-resistant oils are then subject to chemical breakdown. Steam turbines operating at these temperatures are reasonably and sufficiently efficient for large-scale power generation.

Apart from that there are no technical problems to be solved that need delay a massive expansion in the production of solar thermal electricity. The problem is not how to produce the power. The only problem is how to reduce the slightly excessive capital costs. With high-temperature solar thermal power generation the sunlight is always concentrated using some form of parabolic mirror system. The construction of these mirrors, the mounting frames on which they are erected, the mechanisms and the pivoting systems needed to track the sun is what costs the money.

Capital costs currently seem to run between a possible low of $5,000 and on up to $20,000 or more per kilowatt of power produced. Daytime only operation has already been factored into these figures.

So basic power generating costs as low as 5 cents is therefore a reasonable expectation. Today, in many places around the world, electricity costs from fossil fuels far exceed these figures. Yet despite this, most countries have stopped funding research that might ultimately eliminate the dubious cost advantage of cheap coal and gas.

To date such systems have not been a serious threat to gas and coal and oil, but with more economical plant design solar thermal energy will emerge as a true threat to fossil carbon fuel sales. If it's allowed.

The largest solar thermal power station in the world is the LUZ plant at Kramer Junction near Barstow in Southern California. The plants were built in the 1980s. Although sunlight is free, the capital cost for power stations of the LUZ design is five and more times the capital costs for a coal- or oil-fired power station. The final electricity cost is dearer but not by much.

The LUZ built solar power station still operates but the company that developed the technology and built the solar generating equipment went to the wall. (See Strategy 31.) Without the existence of the original manufacturer it initially became difficult to maintain optimum output at Kramer Junction. Full power production was finally restored after many years of component supply problems.

The LUZ technology is still extremely good and can easily be reestablished. It is a totally proven technology. All that is needed are long-term contracts at prices that reflect the real costs of global warming. The horrendous costs we now have to bear resulting from increases in droughts and floods and fires are higher than the few extra cents a kilowatt hour we would pay to return the world to normal.

Solar thermal systems cannot produce power at night and will cease power generation in overcast weather. Solar generated electricity is therefore best sold directly into the grid. As with all noncontinuous power generation the grid itself becomes the best backup.

Although solar thermal systems cannot normally operate on a totally stand-alone basis, there are a couple of very practical and effective ways they can. Solar thermal systems generally use conventional steam turbine-driven generators and this gives them a very advantageous versatility. If at any time steam temperatures and quantities drop below electrical load requirements then either ethanol, natural gas or oil can be used to top up steam temperatures to turbine requirements. A solar thermal power generating installation therefore only requires a set of burner nozzles as stand-by equipment. A totally separate and independent power generating facility is thus not required for a stand-alone power plant.

The other concept is to produce hydrogen gas from the midday excess power supply and burn this to drive the power generating machinery at night. Alternatively the excess energy can be used to pump water up to a high dam for overnight hydroelectric power. Electricity prices would then be more expensive at night than, as now, by day.

The cost of solar thermal systems is based almost entirely on the initial capital cost. Getting the capital cost down is the supreme objective for solar power. I looked at these cost structures a few years ago. No system existed with a sufficiently low enough capital cost structure to seriously compete with very low cost coal-fired power stations.

I then became interested in the development of practical and economical solar power and have been developing a high-temperature solar thermal system ever since. Several million dollars has been spent on the project and it has been helped by sizeable grants from both the Queensland State Government and the Australian Federal Government. I'm now happy to say that all the basic research is complete.

The concept uses thousands of narrow glass mirror strips cast into the top surface of thin concrete floating rafts. The assembled rafts float in a shallow pond and because they are floating they are able to rotate to align with the sun.

It is structured like a low-cost floating boat marina. A complete modular unit is 375 feet (112 m) in diameter and contains 7,500 square metres (nearly 2 acres) of mirrors. The structure is like a football field fenced in with a low concrete fence, filled with water and covered with floating mirrors. The mirrors concentrate the sunlight onto tubular collectors. Each module can produce up to 6 tons of high-pressure steam per hour at temperatures approaching 600°C (1,100°F).

For extreme weather and hail protection the entire array is designed to be flooded and thus to be sunk under the water in a matter of minutes. We conducted tests with 3-inch (75 mm) diameter ice spheres as simulated hail stones and these couldn't shatter the glass mirrors under the water cover. Patents covering these various concepts are already granted, or pending in numerous countries.

The system is designed to comfortably produce steam at 500°C and 1,000 psi to conform to modern power station configurations and efficient steam turbine designs, although we have produced steam for a few minutes at temperatures up to 720°C (1,328°F).

It could have an application functioning as a dual purpose unit producing both electricity and desalinated water.

At this time of writing I have not heard of a high-temperature solar thermal system anywhere, built or being considered, with lower initial capital costs. That was the original objective in the project and is now the system's major advantage. Depending on location, power cost estimates appear to be comparable with fossil fuels and nuclear power. Only time will tell for this particular venture.

In any relatively flat and cloud free locations, practical twenty-four hour power generation would be easily achievable with around 70% being solar derived, with current technology. Fortunately sunny locations also have higher day power loads than night loads.

To achieve any stand-alone solar thermal based system it is currently necessary to include a storage heat sink or other energy input system to smooth out the normal daily variation in solar energy delivery. Ideally the standby energy system should be based on ethanol or biodiesel. But even using oil or gas, an almost instant 70% reduction in greenhouse gas emissions is an incredible start. When ethanol and biodiesel fuel supplies exceed motor vehicles and transport requirements then the oil or natural gas can be phased out.

However, depending always on specific circumstances, I do believe that commercial solar power generation will only ever rank as a minor source of industrial power in advanced societies. Nuclear power will dominate as soon as widespread public acceptance of nuclear power generation develops.

11. Nuclear energy

Nuclear power systems are safer than any other large-scale power generating system ever built and we can only avoid catastrophic global warming by large-scale adoption of nuclear power systems.

The nuclear proliferation debate is over. The cat is already out of the bag. There are about three dozen countries that have nuclear reactors now. Some of them have dozens of reactors. All those countries could build nuclear bombs. If they were governed by a power-crazed totalitarian administration they might want to. Mining more, or mining less uranium won't stop nuclear proliferation. Only international inspections, international sanctions and the elimination of totalitarian regimes based on bigotry will. And that's all happening, and when it's over, the world will be a safer, better and happier place for all. Nuclear energy is going to produce more and more of our ever-expanding electrical needs.

In chapter 10, the subject has been considered in detail. This is mainly a summary of the concepts and considerations in that chapter.

In a nuclear power station, nuclear energy is harnessed to boil water and produce useful steam. The steam turbines and the generating equipment used is much the same as in any other power station. However, generally the steam temperatures and pressures in a nuclear power station are slightly lower than those in a coal or gas-fired power system. Adjusting power output to suit electricity load requirements is as simple as in oil or gas-fired plants, and far easier to adjust than in coal-fired plants.

It is nonsense to propose we should wait the development of hydrogen fusion reactors to replace fossil fuels. Fusion reactors will have similar waste disposal problems as fission reactors. We will only hear about them if and when a sensible and practical fusion reactor is ever developed. But it is most unlikely that the hydrogen fusion system we are spending so much money on will ever happen.

The safety requirements in current fission nuclear power stations have become many times more stringent than those mandated for any other human endeavour. This is undoubtedly due to the money and muscle in the oil-lubricated antinuclear movement. As a result capital costs for nuclear power stations were grossly inflated to between US$4,000 and US$8,000 per kilowatt of power-generation capacity. That equates to an electricity cost of about 4 to 8 cents per kilowatt-hour.

In the last few years nuclear energy costs have dropped considerably. In many instances they are as low as 1 or 2 cents per kWh. That's cheaper than the cheapest coal power. This is mainly because the nuclear plants are proving more reliable and longer-lasting than many expected, so capital depreciation costs are much lower. Power costs also depend on the funds that have to be allocated, usually arbitrarily and exorbitantly, to the mythical "nuclear waste disposal problem".

Nuclear energy is safe. It is not only safe but it now seems clear that low-level nuclear radiation is actually a health benefit (see chapter 10).

Well-documented studies of nuclear power workers seem to conclusively demonstrate both an increase in health and in longevity when nuclear radiation levels increase several fold above world averages.

Of course exposure to radiation levels thousands of times higher than normal can certainly be lethal and cause death within short time periods. Survivors of exposure to extreme radiation levels also have statistically higher reported cases of deaths from a variety of cancers. But reality is that people exposed to massive radiation levels and survive are only slightly more likely to get cancer than are the general population. Statistics show that survivors, just like other people, face far greater risks from dying by being run over by a car, or being a passenger in a car, or falling over in the bath, or being struck by lightning.

No radiation danger exists from low-level nuclear waste. Most natural granite used in building construction, and even the human body, emits more nuclear radiation than most nuclear power stations' low-level waste.

High-level nuclear waste is extremely hazardous, but even it is far less hazardous than many industrial chemicals and biological products. Dangerous chemicals remain hazardous for ever. Nuclear waste gets safer as each year passes.

Commercial nuclear-fired power stations have been operating for almost half a century already. If you threw in an extra half a dozen or so Chernobyl accidents, using the actual accident figures, not the invented deaths, the calculation on nuclear safety shows nuclear energy would still be the safest, most reliable electricity supply system ever created. (See also Strategies 32 and 33.)

Not to class nuclear energy as both alternative energy and sustainable energy shows a level of gross irresponsibility that is frightening. Are we supposed to believe our sun is not sustainable? Our sun is just a very big nuclear reactor.

If global warming has not wiped out mankind beforehand, then there is enough easily accessible uranium and thorium in deposits all over the world to fuel human civilization for thousands of years. In addition normal seawater contains an absolutely unlimited supply. Existing technology today guarantees that nuclear energy will be powering all future human civilizations, and that's completely discounting any new technology.

12. Self-contained power supplies and power storing

Along with the problems of how to produce usable power to do work or to generate electricity often comes the problem of storing the energy involved.

Here we are only considering major energy storage and ignoring minor storage systems. We are not discussing watch springs and small batteries. Usually the items they power are small but relatively expensive and use tiny quantities of power. High specific energy storage costs are irrelevant in such circumstances.

With all systems of power-generation, provision has to be included for fluctuations in power demand. Where power stations supply a city, the city itself actually acts as a cushion. Millions of individual loads average out. See "Extra: total power use and the electricity grid system" (page 594).

Power stations supply alternating current. The frequency, or cycles per second, of the current is kept within extremely tight tolerances. The timing of electric wall clocks is controlled by this frequency. The frequency does vary slightly but the numbers of cycles are actually counted and if the total is slightly down, the frequency is increased a tiny amount so the absolute total over any time is consistent. The clock always ends up being right.

When a sudden spike occurs in the total load the frequency stays almost the same but the voltage drops. Every light in the city dims slightly. Every heater puts out a little less heat. Everything being moved, pumped, pushed or pulled is delayed or retarded very slightly. Then when the spike, or sudden peak load passes, all the city systems speed up again, or pump out slightly more heat, or whatever. In most cities it is quite common to experience a 5% or 10% voltage drop in the power supply as an hourly or daily occurrence. The city thus rides out the overloads until the turbines wind up to produce the extra power.

A totally different problem results from the very large daily fluctuations between the maximum daily peak power use and the overnight minimum power use. Power stations operating full bore, burning oil or natural gas, are able to handle major decreases in power demand by turning down or turning off some of their steam-producing furnaces.

With coal it's not so easy. Power engineers do not like to fluctuate the rate at which coal is fed to a furnace. If a coal-fired furnace is stopped and cools down, it can be difficult and time-consuming to restart. Some furnaces if stopped accidentally can become so damaged they need rebuilding before restarting. It is therefore more economical to keep coal-fired furnaces running almost full bore twenty-four hours a day, seven days a week.

Coal is cheap and so has become the most common fossil fuel used in power generation. In consequence of this need of coal-fired power stations for continuous operation, excess electricity is usually produced. Every day electricity production goes into massive over-supply at night. The excess has to be sold or wasted. This is the reason we are all encouraged to buy this artificially cheap off-peak power. Its contribution to global warming is frightening. As the coal is burnt, about $3\frac{1}{2}$ units of heat energy is consumed to produce about $1\frac{1}{4}$ units of useful electricity. This electricity is then virtually wasted to produce 1 unit of off-peak hot water just to wash dishes and supply warm bath water. The off-peak electric hot-water system is an appallingly wasteful system for consuming and in effect storing energy. The system is a huge contributor to global warming.

In the case of non-fossil-fuel energy systems, catering for storage and load fluctuation can be more specific. Both peak loads and off-peak loads with hydroelectric power are handled by turning up or down what in essence is just a very big water tap.

In times of flooding or excess water supply, excess power can be used to pump water to storage dams at higher altitudes. When dams are positioned at much higher elevation the energy available for power generation is many times higher. Such high dams can be considerably smaller. And in contrast to the main dams, they require negligible catchment areas.

With hydroelectric power generation there is no built-in theoretical thermodynamic efficiency loss as exists when burning fossil fuels. The only efficiency loss with hydroelectric systems results from things like pipe friction.

The "hydrogen economy" advocates argue that the excess electricity from coal plants could be used to produce hydrogen gas. Then by using some not-yet-developed fuel cell, the advocates suggest the hydrogen gas stored in the yet-to-be-invented commercial storage containers be reconverted back to electricity. Currently it is totally impossible to economically store hydrogen gas in the quantities required for industrial power generation.

Even then, converting that gas back to electricity is at best about 35% efficient. Then instead of 1 ton of coal producing a quantity of electricity and 3.66 tons of carbon dioxide we would be burning 3 tons of coal to produce the same usable quantity of electricity and in doing so produce well over 10 tons of CO_2.

Fuel cells have many problems that are rarely talked about. Fuel cells, like photovoltaic cells, produce direct current; not the more practical and versatile alternating current now used in all power grids. The DC power has to be converted to AC and the equipment is expensive. Thomas Edison, the famous American inventor, did make a few mistakes in his exceptional career. One was setting up power supply systems for cities using direct current.

During the 1880s a battle raged between Edison, opting for DC (direct current), and George Westinghouse, opting for AC (alternating current). The Westinghouse Company won. In 1892, under some financial pressure, Edison switched to AC in a merger with AC purveyor Thomson-Houston. That merger became General Electric.

Like hydroelectric power generation, nuclear power generation can be increased or decreased almost by adjusting a tap or moving a lever. The problem of energy storage does not exist.

Solar thermal power generation on the other hand needs short-term energy storage of some form or another to spread the high midday heat more evenly through the day. They need only be relatively simple systems such as heating blocks of concrete, or even rocks or scrap metal, and should not be too expensive. But even with short-term heat storage there are still serious problems to be solved.

It is pointless for a solar thermal power station to have the capacity to store sufficient heat to function as a twenty-four hour power supply system. Overnight storage is not the real problem. With solar power generation it is inevitable that periods as long as weeks will occur when cloud cover prevents meaningful power generation. That is the real problem. Heat or electrical energy storage over such extended time periods is currently totally and completely out of the question.

It is also unnecessary. Solar power shines best as part of a composite or hybrid system. Such systems are inherently practical. They are economical and can be sufficiently reliable to function as stand-alone installations.

As mentioned, this is sometimes done by incorporating a final heating phase powered by natural gas or liquid fuel fired burners. This auxiliary heating is then available to ensure power production even during prolonged periods of sunless days.

Wave power and wind turbines can only be used to generate power to feed into an integrated grid system. If they are ever constructed as part of a stand-alone twenty-four hour power supply installations, then they would need a full-sized backup system using a totally unrelated design concept. Naturally this would mean excessive over capitalization and becomes impractical.

Apart from collecting rain in a dam to run a hydroelectric system, energy storage is an incredibly irritating problem for energy engineers. Certainly there are ways of storing collected energy but they are all excessively uneconomical and impractical.

It is never an efficient process to turn energy, from some primary energy source, into useful work. It usually has first to be converted into electricity. It is also surprisingly inefficient to convert generated energy into a form that can be stored. It is even more frustratingly inefficient to turn such stored energy back into useful electricity. In consequence it is always better to produce energy only where and when it is required. But even that is not particularly easy as invariably some storage or some energy backup is desired or needed.

Apart from nuclear energy, there are really only four basic principles by which energy can be held or stored. They are mechanical, chemical, thermal, or electrical.

Holding water in elevated reservoirs is the most common form of mechanical storage. When excess energy is available it can be used to pump water into the reservoir. Using electric motors to pump water into an elevated reservoir and using the downflow of that water is about as good an energy storage system as currently exists. Even in this process around 30% to 40% of the energy is lost in the process.

Energy can be stored as heat, but apart from using the energy to produce hot water, energy recovery is very difficult. Storage temperatures have to be very high, and even then converting the heat into useful power is maddeningly inefficient.

Then there is chemical storage. Energy is stored as a potential chemical reaction. Generally in this we have two chemicals that react together and release energy, either as heat or as electricity, or sometimes a bit of both. A battery stores energy as a potential chemical reaction which can, when required, produce electricity.

With common fuels the energy is chemically stored, often for millions of years, and is released by burning to produce useful heat. Such fuels are diesel, petrol, coal, natural gas, ethanol, biodiesel, wood and hydrogen.

Hydrogen can be either burnt to produce heat energy or it can be combined with oxygen in a fuel cell to produce electricity.

Holding energy in the form of stored potential chemical reactions is an extremely compact phenomenon and is usually the most convenient. When the substance containing the energy is a liquid it's even better. Solids and gases are less convenient. Liquid fuels are so easy to move and handle.

Unfortunately when we have power being produced in excess of our immediate requirements and the flow can't be throttled back, then for all practical purposes converting that power into a high-chemical-energy liquid for storage is impossible. If the power produced is electricity, hydrogen gas can be produced by electrolysis and stored. Converting the hydrogen back to electricity can only be done by using it as fuel in a gas turbine or internal combustion engines to drive generators. Efficient, commercial, and viable high-power-output fuel cells don't yet exist. Such cells are at least ten years off, and that's being optimistic. Fuel cells were actually invented way back in 1836 by Sir William Grove, a highly respected British physicist of the time. We are still waiting.

In contrast to battery energy storage, liquid-hydrocarbon-based chemical energy systems have a massive advantage. The ideal hydrocarbons are the ones that prevent global warming. They are ethanol and biodiesel. The second chemical in the reaction to release energy from a hydrocarbon is the oxygen in the air. The air doesn't have to be prepackaged. A battery on the other hand contains within itself both of the reacting chemicals. That's why batteries are heavy.

Higher than about 10 miles (16 km) the air is very thin. There are negligible quantities of readily available oxygen. For space flights the vehicle has to carry its own oxygen. That's why they are so huge and heavy at lift off. If a jet transport plane had to carry its own oxygen it would have trouble just getting off the ground. Carrying commercial cargo would be impossible.

Nearer the ground hydrocarbon fuels, especially ethanol and biodiesel, will be the most sensible fuels for decades to come. They store solar energy in a way that is compact, efficient and extremely versatile.

There are other possibilities that are constantly discussed. In the transport sector the worth of an energy storage system comes down to quantity of energy stored per unit of container weight, and of course how easily it can be recharged. For very short-range operations and operations confined to urban use, the common car battery can sometimes suffice. Long-range viability using batteries however, is a very long way off.

Very sophisticated flywheels have been constructed that spin at astounding speeds. Some of these are already in use in short-range experimental transport systems. Their energy density to weight ratio actually rivals conventional battery designs. Flywheel energy does slowly dissipate so long-term storage is not possible. Flywheel systems might be practical for unique or special applications.

Energy can also be stored directly as electricity. Here we are not referring to batteries, we are referring to electrical capacitors. Electricity is electrons flowing in a wire. A capacitor can therefore be considered as a bucket full of electrons. Currently the amount of energy that can be stored in such devices is low, but it is not minute. Some really big capacitors might only run a car for a few minutes but nevertheless, might suit other applications.

It can be seen that for self-contained motor transport, currently and for any immediate future, a liquid hydrocarbon is far and away the most convenient fuel form currently existing. Practical automotive hydrogen storage tanks as yet don't exist. So to stop global warming, we fill our fuel tanks with ethanol or biodiesel.

To summarize: Apart from elevating water in a hydroelectric application there is as yet no system for large-scale energy storage suitable for storing power-station-generated power. It needs to be used as it is produced.

13. Ethanol

Ethanol can replace petrol in motor vehicles and that would end the production of greenhouse gases from all the cars in the world. We must make it happen now. Ethanol is actually a cheaper fuel when oil prices go over $45 a barrel.

Virtually all motor vehicles, other than those in Brazil, today run on either petrol, diesel or LPG (liquefied petroleum gas). And they are all fossil fuels. To stop global warming these fuels have to be replaced. What is amazing is just how incredibly easy and practical it is to do so.

We could easily cease using petrol or gasoline tomorrow simply by running our cars on ethanol. Brazil has been doing this for years. Only minor modifications are required to internal combustion engines to run on almost straight ethanol. The majority of cars in Brazil run on pure ethanol or high ethanol blends. The ethanol boosts the octane rating and the cars run cooler, cleaner and better.

Ethanol (i.e. ethyl alcohol) is the alcohol in alcoholic drinks. It is the main ingredients in methylated spirits. We have been brewing alcohol for thousands of years. Ethanol is made by the yeast fermentation of sugars or starches. It can also be made by the acid hydrolysis of cellulose matter with bacterial fermentation, but this is not as yet well developed and has consistently lacked significant funding. Any country can produce ethanol. It can be made by the fermentation of sugar from sugar cane in warmer climates and from sugar beet, or any of the grains, especially corn or maize, in cooler climates.

Virtually any carbohydrate can be economically fermented into ethanol. The best crop varieties vary depending on local soil types, rainfall patterns, harvesting procedures and prevailing temperatures. A good ethanol fermentation facility can handle almost any grain type, even mixed grains.

Seventy-five percent of the population of this planet live in the tropics.

Mostly these are poor countries in need of income. Many live in countries or on islands where rainfall is ideal for sugar cane production. Sugar cane thrives in the wet tropics and subtropics, and sugar cane production is by far the most efficient conversion crop of solar energy into fermentable sugars. When sugar cane is in its full growth phase it converts sunlight into energy to easily rival photovoltaic cells.

Now in Brazil, and in any other efficient sugar-producing country, from a hectare of sugar cane they can produce 5,500 litres of ethanol per year, that's 35 barrels of motor fuel. On a per acre basis, that's 14 barrels or 600 U.S. gallons.

The total world oil consumption is 4 billion tons per year. That's two thirds of a ton of oil per head of population. It is the equivalent of one car for every four and a half people on the planet. There is actually only about half that number of transport vehicles in the world. The rest of the oil is used for heating, petrochemical production, etc.

What does this all mean? As an exercise, let's say we drive 16,000 miles per year and get 20 miles to the U.S. gallon (26,000 kilometres at 12 litres per 100 k). That's about 3 tons of fuel per year. Then to grow the ethanol or biodiesel we would need to allocate two thirds of a hectare, that's under one and a half acres per motor vehicle. That's 0.13 ha or 0.33 acres per person. That would require an area of sugar cane farms 2,750 kilometres square or 1,700 miles square. That's about the size of the Amazon basin and we will have cancelled our need for petroleum-derived transport fuel.

The Amazon basin, if it was all cleared, could produce enough ethanol and biodiesel every year to run every car, truck, tractor and airplane in the world. And that area requirement will be halved as we switch to hybrid automotive engines. Nuclear can supply us with electrical energy. Nuclear energy could then possibly supply hydrogen gas, if at some future time fuel cells become practical for motor vehicles.

But better still for transport, why don't we let the Third World tropical countries become the new fuel suppliers to the Western world? The bagasse they produce in the production of the ethanol could then easily fuel the future power stations they might want to build. There are already many small power stations running very successfully on bagasse in several countries around the world.

What better way to insure such tropical Third World countries rapidly emerge from poverty and become prosperous and affluent members of human society?

"No pollution is more destructive of the natural environment than the pollution of poverty" —Edward Teller, nuclear physicist, in his *Memoirs* (Perseus Press 2001).

Cars can be modified or initially manufactured to run on ethanol but for immediate action they can run on a blend of ethanol and petrol. The more modern flex-fuel engines can run on a wide variety of blends from

85% ethanol (E85) to straight petrol.

Blending ethanol with petrol has come to be called gasohol. Gasohol contains up to 25% ethanol. Cars need no modification to run on petrol containing up to 15% ethanol, described as E15. From there on up to 25% ethanol, or E25, slight engine modification is usually required.

Gasohol is already produced and marketed in Brazil as E25. In the United States and in several other countries, E10 gasohol is produced.

Henry Ford built his Model T to run on either ethanol or gasoline. Half a century later Boeing B-17 Flying Fortress bombers, fuelled with gasohol, operated very successfully out of North Queensland during World War II. Their super-sophisticated, high-precision aircraft engines ran cooler on the brew and their range and performance were enhanced.

In 1975, during the "energy crisis" caused by the Middle East oil cartel's manipulation of prices, the Brazilian government set up a program called Pro-alcohol. The program was incredibly successful and created a precedent and created a guide that other nations can and must adopt. The object of Pro-alcohol was to make Brazil self-sufficient in automotive fuels. Cars would switch from running on petrol to running on ethanol. Ethanol would be made from sugar. Sugar cane grows extremely well in tropical Brazil. At that time the national average sugar cane harvest in Brazil was over 30 tons per acre or 75 tons per hectare. Improved varieties were expected to easily increase this national average. They most certainly did, now over a 100 tons is common.

In 1979, Brazil produced the first all-ethanol cars. By 1985 over 80% of cars produced in Brazil by such companies as General Motors, Ford, Volkswagen and Fiat were pre-built to run on ethanol blends. By the mid-1990s, there were 4 million cars in Brazil running on straight anhydrous ethanol and there were several million more running on gasohol. (Anhydrous ethanol is ethanol that has had all traces of water removed.)

Gasohol and ethanol are the only gasoline replacement fuels we can switch to that require no change in our current fuel-distribution system. Nor is there any significant change or even significant adjustment of current automobile engine design. Engines designed for pure petrol use are OK, or even improved when running on ethanol-petrol blends. Running cars on straight ethanol E100 or E85 however, does require minor engine modifications.

Converting an automobile engine or even an aircraft engine to run on straight ethanol is surprisingly simple. Ethanol has a higher octane rating than most petrols so higher and therefore more efficient compression ratios are used. Shaving the head to increase compression will result in a gain in fuel efficiency. Some timing and some carburetor or injector adjustments are also necessary to run the slightly richer mixture needed. And that's it.

For new cars the changes mean only a slight modification to the machining and assembly process. There is no actual additional production cost. The result however, is that after initial manufacture, we have a totally greenhouse-neutral automobile.

Weight for weight, petrol contains slightly more energy than ethanol, so fuel consumption rates increase slightly, but the difference is not enough to warrant altering fuel tank sizes. As compensation, the slightly higher engine efficiency using ethanol-boosted fuels lowers fuel consumption.

There is a much more important design concept that has developed over the last few years. The standard internal combustion engine used in cars was slightly altered in the combustion area and then the engine was equipped with some clever and inexpensive electronics. The latest version of this configuration can continuously and successfully run on either ethanol or petrol or any mixture whatever of the two. The machine then becomes a flex-fuel vehicle.

Amazingly to many, in the United States flex-fuel motor vehicles have actually been on the market since General Motors introduced its first flex-fuel engines in 1992. The GM engine was perfectly successful. Other companies soon followed. Since then flex-fuel vehicles produced in the United States include, in the Ford range, the Taurus, the Explorer, the Supercab Ranger and the Mercury Sable. Daimler/Chrysler produced flex-fuelled models. Their flex-fuel Chrysler Sebring comes in sedans and convertibles. Also produced were the Chrysler Voyager minivans and both Dodge minivans and Plymouth minivans. General Motors produced a 5.3-litre V8 Sierra half-ton utility (or pickup), a 5.3-litre model Suburban, a Tahoe, a Yukon and several XLs. GM also produced some 2.2-litre Chevrolet models. Both Mazda and Isuzu also produced flex-fuel cars for the U.S. market. Today there are now about 2 million flex-fuel automobiles on U.S. roads. The legislation governing their production allowed for up to 15% gasoline in the fuel mix as originally very cold starting was sometimes a problem with pure ethanol.

The Brazilians have since solved the ethanol cold-weather starting problem and flex-fuel vehicle production in Brazil is really rolling. These cars will happily run on pure ethanol, pure gasoline or any mixture of the two. The Brazilians would prefer to call their cars "total-flex". The Volkswagen Gol hit the showroom floors in September 2003. It runs on 100% ethanol, or any mixture through to 100% petrol. By June 2004 sales had reached 300,000 cars a year and climbing. Buyers love them. They sell at around the same price as mono-fuelled vehicles (that now aren't selling well at all).

Relative to the petrol we now use, running a car on ethanol produces an extremely clean exhaust. Using pure ethanol means that no greenhouse gases are added to the atmosphere. No additional carbon is added the earth's biosphere it being a use, grow, reuse process.

Another advantage is that between 20 and 30% less carbon monoxide is produced. Carbon monoxide is the gas that kills people in confined spaces. Petrol powered cars discharge toxic sulphur dioxide from their exhausts.

Robinson 44 helicopter flown by the author. These aircraft are fitted with six-cylinder Lycoming IO 540 aircraft engines. The Brazilian aviation authorities are now approving a modification to the Lycoming engine for aircraft operations using sugar-derived ethanol. Worldwide, Brazil is second only to the US in the general use of light aircraft and many of those aircraft will soon be flying on ethanol.

In the atmosphere this gas becomes sulphuric acid and ultimately falls as acid rain. In most cities, car exhaust fumes are the major source of sulphur dioxide. Ethanol does not contain sulphur compounds and sulphuric acid can't be produced. The United States 1990 Clean Air Amendments Act actually nominates high ethanol content blends, such as E85, as "clean fuel".

Unburnt petrol in the exhaust is a significant pollution hazard. Unburnt ethanol is not. It is about as hazardous as spilling a glass of beer. Also, unlike diesel or petrol, ethanol produces only tiny quantities of carbon particles in the exhaust. In addition, by switching to straight ethanol there is a 15% drop in the formation of nitrous oxide compounds. In the air these compounds turn into nitric acid, an additional contributor to acid rain.

In 2003 Neiva, a subsidiary of the giant Brazilian aircraft company Empresa Brasileira de Aeronautica SA (or Embraer) unveiled their ethanol powered Ipanema EMB 202 crop dusting aircraft. Embraer is the world's number four aircraft producer. The aeroplane was fitted with a modified American Textron Lycoming six-cylinder, overhead-valve, fuel-injected aircraft engine, an IO 540. (see *Aviation Now* September 2003). The aeroplane uses slightly more ethanol than the avgas (aviation gasoline) version but in Brazil avgas can cost US$2.00 a litre whereas aviation ethanol is available at US$0.35 a litre.

Brazilians are second only to Americans in their use of light aircraft. The suggestion in Brazil is that all their light aircraft should be converted to operate on straight ethanol. There would be huge savings. Avgas in Australia generally costs around $1.00 a litre, so we could do the same (except for the behind-the-scenes influence of oil companies on successive Australian governments).

It is easy to totally phase out gasoline or petrol. Brazil has shown the way. The country is now the world's largest producer of sugar cane. A massive two thirds of that total sugar production is used to produce ethanol. They produce about 16 billion litres per year.

At say 2,500 litres per motor vehicle per year, that quantity will fuel more than 6,000,000 automobiles for a year. And no carbon dioxide whatever is added to the atmosphere from all those millions of cars.

In Brazil, ethanol is being produced and sold ex-distillery at between US$0.20 and US$0.25 a litre or between US$0.76 and US$0.95 per U.S. gallon. From late 2000 to early 2001 the Brazilian government purchased 70 million litres of their home-grown ethanol to maintain safe national stock levels. They paid approximately US$0.30 per litre for the slightly dearer anhydrous form. The sugar cane farmers of Brazil and the whole Brazilian economy benefited.

As mentioned before, ethanol can also be made by the acid hydrolysis of cellulose matter with bacterial fermentation. A new bacterium was discovered at London Imperial College UK a few years ago that can digest almost any plant material and convert it to ethanol. It was reported the bacteria functioned best at around 70°C. That's a very easy process temperature to maintain. With bacteria like that a whole sugar cane crop could be converted into ethanol, not just the sugar (*Science* Vol. 264, April 1994). So to even consider continuing the widespread use of petrol and diesel is ludicrous, especially with bacteria like that on the horizon.

Where our research dollars should be spent is on bacteria like that, not on some extravagant, fuel cell, Star Wars type hydrogen-economy dream.

Simple fuel tax changes could initiate an almost instant switch to gasohol and ethanol. But citizens have to demand it or it won't happen. Few politicians have the guts to buck the oil companies. Brazil is the exception. Brazil does produce about 30 million tons of oil a year but that's not really very much. It certainly would not be enough to supply the energy needs of fossil-fuel-guzzling Australia with only 20 million people, and definitely not enough to power Brazil with 150 million people.

Brazil drives on ethanol and is therefore the most greenhouse responsible country on earth. But for Brazilians, only the Amazon rainforests get publicity, and that's invariably critical. It's always critical because rainforest stories have such an entrenched structured anti-timber bias. But more probably because such areas are great places to grow sugar cane to fuel what are, in essence, solar-powered cars.

Massive increases in ethanol production from agricultural crops must be given top priority. Using ethanol and biodiesel—which we talk about next—is the only quick and easy, safe and practical action we can take to eliminate carbon dioxide buildup from our world's motor transport systems (see Strategy 29).

14. Biodiesel

Vegetable oils chemically combined with ethanol can totally replace petroleum-based diesel and at about the same price. In a fuel tank biodiesel also happily mixes with conventional diesel refined from mineral oils.

When Rudolf Christian Karl Diesel invented his engine in 1897 he ran it on peanut oil. Straight vegetable oils were soon replaced with products derived from mineral oils. Eventually these became the diesel fuels we know today.

Even the best vegetable oils gum up diesel engines and so are never used. Biodiesel however, is a very different product both chemically and in use. It is generally accepted that straight biodiesel is somewhat better than mineral diesel in conventional diesel engines.

Any vegetable oil can be used to manufacture biodiesel. Animal fats can be used, and even what are generally considered as useless waxes can be used. The manufacture of the liquid we call biodiesel is an amazingly simple and efficient process.

Probably like most of you, I simply had no idea, no inkling at all how easy and how simple is the process. I only learnt about biodiesel recently. In Australia I have friends in the liquid waste disposal business and they knew nothing about the production of biodiesel. To home brew a good beer is a nightmare compared to producing biodiesel.

This is the recipe: take three measures of any vegetable oil, or animal fat, oil or wax, even waste oils are OK, add one measure of ethanol. Then add a pinch of caustic soda and warm the mixture. Shake vigorously for a couple of hours and allow the brew to settle. A mixture of biodiesel and glycerin is soon produced. The glycerin separates to the bottom. Drain off the glycerin and strain both liquids. That's about all there is to it.

The biodiesel can go straight into any diesel engine. The glycerin (technically it's glycerol) is not even a waste product. It is often more valuable than the biodiesel. Glycerol is a commonly used raw material in the production of cosmetics and plastics, such as cellophane, polypropylene and PVC.

When using vegetable oil, the oil seed is first crushed and the oil extracted. With many crops the residue material from the oil crushing plants has a high protein value and so makes an excellent cattle feed. There is no waste anywhere in the whole biodiesel production process and not one atom of carbon is added to the earth's biosphere. Net carbon dioxide production from diesel engines, throughout the world, could stop for ever.

Extra: basic biodiesel chemistry

Most plant and animal oils, fats and waxes are classed chemically as esters or triesters. Esters are organic compounds that are derivatives of fatty acids. A triglyceride is a compound of three vegetable oil esters attached to a glycerin molecule. These esters are able to react with other alcohols, such as methanol or ethanol, and form new esters and in so doing they release the bonded glycerol.

In the process, the often sticky and viscous, high-molecular-weight ester, which is always susceptible to polymerization (making it gummy), is converted to a less viscid, lower-molecular-weight ester. Potassium hydroxide or sodium hydroxide (caustic soda) is needed as a catalyst to make the reaction proceed. Thus a viscid oil, or even a solid wax, can be converted into a much thinner and very useful liquid—biodiesel.

It is a very commercially viable operation and makes good sense.

3 triglyceride ester (vegetable oil) + 1 ethanol (alcohol)
= 3 ester (biodiesel) + glycerol, $C_3H_5(OH)_3$ (glycerin)

The ester or biodiesel is usually described by preferencing the name with the oil used, followed by the type of alcohol. For example, using canola seed (rapeseed) and methanol we get Rape Methyl Ester (RME). From soybean oil and ethanol we get Soy Ethyl Ester (SEE), and so on.

The biodiesel manufacturing process has two major cost inputs, ethanol and vegetable oil. Methanol can be used but this defeats the purpose of halting global warming, as generally methanol is a fossil carbon product. Methanol is the "methy" in methylated spirits. It has been used for decades to make it undrinkable. Better substances and colourings are now used to distinguish ethanol and make it unpalatable.

The biodiesel manufacturing process results in three saleable commercial products: animal feed, glycerol and biodiesel.

The following are illustrative costings, in which all fuel taxes, tariffs or subsidies have been removed to obtain meaningful comparisons.

Ethanol can easily be produced from sugar cane for less than US$0.35 a litre as we have seen. World prices for various edible vegetable oils range between as low as US$0.40 a litre to about US$0.60. Nonedible oils are cheaper. The quantity and cost of the caustic soda catalyst is close to insignificant.

In Australia, in reasonable seasons farmers will grow and produce any amount of canola seed, provided seed prices stay above around A$340 a ton or about US$250. Current varieties of canola seed (rapeseed) contains between 35% and 45% useful oil. After the oil is extracted the crushed canola meal wholesales for above A$250 a tonne. It rarely drops below A$200. By selling the meal at the above prices the oil costs work out at about US$0.33 a litre or US$1.25 a U.S. gallon.

There is a market for the glycerol produced as a byproduct. Glycerol, 99% pure, is a premium product traded internationally. Over the last several years prices moved between US$1,300 and US$2,400 a ton. In the United States the price of non-premium glycerol, as produced in the manufacture of biodiesel, is around US$500 a ton, about US$0.53 a litre. (Simply multiply litre prices by four to get slightly over U.S. gallon prices; about 5% over.)

If we consider the imputed costs of ethanol at between 30 cents and 40 cents U.S. a litre and the imputed costs of palm or grain oil at between 35 cents and 45 cents U.S. a litre, and allowing a mix ratio of three to one, oil to ethanol, we would be producing both glycerol and biodiesel at between 37 cents and 45 cents a litre. Mixing the materials and separating the end products incur negligible costs—maybe a cent or so a litre. The bulk price for biodiesel would range between $1.45 and $1.75 a U.S. gallon.

Prices could even be lower. A canola crop produces around 150 U.S. gallons of oil per acre, around 1,400 litres per hectare. But top canola crops produce 2,000 litres per hectare. The very best oil producer is the tropical oil palm at around 250 U.S. gallons per acre or 5,000 litres per hectare. That's over thirty standard barrels of vegetable oil off one hectare. A farm returning US$1,000 per hectare would be producing oil at US$32 a barrel. Given some practical guarantee on prices, tropical farmers could grow all the oil we need.

For biodiesel production the preferred alcohol is ethanol fermented from sugars and grains. This eliminates all carbon dioxide additions to the atmosphere. Methanol is a petroleum product and its use would add carbon to the biosphere. The use of methanol to produce biodiesel should be actively discouraged by taxation measures. Methanol is also a very poisonous material, even externally.

It is obvious that methanol will always be the alcohol suggested by the oil and gas companies as methanol is one of their "own". Europe and the United States generally use methanol to make biodiesel (*Australian Sugar*, November 2000).

To totally eliminate the use of petroleum-based diesel fuels all we have to do is to structure a system that compensates for manipulated fluctuations in world oil prices and give just a little subsidy or tax incentive to the fuel-producing farmer. Preventing oil price manipulation is an absolutely necessity as we must totally end the ability of oil cartels to juggle oil and gas prices to deliberate and systematically forestall the development of alternate fuel systems.

It follows that a wise and responsible government should never, within their national borders, allow the price of crude oil to drop to or below say

US$50 a barrel, even if the world price of oil drops to nothing. Governments could probably cut every other fuel tax and make up the shortfall by collecting the difference between world prices and the $50 a barrel.

It is essential we encourage farmers throughout the world with meaningful or even exaggerated incentives so as to guarantee they grow these fuel-producing crops that the world now needs.

Today ethanol and biodiesel are very simple, safe, cheap and easy fuels to produce. We have to accept totally that they are the transport fuels for any pleasant, foreseeable future. We also have to make that fact a reality (see also Strategy 29).

15. Solar photovoltaics (PV)

The previously mentioned EU Green Paper on electricity costs lists electricity from solar cells in 2000 at 70 cents U.S. per kWh. That's ten to twenty times the cost of wind, solar thermal, hydro, geothermal, nuclear or fossil-fuel electricity generating systems. Solar (PV) cells are impossibly expensive. Prices haven't changed much since that 2000 report.

Even in the very long term, solar cells are most unlikely to ever be a viable source of commercial power. To have governments subsidize their use (as is now happening in Australia and in other countries) on the pretence they might somehow moderate global warming is an almost criminal waste of tax dollars. The commercial use of PV for significant power production is a fairyland fiction.

In a solar cell, layers of materials, similar to the materials used in transistors, are bonded together. There are usually two layers and each is connected to an external circuit. When sunlight falls on a solar cell, electrons are jostled between the layers and are forced to flow out through one of the terminals. They flow through the device to be powered and then finally back into the other terminal. The solar cell is acting like a small self-charging battery. In a battery, stored chemicals within the battery make the electrons flow. In a solar cell sunlight makes the electrons flow.

The current produced from a photovoltaic cell has a very low voltage and does of course flow only one way. They therefore produce direct current (DC). Modern electronic devices consume amazingly small quantities of electrical power and these are always the applications where solar cells really shine.

Individual solar cells are generally never more than a few square inches or square centimetres in area. Only about one or two volts can be generated in any one cell, and only tiny electric currents can be produced. To obtain any reasonable current and even a moderately high voltage, a large number of cells have to be assembled and wired together.

In order to use PV power in household and industrial applications it must be converted to alternating current (AC), and at a much higher voltage (110 volts in the USA, 240 volts in Australia). The conversion to high-voltage alternating current requires a fairly complex piece of electronic equipment called an inverter. Inverters by their very nature are expensive. Then if the converted power is to be on sold into the power grid, the voltage and the alternating current frequency has to be synchronized to the grid.

In the production of solar cells large silicon crystalline structures are first "grown". From these grown crystals thin wafers are sliced. These processes can only be satisfactorily achieved in ultra-clean laboratories. Most solar cells today are made from these silicon wafers.

There is often a lot of fanfare about producing more efficient solar cells, but even just slightly more efficient cells become prohibitively expensive for general use. In most practical applications today, best power conversion efficiencies are around 15% sunlight energy to electricity. Generally it makes considerably better economic sense to simply use more of the less efficient but cheaper cells. High-tech cells are made that achieve a 24% efficiency. These high efficiencies are about 65% of the theoretical maximum efficiency considered possible. Generally good quality commercial solar cells operate at around 12% efficiency.

There are other photovoltaic cell technologies besides that based on silicon, but most of these have yet to prove economically viable. They also have numerous design and production hurdles to overcome. Gallium arsenide is a semiconductor, and cells made with it have somewhat higher theoretical efficiencies. By using gallium arsenide 30% efficiency has been achieved in laboratory experiments.

Gallium arsenide cells are extremely expensive to make. They can however be made to absorb sunlight concentrated as high as 400 times. Their use therefore is generally only considered in conjunction with optical concentrating systems. Such solar cells are called multi-sun cells. The 70% not converted to electricity simply heats the solar cell so they have to be water cooled.

In the field, solar cells have to be protected from weathering, and in large solar cell installations, from possible hail damage. For such installations the cells need some form of strong cheap and substantial transparent protective sheeting, which has yet to be developed. Alternatively they need easily movable covers that must of course be capable of withstanding periodic gale force winds. Such a covering obviously needs to be more substantial than the materials in a motor vehicle body. There is simply no cheap, economical and commercial way of protecting large areas of solar voltaic cells from substantial hail damage.

Solar cells should face the incoming sunlight for best efficiency, so a cheap tracking system is desirable. Even large-scale solar cell tracking systems are not yet considered economical.

All these costs must be added to the basic price of any solar-cell installation. Vociferous advocates of solar-cell systems rarely do.

Recently photovoltaic cells have been incorporated onto flexible substrates. Cells have also been developed that are partly transparent and so can be made into vertical windows. The concept is that they be used in building construction to form both windows and cladding. The cells are expensive and less efficient than conventional silicon cells. The cost of the electricity produced is exorbitantly high.

Solar cells have always been inherently costly to make but prices have dropped dramatically as manufacturing became more streamlined. To produce power at even three times other alternative energy systems means insurmountable cost barriers must still be overcome.

Stand-alone systems capable of continuous operation with no backup power source are not possible with photovoltaics. This is another disadvantage. When considering photovoltaic power generation a completely independent, full-load backup system is necessary. In this regard it is like wind energy. Storage batteries may be sufficient for small-scale overnight operation but no storage system can cater for long periods of overcast weather.

The main advantages of solar cells are their extreme reliability and convenience. They can be left unattended for years with little worry. Although interplanetary probes use nuclear-powered batteries, satellites and space probes usually have their electronic equipment powered by photovoltaic cells. One advantage solar cells have in space is that the sun doesn't ever set.

With a solar cell with any light present, from any direction, the cell will produce some small amount of power, and this can be crucial. In situations where the raw cost of power is relatively insignificant then solar cells have an excellent function.

For large-scale commercial power generation where it would be necessary to buy them by the acre, photovoltaic cells are prohibitively expensive. A small town, of say 10,000 people, would need 25 acres (10 ha) of the very best high-tech electronic photovoltaic cells, plus enough batteries to power the town overnight, plus an inverter to turn the DC current into household voltages and frequencies. It's impractical and will be for a very long time.

There appears to be only one conceivable way that solar cells could produce remotely economical commercial power. Sunlight could be concentrated using arrays of inexpensive glass mirrors set on simple tracking systems. So using concentrated sunlight and multi-sun cells the number of cells could be reduced, possibly fifty-fold. Such cells would of course require cooling. Currently multi-sun cells are way too expensive even for this option and are likely to remain so for many years.

Solar cell manufacture has managed to become massively subsidized by governments all around the world. That has produced short-term lower selling costs. Their costs are artificially lower because of another factor. The silicon wafers used in solar cell manufacture have generally been scrap materials from the computer chip industry. Additionally a decline in demand from the electronic industries for polycrystalline silicon chip materials has meant that the photovoltaic industry has been able to enjoy a miniature low-cost boom. Solar cell manufacturers were able to buy first-quality silicon at scrap quality prices. The solar cell cost structure became somewhat artificial. Approximately half the solar cell production, starting about 1999, relied on the availability of artificially cheap, high-quality polycrystalline silicone.

The current result is that the cost of solar cells is now artificially low, and the supply of raw materials for their production is now artificially high. This situation won't last, so solar cells became as cheap as they will ever be for many years.

The total world production of solar cells has boomed in recent years, probably in consequence. Despite the boom, reality in terms of electricity-generating capacity is infinitesimal. At 2001 world solar cell production rates, it would take half a century of full-scale production to create a generating plant to cater for just one large city.

At this stage, using single-sun photovoltaic cells, there is absolutely no way that installations will ever become an energy-competitive system capable of even vaguely assisting in the prevention of global warming.

This is why now, and at least for any foreseeable future, the fossil carbon fuel suppliers see it as inconceivable that single-sun photovoltaic cells are a significant threat to their industries. Why else does photovoltaics and the fiction of "free power from the sun" receive such unjustifiable support and publicity?

16. Fuel cells and the hydrogen economy dream

The concept of the hydrogen economy is just a huge confidence trick. It's designed to placate us into believing that a totally safe, environmental benign and unlimited energy supply is just around the corner. The "hydrogen economy" is a carefully marketed public relations fiction. It is not based on facts and realities. It is based on sound bites and science fiction.

A hydrogen-oxygen mixture will burn and release heat and energy as the gases combine to form water. If you put a couple of electrodes into a jar of water containing a little table salt and turn the power on, the electrical energy flow is consumed by splitting the water back into hydrogen and oxygen. You can see the gases bubbling up from the electrodes. The process is called electrolysis. A fuel cell tries to reverse this process using hydrogen gas and air.

Currently all viable proposals, and all methods used for the low-cost large-scale production of hydrogen gas, are based on the use of fossil carbon compounds as the raw material. Producing commercial hydrogen by electrolysis is, and has always been, impractical and prohibitively expensive simply because of the cost of the electricity used. When generating electricity by burning solid, liquid or gaseous fuels, about two-thirds of the fuel energy goes up the chimney. That cannot be avoided. It is ordained by basic thermodynamic theory.

If excess electricity is generated at a power station it can be used to produce hydrogen gas. But why, for currently we have no practical way of storing hydrogen?

Converting the hydrogen gas into useful energy is never better than 50% efficient and usually more like 30% efficient. Only one-third of the original energy ends up as useful power, and as we only get 30% of that energy recouped we are left with 90% of the original energy being quite unavoidably wasted. So it can be considered that 3 tons of coal effectively produces only $\frac{1}{3}$ ton of original coal energy, but a very real 10 tons of carbon dioxide. All this waste and effort to run fuel cells is just ludicrous.

The action in a fuel cell is like electrolysis in reverse. The fuel cell is a tricky device wherein the hydrogen and oxygen burning or combining reaction can be slowed down in such a manner that, under certain conditions of temperature and pressure, electricity is produced. It is a conversion direct to usable electricity.

In a fuel cell, hydrogen combines with oxygen but no flame is produced. Generally however, fuel cells do need to operate at several hundred degrees, although still well below flame temperatures. In a burning process, hydrogen combines with oxygen and produces usable heat and waste water. In a fuel cell process the gases produce electricity and waste water and small quantities of waste heat.

Hydrogen can be removed from some hydrocarbons such as ethanol and methanol. Ethanol, for example, can be passed through a reformer containing a special catalyst maintained at 800°C. A mixture of hydrogen gas, carbon dioxide and carbon monoxide emerges.

Researchers are endeavouring to develop fuel cells to run on gases such as methane and ethane as well as on methanol and ethanol. Experiments are being vigorously pursued to build cells that will run on petrol. Within these systems hydrogen has first to be extracted from the liquid fuel to feed the fuel cell. This is done in the reformer. Reformers have to be supplied with heat energy at high temperatures. The reformer ultimately has to become part of the fuel cell package.

Fuel cells running on any hydrocarbon will exhaust carbon dioxide and water in exactly the same quantities as if the fuel was burnt in an internal combustion engine, or in a furnace. The only possible advantage is that energy production might be slightly more efficient. Otherwise, as a means of even slowing global warming, fuel cells running on anything other than non-fossil-fuel-derived hydrogen are useless. This is one of the unmentionables in the "hydrogen economy dream", or should we say nightmare?

Automotive transportation systems using fuel cells are at best also a thing for a distant tomorrow. The catalytic membranes that separate the two gases in a fuel cell are delicate and can't handle any impurities in the system. The cells have to run at high temperatures. Their efficiency in converting hydrogen into electricity is, at their laboratory best, about 50% to 60%. The very best and most expensive commercial cells are around 30% efficient. It would make more sense to use any hydrogen available to run standard internal combustion car engines.

Fuel cells to power a motor vehicle have to be able to produce huge quantities of electricity to run the powerful electric drive motors and their gear systems. Normal inefficiencies are inherent at every stage. The overall efficiency of raw energy to rotating wheels, utilizing the most exotic fuel cells available, is believed to be marginally better than running an internal combustion engine or a gas turbine on that very same hydrogen. Admittedly there is an expected reduction in nitrous oxide production by using fuel cells. But global warming effects would not be reduced, not one iota.

One way or another a fuel cell has to be fed hydrogen gas. Hydrogen, by itself, does not exist on this planet except in trace quantities. It is not available to be mined, or drilled for, or even harvested. Hydrogen is not and never can be an original source of energy. Except in minute quantities, straight hydrogen doesn't exist anywhere on this planet. It has to be made. The energy to make it is then the only energy it contains. It is also impossible to get back all the energy from the hydrogen gas as was needed to produce it in the first place.

Just maybe, in some future time, bacteria might be developed that could somehow turn sunlight direct into hydrogen gas. But that is a pipe dream for some distant tomorrow. It can't help us now with our destabilizing world weather problems.

No matter what, hydrogen can only ever at best be a means of either storing energy or transporting energy. Manufacturing hydrogen is like charging up a car battery. It's like pumping water into some elevated dam for later power generation. Hydrogen is never a source of power.

Hydrogen gas is also not the benign material we are encouraged to believe. Recently serious concerns have been expressed on the unique and unpleasant dangers in handling hydrogen. The tiny hydrogen atom is the smallest atom that can possibly exist in all the universe. Hydrogen gas can actually seep through solid steel. Normal valves used for controlling gases such as oxygen, carbon dioxide, nitrogen and LPG let hydrogen leak through. Hydrogen is totally invisible and totally odourless. So hydrogen leaks can go dangerously undetected.

Colouring or strong smelling compounds are added to gases to make serious or significant leaks noticeable and detectable. With hydrogen such measures are automatically doomed to failure. The additives can't get through the minute passages through which the hydrogen happily permeates. So hydrogen leaks go undetected. Also any of the common compounds normally added to gaseous fuels to detect leaks, if added to the hydrogen, will almost instantly clog and disable the delicate catalytic surfaces used in fuel cells.

Leakage in the commercial handling of any gas is an accepted ongoing cost factor.   Cost of the leaked gases is balanced against the costs of leakage minimization. Total prevention is rarely feasible. Actually, leakage allowance figures of around 10% are not unusual in the LPG industry. Hydrogen would be worse without exceptional and precise handling procedures.

Hydrogen-air mixtures have a far wider, and therefore more dangerous explosive mixture range than all other conventional gaseous fuels in use anywhere in the world, or even proposed anywhere. Hydrogen burns with an exceptionally hot flame, and the flame is almost invisible.

Therefore, from a safety angle, the use of hydrogen gas by the general population is not desirable. Insurance would be a problem and premiums would always be high. Insurance and safety factors are other unmentionables in the big "hydrogen economy" sell.

The hydrogen economy scenario has other serious problems. A report in the 13 June 2004 issue of *Science* by a panel from the California Institute of Technology and its allied Jet Propulsion Laboratory considers the effect of all the extra hydrogen gas entering the biosphere resulting from the creation of an international hydrogen economy. The mathematics indicates that the ozone hole would get much bigger and deeper. They also predict that the ozone hole would persist for longer periods. Additionally it would negate any immediate beneficial effects on the re-establishing of the ozone shield by the current worldwide reduction in the use of CFCs.

The report suggests that extra hydrogen gas in the upper atmosphere will obviously affect high-altitude cloud formation and in consequence atmospheric optics and in turn global warming. What could happen is unknown and scenarios are vague and speculative. It also notes that there could be effects on plant growth resulting from "unforeseen effects on microbial communities" within the soil.

There are 100 million vehicles in the United States and if they are all to be replaced with electric vehicles magically powered with hydrogen fuel cells then for each and every fossil fuelled electric power station in existence, both in the United States and in Europe, we would have to construct another one just to produce the hydrogen gas required. And even that is unlikely to be sufficient.

If we don't want all these new power stations to run on fossil fuels and if nuclear energy is not an option, where would all the energy come from? The hydrogen economy advocates say solar energy. But that's just another dream. There is only one commercially operating large-scale solar power station complex in the world, and it's just one quarter the size of our "standard" one-million-people power station. It was intended that more of these reasonably successful quarter-size solar power stations would be built.

But somehow, as we saw, their construction was stopped.

Believing the hydrogen economy story, and believing it will save the planet, is believing the king was actually wearing those magic clothes.

Manufacturing hydrogen to use as a fuel has all these many problems but hydrogen does have some notable attributes. Although it is more bulky, weight for weight, hydrogen contains about three times as much energy as most liquid fuels.

The problem with hydrogen systems is that there is no practical way of storing it in usable quantities. Certainly it can be compressed and stored in high-pressure cylinders but just as assuredly not in useful quantities. Such cylinders are totally impractical as automotive fuel tanks. They are too heavy, too dangerous and a car would need too many to go any acceptable distance.

A system needs developing where somehow the gas is dissolved into some form of sponge or in something that can hold a quantity of energy at least near that held in an automobile fuel tank. If and when a reasonably low-cost system is developed it will almost certainly be well received and could well be widely adopted. Commercial jet aircraft of all things could be built to run on hydrogen and they would have surprising and practical advantages. They would fly further, carry less fuel and carry more cargo. Handling the dangerous gas by trained aviation personnel is also more feasible.

If the hydrogen storage and transport problem has no practical solution, then research on hydrogen power systems is close to pointless. Only with a handling system that is yet to be invented are fuel cells, or internal combustion engines running on hydrogen, likely to ever become a real possibility. It will be a long time before that happens and a longer time before an infrastructure to distribute the hydrogen fuel could be established.

We don't have that sort of time. And we can't ask the planet to hold its breath waiting.

12

To beat global warming: things we have to know and things we have to do

WE must now recognize and appreciate two things; firstly, global warming can be stopped, and secondly, stopping global warming can be done at negligible cost. Our personal aims therefore, also become twofold: each of us must immediately commence doing those things that insure that our planetary overheating stops. And secondly we must convince others that the goal of restoring climatic stability is both possible and practical. We must in turn insure that everybody accepts his or her own measure of responsibility in being part of winning the battle against the cancer of global warming. We must ensure that everybody knows clearly how he or she can help.

The utterly inevitable alternative is a thousand years of never-ending world climatic change, a thousand years of utterly unpredictable weather: an incomprehensible future of endless supposedly natural disasters.

Restoring stability to our weather systems can only be accomplished by the will and determination of what must become an ever-growing number of thoughtful, responsible and decisive people. It is imperative we make those numbers grow fast.

I think most of us want to live in a safe, free and interesting society, a society in which opportunities to better oneself by supplying others in our society with cheaper and better goods and services is the natural order of things. I believe most of us want to live in, and be part, of a world civilization based on high levels of sustainable affluence.

Global warming and its consequential climate destabilization are threatening everything we aspire to and everything we hold dear. The resultant changes to world climates and weather patterns present the greatest threat civilized man has ever faced.   And it must be clearly understood that global warming also presents the greatest current threat to all our world's ecological systems.

Global warming and its resultant cancerous climate change are already causing devastation and havoc in places all across the world. No place is immune. Damage costs are already exceeding any cost benefit claimed for fossil fuel energy systems.

The paradigms of fossil fuel use, the reliance and apparent dependency on agricultural chemicals, and the almost universal structured aversion to anything nuclear are so pervasive, so all-embracing, they seem impossible to challenge.   But challenge them we will, and change them we must. Skeptics we must become. No longer can we tolerate our thin, vulnerable, almost negligible but very valuable atmosphere being used as a dumpsite for fossil fuel waste and the carbon dioxide spewing from the destruction of our world's soils.

It is now blatantly obvious. Global warming is caused by a net increase of greenhouse gases entering the atmosphere. Those gases come from us burning fossil fuels and us destroying soil fertility (see chapters 5 and 6).

Carbon dioxide levels in the atmosphere today now exceed 370 parts per million. For the previous few million years they were around 270 ppm. We have to get them back under 300 ppm to restabilize world weather.

The program to do so has two main thrusts. First, we modify our agricultural practices to increase soil fertility levels, instead of as now, decreasing them. This process will extract massive quantities of carbon dioxide out of the atmosphere and return levels to near normal. That could be achieved in little more than a decade. Secondly and concurrently, we must change our energy systems away from fossil fuels to other energy systems to prevent dangerously high levels of greenhouse gases from ever recurring.

If as individuals we do nothing but blindly put our faith in governments and their bureaucracies, it will never happen in time. And then, all too suddenly, it will be too late.   Constant climatic instability with all its deadly consequences will become irreversible. Institutions ignored by the people for too long can no longer be trusted. Our governments have been systematically manoeuvred to consistently comply with the requirements of cash-loaded fossil carbon interests. The big interests themselves are steered by their own internal, inherent self-interest and their own big money predilections. Unfortunately there is no concentrated big money interest in stabilizing world weather. There is thus no financial balance. Balance has therefore to come from people power actions. People power is millions of individuals creating a new political imperative.

We all vote and we have three ways we vote that affects our society. We vote at the ballot box, we vote with our wallets, and we vote with our voices, our pens and our protest. So individually we modify our buying patterns and make our wallets send the message. Simultaneously we harass our local members of parliament to move and manoeuvre in the way we demand. And so we change things and create systems and structures that insures global warming comes to a speedy end.

The concept is being vigorously promoted that it is indeed pointless, and therefore too disheartening for us to even attempt to combat global warming. The message is that the massive increases in fossil carbon use by China and India will make our comparatively minuscule efforts utterly irrelevant. Those two countries today are certainly becoming big consumers of fossil fuel, but they didn't create the global warming problems we now have. By consuming huge quantities of fossil carbon materials throughout the last half-century, we in the West created the problem. We are the biggest culprits. The 80 ppm of carbon dioxide in the air causing global warming has to be removed. Increasing soil organic matter content by enhancing soil fertility is the only viable mechanism for removal that we humans have. That trees could do it is a PR-fabricated fiction. We would need to plant about two trillion trees. World food production would have to totally end to make available the land needed to grow them.

Those responsible for putting the carbon dioxide in the air must be responsible for removing it. And of course that responsibility has to be apportioned justly.

This is what we do. Let's decide 1950 to 2000 as our half-century baseline period. Fortunately each individual country's use of fossil carbon materials in that period is well documented. *World Resources 2005: The Wealth of the Poor—Managing Ecosystems to Fight Poverty* is a publication produced by the World Resources Institute in collaboration with the United Nations Environment Programme, the United Nations Development Programme, and the World Bank. It contains all the relevant information from which it became possible to assess each country's specific contribution to the planetary predicament of global warming, or more benignly "climate change".

Each country must accept the responsibility of removing the carbon dioxide that it individually added to the atmosphere and this has been catalogued. In the Appendix (page 674) is a table listing each of the world's countries, along with their individual contribution to global warming. It's shown as a percentage. Next to it is shown the number of parts per million of carbon dioxide each country is obliged to remove. The agricultural land area, comprising both croplands and grazing lands available to sequester the CO_2, is then listed. Finally, the increase in soil organic matter needed in that land to honor the country's responsibility is listed, as the percentage point increase required. That increase in soil organic matter is required to a depth of 1 foot or 300 mm. That depth of soil weighs about 4,000 tonnes to the hectare, or 1,600 tons to the acre.

Carbon is slightly over half the weight of soil organic matter, and only a quarter of the weight of carbon dioxide. So, using ballpark approximations, we can halve the percentages if we're talking about pure carbon, and double them if we're talking about carbon dioxide.

Let's consider examples. In the last half-century India discharged into the air approximately 2.3% of the world's production of carbon dioxide from fossil fuel use for all transport, industry and cement production. The world's problem is 80 ppm too much carbon dioxide in the air, so India's responsibility is 2.3% of that, or approximately 2 ppm. Carbon dioxide from cement production is generally around 2 to 3% of a country's total carbon dioxide emissions. For India, cement production would contribute approximately one sixth of one part per million. Cement production we can tolerate until a substitute becomes available. The farming and pasturelands of India add up to 181 million hectares. So India has to increase the fertility in those soils by less than one percentage point to be totally innocent of any contribution to our current global warming mess.

Australia discharged 1.2% and is thus responsible for removing 1 ppm. China discharged only 9.2% so it must remove 7 ppm. United States discharged 27% so must remove its 22 ppm. Europe discharged a whopping 38% so must remove 30 ppm. Thus the United States and Europe will be obliged to enrich soils in other countries as well as their own to satisfy their international obligations.

Many affluent countries won't have enough land to sequester their accumulated apportionment so those countries must pay for and develop soil fertility in the countries that do have the land. As they're generally Third World countries, that also becomes the perfect aid package. It's totally fair and it's totally just, and we create a wonderful, fertile and healthy world. Then to keep it wonderful we simply stop mining fossil carbon material and in turn stop dumping the waste greenhouse gases produced direct into our vulnerable biosphere.

We can and must make nations accept their responsibilities and act on them. Apart from the obvious moral and ethical considerations, there can be other inducements. For example a country may have a valuable tourism trade, so let's not visit them, and tell them why. Tourism is big business and we are the tourists. We can make the tourist trade our own personal very big stick.

There will be a lot of opposition to doing what we must do. Power and very big money is involved. But no matter, individuals in concert can move mountains. You must never believe your effort and your voice and your vote can't amount to much, for you would be wrong. The writer Betty Reese gave us an apt quote: "If you think the efforts of one individual will be nothing, then you have never been in bed with a mosquito".

Once we appreciate what we need to do, start doing it and tell others how they can help. Things will then change. Climates will begin to stabilize. Sea levels will stop rising. Wild, freakish, unpredictable weather phenomena can stop being a constant expectation. And people will again take control over their destiny.

Preventing global warming is an immediate and absolute planetary necessity. Therefore we now must accept as irrelevant the myriads of inconsequential environmental issues out there, issues that cloud the all-pervading dangers of destabilizing the world's climate.

Energy supplies for transport, motor vehicles, ships and planes

When the car market is near saturation, as in most Western societies, how can an oil company sell more fuel? The obvious answer is to have the engines made bigger and the vehicles heavier. Then hopefully sell the concept of four driving wheels. Then sell this very enlarged, over-engined package as "increased safety". In addition bribe, coerce or inveigle legislators into tax breaks for such fuel-hungry vehicles. It's happened. A good example: in rural Australia where distances are great, one might presume gas-guzzlers would be a disincentive. So taxpayers are manipulated to fund tax breaks on country fuel consumption. And the automakers also love it!

We want self-contained motor transport, and self-contained systems need fuel they can carry on board. For that we have to select suitable non-fossil fuels. The only both excellent and viable choices are ethanol and biodiesel. Hydrogen is at best a vague and distant possibility. Hydrogen is too far down the track to be of any relevance whatever in stopping global warming. The "hydrogen economy" is a marketing gimmick designed to placate nontechnical but responsible citizens. It is also used to enthuse nontechnical antinuclear crusaders.

The absolute ideal motor vehicle design for the near future should have engines that run on either biodiesel or high ethanol blends. The perfect automobile is to be a hybrid using a flex-fuel engine—a hybrid being an internal combustion engine in combination with a battery electric drive. Both engines produce minimal to absolute zero net carbon dioxide emissions. Hybrid engines will also deliver exceptional miles per gallon. Hybrid cars are now on the market. Flex-fuels car have been on the market for a decade or more. Which company will be first with a flex-fuel hybrid? Whoever it is, support them. Support them by buying their cars and advocating others to buy their cars.

With those cars, if everybody on earth suddenly had a Western standard of living and drove cars the way we do in Western nations now, fuel supplies would not be a problem in any way, shape or form. Several tropical countries could individually grow enough sugar cane and produce enough ethanol to fuel every single one of them. Ethanol and biodiesel production has never been a problem and could never be. Every wet and warm country on the planet can become an energy supplier.

How do we force a rapid widespread change to ethanol and biodiesel? There are many things we can and must do.

Cancel biofuel restrictions

Every law that restricts the amount of ethanol in an automotive fuel must be cancelled immediately. Simply label the blend ratio and let us, the customers, decide what we want to buy.

Petrol and ethanol prices

Explain to people that to combat global warming, the price of petrol must be restructured and taxed so as to be always dearer than ethanol fuels at the pump.

The gasoline manufacturing process itself requires oil to run it, so with oil at say US$55/ €50 a barrel, gasoline's raw material costs hover around US$0.28 a litre or US$1.06 a U.S. gallon. (In the oil trade a barrel is taken as 42 U.S. gallons or 159 litres.) To those costs must be added manufacturing costs, shipping costs and the often numerous hidden subsidies the oil industries have acquired. Gasoline costs are therefore closer to US$0.40 per litre. To these also, and quite rightly, should be added the military costs incurred in defending the oil production and delivery structure. And we know by recent experience they can be considerable. This must be understood by all.

Ethanol costs are around US$0.25 to $0.35 per litre at the distillery. So people rightly ask, "Why isn't ethanol at every service station?"

One reason is that oil prices are too easily fluctuated so as to destroy any reasonable continuity in market supply and demand for ethanol. Start serious ethanol production and the oil producers simply fluctuate the world price of oil. They drop it for a few months and create huge cash flow problem for any ethanol industry startup, and in doing so they bankrupt them.

Private investment in large-scale ethanol production is too risky without our own governments intervening with suitable protective legislation. Protective legalization is necessary and is indeed perfectly justifiable. Individual businesses can't fight tightly structured foreign governments that control world markets. We must tell our government we want our vulnerability to nation-sized industrial sabotage to end. Global warming and good old horse sense must become the major factor in determining and insuring independent and assured fuel suppliers for our transport industries. Inform people of these realities. Oil producers have been holding us over their barrel for too long. Tell your government you want it to end.

Point our how the world price of oil never significantly exceeded $45/€45 a barrel for any length of time because oil producers know that much above that price, biofuels become competitive and a biofuel industry could become established. For the oil producers, the West is the goose that keeps laying the golden egg. Why would they spoil it?

The only possible exception is if they decide that biofuels are so inevitable that they might as well get as much money as they can before that inevitability becomes a reality.

What is biodiesel?

Most people, at least in my country, have no idea what biodiesel actually is. So tell them. Uninformed people cannot make wise decisions and global warming simply cannot be ignored. Explain that diesel engines can actually run on ordinary vegetable oil: canola oil, coconut oil, whatever. But refined diesel works better and biodiesel is better still. Explain that any vegetable oil (even used cooking oil) mixed with ethanol and warmed with caustic soda undergoes a chemical reaction. The two substances formed in the reaction are glycerol (ordinary glycerin) and a modified oil called biodiesel. Also, unlike petroleum-derived diesel, spills of biodiesel eventually completely biodegrade. (The *Exxon Valdez* spill would not have been a problem if the ship had been carrying biodiesel.) Glycerol, the byproduct in biodiesel production, is a valuable raw material in the plastics and pharmaceutical industries. Tell your friends.

Motorists to choose what fuel

As an immediate start, every service station should have ethanol blends available now. Biodiesel must rapidly follow and both fuels must be cheaper at the pump than straight petroleum fuels. At the very least, energy for energy, they must be no dearer. Then the decision will be ours. Then ask for biofuels every time you fill up. Convince your friends to do likewise. They live here too.

"No added ethanol" marketing signs

If at a service station you see a sign "boasting" no ethanol in their fuel, tell them you don't appreciate the anti-ethanol marketing campaign. Tell them to get rid of the sign or you won't be back.

Your existing vehicle

Check with the manufacturer: can your vehicle operate perfectly on ethanol blends, or for a diesel car, on biodiesel? If so, always demand these fuels when filling up. If your service station doesn't stock ethanol blends and biodiesel now, constant asking ensures they soon will. It can be the same at marinas. Make it happen by demonstrating how they can make you a happy and regular customer.

Diesel powered vehicles

For ease of mind check that the manufacturer's warranty covers biodiesel use. Almost invariably they do, as biodiesel is better for the engine. Then use it in your vehicle and start the halt on global warming. As an extra bonus your engine will last longer.

When your vehicle is not compatible

If the manufacturer says they didn't make your particular automobile ethanol-blend compatible, that's unfortunate. But you can still refuse to fill up at a service station that doesn't have ethanol blends available for others. When you get your next car you can then be assured there will be plenty of biofuel outlets.

Buying a new car

Before you buy a new car make sure it likes ethanol blends. Even better, go for flex-fuel engines that can operate on up to E85 (85% ethanol). Flex-fuel engines that can use E100 are only now becoming available and then only in Brazil. An E85 flex-fuel hybrid vehicle is close to perfect and at a negligible, if any, increase in initial cost. Fuel cost savings with hybrids more than compensate. Don't ever buy a car that isn't compatible with some measure of ethanol enrichment. If they are not immediately available, ask anyway. That way you'll get them thinking. That way you'll get their wheels moving.

High-powered cars

Some people like to drive big cars with big engines. That's fine, provided they run on biofuels. People driving big cars with big engines engineered solely for petroleum fuels are the oil industry's puppets. They are dancing exactly how the PR image builders planned. Make the change. Demand your new big V8 is tuned for ethanol. It can deliver more power and also shows the owner is no fool. Let's tax big petrol engines out of existence now.

Secondhand vehicles

Ask the dealer "will it run on ethanol blends?" Get a suitable warranty. Remember, in the very near future cars that can't use ethanol blends, or don't accept biodiesel, won't hold their price as easily as cars that can.

Outboard motors, mowers, tractors, aeroplanes

Demand they be ethanol compatible. Or if diesel, they must accept biodiesel. If enough of us demand these things, they will happen.

Race cars and race boats

If methanol based, get your sports organization to switch from toxic, corrosive, fossil-derived methanol, to safer noncorrosive, nontoxic, biologically

derived ethanol. This will also enhance the responsible image and community acceptance of your sport.

Biodiesel in commercial jet planes

Biodiesel can now be produced that can readily blend with Jet-A aviation
fuel. But the international treaty on zero taxes for aviation fuels effectively
guarantees fossil fuels be used in international air travel. That's madness.
That insane and poisonous treaty must be rescinded. Taxes should be
structured to ultimately eliminate petroleum fuel use from the air transport
industries, not encourage it. How this could be achieved needs some astute
thinking by wise and thoughtful people more familiar with the industry.
Somebody must do it. Can you?

Oil-powered ships

Most ships now have diesel engines. They are either internal combustion
engines or turbines. Either can operate perfectly well on biodiesel. When
you book a passage on a passenger liner or on a cruise liner, first ask if it
runs on biofuels. If not, think about a different holiday. Tell your friends to
do the same.

Nuclear-powered ships

Antinuclear activists have been loud in their condemnation of nuclear
powered ships. For example, New Zealand decided some time ago to not
let British or American nuclear-powered ships into its harbours. The New
Zealand Committee on Nuclear Propulsion, after careful deliberation and
after recognizing the thousands of safe ship-years already logged by nuclear-
powered vessels, finally concluded they were safe. They were then allowed
to berth in New Zealand ports. However the fossil fuel antinuclear lobby,
with their finely tuned and well-trained expertise, won the political battle.
The New Zealand Government chickened out politically and banned their
entry, but they are now removing their blinkers and relenting. Don't let your
government be so easily manipulated.

Nuclear-powered passenger liners would be safe but possibly not yet
sufficiently safe against hijackers. Book a holiday on the first nuclear-
powered cruise ship when they become utterly pointless to hijack. As soon
as nuclear energy becomes more generally accepted, such ships will most
certainly be developed.

Make petroleum fuels non-tax-deductible

All taxpayers are being made to pay for the results of climate change caused
by burning fossil fuels. Why? It should be paid by those using the fuel.
Currently, when burning fossil fuels in a business enterprise, the fuel cost

is tax deductible. Let's keep the business cost of ethanol and biodiesel a deductible expense, but not fossil fuels. Make sure your political representatives know that's what you want and why, and then demand action from them.

Subsidies and tariffs

Our world is at war with global warming and the world must win. To win, it is essential that biofuels must be kept more than competitive against petroleum-based fuels at the pump (or in Australia, the petrol browser). Remember, subsidies and taxes are legitimate weapons in time of war. So let's use them to beat global warming.

Our policy must always be to use inflated petroleum taxes to subsidize the change to biofuels. The oil lobby will try to promote this as an attack on "innocent motorists". Or they will suggest great harm to the national economy. They will probably recruit wilderness societies or biodiversity advocates and invent new causes. These tactics must be expected. Always dispute such manufactured fictions. We must no longer let the usual lies and half-truths sink the adoption of biofuels.

The world price of oil is generally manipulated to hover around US$45/€45 a barrel, never above for any extended period. So we simply play the game in reverse.

It would depend on individual countries and their ethanol production facilities, but let's take ethanol as viable to produce at US$0.35 a litre. Per barrel that's US$55 for finished bulk ethanol at the distillery.

Two possible systems: First, if the world price of oil is below, say $55 a barrel, then pay the ethanol producer the difference as a subsidy. If oil is $40 or $0.25 a litre it will be cheaper at the pump so pay the ethanol producer a subsidy of $15 dollars a barrel or $0.10 per litre for every litre sold.

If the world oil price is dropped to $10 a barrel, oil at the pump will be cheaper, so again pay the producer the difference, which would be $45 a barrel or $0.28 a litre.

Ultimately the price at the pump will be determined by the actual cost of ethanol, not some cynically manipulated world oil price.

Secondly: An alternative that governments would obviously prefer. Have the state collect an excise tax on imported oil so that the effective oil price landed and passed through customs is always US$55 a barrel. The tariff, excise or subsidy to producers could be based, for example, on world oil price averaged over the previous three months. If world oil prices are $40, the state charges $15 a barrel excise. If $30 they collect $25 a barrel. Changing to biofuels thus becomes self-funding.

If a country can't produce enough ethanol, or local production is inefficient, import it. If it is decided the local ethanol industry needs additional support, then support it the same as with any other local industry. But always keep oil more expensive, and for a long overdue change, make oil taxes pay alternative energy subsidies.

Some states tax automotive fuels at the final distribution point. This too is easy. Simply tax the petroleum content higher than the biofuel content. Always insure the petroleum option is noticeably more expensive.

The above are just some suggestions: Taxes, tariffs, excise, subsidies or whatever, one way or another, ethanol must always be made the cheaper fuel at the local service station for spark ignition engines and biodiesel must always be cheaper than petroleum diesel.

Ethanol not from sugar cane

Making ethanol from grains or sugar beet is generally more expensive than from sugar cane. But we want the ethanol. If it is deemed necessary to assist grain or beet producers, then pay them a subsidy.

But be aware. The preferred option of the oil and gas companies is to impose a surcharge, tax or excise on imported sugar or ethanol to "assist local grain ethanol production". This is what they always lobby for as such a surcharge always results in artificially forcing up local ethanol prices way above petroleum prices.

The final outcome being that total ethanol production will actually fall while politicians at the same time boast they are "subsidizing ethanol". Don't be fooled.

Long-term government commitment

Incentive systems and subsidization systems set up to encourage a change to biofuels must be long-term. When taxation laws are structurally changed with the aim of preventing global warming we must ensure that those laws are also long-term. Biofuel capital works have to be recouped over time.

In the past it has been a common manoeuvre by government bureau-cracies to create assistance and grant systems for the development of non-fossil-fuel initiatives. But it is also standard, sleight-of-hand practice to limit the duration of such assistance in manners that effectively nullify their meaningful implementation. Politicians have thus appeared to be concerned about global warming while concurrently acting in ways that worsen it. The reality being that they continue to comply with the dictates of the fossil fuel dollars.

Don't let them continue to get away with it. Look for it in their actions. Be ready to oppose all forms of such oil-inspired political and bureaucratic skulduggery.

Limited oil reserve fiction

A conviction is quietly promoted that global warming will self correct as the world will run out of oil some time in the near future. So why worry? That is what they want us to believe. Maybe in half a century or so we might indeed eventually run out, but that's not anywhere near soon enough. It can't happen in time to prevent world climatic havoc. It won't stop the damage, the deaths, and all the destruction.

There is so much oil out there that there's currently little enthusiasm for searching out new deposits. In addition, old, supposedly worn-out fields often contain several times previously extracted quantities. New techniques can get that oil out.

Everybody must appreciate that reliance on fossil fuels has to end and not because of any meaningful drop in supply. Not because we might run out of the stuff, but because the limiting factor is the vulnerability of the heat flow and optical characteristics of our atmosphere, and that limit has already been exceeded with expensive and escalating consequences.

Building Third World economies

The concept of solving tropical Third World countries' economic woes by having them grow sugar cane and oil palms to produce ethanol and biodiesel for world markets has tremendous promise. We can decide to buy our ethanol and biodiesel from any Third World country that is now a free democracy, or is moving towards being a free democracy. It will make for a safer and more prosperous world for all of us.

The now common African oil palm trees, *Elaeis guineensis*, are considered the most prolific producers of vegetable oil. The oil admirably suits biodiesel production. They are a tropical plant. The fruit of the oil palm can produce over 5 tons of oil per hectare. And that's equivalent to 5 tons or 5,000 litres of biodiesel per hectare, or over 500 U.S. gallons per acre.

Edible vegetable oil prices vary around US$0.55 per litre (US$2.00 per gallon), and sometimes higher. But as human consumption is not an issue, biodiesel-suitable oil can be produced for as low as US$0.30 per litre.

Glycerol is a fossil-carbon-free byproduct of biodiesel production and is a versatile raw material in the chemical industry. The two products mean biodiesel can be produced at costs similar to petroleum diesel. Therefore we should actively support a plastic industry based on glycerol. Give them a tax break, or what ever they want to make it happen. Ask them. Let them say what they want or need to economically switch to a planet-protecting raw material.

Biodiesel can become even more viable when oil-producing algae farms are guaranteed an assured market long-term. Algae oil production has the potential to lower biodiesel costs dramatically. Unfortunately preventing global warming can't wait. We will simply have to tolerate paying high subsidies to all biodiesel producers pending these hopefully inevitable developments. That way at least gets us the infrastructure in place and Third World countries on their feet and prospering.

Industrial energy and power generation

All nations aspire to the type of living standards current in the West, and they will eventually achieve those living standards. They will require a huge supply of energy, just as ours does. That new energy must not come from burning fossil fuels. That is just as important as recognizing that our energy must cease coming from fossil fuels.

We in the West use about the same quantity of fossil fuel to generate our electricity as we use to power our transport systems. We can easily grow all the sugar, grain and vegetable oils we need to power our transport systems. And they are safer and better fuels than those from petroleum. But like petroleum fuels, ethanol and vegetable oils are too expensive for generating industrial electric power. Natural gas produces about the same quantities of greenhouse gases as oil but is cheaper. Natural gas use is slightly limited by delivery difficulties and considerable dangers.

Basically we have to make the decision: it's nuclear energy or it's coal and gas. To prevent constantly accelerating climatic destabilization it has to be nuclear energy. For large-scale industrial power generation there is absolutely no other choice.

We all have to accept the realities of power generation. Dreamland science won't solve global warming. Reality just won't go away.

Conventional alternative energy is very limited

Explain to your friends the limitation on industrial energy production from solar, wind, wave, tidal, hydroelectric, geothermal and the other non-nuclear alternative energy concepts. Point out that all of them in total can only ever constitute a minor role in world industrial energy production, at least in developed nations. Energy use is expanding a hundredfold faster than alternative energy production. It is probable that low-cost solar-thermal power generation could be viable in developing countries, especially where electric grid systems are poor or simply don't exist.

Solar hot water heaters are great

In areas where energy is fossil fuel derived, solar hot-water systems must become the norm. We must make our legislators legislate to make that happen quickly. Arguments against such laws will undoubtedly germinate in the brains of the fossil fuel PR people. So be aware. Don't be fobbed off with carefully structured systems designed to sound good, but in reality be too hopelessly cumbersome and impractical for general acceptance. We don't want solar hot-water systems to be simply competitive. We want fossil fuel based hot-water systems to be hopelessly uncompetitive. Legislators, we are telling you: "Do it, make it happen".

Natural gas is no answer

Natural gas is not the "clean" fuel it's purported to be. In many ways natural gas is more dangerous and more damaging than oil. As a source of carbon dioxide, burning natural gas is only slightly better than burning oil. But because of unavoidable methane losses in transport and storage, natural gas can actually be worse than oil in generating greenhouse gases. It is promoted as "less polluting". Not so. Certainly it's free of some of oil's more obscure naturally occurring impurities such as sulphur, so acid rain effects are reduced. But that's it. For electricity generation, gas produces about the same quantities of greenhouse gases as does oil. (Although neither are as bad as coal.)

Don't believe the advertising, natural gas is in no way a safe and benign energy source. This manufactured fiction that natural gas is somehow safe has to be corrected. Natural gas is as bad in both power stations and automobiles as is oil and petrol. It is essential that this be understood and appreciated by all. The safety and environmental desirability of gas is a marketing gimmick. Make sure people recognize the ploy as just a simply, subtle and astute public relations image manipulation.

Nuclear energy must happen

There is nothing wrong with nuclear energy, as we saw in chapter 10.

Nuclear energy can replace fossil fuels easily, and thousands of people will live that fossil fuel use would have killed.

We all must appreciate that for years there has been a well planned and deliberate campaign to create an image in people's minds that nuclear energy is very much more dangerous than any other mass energy production systems in existence. That's rubbish. Make yourself aware of the true facts and tell others. Tell them how it happened. Tell them what Sir Fred Hoyle argued and remind people of its relevance in our current world. Point out how the Kremlin supported and funded the antinuclear movement and how this probably explains the extreme left-wing bias in these organizations. Talk about the sickening logic of an unholy alliance between the extreme left and big oil, on so many environmental platforms. Argue with those who constantly mouth antinuclear clichés. Don't let them get away with blatant lies and misrepresentations.

Explain that disposing of nuclear waste is far less hazardous than disposing of the hundreds of other industrial waste materials we handle every day. Point out that radioactivity wears out. Explain how if you dump equal quantities of radioactive waste every year at a site the radiation levels at the site will obviously increase, but after fifty years of continuous dumping the levels will reach a peak. From there on radiation levels will be dropping as fast as new materials are added. That means the same site can be used forever, or while there is room available. The site reaches a maximum radiation level and can't get worse. Radiation levels are always in constant decline. It is the nature of nuclear radiation. So eventually the radioactivity at the dumpsite declines as fast as new radioactive material is added. In total contrast, all non-nuclear dangerous materials simply accumulate endlessly, and stay dangerous forever.

Tell people how safe and sensible it is to exploit subduction zones for all forms of waste disposal, both nuclear and chemical.

The fiction of nuclear accident dangers

Many a bad bus crash has killed more than have died from all the world's nuclear accidents. Coal mines are infinitely worse killers than buses—killing people constantly. You can point out that coal mines in China kill 5,000 miners every year.

Tell people the truth about the world's three worst nuclear accidents and tell them how many died. Only Chernobyl would have rated a news story had they not involved nuclear facilities. These are the worst of all the so-called nuclear disasters.

1957. Sellafield-Windscale in the United Kingdom; no deaths.

1979. Three Mile Island in the United States; no deaths.

1986. Chernobyl in the former USSR; maximum 48 deaths.

The often-mentioned "estimated thousands of deaths from Chernobyl" is a total fiction. It's more than a fiction; it's a carefully structured lie. The United Nations Scientific Committee on the Effects of Atomic Radiation has been monitoring the accident and its effects continuously since 1986 and confirm the above numbers. Mention the thousands of deaths from petroleum fuels and coal and the almost forgotten Union Carbide chemical accident in 1984 at Bhopal, India. That death toll was 20,000 people. The toxic gas that killed everybody formed from the pesticide and herbicide raw materials held at the plant. Bhopal was worse than 500 Chernobyls and people are still dying from the Bhopal chemical spill. People forget what they are not deliberately reminded of. Chernobyl is constantly resurrected by the media. Bhopal almost never.

Nuclear radiation health benefits

Explain that people exposed to radiation up to a hundred times higher than normal background levels are healthier and live longer. They may not believe you, so tell them to check it out. Then they will know the facts and can decide for themselves. Explain that nuclear radiation is like sunshine. Many times more than we now generally receive is good for us, but way too much can kill. Also explain that people exposed to extreme levels can die within weeks, but if they survive the first month or so then complete recovery is nearly certain, and with no aftereffects whatever. The antinuclear lobby either simply do not have the facts, or they deliberately lie about radiation mortality and dangers. So you tell people the facts.

Many nuclear explosions

Few people are aware that we have exploded 2,000 nuclear devices on this planet to date. So remind them. Note that they were detonated in the atmosphere, on the land surface, on remote islands, underground and under the sea. Thirteen were exploded in space at a whole range of distances out from the earth. Man-made lakes have been produced using nuclear explosions. They are used for fishing and recreation, and they are safe. They are considered as health resorts.

In spite of the horrific images we associate with nuclear explosions, the physical world hasn't changed in any way for the worse because of them. Not one iota. The increase in background radiation over the planet is utterly negligible, yet those detonations were never "cleaned up". Neither was the waste from the explosions stored in glass or concrete, or steel drums, or buried in salt mines, as is mandated for nuclear power station waste.

Nuclear power reactors everywhere

People must become informed. People must be made aware that there are around 440 operating nuclear power stations generating electricity across the world. If we had just five times as many we could completely stop using fossil fuels to generate our electrical power. It's as simple as that. People don't know this, so tell them.

There are already 31 countries in the world that have operating nuclear power stations. There are about 60 nuclear power stations in France, over 100 in the United States. In Lithuania over 80% of the electricity generated in the country is nuclear. Some of the reactors in the former USSR are of the old Chernobyl design, but now they have the stupidity factors removed and they're OK. All later nuclear power plant designs now, and from anywhere, are extremely safe. So safe that even some near impossible, hypothetical meltdown in one would not be a particularly life-threatening accident to anybody. A nuclear power station cannot be turned into a nuclear bomb. Explain this to people. This sort of common sense information has to become more widely recognized. Tell people the facts; explain them. The never-ending flood of disinformation fuelled by the fossil fuel brokers has to be countered to stop global warming.

Nuclear reactors in hospitals

As an example of nuclear use tell people about the TRIGA isotope and research reactors described in chapter 10.

There are over 80 installed at universities and hospitals all over the United States. They are not only safe for use, but are routinely used by hospital staff and university students.

Reactors deep underground and buried

People should be aware of reactor design options. One system really worth knowing about is the concept for building automatic, self-limiting power reactors deep underground so they could be sealed off and left there indefinitely. It would be perfectly feasible and safe to install such reactors in an unfriendly or politically unstable country to supply the economy with reliable but militarily useless nuclear power.

The antinuclear movements

The whole antinuclear movement is in absolute compliance with the objectives of the oil and fossil fuel lobby. This may be an incredible coincidence or it may not be, but it is a very real fact of life. Ask your friends to start thinking and stop naïvely believing the propaganda.

The PR organizations heap upon us some imagined guilt of increasing radiation cancer risks to our distant descendants. Don't ever feel guilty. The best and safest thing we can do for our children and grandchildren and all our ongoing descendants is to responsibly embrace the concept of a totally nuclear-powered society. The future dangers they sell are fabricated fictions. That mankind faces a nuclear waste disposal problem is also a cruel and fabricated fiction. When the relatively minute quantities involved are taken into account, antinuclear waste disposal arguments are seen to be senseless, and all too often childish.

Today, if it so wishes, any country can build a nuclear reactor structured to produce weapons-grade materials. And we could be utterly unaware of such action. In the past, that has already happened in at least four countries. Yet having oil available to make weapons-grade chemicals should be much more frightening than having uranium available to do the same.

People need to start thinking these things through, so get them thinking. The generation of power by using nuclear energy is essential if we intend to stop global warming. Even a nuclear war wouldn't kill as many people as would die from limiting our reaction to global warming to a naïve compliance with Kyoto-type protocols (see chapter 10).

Bringing greenhouse carbon dioxide levels back to normal with soil

The answer is increase soil fertility

Explain to people that soil humus and soil organic matter is mainly decomposed plant life and is 58% carbon. Explain that the only source of carbon for life on the planet is the carbon dioxide in the air. All we have to do is turn atmospheric carbon dioxide into humus as cheaply and as efficiently as possible. We are then recreating soil fertility and there is nothing new or magic in that process. It's been happening naturally for billions of years. We just help the process instead of hindering it (see chapter 5).

It is simple and easy to increase the organic matter content of soil and so sequester carbon dioxide from the air. Our world's agricultural land areas are more than ample to return atmospheric carbon dioxide levels to normal. We have to raise the organic matter content of the world's soils we cultivate and manage by 1.6% and the greenhouse problems now destabilizing world climates and weather systems will vanish. That must happen now for very soon global warming will be irreversible and uncontrollable. But we can do it. If just the U.S. grain belt was somehow managed throughout the next decade to recreate deep soil with a 20% organic matter content, the carbon dioxide in the atmosphere of the entire world would be returned to a safe preindustrial era level. And global warming would be fixed.

Chemicals destroy fertility

We must all appreciate that the vast majority of agricultural chemicals kill soil biological activity. And that is exactly what we don't want. The majority of rural agricultural fertilizers break down soil humus and turn it into carbon dioxide. That must stop, so we buy farm products that are labelled "organic" (or Priority One if the term is adopted).

Irresponsibly restricting agricultural land area

There is an unpleasant and unsavoury motive behind the concept: agrochemical companies are convinced that enormous increases in the demand and use of agrochemicals will result from the spread of intensive agriculture. It is therefore smart for them to instill and support policies that minimize available agricultural land area. The creation of huge wilderness areas and enormous but mostly uninteresting national parks, and such similar concepts, ideally suit their agenda. For the agrochemical companies and their green supporters the ultimate dream is to have all food and farm produce grown in vast chemical vats. Sadly for the atmosphere, market acceptance of such hydroponically grown food is rapidly becoming established. That trend must stop.

A catchall phrase to promote the agricultural land minimization agenda is the beautifully marketable and convenient concept of labelling anything agricultural as a "threat to biodiversity". Not so. The catalogued figures show that the actual number of species lost over the last hundred years is almost infinitesimal. The so often claimed thousands of losses is a PR fiction (see Strategy 50). Remind people that the word *biodiversity* was not even in *Webster's Dictionary* of the English language prior to 1986. Now it is the chosen religious icon of most green movements and is the banner under which they claim over 90% of the planet as their "sole responsibility". This craved-after influence must shine as an emblem for the "power trippers" in the biodiversity industries.

When you next see land being confiscated on some green cause pretence, object to it. That would make *you* the one "saving the planet".

Fixing salinity and fixing soil erosion

Most people are utterly unaware of the causes of salinity. Explain how salinity problems result from monocropping, excessive use of water, agrochemicals and turning the soil. Explain how reversing these practices will rapidly fix salt problems at no cost (see in chapter 8).

Inform your friends that the best and assured defence against soil erosion is to create fertile soil. Point out that planting trees and scrubs has negligible erosion benefits. Even if planting worthless trees did work, one must ask, what ultimately would be the point? Increasing soil fertility on the other hand makes real sense.

Buy organic if available

Organic farm produce grows best in humus-rich fertile soil so, apart from minimizing agrochemical use, buying organic produce forces the farmer into developing the fertility of his soil. Some plants won't even grow in other than humus-rich soil. Increasing soil fertility thus becomes more profitable for farmers. Our job is simply to be a health conscious and responsible customer.

A "Priority One" logo

The organic label is excellent so always choose a product so labelled. However, "organic" covers too narrow a band. There are a whole range of products and processes where organic is not applicable. Without a label or logo it is more much difficult for us to manipulate the marketplace in the way needed to halt global warming. For goods and services that suit our purpose but where organic can't be used, I suggest we use Priority One (P1 or P.one) as our logo. Let's try it.

Various terms specific to global warming may develop over time, but for now adopting the logo Priority One would get things rolling.

When we select a product, a process or a service, that selection should be predicated to the prevention of global warming and should be labelled Priority One. On aluminium and other materials that require huge electricity inputs whose power source is non-fossil, they too should carry a Priority One logo. Aluminium saucepans and similar items made from these materials should also carry the logo. Motor vehicles that run on ethanol. Any of the range of hybrid vehicles now coming online. Solar hot-water systems. Nuclear power stations and high energy users that use their power, produce grown in soil where fertility levels are rising. All are Priority One in the prevention of global warming and climate change.

If you yourself produce goods or services that sequester carbon dioxide, or prevent its original formation for one reason or another, your product should be labelled Priority One. Be proud, do it now, advertise your reasons and confidently believe that responsible people will make responsible selections and buy your product, your process or your service.

A simple certification procedure will have to eventually come into being. Maybe you are in a club or organization that could help create a sensible and encouraging certification process? If so the whole world needs your help. Contact us through Keyline Publishing Co at Surfers Paradise, Australia.

Chemicals non-deductible

Ensure that your tax dollars don't fund chemically dependent agricultural practices. So contact your political representative and insist that the use of agrochemicals that destroy soil fertility must no longer be a tax deductible item. Let's get those taxation laws amended now.

No farm subsidies based on land area

This is surprisingly important. Insist that subsidies are to be paid on quantity of farm produce actually produced, and subsidies must never again be pegged to land areas. Explain why and how land area subsidies encourage excessive use of chemicals. To ensure that such changes happen quickly, have legislators modify subsidy systems so farmers are not only not penalized, but do better by adopting fertility-enhancing practices. After all, our food will be tastier and more nutritious. Also point out how easily such a change can be made. If you personally know somebody with any influence whatever in government, then do some lobbying (see chapter 6).

Save a tree fictions

Explain to your friends, explain to whoever will listen, that soil enrichment can entrap carbon dioxide quicker and more efficiently and at vastly less expense than by growing useless trees—useful trees maybe. Point out that only by harvesting useful trees containing useful wood are trees of any use in combating climate change. If the wood in a forest is not constantly harvested then a forest system is totally worthless in combating global warming. Explain why.

Forests don't produce usable oxygen

Explain how both a mature tree and an established forest breathes out as much carbon dioxide at night as it breathes in carbon dioxide during the day. It will also get worse, for with global warming temperature rises, forests are drying out and starting to burn. Getting the timber out before they burn is common-sense environmentalism.

Wood is beautiful

By using wood we create a carbon sink. We must champion the harvesting and use of wood from wherever it comes. If wood will do the job, then use it every time. Let people know you like wood and why they should too.

Clearing scrub and forests

Clearing and enriching the soil with grass and crop production is a net carbon dioxide entrapment process. Actively preventing the clearing of scrubland and so preventing the absorption of carbon dioxide into soil shows a cynical, or at best naïve, disregard for the planet's total environment. Recognize that the true motive, the behind-the-scenes motive for preventing land clearing to create grazing and general agricultural land, is to encourage more intensive chemical agriculture. And that is exactly what we don't want.

Fertilize with sewage

Remind people that human excreta, like any other animal excreta, is an excellent fertilizer. Point out that except in our Western chemical-agricultural systems, human waste has been used in the growing of food in every society and every civilization that has ever existed on the planet. Any possible impurities such as the mythical monster known as heavy metals or even pathogens are neutralized in fertile soil. It is simply the nature of fertile soil and the nature of the animals and people that evolved with it. Pathogens do not like fertile soil. They soon die. They survive best in stagnant infertile environments such as wetlands and polluted ponds. Raw sewage, no matter how contaminated with pathogens, will self sterilize as soil fertility levels climb. With the extra thousands of tons of humus, heavy metals will safely chelate onto the abundant humic acid molecules in the soil, just like salt.

If we aren't going to use sewage to fertilize edible crops then it should be used for growing nonedible crops, trees for timber, cotton for clothing, vegetable oils for biodiesel and especially sugar cane for ethanol production.

But let's stop wasting it. In a modern sewage plant we turn this excellent fertilizer into carbon dioxide and discharge it into the air. Anything left we bury deep, or we burn. Against the inevitable opposition of the agro-chemical industries, we must all support propositions that utilize any use of sewage that stops its rapid conversion to atmospheric carbon dioxide.

Combating myths and manipulated environmentalism

Manipulated biodiversity causes

Allow me to repeat and reiterate: global warming, with its consequential destabilization of world climates, is by far the biggest threat to biodiversity on the planet. Nothing else is remotely comparable. Too often, organizations that profess to be protecting some facet of biodiversity are forcing more global warming, forcing more cancerous climate change and guaranteeing less biodiversity.

They are indirectly, and hopefully inadvertently, supporting increased sales of oil, coal and gas. Too often that's been the way things have been systematically contrived.

If a "cause" results in more fossil fuel use, more intensive or more agrochemical-based agriculture, or the expansion of oil- or fossil-carbon-dependent products, think of the bottom line. Does it in any way contribute to fixing the atmosphere? If not, don't support it and don't trust it (see Strategy 50).

Manufacturing and reinventing wilderness

Remind your friends that modern man first appeared and began colonizing the whole planet around the middle of the last ice age. Over the tens of thousands of years of that colonizing process, man massively modified the environment and the ecology of every continent on earth. It was mostly done with fire. Our early ancestors were not particularly altruistic. To hunt down a meal they would happily burn a million acres. Some burning simply changed things to be more suitable for our species. Some burning made it worse.

It must be appreciated by all, that outside of the world's deserts of sand or ice, no pre-human wilderness exists anywhere on this planet. Protecting wilderness areas is fiction (see Strategy 50).

Environmental protection agencies don't

EPAs are supposedly set up to protect the environment. But their developed aim has become to acquire power, acquire undue influence and to protect themselves and their money supply. No EPA anywhere, in any country seems seriously concerned with global warming, and global warming is disrupting the environment of the whole planet. The oil industry is behind the scenes of too many green movements and EPAs. For them it pays to be.

With state and federal EPAs, it is now time for us to query: what part of our environment do their officers so selectively try to protect, and for whom? EPA officers, in the pursuit of usually illogical and unworthy aims, are granted excessive and unjustifiable power over ordinary citizens. And when you pause and observe, it becomes obvious that in too many cases their causes seem to be excessively in line with the dictates of the fossil fuel and petrochemical industries. EPAs impose restrictions that are all too often quite irrational. Global warming is the only extremely serious environmental issue facing life on this planet, yet it is rarely of interest to an Environmental Protection Agency anywhere. EPAs simply plug for huge budgets for never-ending, ongoing research into pointlessly ever-expanding wilderness grabs.

Unfortunately an EPA is too often the source of environmental advice to a government. The reality is, while most of their officers live in small private worlds of their own, they nevertheless wield immense bureaucratic power in pursuit of their all-too-irrelevant issues.

EPAs are just like most agricultural departments and have to be taken with the proverbial grain of salt. Both are excessively influenced by the tentacles of the fossil carbon lobbies. For example, the U.S. EPA lists compressed natural gas (CNG), liquefied petroleum gas (LPG), methane and propane as alternative fuels. With tiny exceptions, every one is derived from some fossil fuel deposit somewhere. Every one produces, at the very least, twice its own weight in greenhouse gases. Americans should therefore ask, whose environment is their EPA protecting? Australia is the same. Australia, for example lists hydrogen gas as an important fuel. It might just as well list Eveready batteries.

Nevertheless, there are people within these government organizations with clearer vision that see the real picture. Let's make their voices heard. Have them run our Environmental Protection Agencies but with the restoration of climate stability and the prevention of global warming as their prime objective. Even then we citizens will still need to monitor them to prevent their capture again by the fossil fuel lobby and their political hacks.

Australian inland rivers

Inland rivers in Australia illustrate how EPAs go wrong. Those rivers don't carry huge quantities of water except in flood times. There is a well-rehearsed movement to prevent the construction of farm dams and the use of the stored water for irrigation and soil development. The proclaimed motive is to "protect" these rivers, seemingly by keeping as much water as possible flowing out to sea. So ask, "Protect them from what?" There is only one utterly logical motive for this suddenly inspired cause of protecting Australia's inland rivers. That is to flush agrochemical-loaded farm runoff water out to sea. By world standards Australian rivers are more like creeks. Agrochemicals are building up in all of them and the buildup will eventually become obvious and ultimately hurt agrochemical sales. So specialized and well tutored green movements demand: keep the rivers flowing. The truth is, their aim is to keep the rivers flushing! We have to make people recognize this "cause" is the worst form of cynically distorted and manipulated environmentalism imaginable. It is not to protect the rivers. It is to protect agrochemical sales. See "The great Australian river scam" in Strategy 2.

Energy conservation fictions

It sounds good, but the reality is that turning off lights, turning down the heat, warming up the air conditioner, etc. etc. etc. only works for a short time. It ultimately becomes another chore, which, in general, we eventually ignore. Such things as improved insulation in buildings is a more sensible, more permanent approach than endless, tiresome personal self-regulation.

Of course only where the energy is fossil-fuel-derived is energy conservation actually relevant. If energy is not derived from fossil fuels then energy conservation becomes simply a cost consideration. And the truth is, the world is not in any way short of non-fossil-fuel-derived energy, and never will be.

Ultimately the most effective way of minimizing fossil-fuel-derived energy is by pricing such energy in tune with its grim cost reality. Yet incongruously, in almost all countries fossil fuel, the single most virulent producer of greenhouse gases is subsidized by the state by using taxes collected from its citizens. That's worse than blind madness, for it's carefully planned and deliberately structured madness. We must stop insane subsidies of that nature and replace them with punitive carbon taxes and fossil fuel excises. The aim must be to consistently and systematically tax fossil fuels out of existence (see Strategy 19).

The Kyoto Protocol and similar myths

The Kyoto Protocol is another fairy story. Ratify it or don't ratify it, it means nothing. The Kyoto Protocol was, or might just as well have been written by the oil and gas industries. For them it was perfect. It has now come into being (February 2005) and is being publicized as a great environmental coup. People are encouraged to feel warm and fuzzy, but oil and gas will continue to flow in ever-increasing quantities, and in more and more countries. For the oil producers it is perfect. For example: Russia is now a major supplier of the world's oil needs. Russia signed up and made that idiotic protocol legal and binding. In doing so Russia absolutely guaranteed itself an ever-expanding market for its huge oil reserves (see Strategy 1).

Bicycles are unrealistic

Bicycles are publicized and heavily promoted by some as the green answer to transport. That's rubbish. The car and oil companies support the concept because it makes them look responsible, yet both know bicycles can never be a serious threat to either. Like it or not, modern Western cities have been built to suit the automobile. In them, automobiles will always be preferred. In cities where a bicycle works best, a motorbike or motor scooter works better. My city has most of its roads plastered with paint stripes to create dedicated bikeways. They cause massive traffic problems but haven't increased the number of bicycles in use. The massive sprawl of dedicated bikeways remain empty.

There are a few situations where dedicated bikeways are certainly worthwhile, for instance near schools when the school day begins and finishes. But these are exceptions. Generally the cost of the delays and the irritation to the travelling public of these incredibly expensive public relations extravagances is enormous. Have the courage to criticize such hypocrisy. Traffic idling for hours in jams and snarls is a gas-guzzling climate change monster.

Recycling has varied worths

While recycling industrial materials is obviously a sensible option, in general it has negligible impact on total atmospheric greenhouse gas levels. Some recycling processes can actually be a net producer of greenhouse gases. (Recycling non-carbon based materials, such as metals, is a wholly separate and often a very worthwhile process.)

Paper is one of our major waste products. It should be either recycled back as reconstituted paper, or simply burnt as fuel. Either way carbon is not added to the biosphere, so global warming effects are minimal. Burning paper to avoid burning a fossil carbon fuel is probably the best paper recycling scenario. Alternatively, waste paper can be mulched and mixed in topsoil, but generally there is just too much waste paper being produced for this option to make much sense. The worst option is to bury the paper in landfills. Paper in landfills decomposes anaerobically into methane, as do nearly all biologically based materials starved of oxygen. The methane gas seeps into the air, and methane is a greenhouse gas twenty times worse than carbon dioxide.

Often recycling is undertaken to prevent excessive accumulation of toxic chemicals and metals. This too is obviously a sensible option but has a negligible global warming impact. Recycling benefits are possibly overemphasized in relation to global warming. This should be watched in education curriculums where global warming is often systematically de-emphasized.

A more sensible and widely supported concept first recognizes that about three-quarters of household garbage is paper and biological materials, food and lawn clippings etc. It then recognizes that these materials can all be happily digested by earthworms. An earthworm can easily eat its own weight every two days. What's left is simply screened off and consists mainly of now fairly clean glass, plastic and metal. All are easily separated for recycling. The worm casts are fabulously rich natural fertilizer. They can be spread on farmland in absolutely any quantity. Chemical fertilizer companies hate the concept and hate any publicity it might receive. It's called vermicomposting. We should embrace and subsidize it. Vermicomposting is a very significant carbon-sequestration and fertility-enhancing process and could easily handle the huge volumes of garbage produced by the largest of cities. We should make vermicomposting of city waste become the standard treatment process.

Natural fibres feel good

It makes sense to use natural fibres if a choice is available. However, woven plastic fibres are not produced in sufficient quantity to seriously affect global warming. Plastic materials are now produced in bewildering varieties and for an incredible range of applications. The plastics industries are not the immense producers of greenhouse gases as is often suggested. Campaigns to ban carry bags at supermarkets, successful or otherwise, will have negligible effects on global warming. Driving to the supermarket uses gallons of petrol. A carry bag might be made from a teaspoon of oil, yet carry bags are hammered as some big environmental issue. Always consider the oil industries' sales assessment of relative importance when you do your own assessing. A can of oil can make either a can of petrol or a can of plastics. An awful lot of useful goods can be made from one can full of raw plastic, whereas the petrol is burnt in a few minutes.

Rethinking asbestos

What is the true story on asbestos? We all "know" the horror story, and we are all ingrained with fear of its use anywhere, any time. But is there more to the story? Could there be ulterior motives and well-structured fiction involved? Is it possible that the asbestos story is not quite that simple? Did asbestos get the antinuclear energy treatment?

The currently mined type of asbestos is as safe as any of its substitutes. It is also much stronger and more reliable. The switch from better-quality asbestos cement building materials to plastic-reinforced cement products might just have been a petrochemical industry master stroke. The money involved is massive. Asbestos fibre substitutes in every fibre cement sheet made today use large quantities of fossil fuels in their production. Asbestos uses none. Asbestos comes out of the ground ready made.

Switching from using virtually heatproof asbestos in brake pads in the family car to far less safe alternatives should never have been permitted. People should be made aware of who benefits from the demise of asbestos. It's a lesson all who understand the dangers of global warming should think about. Like many things in the environmental and green crusades, we need to keep an open mind on asbestos (see Strategy 41).

Carbon sequestration fictions

To continue to dig up and sell oil, gas and coal, it is smart policy to have people think it likely that the carbon dioxide produced can be simultaneously pumped back into the ground. The concept is utterly ridiculous. The costs would be astronomical and the storage risks would make storing nuclear waste look like a weekend picnic. Also the concept of pumping enormous quantities of carbon dioxide down into deep oceans has some terrifying possible consequences. Absolutely huge amounts of our tax money is being wasted on these oil/coal/gas inspired PR extravaganzas.

To illustrate how ludicrous the concept is of the mechanical sequestration of carbon dioxide, point out to people that a power station sufficient to supply a modern city of one million people requires two long trainloads of coal each week to fuel it. Let's presume it is somehow possible to collect, and freeze into dry ice, all the carbon dioxide produced at the power station. Our power station then has to ship back out the back door those same long trainloads, now somehow filled with dry ice, and do it every single day. Not just twice a week. Then we point out that the dry ice has to be dumped into some absolutely safe, airtight underground hole three times as big as the mine tunnel or open cut that the original coal came from. It's crazy.

Immediately, electricity from burning coal would be a dozen times more expensive. Peanut butter would be a more logical fuel, and it's a biofuel. Coal and sequestration would be more expensive than even the dearest nuclear energy, and that's with nuclear energy waste disposal costs assessed at the most hopelessly exaggerated cost imaginable.

Similarly, an oil well wouldn't accept back even half the carbon dioxide that burning the extracted oil would produce. Petrol would suddenly cost three times as much as ethanol. The futility of carbon sequestration, other than by the creation of fertile soil, is considered in detail in Strategy 21.

It is already appreciated, by those that seriously do the sums, that alternative fuel costs are far lower than the cost of burning fossil fuels and then somehow sequestering the resulting carbon dioxide. And that's by using the very best of the hypothetical sequestration concepts bandied around. Sequestration arguments can confuse because on face value the basic arguments sound logical. The problem is just that the practicality and fundamental economics are insane. Yet the United States and Australia are both allocating incredible sums to research on carbon dioxide sequestration. It will get nowhere. It will dangerously placate fears of global warming for those unaware of the futility of the exercise. Carbon sequestration is being made the carrot on a stick to a blinkered donkey. Let's not be the donkeys; throw away the blinkers.

Blowout in insurance costs

We must tell people of the rapidly escalating costs of weather-related insurance. Insurance bodies are telling us that weather-related costs are rising at 10% per year. Arithmetic therefore shows they will double every seven and a half years. It seems many of us will live to see climate-change-related damage costs eventually exceed world GDP, as has been predicted. Today, already many homes and buildings are becoming uninsurable. In a free enterprise system, capital assets are an important means of securing borrowings needed to generate wealth. An uninsurable asset thus becomes a financial millstone around one's neck. In consequence the gross national wealth is decreased. As always, everybody pays, so let's all draw the line. Global warming has to stop now.

Hammer talkback radio

Get the message across on how simple it is to prevent global warming. Whenever you hear pseudo-environmental arguments being expounded, phone in. Don't let them get away with environmental fictions structured to sell fossil fuels and petrochemicals.

Counter blatant TV bias

When you see TV productions that are subtly or blatantly biased against alternative energy such as "wind turbines might kill endangered birds", phone in, write in, complain. Remember the quote? Let's try being the mosquito!

Letters to the editor

Write in. This can help, though letters are always vetted and all too often to the advantage of the fossil fuel advertisers. However keep trying. Good ones will get through. Always write in when you see environmental issues being pushed that either sell oil or hinder and delay alternative energy systems from implementation. Don't let them get away with it. Continue to demonstrate you want practical action on global warming, not platitudes.

We should keep substantial oil reserves

We can't let running out of oil ever happen even if it sounds like a good thing. For future generations it is imperative that we keep massive reserves available. At some time, some unforetold astronomical event, or some unsuspected geological occurrence might tweak the atmosphere towards generating a freakish world cold. It has happened at least a couple of times before in our Earth's long history; our planet completely froze over. It's called the Snowball Earth phenomenon. The Snowball Earth effect is much more sensational than a simple ice age.

During a Snowball Earth cycle information suggests the world freezes over in maybe a thousand years. Average world temperatures then plummet to $-50°C$ and Earth's temperatures are as cold as those on Mars at midnight. The extreme cold apparently lasts a few million years. Ultimately ongoing volcanic activity means carbon dioxide levels rise unchecked by biological sequestration. A critical point is reached and the ice starts a rapid melt. The Earth thaws out in as little as hundred years and world temperatures rapidly soar from an average $-50°C$ to an average of $+50°C$ ($-60°F$ to $+120°F$; see chapter 1).

Whenever and for whatever reason, if something like global freezing ever got started we now know how to stop it. We could deliberately generate controlled global warming. We already know how to, and we know it works, for that's what we are doing right now and have been doing for the last seven decades, without realizing the heating consequences.

So humans must have readily available fossil fuels to switch to and to use for however many decades it takes to prevent some such deadly creeping catastrophic ice age from happening. We must keep the oil we have left. Fossil fuel reserves may be humanity's only life raft if something like that ever got started.

What research and development should we fund?

We are spending vast sums on research about global warming. Politically this looks good. The money usually goes to a variety of universities where professors and students dream up research projects for their doctorate degrees. Fixing global warming for them is not the issue. For them, writing reports, studying statistics and dreaming up projects that qualify for even more funding are the important things at issue. That's how universities work. We don't need further research to prevent global warming. We simply need to stop it, and to stop it what we need is personal determination and political will.

If they are going to spend our money on global warming research then let's spell out what could be, and what couldn't be useful.

In this we are only considering what governments have collected from us in taxes and how any research money should be spent to stop global warming. In general, private or industrial funded research is their own business as it's their own money. However private research that contributes to the prevention of global warming should be assisted by our tax money as such funding is usually less wasteful than government organizations.

Research and development is fine, but no new R&D breakthroughs are necessary to halt and correct global warming. The claim that more R&D is essential is an oil PR delaying tactic.

In the following, global warming research and development has been given a Yes or No; we spend money on it or we don't. The requirement is that we do not squander our research dollars on pointless and irrelevant concepts.

Research and development for the transport sector

Automotive power systems? No.

Automobile companies, aircraft companies and ship builders handle engine design better.

Ethanol? Yes.

We would like research undertaken to develop biological processes for turning cellulose type material (like grass) into ethanol fuel. Producing ethanol automotive fuel from the fermentation of sugars and starches works well and will do us for now, but other processes that might ultimately prove better or cheaper, or use more easily grown raw materials should be researched, investigated and developed. Ethanol made by the acid hydrolysis of cellulose matter with bacterial fermentation, is one example.

Biodiesel? Yes.

Biodiesel is manufactured from ethanol and vegetable oil. A better oil-producing plant, either a new type or an existing plant selectively bred for higher oil yields would be good. Plants could probably be genetically modified for massive oil production. Remember however that the oil public relations people will try to hinder such research and development. They might enlist and fund the anti-GM groups if plants showed promise.

Some types of algae are efficient at producing suitable oil. These should be studied and developed and promoted. The oil need not be palatable. It is not for eating. It's simply a biological solar energy collecting process that we wish to improve.

Biodiesel for jet turbines? Yes.

We need official research done quickly to ensure rapid approval and authorization to have biodiesel or biodiesel blends authorized for commercial use. Oil companies won't like this and aeroplane engine makers are in no hurry, so in this the use of government research agencies is therefore necessary. It will also totally confirm the safety and reliability of biodiesel fuels in ground-based gas turbines. (The term *gas* refers to burnt gases spinning the turbines, and not the fuel itself. Steam turbines, by comparison, are driven by steam.)

Hydrogen storage? Yes.

Hydrogen gas is a good energy holding material. Hydrogen is not an energy source. Hydrogen has to be manufactured by using an energy source. One problem with hydrogen is that there is no way yet discovered to economically contain the substance. It either has to be stored at extremely low cryogenic temperatures, or has to be stored at extremely high pressures in heavy metal bottles—like the familiar oxygen bottles used with oxyacetylene torches. The problem is that such bottles can hold only relatively tiny quantities of gas. Also, over time hydrogen gas will leak out through the microscopic pathways within the actual metal. A viable, practical, inexpensive and safe system for holding hydrogen gas has yet to be invented. It is worth spending money on dreaming up and producing such a system, but it is almost certainly a long way off.

Hydrogen production? No.

A bottle of hydrogen is in essence a car battery or torch battery. The chemical energy within the hydrogen gets used up and the battery has to be recharged. Hydrogen gas has to be manufactured and the manufacturing process consumes more energy than you can get back out. If hydrogen gas was produced from electricity from a nuclear power station (or any power station for that matter) its base energy cost, with no production charges, would be the equivalent of oil at over $100 a barrel. Hydrogen would be three, four or more times the price of ethanol or biodiesel.

However, practical hydrogen storage is a problem worth researching by government. More efficient production of hydrogen is not. That would be no more than a nicety. Industry can handle such problems easily.

Fuel cells? No.

Industry can and is handling their development. They will be available for motor transport if and when hydrogen becomes safe, practical and economical to store and use. It must be understood that despite all the orchestrated hype and publicity, practical, efficient, high-output and vaguely reliable fuel cells that could run a family car simply don't exist and never have. Fuel cells are like the myth of the perpetual motion machines and like them have been around for a long time. Remind people that fuel cells are not only not new, but have been around already for seventy years. See in chapter 11, section 16: "Fuel cells and the hydrogen economy concept".

Liquid fuel from coal or gas? No.

This is a total and absolute waste. It is designed to consume research dollars that might be spent on more important non-fossil-fuel concepts. If such fuels were ever produced such an energy would be far worse a greenhouse gas producer than even the worst and dirtiest coal-fired power station now existing.

Research and development for the power generation sector

Hot fusion? No.

As a consumer of research funding, hot fusion concepts are a bottomless pit constantly gobbling billions. In addition, and contrary to what is advertised, hot fusion would produce nuclear and chemical waste much the same as our current nuclear fission energy systems. (But also, like current nuclear systems, the waste would not be a serious problem.) So despite all the inferred claims, appreciate and remember that hot fusion is not a magical waste-free process. The antinuclear, antiproliferation enthusiasts should pause for a second and try to imagine the consequences of some new, cheap, incredibly deadly but compact hydrogen bomb concept being developed as a result of fusion energy research.

For somebody in the fossil fuel industry, hot fusion is absolutely and undoubtedly the safest place for governments to waste alternative energy research money, and at the same time still have their government looking responsible.

Cold fusion? Yes.

Cold fusion and the latest possibility, sonofusion, might be long-term gambles and possibly of dubious merit, but if some cold fusion process could be made to work, it would be the greatest energy discovery ever. The money needed to fund cold fusion research is minuscule by any other nuclear energy comparison so we should let cold fusion researchers have their heads. Success would be like a monster lottery win.

Cold fusion must really scare the fossil fuel conglomerates. So cold fusion, if ever mentioned, seems always to be consistently ridiculed in the media.

Totally safe, utterly rogue-proof, politically correct nuclear reactors? Yes.

Sadly this is probably a necessary public relations exercise to hopefully satisfy the extreme antinuclear proponents. It does however fill a need where totalitarian regimes demand a right to use nuclear power simply as a cover for weapons development. We already have simple, robust designs that have stood the test of time. This research would be to merely provide designs for extreme situations and also uncompromising critics.

It is not at all difficult to build a totally safe, completely self-regulating, totally automatic nuclear reactor. A reactor built so that even if it broke down it could simply be abandoned and left where it was; a reactor that would be utterly useless to nuclear weapons-minded rogue governments or terrorists. A nuclear reactor that would never be worth digging up or maybe built so that it's too risky to try. Something that would be useless to anybody, even if they tried. Inaccessible nuclear reactors, buried a thousand feet or more underground could power any First World, Second World or Third World city and we need never worry if in the future some rogue governments or gangsters took the place over.

We should get reactors like that onto the market, post-haste. My government and your government should place orders for some now. We don't want manipulated delays. We want them coming off production lines ASAP.

Heat and energy storage? Yes.

This is an important problem to be solved in our energy future. It needs a lot of lateral thinking and clever innovation. The costs of wind energy and solar energy (both photovoltaic and solar thermal) will continue to gradually drop, but probably not dramatically. Neither will they ever be much less than twice the cost of efficient nuclear power systems. Photovoltaics will continue to be impractical as a high energy source for many years, possibly for ever. Wind and solar thermal have a big application in developing countries, especially those lacking an efficient and comprehensive grid system.

The problem is storing power to cover breaks in supply. The sun goes down or the wind stops. Wind energy can only be stored as electricity or pumped elevated water. Solar thermal energy can use both these and also stored heat. But neither is really good enough to power well-developed nations. The development of practical and economical systems for energy storage is desirable to give a broader spread of energy delivery and allow for inevitable demand fluctuations for such alternative energy systems. For the millions in developing countries, solving energy storage problems will ultimately be essential for twenty-four-hour delivery.

The hydrogen economy fiction? No.

The hydrogen economy is a money-hungry fairyland. The whole concept is a manufactured myth and has to be recognized as such. Hydrogen fusion and hydrogen fuel cells are grouped together as an energy system panacea. It's a piece of PR sleight of hand, for without a reasonable understanding of both the physics and the economics, both concepts are confusing and tricky to assess. It's a house of cards structure, designed to give a consoling promise of some hypothetical dream solution to both global warming and world energy supply. It's an irrational dream. Safe and viable hydrogen fusion is a marketing fiction supported only by the fossil fuel lobby and the selected academics happily playing forever with the incredibly expensive toys we buy them.

Also having hydrogen gas promoted as the safe motor fuel for the future is in effect the same as arguing that batteries are the energy for the future. The mythical hydrogen economy dream is based on fusion energy and fuel cells. Today, and at least for any immediate future, both are PR fictions.

Carbon dioxide sequestration? No.

Harry Potter science is closer to reality than carbon dioxide sequestration into storage chambers or hypothetical geological structures. Such concepts are just feel-good PR creations. Wasting vast sums of money on such research must stop now. Let's be logical. Carbon dioxide disposal is an integral part of the cost of using fossil fuels so the fossil fuel industries themselves should finance any such experiments. That's even in the unlikely event that they seriously believe it to be viable.

Subduction zones for nuclear waste? Yes.

Subduction zones subduct. They draw in or suck in whatever falls into them. Anything dropped in will subduct to effectively vanish forever. The only research really of interest is which zone might be more effective or more convenient in subducting the waste. By comparison with almost any human waste issue, nuclear waste disposal is a very tiny problem and huge subduction trenches occur all over the world solve it. Almost all would be excellent nuclear waste disposal sites.

As all will be targeted by the antinuclear movement, so the better ones might as well be researched to forestall theosophical and other arguments. (But not as a delaying tactic.)

Is it safe? Utterly. Only in tens of million of years is it even theoretically possible for the waste to re-emerge in the earth's upper mantle. It has then to get up through the mantle to the actual surface. Naturally, after a few million years the waste is not only no longer radioactive, but being semi-liquid for millions of years is mixed in the billions of tons of surrounding molten magmatic soup.

Non-subduction nuclear waste disposal research? Yes.

It may be more convenient and less expensive to dispose of nuclear waste nearer home. Such research will also demonstrate how easy and safe are the many varieties of nuclear waste disposal systems already available. It might even convince the skeptics that nuclear waste disposal is in reality not a problem.

The supposition that waste buried in deep holes might get into groundwater and travel to distant places while it is still radioactive to any hazardous degree is nonsense. Even in sand, groundwater moves sideways at surprisingly slow rates. In most other geological materials, speeds are in metres per thousand years. Research is necessary for selecting sites where groundwater movement is negligible to the degree where even remote risks become obtuse hypotheticals.

A summation of energy and agricultural costs, consequences, benefits and bonuses

Anthropogenic greenhouse gases in the main come from three things: soil deterioration, power generation, and transport vehicles. The costs here considered are simply the short term, accounting style costs. It must be appreciated that the real costs of not rapidly moving away from fossil carbon fuels and products and chemically based agriculture will mount rapidly, until catastrophic climate changes become unstoppable at any price.

Agriculture

Increasing the fertility of soil reverses the discharge process and so removes carbon dioxide from the atmosphere. Growing agricultural produce by concurrently enhancing soil fertility is no more expensive than spending sums on agrochemicals that destroy soil fertility. So the agricultural changes and costs necessary to stop and correct global warming are minor.

We must consciously discount the lobbying and the politics that infers otherwise, and we must stop the insidious educational bias that teaches our children such falsehoods.

We must fully appreciate that the fertility of our soils can easily be re-established to at least their former levels, it can be done quickly and there are wonderful bonuses and benefits.

1 Removing the existing excess carbon dioxide from the atmosphere and ending its input from soil fertility decline is the big bonus. In so doing we are returning our planet and our weather to normal.

2 There will be a profound and wonderful change in the nature of our food. It will taste better. It will be more nutritious. It will make us all healthier and give us all a longer life.

3 The salinity problems we have inadvertently created all round the world, will be solved and the damaged land returned to healthy productivity.

Power generation

We can eliminate all gas, coal and oil power generation by simply building, over the next twenty years, five times as many nuclear power stations as we now have on the planet. Many would be no more than replacing old worn-out coal units that fall due for replacement. The rest are new power stations that will be required anyway.

These new power stations would effectively end carbon dioxide and related greenhouse gases produced by electric power generation from ever again distorting our atmosphere.

Only because fossil fuel systems are permitted free-to-air disposal of their main waste products, on average, are mining, power generation and waste disposal costs for nuclear energy about the same as for fossil fuel systems. Total extra cost of the change is therefore negligible.

4 The big bonus for power systems is that we eliminate the first half of all anthropogenic greenhouse gases entering the atmosphere.

5 We eliminate mercury and all the other chemicals contained in coal from the food chain. Ocean fish become safe to eat again. We also end acid rain and all its nasty consequences.

Transport

Ethanol replaces gasoline/petrol: Presuming world oil prices at around $40 a barrel, ethanol will wholesale about five to ten cents a litre more than petrol on an equal energy basis. Much above $45/€45 a barrel and ethanol becomes cheaper.

Biodiesel replaces diesel: Biodiesel's wholesale price will partially depend on utilizing the glycerol by-product. Initially biodiesel should wholesale about the same as petroleum diesel, again presuming oil at around $45 a barrel. Biodiesel could increase in price a little but only if glycerol demand can't keep ahead of the increased supply. Crude palm oil typically wholesales for around US$275 to US$325 per tonne. That's about US$0.27 per litre. That would make biodiesel wholesale at around US$0.35 per litre.

Switching to straight ethanol and biodiesel would add, at most, between 5 and 15 cents U.S. more per litre, or between 18 and 56 cents per U.S. gallon, all taxes omitted. This is again based on a $40 a barrel oil price. At anything much over about $45 a barrel, both biofuels start to become cheaper than petroleum fuels.

6 We eliminate the other half of anthropogenic greenhouse gases entering the atmosphere.

7 We create a huge farming and fuel industry for Third World tropical countries. The oil rich countries have had an income bonanza for years and should by now be industrially healthy and self-sufficient. It's now somebody else's turn.

The wealth of the fossil carbon industries insures that vast sums of money are always allocated, and immense social and political leverage is always applied to fashion public opinion in their favour. Money is used to influence federal and state legislators to achieve these aims.

The fossil carbon industries and the agrochemical industries are in the business of selling their products. Their actions are therefore frighteningly understandable. Whether their advertising campaigns and lobbying activities, and whether their effects on both legislators and the general public is conspiratorial, or simply (for them) fortuitous randomness can be debated. The end result however is exactly the same. That end result is increasing global warming. It is ever-worsening world weather with escalating violence and instability. Let's get our priorities right, these things must now stop.

If enough of us do just some of things advocated in this book, if enough of us convince others to do the same, we will be on a new road, a new pathway, a highway to the prevention of climate destabilization and global warming. At the end of the journey we will have recreated a more stable and much safer and more friendly Earth.

So hopefully now this is not The End, it is *The Beginning...*

Appendix: apportioning the responsibility for global warming

The following table shows the increases in organic matter required to reduce atmospheric carbon dioxide levels to the magic "two nines" (299 ppm) where the problems of global warming and climate change end. Atmospheric carbon dioxide used to be 280 ppm. It's now climbing past 380 ppm.

The measure of a country's obligation must be determined by how much carbon it is responsible for extracting from deep within the Earth and adding it to the planet's biosphere. It is imperative that every country must cease consuming fossil-carbon-based materials and adding more carbon to the biosphere. However, our immediate global warming problems are caused by the carbon dioxide that is there now, and that quantity of carbon we are stuck with. So our immediate and urgent requirement is to realign the proportions of carbon within the biosphere. Atmospheric carbon must become soil organic carbon. We have no other option. Each country must accept its individual responsibility and make that realignment happen.

The Two Nines Table—299 ppm

% contrib. = country's percentage contribution to global warming through fossil fuel consumption, 1950–2000

ppm = country's contribution to global warming in parts per million of atmospheric carbon dioxide

land = crop and pasture land available to fix global warming, in millions of hectares (1 hectare = about 2.5 acres)

OM = organic matter percentage point rise, in the top 12 inches of the country's crop and pasture land, to end global warming

Country	% contrib.	ppm	land	OM
World	**100**	**80**	**5096**	**1.6***
Europe	37.4	30	474	5.9
Albania	0.02	0	1.12	1.5
Austria	0.32	0	3.39	7.0
Belarus	0.43	0	8.92	3.6
Belgium	0.72	0	1.54	35
Bosnia	0.08	0	2.10	2.8
Bulgaria	0.36	0	5.31	5
Croatia	0.09	0	3.13	2.25
Czechoslovakia	0.86	1	4.33	15
Denmark	0.32	0	2.67	8.9
Estonia	0.11	0	0.72	11
Finland	0.26	0	2.13	9
France	2.38	2	29.7	6
Germany	6.01	5	16.75	27
Greece	0.27	0	8.51	2.35
Hungary	0.39	0	5.89	4.9
Iceland	0.01	0	2.31	0.34
Ireland	0.15	0	4.41	2.6
Italy	1.87	1	15.6	9.0
Latvia	0.06	0	2.48	1.9
Lithuania	0.1	0	3.50	2.0
Macedonia	0.05	0	1.25	2.8
Moldova	0.08	0	2.53	2.4
Netherlands	0.82	1	1.97	31
Norway	0.15	0	1.23	9.4
Poland	2.0	2	18.1	8.4
Portugal	0.16	0	4.21	2.9
Romania	0.75	1	14.7	3.8
Russia	9.8	8	203	3.6

Country	% contrib.	ppm	land	OM
Serbia	0.22	0	5.61	2.9
Slovakia	0.29	0	2.50	9.2
Slovenia	0.06	0	0.50	9.5
Spain	0.98	1	30.0	2.5
Sweden	0.39	0	3.29	8.8
Switzerland	0.22	0	1.54	10.8
Ukraine	2.7	2	41.7	4.8
United Kingdom	3.8	3	16.9	17
Europe excl. Russia	27.6	22	272	7.61
North America	29.3	24	470	4.7
Canada	2.21	2	64.5	2.6
United States	27.13	22	412	4.9
Cent. Amer. & Caribbean	1.57	1	143	0.82
Belize	0.001	0	0.137	0.70
Costa Rica	0.01	0	2.86	0.35
Cuba	0.15	0	6.59	1.68
Dominican Republic	0.04	0	3.68	0.83
El Salvador	0.01	0	1.70	0.63
Guatemala	0.02	0	4.55	0.35
Haiti	0.004	0	1.60	0.19
Honduras	0.01	0	2.91	0.29
Jamaica	0.03	0	0.51	5.1
Mexico	1.18	1	107	0.83
Nicaragua	0.01	0	7.04	0.11
Panama	0.02	0	2.23	0.60
Trinidad and Tobago	0.05	0	0.133	28
South America	2.65	2	630	0.32
Argentina	0.55	0	178	0.23
Bolivia	0.03	0	36.9	0.05
Brazil	0.94	1	262	0.29
Chile	0.15	0	15.0	0.77
Colombia	0.23	0	45.7	0.38
Ecuador	0.05	0	8.03	0.50
Guyana	0.008	0	1.77	0.32
Paraguay	0.009	0	25.0	0.03
Peru	0.11	0	30.7	0.26
Suriname	0.01	0	0	–
Uruguay	0.03	0	14.9	0.16
Venezuela	0.54	0	22.0	1.8

Country	% contrib.	ppm	land	OM
Oceania	1.31	1	467	0.21
Australia	1.17	1	446	0.20
Fiji	0.003	0	0.475	0.53
New Zealand	0.12	0	17.4	0.51
Papua New Guinea	0.008	0	0.906	0.70
Solomon Islands	0.0005	0	0.112	0.34
Asia excl. Middle East	22.4	18	1323	1.3
Armenia	0.028	0	1.4	1.5
Azerbaijan	0.21	0	4.6	3.4
Bangladesh	0.05	0	9.1	0.5
Bhutan	0.0005	0	0.6	0.06
Cambodia	0.002	0	5.3	0.03
China	9.17	7	560	1.23
Georgia	0.04	0	3.0	1.0
India	2.33	2	181	0.96
Indonesia	0.54	0	45.3	0.9
Japan	4.75	4	5.1	70
Kazakhstan	1.1	1	208	0.4
Korea, North	0.64	1	2.65	18
Korea, South	0.89	1	1.97	34
Kyrgyzstan	0.05	0	10.7	0.32
Laos	0.001	0	1.85	0.06
Malaysia	0.22	0	7.89	2.1
Mongolia	0.032	0	132	0.02
Myanmar	0.03	0	10.5	0.2
Nepal	0.004	0	5.0	0.06
Pakistan	0.23	0	27.0	0.65
Philippines	0.19	0	12.2	1.2
Singapore	0.12	0	.002	4360
Sri Lanka	0.03	0	2.4	0.8
Tajikistan	0.06	0	4.34	1.0
Thailand	0.3	0	20.4	1.1
Turkmenistan	0.18	0	32.4	0.43
Uzbekistan	0.64	1	27.3	1.8
Viet Nam	0.11	0	9.44	0.9
Middle East & N. Africa	3.54	3	465	0.57
Afghanistan	0.01	0	37.8	0.02
Algeria	0.20	0	38.1	0.39
Egypt	0.31	0	2.99	7.8
Iran	0.71	1	60.5	0.87
Iraq	0.22	0	10.1	1.6
Israel	0.15	0	0.59	19.3
Jordan	0.03	0	1.1	2.4

Country	% contrib.	ppm	land	OM
Kuwait	0.15	0	0.16	70
Lebanon	0.04	0	0.34	9.4
Libya	0.11	0	15.8	0.53
Morocco	0.083	0	30.3	0.21
Oman	0.033	0	0.93	2.6
Saudi Arabia	0.52	0	174	0.22
Syria	0.11	0	13.6	0.62
Tunisia	0.050	0	9.79	0.38
Turkey	0.52	0	41.6	0.94
United Arab Emirates	0.13	0	0.59	17
Yemen	0.03	0	17.4	0.14
Sub-Saharan Africa	1.77	1	1016	0.13
Angola	0.02	0	57.3	0.02
Benin	0.003	0	3.32	0.06
Botswana	0.007	0	26.1	0.02
Burkina Faso	0.002	0	10.4	0.02
Burundi	0.0006	0	2.36	0.02
Cameroon	0.01	0	8.84	0.08
Central Africa	0.001	0	4.98	0.01
Chad	0.001	0	49.1	0.001
Congo	0.004	0	10.2	0.03
Congo, Dem. Rep.	0.02	0	22.7	0.064
Côte d'Ivoire	0.02	0	20.0	0.064
Equatorial Guinea	0.0006	0	0.34	0.14
Eritrea	0.0008	0	7.47	0.008
Ethiopia	0.009	0	31.0	0.023
Gabon	0.009	0	5.15	0.13
Gambia	0.0008	0	0.72	0.08
Ghana	0.016	0	14.8	0.08
Guinea	0.005	0	12.3	0.03
Guinea-Bissau	0.0008	0	1.60	0.04
Kenya	0.03	0	26.2	0.09
Lesotho	0.0004	0	2.34	0.01
Liberia	0.005	0	2.60	0.13
Madagascar	0.006	0	27.3	0.02
Malawi	0.004	0	4.33	0.06
Mali	0.002	0	35.4	0.004
Mauritania	0.007	0	39.0	0.01
Mozambique	0.01	0	48.6	0.02
Namibia	0.002	0	38.7	0.004
Niger	0.003	0	16.5	0.02
Nigeria	0.14	0	72.0	0.14
Rwanda	0.001	0	1.85	0.06

Country	% contrib.	ppm	land	OM
Senegal	0.01	0	8.09	0.10
Sierra Leone	0.003	0	2.79	0.08
Somalia	0	0	44.5	0
South Africa	1.3	1	99.6	0.98
Sudan	0.02	0	133	0.01
Tanzania	0.01	0	40.6	0.02
Togo	0.003	0	3.59	0.06
Uganda	0.005	0	12.4	0.03
Zambia	0.02	0	34.9	0.05
Zimbabwe	0.06	0	20.5	0.22
World	**100**	**80**	**5096**	**1.6***

SOURCES: Percentage contributions, 1950–2000, were calculated from table 8 (p. 204) of *World Resources 2005: The Wealth of the Poor—Managing Ecosystems to Fight Poverty* (World Resources Institute). Cropland and pastureland figures were taken from table 11, p. 216.

---

*We can allow for a nominal 10% extra to cover the rise in the greenhouse gases other than carbon dioxide that also derive from fossil carbon sources. Then to cure global warming the percentage point increase in organic matter content in the top 12 inches of the world's agricultural soils needs to average 1.6%.

Index

Lightning Source UK Ltd.
Milton Keynes UK
12 April 2010
152558UK00001B/2/A